Healthy Foundations
in Early Childhood Settings

FOURTH EDITION

Barbara Pimento
George Brown College

Deborah Kernested
R.N.

D1413534

NELSON / EDUCATION

NELSON EDUCATION

Healthy Foundations in Early Childhood Settings, Fourth Edition
by Barbara Pimento and Deborah Kernested

Associate Vice President, Editorial Director:
Evelyn Veitch

Editor-in-Chief, Higher Education:
Anne Williams

Senior Acquisitions Editor:
Lenore Taylor-Atkins

Marketing Manager:
David Tonen

Developmental Editor:
Sandy Matos

Photo Researcher:
Marian Evans

Director, Asset Management Services:
Vicki Gould

Permissions Coordinator:
Marian Evans

Content Production Manager:
Christine Gilbert

Production Service:
Macmillan Publishing Solutions

Copy Editor:
Holly Dickinson

Proofreader:
Barbara Storey

Indexer:
Maura Brown

Manufacturing Manager- Higher Education:
Joanne McNeil

Design Director:
Ken Phipps

Managing Designer:
Franca Amore

Interior Design:
Dianna Little

Cover Design:
Dianna Little

Cover Image:
ImageZoo/Images.com

Compositor:
Macmillan Publishing Solutions

Printer:
Edwards Brothers Malloy

Library and Archives Canada Cataloguing in Publication Data

Pimento, Barbara
   Healthy foundations in early childhood settings / Barbara Pimento, Deborah Kernested. — 4th ed.

Includes bibliographical references and index.
ISBN 978-0-17-644113-5

1. Children—Health and hygiene—Canada—Textbooks.
2. Early childhood education—Health aspects—Canada—Textbooks.
3. Health promotion—Canada—Textbooks. 4. Child welfare—Canada—Textbooks.
I. Kernested, Deborah, 1957- II. Title.

HQ778.7.C3P55 2009
613'.0432   C2008-906790-8

ISBN-13: 978-0-17-644113-5
ISBN-10: 0-17-644113-1

CONTENTS

UNIT 1   HEALTH PROMOTION

UNIT 2   OCCUPATIONAL HEALTH

UNIT 3   ILLNESS PREVENTION

UNIT 4   ILLNESS MANAGEMENT

UNIT 5   NUTRITION

UNIT 6   HEALTHY ACTIVE LIVING

UNIT 7   SAFETY PROMOTION

UNIT 8   PREVENTING CHILD MALTREATMENT

UNIT 9   SUPPORTING CHILDREN'S DEVELOPMENT

LIST OF EXHIBITS AND APPENDIXES

Tables

Figures

Appendixes

BEFORE YOU BEGIN

Health is a complex subject that is interesting, challenging, thought-provoking, and sometimes complex. It includes a wide range of perspectives. We are confident that this edition of *Healthy Foundations in Early Childhood Settings,* like the previous ones, reflects all of these attributes and addresses more fully those issues that are of greater concern today. As the title of this book implies, health is a cornerstone in ensuring high-quality early childhood education. Development and learning are fostered and supported when children are healthy and able to participate fully in a child-centred, play-based curriculum. Health is integrated with children's growth, development, and cultural realities, and each of this book's units reflects this belief.

In collaboration with families, educators have an integral role in maintaining or improving children's overall health status through a health promotion philosophy. This role requires an anti-bias attitude, respect, and sensitivity to diverse ethnocultural and family health beliefs and practices. Each of us has a responsibility for our own health, yet we can't dismiss the responsibility of our communities and society.

The third edition of *Well Beings: A Guide to Health in Child Care* (2008), by the Canadian Paediatric Society, provides the Canadian early childhood education community with a comprehensive health resource manual. The book's audience extends beyond directors and educators to include child care office personnel, public health staff, physicians, and early childhood education instructors and students. As with previous editions, we refer to *Well Beings* and use selected material from it throughout this textbook. *Healthy Foundations in Early Childhood Settings*, Fourth Edition, provides you with an overall health promotion philosophy, entry-level knowledge, and skills and introduces you to *Well Beings*, Third Edition, which you will use as a resource manual upon graduation to expand your knowledge and skills.

The emphasis in *Healthy Foundations in Early Childhood Settings* is on the overall health needs of all children. We have not included discussion of physical, cognitive, or socioemotional challenges and long-term medical conditions such as epilepsy or diabetes. In most, if not all, early childhood education training programs, students are required to complete a course on working with children with special needs and working effectively with families and others involved in their care. Students then combine the knowledge, skills, and attitudes that they learn in their courses and program placements to meet the physical, emotional, and social needs of each child. Most training institutions also offer post-diploma education in this area. Special Link: The National Centre for Child Care Inclusion provides researchers, policy makers, parents, and early childhood educators and directors with the best inclusive practices on the frontlines of Canadian child care. Their findings are available to everyone at http://www.specialinkcanada.org.

Healthy Foundations in Early Childhood Settings, Fourth Edition, reflects a national perspective while recognizing differences among the provinces' and territories' child care regulations. As a result, we have selected a number of terms that are used throughout the textbook.

Educator

Regardless of the term used officially in any particular province or territory, people working in the field use different titles for their profession. Here are a few:

- educator
- educarer
- facilitator
- teacher
- caregiver
- child care worker
- child care provider
- child care practitioner
- early childhood educator
- child care professional

At the national level, there is ongoing discussion about selecting one term that can be used to designate a person who has formal early childhood education training, one term that reflects the complexity of roles in working with children and their families in child care programs. Two suggestions are "early childhood educator" and "early childhood care and education teacher." Although there is no national consensus as yet, the province of Ontario has decided to legislate the term "early childhood educator." Ontario's new College of ECE is the first regulatory college for early childhood educators (ECEs) in Canada. The College will monitor and support high standards in early childhood education. It will also help ensure that Ontario's children who attend early learning and care programs are being cared for by qualified professionals. Complicating the discussion is the fact that in most of the literature, the term "early childhood" applies to the ages between birth and 8 years, thus excluding school-agers between the ages of 9 and 12 and, by extension, those who work with them. We have chosen to use the term "educator." We recognize that trained, qualified professionals who work in early childhood education programs care, support, facilitate, and educate.

Director

The daily operation of an early childhood program is often determined by the number of children enrolled and the organization's management style. As a result, in some situations, the director is responsible for the program's overall administration, is responsible for the supervision of staff, and sometimes also works with children. In other situations, the director oversees the finances and policy and staffing decisions and takes primary responsibility for networking in the community and formally representing the program. In addition, one or more supervisors oversee the staff and work directly with children and families for all or part of each day. The term "director" refers to the individual who has primary responsibility for supervising educators and managing day-to-day operations. Programs that operate as cooperatives do not have directors. In these programs, "director" refers to the collective that makes decisions.

Program and Facility

In this edition, we use the terms "program" and "facility" rather than "centre."

The term "program" refers to the learning environment planned and implemented by educators, who base it on the children's emerging needs and interests. The term is also used to refer to the program in a more general sense, as an early childhood education program that is licensed by a province or territory. The use of "centre" is an exclusive rather than an inclusive term in relation to educators. Educators work not only in child care centres but in a variety of programs, such as family resource centres, family daycare homes, and nursery school programs.

The term "facility" refers to the physical space—the structure, the building—that houses the program.

Parents and Families

The terms "parents" and "families" refer to any adult who has primary responsibility for the child. The terms encompass legal guardians and foster parents. We recognize that the child's immediate family may comprise individuals other than biological or adoptive parents, and we hope that our use of these terms reflects inclusiveness.

Child Care Office

The term "child care office" refers to the office or agency primarily responsible for licensing programs in individual provinces and territories. When we refer to child care regulations, we mean those that apply to your province or territory.

Age Groups of Children

Classifications for age groups vary with child care regulations. We use these definitions throughout the textbook:

- infants: birth to 12 months
- toddlers: 12 to 24 months
- preschoolers: 2 to 5 years
- school-agers: 6 to 12 years

New to the Fourth Edition

The new edition contains updated information and statistics in all units. Other significant changes are as follows:

- Unit 1: The social determinants of health concept has been introduced, which identifies the five determinants that are most applicable to early childhood programs and promotion. The *Reaching for the Top: A Report from the Advisor on Healthy Children and Youth* (2007) report is introduced. Two concepts have been defined: population health approach and developmental health. The issue of mixed and competing messages that abound for educators and families is also introduced and continued in Unit 3.

- Unit 2: Occupational Health expands on the workplace–personal life juggle/balance and the costs of an unhealthy workplace. There is a new checklist to evaluate health information on the Internet (Appendix 2.1). The health promotion checklist for you and your employer is updated (Appendix 2.2).

- Unit 3: The immunization schedule has been updated with the most recent Canadian standards. A discussion on the environmental and health concerns related to sanitizing and antibacterial products is included.

- Unit 4: The Management of Illness table (Appendix 4.1) is updated with the most current exclusion criteria from *Well Beings* (2008).

- Unit 5: Updates are provided on all aspects of *Eating Well with Canada's Food Guide* and nutrition issues. The importance of breast-feeding is expanded. Strategies to promote lifelong healthy eating habits in the early childhood program and menu planning to support these habits are identified. Appendix 5.2 Nutrients: Their Functions and Food Sources is updated and expanded.

- Unit 6: Healthy Active Living is new. It outlines issues such as the concerns about an epidemic of childhood obesity; lack of adequate physical activity; unhealthy eating habits, including trans fats, carbonated and other low-nutritive drinks, and insufficient intake of vegetables and fruit; and the time spent in front of a screen. The relevance of each of these issues to early childhood programs and strategies for educators and parents to address these concerns are discussed. Greening of the outdoors is highlighted. There are physical activity guidelines and suggestions for each age group.

- Unit 7: We have included relevant information from the most recent Canadian Standards Association (CSA) standards for playgrounds. As well, there is an expanded section on environmental contaminants with a link to an environmental child safety checklist developed by the Canadian Partnership for Children's Health and Environment (CPCHE).

- Unit 8: The term "child abuse" has been replaced with "child maltreatment" due to the prevalence of the term in government documents (e.g., The Public Health Agency of Canada's publications) and research in this area. We have expanded on the prevention of child maltreatment, and concerns regarding Internet sexual exploitation are introduced. The *United Nations Convention on the Rights of the Child*, written in user-friendly language, is introduced in Appendix 8.1.

- Unit 9: In addition to updates to reflect new information, the content in dental health education has been expanded to highlight the importance of dental hygiene to overall health and well-being.

Three or more Critical Thinking questions are asked in each unit, enabling students to explore the issues introduced.

Updates to resources, including websites for further reference, are available at the end of each unit.

Learning Outcomes

Educational reform and initiatives across Canada—such as prior learning assessment, standards, and outcomes—are catalysts for some educational institutions to embark on the process of establishing learning outcomes. These are clear, broad statements that embody the necessary and significant knowledge, skills, and attitudes that learners are expected to demonstrate to successfully complete each course or program.

We have examined this textbook for significant learning statements. On completion of this textbook, in conjunction with studies in health, it is expected that students will have demonstrated the ability to

1. represent the holistic nature of health through examining its physical, emotional, and social dimensions

2. identify the scope and limits of the educator's roles with regard to health in early childhood education, recognizing the importance of sensitivity and respect for the primary role of parents and family

3. apply the principles of a health promotion philosophy to their own lives as well as to their work with children

4. promote children's health based on knowledge of child development and observation within the context of the family culture

5. assimilate the importance of collaborating and networking with other professionals and agencies on an ongoing basis to enhance health in early childhood education and care programs

6. transfer the principles of essential health policies and practices to new situations in early childhood education

ACKNOWLEDGMENTS

The knowledge I gain continually through my relationships with family, friends, colleagues, and students is more meaningful to me than I can put to paper. Michael is wonderful—always there to listen, share ideas, and offer his wisdom and support in countless ways. Taryn's and Taylor's love for life and budding passion for social justice issues that affect all of us give me strength and make me proud.

Thanks to my colleagues at George Brown College, who are incredible individuals and are always so supportive. Special thanks to Marie Goulet, Lynn Wilson, Rita Barron, Diane Bergeron, and Connie Winder for their helpful feedback, resources, and ongoing encouragement. Patricia Chorney Rubin, as always, is incredibly supportive and offers many thoughtful and innovative suggestions. I also very much appreciate the benefits of shared knowledge and a broader perspective in health promotion practice from my brief secondment to the George Brown College Community Learning Centre for Healthy Living. Thanks so much to the wonderful faculty, staff, managers, and, of course, students from across the college and others with whom I had the opportunity to meet and work.

Beyond George Brown, I have very much appreciated the commitment and expertise of Pearl Rimer, Manager of Resource Development, Research & Training at BOOST Child Abuse Prevention and Intervention (formerly The

Toronto Child Abuse Centre). Pearl put in many hours ensuring that Unit 8, Preventing Child Maltreatment, had a full critique. Also, Carol Harrison, a registered dietitian and Toronto-based nutrition consultant specializing in nutrition communications, continues to be a wonderful resource person to me, as well as to George Brown College's School of Early Childhood, via her annual involvement in the GBC Child Care Cooks' Conference. Sue Weststrate from The Best Start Resource Centre brings passion to health promotion and has been a great resource, particularly in the area of physical activity for young children. Janine Kirby, faculty at Lambton College in Sarnia, also offered helpful suggestions for this edition, as did Donna Michal of the Early Childhood Work Group, Health and Learning Knowledge Centre.

Deborah and I continue to work a province apart, but it feels as if we are sitting side by side. When we work together, it's magic! I marvel at Deborah's many strengths.

—Barbara Pimento

To Ali, thank you for your patience and support and for taking care of me through all of those time crunches. To my mother Rhoda, my sister Carla, and my niece and nephew Anastasia and Erik, along with my friends, thank you all for your love and encouragement. Barb and I have now written three editions while being separated geographically. Even with that experience, we are still confronted with unique challenges, some of which were easier to meet with computers, the Internet, and e-mail. Thank you, Barb, for taking the lead on the fourth edition. Your commitment, dedication, and tenacity made this edition a reality. I've said this in each edition and do so now, but I couldn't have asked for a better writing partner and friend.

—Deborah Kernested

There are many we would like to thank for sharing their knowledge in the development of *Healthy Foundations in Early Childhood Settings,* Fourth Edition. In addition to the kudos already mentioned, special thanks to the colleagues at George Brown College who have continued to share their expertise, especially Rita Barron, Diane Bergeron, and Sandra Fazio, who have used the textbook and offered ongoing feedback and suggestions. Rob Caspary, Chef at George Brown College, School of Early Childhood, has shared his talents by providing us with a delicious new menu for a week (Appendix 5.4). Thank you to Patricia Chorney-Rubin, and the fabulous managers and staff at the George Brown College child care centres. What a team! To Carla Kernested, Child Care Safety Specialist, Manitoba Child Care Program, Family Services & Housing, thank you for your consultation on issues throughout the textbook. To Mike LeBlanc, Chief Public Health Inspector, Manager—Health Protection Unit, Environmental Health Branch, Manitoba Health and Healthy Living, and his student, who came through at the 11th hour with references that seemed impossible to find. Jennie Strickland, Publications Coordinator for the Canadian Paediatric Society (CPS), was responsive and collaborative in communicating between CPS regarding *Well Beings,* Third Edition and us—thank you, Jennie. To Sandy Matos, our Developmental Editor, whose enduring patience and support while moving us along the development schedule deserve our admiration and thanks! Your incredible competence and willingness to pitch in and assist us on the administrative tasks of writing a textbook were invaluable. Thanks also to the many others at Nelson, especially Cara Yarzab, our Publisher, whose hard work helped make this book possible. We would also like to thank the other members of the team who have made the publication of this book possible: Lenore Taylor-Atkins, Acquisitions Editor; David Tonen, Marketing Manager; Christine Gilbert, Content Production Manager; Holly Dickinson, Copy Editor; Vicki Gould, Director, Asset Management Services; Marian Evans, Permissions Researcher; Barbara Storey, Proofreader; and Maura Brown, Indexer. Special thanks to Angela Cluer, Executive Director, Media Development and Jennifer Leung, Designer, who took the many photographs in the fourth edition.

A textbook is not complete without its photographs. Thank you so much to the children, families, and staff at the early childhood education programs who generously welcomed us into their wonderful programs—in particular, staff at the Scotia Plaza Child Care Centre and the University of Toronto, Child Care "on Charles Street," who opened their doors for us to capture photos depicting best practices. This is very much a tribute to managers Carol Thorpe and Debbie Wilson. Some of the photographs in this book are courtesy of Carla Kernested and Anastasia and Erik Pindera, Winnipeg; Sister Celeste, Fort Norman, N.W.T.; Marie Goulet, Toronto; Lynn Wilson, Toronto; the Nolan Family (Victoria, Eamonn, Tarabh, Ceilidh, and Angus, Victoria's guide dog), Toronto; the Manitoba Child Care Association, Winnipeg; Ryerson University's Early Learning Centre's Sally Kotsopoulos; and Health Canada.

Finally, thank you to all who reviewed the third edition of this text to provide us with the direction required to develop the fourth edition. The information and insight provided by these reviewers proved invaluable in ensuring the quality of this resource and, most of all, in keeping us abreast of the needs of our colleagues, who bring this material to life. Special thanks therefore go to the following:

Judith Boyd, *New Brunswick Community College*
Christine Boyle, *Mount Royal College*
Lynn Caruso, *Seneca College*
Angie Commeford, *Sheridan Institute of Technology and Advanced Learning*
Leslie Corbet, *Sheridan Institute of Technology and Advanced Learning*
Rosemary Heenan, *St. Clair College*
Lisa McCaire-Watters, *Centennial College*

Health Promotion

CONTENTS

P romoting the health of children and families in early childhood programs is one of the most important roles of educators. So much of what educators do is interconnected with health and well-being. In this introductory unit, we explore what health is, and we look at what determines our health. We explore health promotion and our changing attitudes toward health. The unit closes with an introduction to the health promotion action plan and how it can be incorporated into early childhood programs. It is important for early childhood educators to recognize their essential role as health promoters. The action plan is revisited in subsequent units.

OBJECTIVE

To identify the World Health Organization's definition of health.

WHAT IS HEALTH?

The most influential definition of **health** in the 20th century was introduced by the World Health Organization (WHO) in 1948. Health, said the WHO, is "a state of complete physical, mental and social well-being and not merely the absence of disease or infirmity" (WHO, 1948). The definition has been criticized over the years because of, among other reasons, its use of the word "state" rather than "process" and for the impossibility of achieving a "complete" state of health. Yet there is no doubt that this definition paved the way for a social model of health and health promotion in Canada, broadening the concept of health from a medical one to one that encompasses quality of life. Quality of life refers to the degree to which an individual enjoys the important dimensions of her or his life, including the fulfillment of physical and emotional needs, social belonging, and the realization of goals, hopes, and aspirations. Quality of life is relevant to all humans, at any time and from their own perspectives (Brown, Raphael, & Renwick, 1998, p. 4).

> In 1984, the WHO revised its definition of health to
> the extent to which an individual or group is able, on the one hand, to realize aspirations and satisfy needs; and, on the other hand, to change or cope with the environment. Health is therefore seen as a resource for everyday life, not the objective for living; it is a positive concept emphasizing social and personal resources, as well as physical capacity. (WHO, 2005, p. 3)

Source: *Health Impact Assessment Toolkit for Cities. Document 1. Background Document: Concepts, Processes, Methods. Vision to Action.* World Health Organization, 2005. Reprinted with permission.

The ever-changing nature of our health means that our adaptability to change is an important lifelong attribute and influences our health. All people are unique in how they define their own health. Health is enhanced by reasonable lifestyles and the equitable use of public and private resources that permit people to maintain and improve their own well-being, however they define health.

OBJECTIVES

To list the 12 social determinants of health, as defined by the Public Health Agency of Canada.

To define the term "population health."

To list the features of a population health approach.

SOCIAL DETERMINANTS OF HEALTH

Health is a basic human right, so why are some of us more likely to enjoy good health than others? To answer this question, we first need to consider health determinants. There are no guarantees of good health, and many aspects of our lives affect our health status. Maintaining our health is the combined responsibility of all of us, as members of our community and of society. In addition to our biology and genetics, there are many factors that influence our health status, and the Public Health Agency of Canada has identified what are known as the (12) **social determinants** of health. A wealth of evidence supports the view that the social, economic, and physical environmental circumstances of individuals and groups are equally or more important to our health status than medical care and personal health behaviour (Federal, Provincial and Territorial Advisory Committee on Population Health, 1999). There is a complex interplay of the social determinants of health; some have a broader impact than others and may be more or less significant to our health at different times in our lives (see Table 1.1).

TABLE 1.1   **PHAC: Social Determinants of Health**

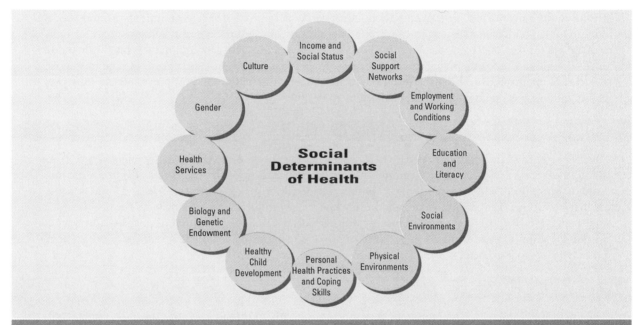

INCOME AND SOCIAL STATUS

There is strong and growing evidence that higher social and economic status is associated with better health. Health status improves at each step up the income and social hierarchy. High income determines living conditions such as safe housing and the ability to buy sufficient good food. The healthiest populations are those in societies that are prosperous and have an equitable distribution of wealth. Why are higher income and social status associated with better health? Considerable research indicates that the degree of control people have over life circumstances, especially stressful situations, and their options to act are the key influences. Higher income and social status generally result in more control and options. And the biological pathways for how this could happen are becoming better understood. A number of recent studies show that limited options and poor coping skills for dealing with stress increase vulnerability to a range of diseases through pathways that involve the immune and hormonal systems.

SOCIAL SUPPORT NETWORKS

Support from families, friends, and communities is associated with better health. Such social support networks could be very important in helping people solve problems and deal with adversity, as well as in

(continued)

| TABLE 1.1 | PHAC: Social Determinants of Health *(continued)* |

maintaining a sense of mastery and control over life circumstances. The caring and respect that occur in social relationships, and the resulting sense of satisfaction and well-being, seem to act as a buffer against health problems.

EMPLOYMENT AND WORKING CONDITIONS

Unemployment, underemployment, and stressful or unsafe work are associated with poorer health. People who have more control over their work circumstances and fewer stress-related demands on the job are healthier and often live longer than those in more stressful or riskier work and activities.

EDUCATION AND LITERACY

Health status improves with level of education. Education is closely tied to socioeconomic status, and effective education for children and lifelong learning for adults are key contributors to health and prosperity for individuals and for the country. Education contributes to health and prosperity by equipping people with knowledge and skills for problem solving and helps provide a sense of control and mastery over life circumstances. It increases opportunities for job and income security and job satisfaction, and it improves people's ability to access and understand information to help keep them healthy.

SOCIAL ENVIRONMENTS

The importance of social support also extends to the broader community. Civic vitality refers to the strength of social networks within a community, region, province, or country. It is reflected in the institutions, organizations, and informal giving practices that people create to share resources and build attachments with others. The array of values and norms of a society influences in varying ways the health and well-being of individuals and populations. In addition, social stability, recognition of diversity, safety, good working relationships, and cohesive communities provide a supportive society that reduces or avoids many potential risks to good health.

PHYSICAL ENVIRONMENTS

The physical environment is an important determinant of health. At certain levels of exposure, contaminants in our air, water, food, and soil can cause a variety of adverse health effects, including cancer, birth defects, respiratory illness, and gastrointestinal ailments. In the built environment, factors related to housing, indoor air quality, and the design of communities and transportation systems can significantly influence our physical and psychological well-being.

PERSONAL HEALTH PRACTICES AND COPING SKILLS

Personal health practices and coping skills refer to those actions by which individuals can prevent diseases and promote self-care, cope with challenges, develop self-reliance, solve problems, and make choices that enhance health. Definitions of lifestyle include not only individual choices but also the influence of social, economic, and environmental factors on the decisions people make about their health. There is a growing recognition that personal life "choices" are greatly influenced by the socioeconomic environments in which people live, learn, work, and play. These influences impact lifestyle choice through at least five areas: personal life skills, stress, culture, social relationships and belonging, and a sense of control. Interventions that support the creation of supportive environments will enhance the capacity of individuals to make healthy lifestyle choices in a world where many choices are possible.

HEALTHY CHILD DEVELOPMENT

New evidence on the effects of early experiences on brain development, school readiness, and health in later life has sparked a growing consensus about early child development as a powerful determinant of health in its own right. At the same time, we have been learning more about how all of the other determinants of health affect the physical, social, mental, emotional, and spiritual development of children and youth. For example, a young person's development is greatly affected by his or her housing and neighbourhood, family income and level of parents' education, access to nutritious foods and physical recreation, genetic makeup, and access to dental and medical care.

BIOLOGY AND GENETIC ENDOWMENT

The basic biology and organic makeup of the human body are a fundamental determinant of health. Genetic endowment provides an inherited predisposition to a wide range of individual responses that affect health status. Although socioeconomic and environmental factors are important determinants of overall health, in some circumstances, genetic endowment appears to predispose certain individuals to particular diseases or health problems. Aging is not synonymous with poor health. Active living and the provision of opportunities for lifelong learning may be particularly important for maintaining health and cognitive capacity in old age. And studies on education level and dementia suggest that exposure to education and lifelong learning may create reserve capacity in the brain that compensates for cognitive losses that occur with biological aging.

HEALTH SERVICES

Health services, particularly those designed to maintain and promote health, to prevent disease, and to restore health and function, contribute to population health. The health services continuum of care includes treatment and secondary prevention.

GENDER

Gender refers to the array of society-determined roles, personality traits, attitudes, behaviours, values, relative power, and influence that society ascribes to the two sexes on a differential basis. "Gendered" norms influence the health system's practices and priorities. Many health issues are a function of gender-based social status or roles.

CULTURE

Some people or groups may face additional health risks due to a socioeconomic environment that is largely determined by dominant cultural values that contribute to the perpetuation of conditions such as marginalization, stigmatization, loss or devaluation of language and culture, and lack of access to culturally appropriate health care and services.

Source: Adapted from *Population Health: What Determines Health,* Public Health Agency of Canada, 2004. Reproduced with permission of the Minister of Public Works and Government Services Canada, 2008.

Reaching for the Top: Reporting on Child Health

Although Canada takes pride in its international reputation for fairness and compassion and is considered one of the best countries in the world in which to live, Canada is doing surprisingly poorly compared with other member countries of the Organisation for Economic Co-operation and Development (OECD) in measures of the health and wellness of children and youth. *Reaching for the Top: A Report from the Advisor on Healthy Children and Youth* (Leitch, 2007, p. 14) states that among 29 OECD nations, Canada ranks

- 21st in child well-being and mental health
- 22nd in preventable childhood injuries and deaths
- 22nd in child poverty
- 27th in childhood obesity

This ranking is appalling, considering the fact that Canada has the resources to be at the top. Canada has too many children living in poverty, too many youngsters who are living in inadequate housing and hungry, too many children whose education is not up to standard, and too many exposed to environmental contaminants. We also have a generation of Aboriginal children both on reserve and in cities who are suffering in all these ways and more (Picard, 2008). *Reaching for the Top* (Leitch, 2007, pp. 25–27) identifies recommendations to improve the federal government's role in child and youth health, including

- streamlining an integrated way to address child health issues rather than the current silo, piecemeal approach,
- using scarce funds effectively by avoiding reinventing what other programs are already doing well, and
- ensuring that the process of evaluation becomes efficient and effective and measures the right things.

Population Health and a Population Health Approach

Population health studies why some groups of people are healthier than others. Populations include large groups of people within a boundary; be that a neighbourhood, a city, or a country. **A population health** approach, now widely accepted by Health Canada and the Public Health Agency of Canada, aims to improve the health of the entire population and to reduce health inequities among population groups. Since those inequities have a lot to do with the social, economic, and physical environmental aspects of life (i.e., social determinants), a population health approach recognizes the essential role of public social policy to reduce the gaps among groups in the population (Public Health Agency of Canada, 2002). "The outcomes or benefits of a population health approach, therefore, extend beyond improved population health outcomes to include a sustainable and integrated health system, increased national growth and productivity, and strengthened social cohesion and citizen engagement" (Public Health Agency of Canada, 2002, p. 2).

A population health approach (Public Health Agency of Canada, 2002)

- recognizes the complex interactions between and among the determinants of health. It uses a variety of strategies in multiple settings and partnerships with sectors outside the traditional health sector to address determinants.

- directs investments to those areas with the greatest potential to positively influence population health status.

- is grounded in the notion that the earlier in the causal stream action is taken, the greater the potential for population health gains. This strategy is called "invest upstream," putting effort into prevention when possible.

- ensures that the decisions made are based on sound and grounded theory, so that limited resources are directed ethically and sensibly.

- promotes the participation of all Canadians in developing strategies to improve health. Public involvement builds public confidence in decision making and increases information sharing, and those Canadians most affected by a health issue contribute to possible solutions early in the planning process.

- ensures regular and timely reporting of results and sharing of information with partners and Canadians, promoting direct communication.

In terms of the health of populations, it is well documented that the wider the gap between the socioeconomic "have" and "have not" groups in a society, the lower the health status of the overall population (Wilkinson & Marmot, 2003). This is evident internationally when we consider the positive population health outcomes in countries such as Sweden, Japan, and New Zealand, whose socioeconomic gap is narrower and health outcomes are better than those of countries such as Canada and the United States.

CANADA'S HEALTH CARE SYSTEM

OBJECTIVES

To list and define the five principles of medicare.

To differentiate between the roles of the personal and public health care systems.

Where does Canada's health care system fit in this picture? As discussed earlier, social, economic, and physical environmental factors have a greater impact on our health than does health care, and improvement in health for populations is strongly linked to policies and programs that address inequities. However, the quality of that health care also influences our health, in both prevention and management of disease and injury.

In Canada, we are fortunate to have a system of universal medical and hospital insurance, one that tries, although it does not always succeed, to provide all citizens with equal access to health care. Canada has made the right to health care one of the priorities on its political agenda. We are treated by doctors and are hospitalized when necessary.

Over the past 15 years, the health care system has reached a crisis point. Every few days, you hear a news story about balancing the budget, spiralling health care costs, hospital closures, staff layoffs, cuts to health care services, and reductions in the quality of care. Canada and the provinces and territories are paying more than they can afford in health services, but they are not seeing the anticipated return in overall health. Health care reform has proved to be an immense task in Canada. Health care reform—rethinking and restructuring—is being taken on worldwide. The somewhat rigid structure of the health care system has not provided the flexibility needed to meet the diverse needs of a rapidly changing society. If our health care system were being established today, the system would likely rely less on hospitals and doctors and provide a broader range of community-based services. A high standard of care remains essential, but simply doing more of the same with less won't work.

All levels of government in Canada are calling for a more community- and home-based approach to health care, yet some of these governments are also cutting social services that are needed in an infrastructure for an integrated and comprehensive system. Simply sending patients home from hospital earlier without adequate support for care at home does not address the problem.

In 2002, the Commission on the Future of Health Care in Canada published a report that emphatically supports the core values of equity, fairness, and solidarity that have defined the health care system in the past and must guide future reforms. This report, commonly known as the Romanow Report,

- recognizes that close collaboration by all levels of governments in Canada is essential;
- calls on the federal government to create an accountable and sustainable system, one that says no to private care and user fees and yes to accountability;
- acknowledges the importance of prevention and health promotion (e.g., regarding smoking, obesity, physical activity); and
- recognizes linking reform to a social equality agenda (Canadian Council on Social Development, 2002, pp. 1–2).

Despite the criticisms, there is little doubt that most people living in Canada have benefited from our medicare system. *Quality of Life in Canada: A Citizen's Report Card* reported that even with concerns about the viability and access problems with our health care system, Canadians continue to rate it reasonably high on many issues (Michalski, 2002, p. 74).

Components of Canada's Health Care System

There are two components of the health care system: personal health and public health.

Personal Health Care System

Although health care reform is affecting change, the **personal health care system** essentially includes conventional medical services available to people who want to maintain their health and seek cures for illness. General practitioners, family physicians, and pediatricians are the physicians we first contact when seeking medical care or advice. In certain situations, these physicians consult with specialists (e.g., gastroenterologists, cardiologists) and other medical professionals, such as physiotherapists, dietitian-nutritionists, and audiologists. We are seeing a movement toward including complementary medical practices in the medical services available through medicare, such as chiropractic services. Social workers and other relevant professionals are often brought into patients' medical care when nonphysical factors affect health (e.g., housing, poverty, substance abuse, child abuse). With wide recognition that the social determinants of health must be integrated into a framework for the future of our health care system, this movement will be expanding with time.

Public Health Care System

In Canada, public health services are provided regionally within each province and territory. Each public health department serves a specific geographic area. Usually, each agency is headed by a medical officer of health, who is a physician with specialty training in community medicine. The medical officer of health is given legal powers to prevent health hazards through provincial/territorial public health legislation.

Public health measures have been responsible for many of the major improvements in the health of Canadians, particularly around issues related to clean water and infectious diseases. Recently, however, the risks to health have been changing. The leading causes of death for all ages are now chronic diseases and injuries. Today's public health challenges include epidemic numbers of obese adults and children, continued high smoking rates, and increasing rates of asthma in children. The threat of infectious diseases has not disappeared, with the return of age-old problems (e.g., syphilis, community waterborne disease outbreaks) and the appearance of new ones (e.g., West Nile virus, severe acute respiratory syndrome [SARS], bioterrorism). Most current public health legislation focuses on the control of infectious diseases. The new reality is initiating legislation directed at public health prevention of chronic conditions such as obesity and asthma (Institute of Population and Public Health, 2003).

The **public health system** provides and supports a wide range of programs, including the following (Institute of Population and Public Health, 2003):

- disease surveillance and responses to outbreaks
- health promotion to advocate for and facilitate healthier public policies, improve skills, and support individual and community-level behaviour change
- immunization programs
- inspection of restaurants and child care facilities

The local public health agency usually provides a variety of services when budgets permit. The medical officer of health designates services to address the public health needs in that geographic area. Large urban communities, for example, have a higher concentration of individuals addicted to drugs than do rural communities. When a region has a number of early childhood programs, ideally, the public health agency responds to each program's unique needs for information, consultation, and education.

As an early childhood educator, you will be involved with the public health system. Public health agencies are responsible for inspecting and approving health standards in early childhood programs, particularly licensed centres. Many centres, however, also actively seek an ongoing relationship with their public health professionals, to maximize the potential for health promotion. Directors commonly seek guidance for infectious disease control, immunization, safety, nutrition, and dental health.

Financial restraints have meant larger workloads for public health personnel. Often the agency's priority for health promotion makes a relationship with an early childhood program mutually beneficial. Directors or educators may need to initiate contacts with the designated public health nurse or inspector due to great demands on the official's time.

<table>
<tr><td>

OBJECTIVES

To discuss a holistic view of health and its effect on Canada's changing health care system.

To describe how complementary practitioners such as midwives contribute to a collaborative approach in health care.

To define the term "natural health products."

To describe the role that the federal government has in regulating natural health products.

</td></tr>
</table>

CHANGING ATTITUDES TOWARD HEALTH CARE

Canada still largely operates an illness care system rather than a health (promotion) system, with a total expenditure on health promotion of only about 5% (Health Canada, 2005a). Of course, treatment and cure needs are essential and require adequate resources. However, when we consider the "invest upstream" population health approach, more and more Canadians are questioning the curative approach to conventional medicine and are considering the merits of a holistic approach to health care. The holistic approach encompasses health promotion as a way of reducing health risks to individuals and the community at large. Reduced health risks would mean that less money would be needed for curative treatments and more money could be reallocated to health promotion measures, which include prevention. Many in the medical establishment resist this change in ideology as the balance of power in decision making over the health of individuals shifts and the health care delivery system is restructured.

Conventional medical care has become established in Western countries only in the past 200 years. Medical care primarily focuses on treating people after they become sick and on health maintenance, rather than on health care based on promotion. Most people seek medical advice only after experiencing the symptoms of illness. Physicians evaluate the symptoms, look for a cause, and decide on a treatment. The recommendations can be narrow in focus. Usually, physicians treat the physical symptoms rather than consider the connections among the patient's dimensions of well-being. Treatments commonly include surgery, medication, physical or occupational therapy, or a change in nutritional habits—or any combination, all of which relate to the patient's physical health. This style of medical care is one in which the doctor is in charge and the patient asks few questions. When a patient is hospitalized, other health care professionals, such as dietitian-nutritionists, occupational therapists, and respiratory technicians, see the patient when the doctor requests a consultation.

Conventional medicine is extremely expensive because of its reliance on highly specialized professionals and institutions (hospitals and clinics). Moreover, it does not care for the patient as a whole. It does not routinely use the expertise and skills of a variety of health professionals within a collaborative team approach; rather, it uses them as consultants if the doctor deems their input necessary. Health promotion costs less than curing or treating illness, especially in the management of long-term medical conditions. For both the individual and the community, avoiding illness altogether makes the most sense.

This curative or health recovery approach was, and still is to some degree, widely held among many in the medical community and society. Many patients expect doctors to be miracle workers—to cure all their ills without patients accepting any responsibility for their unhealthy lifestyles. But another health care delivery system is gaining support, one that takes a holistic or broader view of health. We are becoming more informed consumers, asking our physicians questions and viewing ourselves as partners or advocates in our health care. Many Canadians are taking more individual control over accessing health professionals—chiropractors, physiotherapists, naturopaths—rather than waiting for a doctor's referral.

Traditionally, health care providers have been the main source of information and advice for patients. Although this is still true, increasing numbers of individuals are using the Internet to do extensive research on their conditions and come to their doctor appointments loaded with printouts and questions. This can result in some patients who then think that they know more than their physician in regard to the condition and treatment. However, without the background health knowledge and experience of a physician, the average Canadian is not prepared to make decisions based on publicly accessible information, since so much of the medical information found on the Internet is unreliable. It is imperative that patients visit reputable websites when using the Internet. Nevertheless, the demand by patients for greater involvement in decision making has made it essential that the public has access to user-friendly, accurate, and current information. In turn, health care providers are called upon to interpret the vast amount of public health information.

An Emerging Collaborative Approach in Health Care

Medicine is a business, and doctors are having to adapt to the changing attitudes and expectations of consumers. Examples of the changing direction in Canada's health care system include a revamping, on the part of some medical schools, of teaching programs to a community-based model, a movement toward community medicine (e.g., community health centres), and the licensing of midwives.

- Midwifery has been a legal and legitimate profession in England for over 500 years, but the publication of the *Midwifery Act* in Ontario on January 1, 1994, was the first legal acknowledgment in Canada of the legitimacy of birthing babies beyond the medical model approach. Pregnancy and childbirth are natural and low-risk processes for most women. Midwives provide continuity of care by supporting the woman and her family throughout the pregnancy, during the birth, and for six weeks after delivery. One of the benefits is supporting families with breast-feeding. If a new mother is able to work through the initial challenges and breast-feed for a longer term, there are substantial benefits to both child and mother (see Breast Milk and Infant Formula, page 251).

- In Canada, the rate of caesarean births has risen steadily over the past three decades in all provinces and territories, with British Columbia having the highest rate (30.4%) by 2005 (British Columbia Perinatal Health Program, 2008, p. 3). Although there are many reasons for high caesarean rates, midwifery care can potentially reduce the incidence of such interventions, resulting in a less medically intrusive experience for women and savings to the health care system and hospitals.

- Women who use midwives can choose a home or hospital birth.

- The positive impact of midwifery in Ontario has resulted in the *Maternity Care in Ontario 2006: Emerging Crisis, Emerging Solutions* recommendation to "attract, support and retain maternity care providers by developing a system that values and respects all provider groups, including midwives, nurses and physicians through harmonization of regulation and liability mechanisms and creation of complementary funding schemes" (Ontario Women's Health Council, 2006, p. 13).

- The majority of provinces and territories in Canada have now legalized and legislated midwifery. Statistics Canada conducted *The Maternity Experiences Survey*, a national snapshot of women's experiences during pregnancy, birth, and early parenthood in 2007. Of the women who had had a midwife oversee their delivery, 71% rated it as a "very positive" experience. Of the women who had had an obstetrician-gynecologist oversee their delivery, only 53% rated it the same way (Canadian Broadcasting Corporation, 2007, p. 1).

Community health centres are another example of a collaborative, community approach to health care. Under one roof, they provide the services of professionals such as physicians, nurses, public health nurses, nurse practitioners, dietitian-nutritionists, social workers, physical and occupational therapists, health advocates, counsellors, interpreters, massage therapists, and pharmacists. These professionals work together to meet the diverse needs of individuals and their families. The health care centres refer patients to and work with other community services, such as job retraining, English as an additional language (EAL) lessons, housing and income agencies, legal aid, and so on. Find out about community health centres in your community and become aware of the diverse services they offer. Often programs related to early childhood and parenting are important components of their organizations.

These and other measures benefit patients and the public by reducing overuse and misuse of the system and by providing alternatives that may be more appropriate for the health and well-being of some individuals. Obviously, the expertise of doctors remains important to Canada's health care system, but a team approach uses the expertise of many health and health-related professionals effectively.

This change moves away from the doctor's office and hospitals to clinics that provide a variety of services in collaboration. Community health centres also make a statement that health and social services should not be separated. Many people, such as those who live in poverty or on the street, who are not fully literate, or who have recently immigrated to Canada, are unable to obtain the level or quality of health care that others can in the conventional medical care system. Ideally, community health centres are designed and administered by the community to meet its unique needs.

Complementary Medicine Practitioners

Historically, **complementary (or traditional) medicine** practitioners such as homeopaths and naturopaths have been excluded from the conventional medical model in Canada. Many alternative practices and products have not been scientifically proven to be effective or safe, so they are unregulated and not covered by medical insurance plans or drug benefit plans. Conversely, critics of conventional medicine question whether some treatments covered by medicare are medically necessary or effective, or at least they question those that are overused (e.g., the high number of sonograms done during healthy pregnancies). Some individuals may assume that using a complementary practitioner is a step toward holistic health; however, that may not always be the case. Anyone who chooses to consult a complementary practitioner—or a physician, for that matter—must be a very conscientious consumer. Moreover, urgent attention on the part of governmental authorities is needed to ensure the safety and effectiveness of complementary interventions.

Natural Health Products

Natural health products (NHPs) are now the most popular form of complementary health care in North America. On January 1, 2004, Health Canada's *Natural Health Products Regulations* came into effect, defining NHPs as

- vitamins and minerals,
- herbal remedies,

- homeopathic medicines,
- traditional medicines, such as traditional Chinese medicines,
- probiotics, and
- other products such as amino acids and essential fatty acids.

NHPs must be safe for consideration as over-the-counter products, be available for self-care and self-selection, and not require a prescription to be sold. Products requiring a prescription will continue to be regulated under Health Canada's *Food and Drug Regulations* unless future amendments to this legislation change this condition (Health Canada, 2007).

"Natural," however, doesn't always mean safe. For example, some NHPs are toxic in large doses; some can cause side effects, allergic reactions, or interact with other medications; and some may be harmful for people in certain circumstances (e.g., with heart disease, during pregnancy). It is therefore important to consult your doctor, naturopath, or pharmacist before trying a product (Tzu Chi Institute for Complementary and Alternative Medicine, 2002, p. 1).

Drugs and Health Care Products: Baseline Natural Health Products Survey Among Consumers, conducted for Health Canada (2005b, pp. 2–3), found the following:

- Seven in 10 Canadians (71%) have used an NHP.

  Vitamins (57%), echinacea (15%), herbal remedies, and algal and fungal products (11%) top the list of NHPs used.

- Personal health concerns and the desire to maintain and promote personal health are primary factors driving the use of NHPs (52%).

  Three in 10 Canadians (29%) feel that NHPs are natural and safe or better than conventional medications. Twenty percent report that they acted on the recommendation of others, such as family or a physician.

- Eight in 10 Canadians (81%) think it is important to respect the role that NHPs play in some cultures.

  A majority (81%) think that the use of NHPs will increase over the next 10 years, and seven in 10 (72%) believe that Canadians have the right to use any NHP they choose.

- One half of Canadians (52%) think that NHPs are safe because they are made from natural ingredients. Three times as many Canadians (62%) disagree as agree (21%) that if a health product is made of natural substances, no risks are associated with its use.

- Nine in 10 (91%) agree that all NHP manufacturers must ensure that the products they sell to consumers are safe.

  A majority of Canadians (84%) agree that the Government of Canada should regulate the claims made by manufacturers of NHPs. Over three-quarters (76%) agree that Health Canada should regulate NHPs in the same way they regulate prescription drugs.

- Over three-quarters of Canadians (77%) agree that it is okay for the NHP industry to put health claims on labels, as long as they are backed by scientific evidence.

- Seven in 10 Canadians (69%) agree that they need more information on NHPs, and an even larger majority (84%) believe that more needs to be done to inform Canadians about the safe use of NHPs.

Source: Adapted from *Drugs and health products: Baseline Natural Products Survey Among Consumers,* Health Canada 2005. Reproduced with the permission of the Minister of Public Works and Government Services Canada, 2008.

The intent of the federal government's *Natural Health Products Regulations* is to ensure that the products are safe, effective, and of high quality. The regulations include

- labelling requirements that place more information about individual products in the hands of consumers and practitioners,
- a premarket approval process to ensure that what is described on the label is actually in the bottle, and
- a requirement that appropriate levels of scientific evidence support any claims on the label about the product's effects (Tzu Chi Institute for Complementary and Alternative Medicine, 2002, p. 3).

Some families in early childhood programs use complementary practitioners and medicines. Remedies and medicines may come either from cultural or traditional backgrounds or from a philosophy that differs from the established medical model. It is important to respect health practices different from your own and to be aware of your role in promoting the health of each child in your care. If you question an aspect of the family's health practices, find out more about it before taking action. However, many, if not most, early childhood programs have written policies restricting the administering of nonprescribed medication in your program (see Administering Medication, page 180).

In Canada, some alternative health care is covered, at least partially, by the discretion of the provincial and territorial health insurance plans (e.g., osteopaths, chiropractors). Some medical doctors are incorporating complementary practices into their patients' care. These doctors are under increasing scrutiny from their licensing body. In contrast, some European countries have progressed further in recognizing the effectiveness of combining conventional and complementary medical practices. The cost of complementary practices is covered by their medical insurance plans.

PREVENTION AND HEALTH PROMOTION

Prevention and health promotion activities have been practised for centuries. In the 1970s, a more committed and conscious movement toward healthy living began in Canada.

What Is Prevention?

As one component of health promotion, "**prevention** involves identifying the factors which cause a condition and then reducing or eliminating them" (Epp, 1986, p. 4). The goal is to have individuals adopt preventive strategies in their daily lives that may lower the risk of occurrence or recurrence of a

OBJECTIVES

To define health promotion according to the World Health Organization.

To define prevention.

To describe how prevention fits into the health promotion approach.

particular illness or injury. Although lowering a risk doesn't guarantee that a disease is prevented, most people recognize the positive elements of this change.

Here are some examples of prevention strategies:

- stop-smoking programs and no-smoking policies for preventing lung cancer and lowering the risk of heart disease and other major diseases
- monthly breast self-examinations and regular Pap smears for women for early identification of disease
- regular dental checkups
- hand-washing and immunization programs for children to reduce the spread of infectious diseases
- the design of play equipment for safety and appropriateness for the ages and number of children using it
- the use of seat belts in cars and bike helmets on bicycles and scooters

There is not always evidence to support cause-and-effect relationships between health behaviour and disease. In fact, the many interrelated factors involved in disease make prevention complex. Also, popular opinion often promotes certain preventive lifestyle behaviours. These situations highlight the importance of the informed consumer, who weighs the pros and cons of specific behaviour. In particular, we cannot assume that every preventive practice recommended for adults can be applied to children.

What Is Health Promotion?

Health promotion is "the process of enabling people to increase control over, and to improve their health" (World Health Organization, Health and Welfare Canada, and Canadian Public Health Association, 1986, p. 1). According to Labonte (1993, p. 6),

> Health promotion is concerned with creating living conditions in which people's experience of "health" (well-being) is increased. To an extent, this also requires decreasing their risk of disease. But disease prevention is not the primary goal of health promotion; it is a secondary goal. A health promotion program can improve health (well-being) without necessarily reducing the prevalence of disease, or of specific disease risk factors such as smoking, high fat intake or lack of fitness.

Areas in which the federal government has implemented healthy public policy are restrictions on the sale and advertising of tobacco, publicity to reduce impaired driving, and a ban of bisphenol A in the making of plastic baby bottles. Over time, our understanding of the factors that contribute to better health has deepened. At first, government policies focused on lifestyle choices and on healthy public policy. Now, largely because of research on the nonmedical social determinants of health and how they profoundly affect health, the focus has shifted to the societal level, beyond factors that are within the immediate control of individuals and communities (e.g., safe and affordable housing, enhanced maternity/parental leave, reduction of environmental contaminants).

With a holistic view of health, everyone can be involved in promoting health. It is becoming increasingly apparent that people who believe they can control aspects of their lives and have choices are more likely to be action oriented and self-confident. It is easy to lose hope or view ourselves as ineffective when we believe we have no control over our destiny. In your work with children, you will model and foster feelings of self-confidence and belief in oneself within a realistic framework of what we may or may not be able to control.

Integrating Prevention into a Health Promotion Approach

You may be saying to yourself, "I have control over most aspects of my life," and that is true to a degree. Many of us didn't succumb to outside influences and start smoking. Perhaps we made other lifestyle decisions based on positive or negative influences. No one can claim, for example, "Cigarette advertising and peer pressure made me smoke." To focus solely on individual lifestyle decisions is to ignore the complex aspects of health behaviour. Nor can society simply blame the victim, absolving itself of its responsibility for coordinating healthy public policy, fostering public participation, and strengthening community health services (Epp, 1986, p. 8). An individual's ability to implement specific prevention strategies and the likelihood of success or failure are directly related to additional factors that affect that person's life. To think otherwise is to blame the victim (e.g., "It is the teenage girl's fault that she has anorexia," or "If he had been stronger willed and stopped smoking, he wouldn't have lung cancer," or "She's fat because she's lazy"). This attitude toward prevention is unacceptable and does nothing to enhance our understanding of health and improve our well-being.

Sarah quit smoking to reduce her health risks. She can't understand why everyone else can't do the same. For others, quitting smoking is more than withdrawal from addiction to nicotine. Malcolm has tried to quit a few times, but he recently lost his job, and smoking helps reduce his overwhelming feelings of stress. Sarah is probably right when she says that Malcolm should find a healthy alternative for relieving his stress, but the issue is more complicated. Most of Malcolm's friends smoke, and their social activities permit them to smoke. Moreover, his father and uncles smoked and lived long lives without developing lung cancer, so he has no firsthand evidence in support of claims made by experts.

A health promotion perspective takes into account the challenges of reducing inequities in Malcolm's life and enhancing his capacity to quit smoking. He enters a job-retraining program that results in meaningful employment. His standard of living improves, as do his self-esteem and outlook on his future. With lowered stress levels, Malcolm is better able to cope with everyday stress by walking to and from work. He now works in a no-smoking workplace. His new friends at work happen to be nonsmokers, and he is involved in different social activities. With the high cost of cigarettes, no-smoking legislation in public places, and concerns about secondhand smoke, smokers are feeling society's pressure to stop smoking. Consequently, Malcolm now has a much better chance of success because so many other factors are in place to support his decision.

In summary, health promotion involves all aspects of a person's life that affect his or her well-being, and prevention focuses on particular risks or behaviour believed to be causal factors in disease or injury.

CRITICAL THINKING

With regard to an adult with asthma, give an example of a prevention strategy within a health promotion framework.

To list and describe the five determinants of health most applicable to early childhood programs.

To identify at least one strategy to promote health in the early childhood setting for each of the five determinants.

To list the elements of quality in an early childhood education program.

To list the purposes of program policies in an early childhood program.

To discuss student and educator strategies to advocate for high-quality early childhood programs.

HEALTH PROMOTION IN EARLY CHILDHOOD PROGRAMS

Promoting health is something we can do to improve the quality of our life and the lives of those around us. How can early childhood programs be part of this movement?

Social Determinants: The Five Most Applicable to Early Childhood Settings

How do the social determinants of health relate to daily work in the field of child and family services? Although all 12 of them are linked, 5 in particular are "present" in early childhood settings on a day-to-day basis:

1. healthy child development
2. education and literacy
3. income and social status
4. social support networks
5. culture

One: Healthy Child Development

Healthy child development is now known to be a key determinant of long-term health (Hertzman, 1998, p. S14). A healthy start in life has a great impact on the well-being of children and throughout life, providing opportunities for children to develop the attributes and resilience needed to mature into healthy adults in our complex society. A child's experiences during early childhood become embedded in the individual's biology. It is known that early childhood is the most vulnerable and influential period of human development, setting in place essential conditions for lifelong growth and development (Keating & Miller, 1999, p. 220). These experiences include a child's exposure to environmental contaminants. Although the complex processes involved in human growth and development are not fully understood, our history with toxic substances such as lead and pesticides makes it evident that even small amounts of some substances can have profound effects that may not appear until long after exposure. The Canadian Institute of Child Health is a known advocate working at all levels to limit unnecessary exposure to environmental contaminants (see Environmental Contaminants, page 421).

Neuroscience is helping us understand how social determinants affect the body through biological pathways. We now know that, although the brain has all its areas and neurons at birth, it is far from fully developed. "Wiring" or setting learning pathways essentially takes place during the first few years of life. The neuron connections strengthen from care and nurturing. Positive relationships with adults in the early years are investments in optimal brain development.

> During this investment phase, children develop language skills, the ability to learn, to cope with stress, to have healthy relationships with others, and to have a sense of self. . . . Failure to provide optimum conditions for a child's development during this time makes the developing brain physically different from the brain of children who have been well nurtured, and these differences can have lifelong consequences. (Hertzman, 1997, p. 6)

Since the central nervous system communicates with all systems in the body (e.g., immune, hormonal, gastrointestinal), it follows that brain development affects long-term functioning of the body—hence the incidence of disease (Hertzman, 1998, p. S16).

Parenting style has long been recognized as a critical influence on healthy child development; nurturing relationships support all areas of development. Fortunately, most children live with parents who have supportive and positive approaches to parenting. In fact, the vast majority of parents score well on a scale that looks at "effective parenting," including approaches to discipline and consistency. The good news is that according to a scale that measures positive parenting behaviours such as talking, playing, and laughing together, 92% of children under age two and a significant majority of older children lived with parents who demonstrated a positive parenting style. However, Invest in Kids (2008) reports that nearly one in three Canadian children under the age of six have a social, emotional, or learning problem. Early childhood programs, schools, workplaces, and governments need to continue to create family-friendly policies that support the changing demands, dynamics, and composition of families (Canadian Council on Social Development, 2006). Agencies such as Invest in Kids translate the science of parenting and early child development into engaging, easy-to-understand, relevant resources for parents and professionals to strengthen parenting knowledge, skills, and confidence (Invest in Kids, 2008).

The "family-time famine," a reality in many homes, is problematic because families need time together to nurture relationships and enhance members' sense of security, belonging, and competence. A 2001 national survey of more than

31,000 employees from medium and large organizations found that half felt that work time and stress have a negative impact on spending time with children and 42% said that they affected their relationships with their children (Canadian Council on Social Development, 2006, p. 14).

Developmental Health

As discussed earlier in the unit, a population health approach recognizes the value of public policy that strives to improve the health of the entire population while reducing inequities among population groups. Developmental psychology studies the biological and environmental factors in brain development. **Developmental health** combines these two fields of study in recognizing the impact of early childhood experiences on lifelong health:

- Developmental health is a new theory of human development that combines developmental psychology and population health. This approach looks at population trends from lifelong health and well-being outcomes in the context of early childhood (Red River College, n.d.).

- Illnesses and disabilities that emerge in adult life have their roots in early childhood and prenatal development (Hertzman & Power, 2004). Measures of physical growth, cognition, and behaviour in early childhood predict health status in adult life (Hertzman & Power, 2004). (Red River College, 2004)

- No socioeconomic threshold exists below which all children have problems and above which all children do well. While children in the lowest-income families are more likely to experience problems with health and development, a high proportion of children in middle income and higher-income families also have problems. Programs that target only low-income children and youth will miss the majority of vulnerable young people. Also the greatest numbers of children having difficulties are actually living in moderate income, two-parent families. Gradients in early development reflect daily experiences and environments that are shaped by family, neighbourhood, and societal factors. [Socioeconomic status (SES)] is a powerful factor but other elements of nurturant or non-nurturant environments and experiences influence the course of development. (Red River College, n.d.).

- Early learning, behaviour and health are markers for brain development. SES gradients in early childhood can be interpreted as evidence of differences in access to developmental opportunities that provide adequate nurturance, nutrition and stimulation (Hertzman & Power, 2004; McCain, Mustard, & Shanker., 2007). (Red River College, n.d.)

Two: Education and Literacy

As future educators, you can likely relate to the fact that the more educated a person is, the more likely he or she is to be healthy. While we care for young children, we also play a tremendous role in their education. Children's introduction to the world of learning is, in partnership with their parents, very often through their first experiences in group-based early learning and child care settings. Children learn through play, and we are great promoters of play! As already mentioned, brain research tells us that the early years set the foundation for lifelong learning, behaviour, and health. Play-based problem solving is an optimal approach to early learning. One of our most important roles is in supporting and promoting early and emerging literacy in young children, through a rich play environment and opportunities for problem solving, especially in pretend play. Also, educators and families are mutual resources, directly and indirectly supporting the child's education. Programs may also hold events with guest speakers, such as the local public health nurse or dietitian, or may offer a book-lending library with parenting titles, all of which benefit the child's education.

Communication skills include the ability to speak and be understood, as well as literacy. In Canada, literacy is defined as being able to read and write in one or both of our official languages, English and French. A large number of adults, well over three million Canadians aged 16 to 65, have problems dealing with printed materials and most likely identify themselves as people who have difficulty reading. A survey comparing literacy statistics from 1994 and 2003 in six participating countries (including Canada), found a significant wage return for higher skill levels (Statistics Canada, 2005, p. 1). Their results highlight the importance of literacy skills.

Adults whose first language is English (or French) may have low literacy skills; so, too, may adults whose first language is not English (or French). These individuals may be literate in their first language (e.g., Mandarin, Italian, Cree) but not in English or French; however, statistically, they are not considered literate by Canadian standards and are at a disadvantage in the larger community.

In addition to the broader disadvantages (e.g., lack of career opportunities, much lower pay) that are associated with illiteracy, there are often specific concerns contributing to poor health, such as the inability to read printed information about health or illness. People who do not speak or understand one of the official languages well are at a disadvantage because they may not seek information or must depend on someone else's interpretation. A person who is illiterate and has no access to an interpreter may be unable to make effective use of health or social services. Some examples are as follows:

- A person may not adequately understand a physician's or pharmacist's instructions.
- In an early childhood program, parents who are not sufficiently fluent in the same language as the educators may not understand when they are asked to bring in their child's immunization record.
- Parents who are illiterate or have low literacy may not disclose that they can't read the program's parent handbook outlining the health policies.

To improve readability, many public materials are now written in plain and simple language. In large cities, or areas where many people speak, read, and write in languages other than English or French, municipal governments often publish pamphlets and other documents in other languages. This service has had a positive effect on the well-being of people in the community.

Health, social services, and educational departments continue to find ways to increase the number of informational resources accessible to those who do not speak, read, and write English or French. As well, individuals and their cultural or ethnic communities have a responsibility to seek language and literacy programs in English or French so they can use the available resources.

CRITICAL THINKING

For the education and literacy determinant of health, give an example of how a program can support families in promoting health.

Three: Social Support Networks

Educators engage in family support and believe in the value of social support networks. Healthy social environments and strong support networks promote the emotional and physical well-being of children. Many early childhood programs proactively establish networks among the parents in their programs, encouraging mutual support and connecting parents with services and supports.

Community as Context

You share a partnership with parents and other family members in enabling the child to be the best that he or she can be—physically, emotionally, socially. The early childhood education program should provide a welcoming community for families in the context of their lives at that time. Parents know their child best, and it is important that you respect their values and parenting practices. After all, the child is part of that family for a lifetime but is part of your early childhood program for only a limited time. Parents are the decision makers about their child's health. Educators, however, may be

able to provide information such as referrals to agencies, books, articles, and other individuals who help parents consider new information or another perspective in their decisions. Building relationships with parents on a daily basis benefits everyone involved.

After you graduate as an early childhood educator, you may at times be concerned about the effects of a family's health values or practices on the child's well-being. You must determine whether your concern stems from a value or practice that is different from any that you are accustomed to. This difference may reflect socio-cultural differences, a term that refers to ethnicity, race, class, religion, or any other aspect of a social group that shapes values and practices. This value or practice may be very different from, or even in conflict with, one that you grew up with. If it is, you must decide whether this value or practice is simply another way of looking at something or is potentially harmful to the child's physical, emotional, or social well-being. You broaden your awareness by learning about other perspectives. You may or may not decide to adopt this value or practice, but it is important that you not judge others solely on the basis of your limited view. Competent educators strive to communicate with families and support each family's values as much as possible while maintaining standards of high-quality early childhood education.

If, on the other hand, you are unsure about the parents' values or practices because of the potential for physical, emotional, or social harm to the child, you have a responsibility to investigate. Effective communication with parents ensures that you understand the value or practice. Ineffective communication frequently results in assumptions and judgments based on incomplete information. It is possible, often with the help of community resources, to make a more informed decision on the issue and decide, likely with the director, on a plan of action. Keep in mind that most parents care about their children and believe that their parenting reflects this care. This principle can be very helpful in deciding what to do next.

You are concerned about Karim's eating habits. You talk with his parents about his total nutritional intake and any food restrictions. You both agree that a dietitian from the public health department may be able to provide educational material and suggestions that will help.

In addition to pre-enrollment interviews, parents and educators find out more about each other through day-to-day communication, regular parent–educator interviews, the parent handbook, bulletin boards, and other communication vehicles. If differences exist between the program's philosophy and policies and the parents' values and practices, the parents might consider using an early childhood program that better reflects their attitudes. In most situations, however, educators and the director will have tried to negotiate a mutually acceptable situation before that happens.

"**Social capital**" is a term that means the power of socially cohesive communities that benefits all children and families, as communities support healthy practices by making a healthy choice the easy choice. The Health Council of Canada's report (2006) *Their Future Is Now* lists and describes several communities of all sizes that have organized with a vision for healthy children. Responding to the United Nations launch of the Child Friendly Cities Initiative, a number of Canadian communities, such as the municipal government of the city of Greater Sudbury, and nonprofit organizations such as the The Society for Children and Youth of British Columbia, have embarked on changes to the physical and social environments that promote health. Accessibility to safe pedestrian networks, free or low-cost recreation, affordable healthy food, and other responsive changes meet the stated needs of children and families. Hundreds of programs across Canada are working together as communities, often with a common language, culture, or needs. Communities are not necessarily geographic but have common goals that promote consistency for children and families. This is often referred to as "communities in context."

In summary, ongoing communication in early childhood settings and socially cohesive neighbourhoods and communities are great ways to build social networks and buffer some of the stressors in the lives of families.

Four: Income and Social Status

Income and social status are well recognized as key factors in determining an individual and family level of health. The more money an individual or family has, the greater the opportunities are to get a good education; purchase adequate food, clothing, and housing; buy recreational equipment and take vacations; and generally make the choices necessary to participate in opportunities that promote healthy child development. Evidence strongly suggests that poverty is the greatest barrier (or threat) to health—people living in poverty are much more likely to develop health problems, including chronic illnesses such as heart or lung disease, and to die at an earlier age than people living above the poverty level.

> When income is restricted, people often select foods that are higher in simple sugar and saturated fat because they are among the least expensive foods. This pattern of eating can contribute to chronic health problems such as type 2 diabetes or cardiovascular disease.

A significant measure of the health and strength of a society is the well-being of its children and families. By that measure, Canada is failing. *The 2007 Report Card on Child and Family Poverty* (Campaign 2000, 2007, cover) states: "At 11.7% the child poverty rate is exactly the same as it was in 1989. 1 in 8 children in Canada - 788,000 - live in poverty when income is measured after income taxes. Before income taxes, 1 in 6 or 1.13 million children live in poverty. 41% of children living in poverty live in families with at least one income earner working full-time all year" *The 2007 Report Card on Child and Family Poverty* (Campaign 2000, 2007, p. 3) continues with the following statistics:

> For every $1 earned by the poorest 10% of families with children, the richest 10% earned $12.57 in 2005. The benefits of a strong Canadian economy have not been evenly distributed among Canadian families. The federal government should invest a portion of the budget surplus in a poverty reduction strategy that helps reduce inequality, instead of implementing tax cuts that disproportionately benefit the wealthiest Canadians.

But the risk of poverty is not the same for all children:

- In families that face systemic discrimination (e.g., newcomers to Canada, Aboriginal families), child poverty rates are as high as one in two children (Campaign 2000, 2007, p. 1).
- Female lone-parent families have the highest poverty rates. Their situation improved between 1993 and 2001 but has deteriorated since then. Children in female lone-parent families have a poverty rate three times that of all children and four and a half times that of children in two-parent families (Canadian Council on Social Development, 2006, p. 18).

FIGURE 1.1   Child Poverty in Canada and the Provinces, 2005

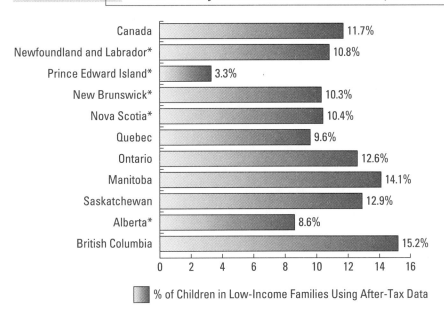

Canada	11.7%
Newfoundland and Labrador*	10.8%
Prince Edward Island*	3.3%
New Brunswick*	10.3%
Nova Scotia*	10.4%
Quebec	9.6%
Ontario	12.6%
Manitoba	14.1%
Saskatchewan	12.9%
Alberta*	8.6%
British Columbia	15.2%

▇ % of Children in Low-Income Families Using After-Tax Data

*Statistics Canada listed the data as "use with caution" due to small sample size.
Source: Statistics Canada's *Income Trends in Canada, 1980–2005, Table 802.*

Source: Reprinted with permission from Campaign 2000 Family Service Toronto (2007), *2007 Report Card on Child and Family Poverty in Canada: It Takes a Nation to Raise a Generation*, 1. (Material from quoted on page 26 is used with permission).

Some children move into and out of poverty, usually as a result of their parents' ability to find and maintain a full-time, well-paying job. Other families depend on two wages to provide basic needs, and even the two combined may be insufficient. The gap between poor and well-off families in Canada has been widening steadily since 1973. This is mainly due to the lack of access to jobs that can support families. Most of the jobs that have been created are part-time, low wage, contract, or seasonal, with few or no benefits. Furthermore, in recessionary times, people who have been gainfully employed for years may lose their jobs, putting them in short- or long-term poverty situations. Consequently, many families are excluded from participation in the economic and social fabric of their communities. This undermines the connectedness that communities need to maintain and build public support for social programs (Campaign 2000, 2002, pp. 2, 3). In households in which one of the adults is physically or emotionally challenged, or must be the primary caregiver for a family member with substantial special needs, that person may be unable to find employment that provides an adequate income—or to find any employment at all. The financial impact of a family breakup or reconstitution also moves families into or out of poverty.

Children who live in persistent poverty are less likely to be academically prepared to start school. When they get there, they have less positive, less successful school lives, with poorer scores in reading, math, science, and writing. They are more likely to have emotional problems and to exhibit anxiety, aggressive behaviours, and hyperactivity (Canadian Council on Social Development, 2006, p. 18). It is not surprising that children who are poor are not likely to enjoy the same feelings of self-worth or quality of life as their more financially stable peers (e.g., they are less likely to participate in sports or other organized physical activities because of high costs).

FIGURE 1.2	Child Poverty Rates among Selected Social Groups

1 in 2 for children in recent immigrant families **(49%)**
1 in 2.5 for First Nations children living outside First Nations communities **(40%)**
1 in 3 for children in racialized families **(34%)**
1 in 4 for children with disabilities **(28%)**
1 in 4 for children living in First Nation communities **(28%)**

Source: Statistics Canada's *Canada Census 2001* and Assembly of First Nations 2006.

Source: Reprinted with permission from Campaign 2000 (2007), *2007 Report Card on Child and Family Poverty in Canada: It Takes a Nation to Raise a Generation*, 2.

Although we know that not every child who grew up in poverty does poorly long term, the preferred long-term strategy is not to build resilience in poor children but to eliminate child poverty. Having choices and control over many of the decisions in one's life contributes to one's well-being, and a degree of control is enjoyed by most wealthy Canadians. It follows, then, that poverty, unemployment, and cuts in social supports have a dramatic impact on the health of many Canadians. A standard of living that fosters well-being is achieved when adults have the opportunity to work at meaningful jobs, have access to affordable housing, and have high-quality early childhood education for their children.

This poverty of opportunity speaks to the reality that, in Canada, we are not usually talking about absolute poverty, requiring the necessities of life. Nonetheless, this is the situation for those living in First Nations communities and homeless families in urban areas. However, a "poverty of opportunity" refers to the relative poverty experienced by more than a million children in Canada:

> In a day and age when education, emotional maturity, leadership, and social and communication skills are prized as essential for prospering in an increasingly knowledge-based society, it is not promising that so many children are starting off with such disadvantage. The skills and attributes valued today require more than a start in life at a minimum subsistence level. (Ross, Scott, & Smith, 2000, p. 3)

The situation of Canada's Aboriginal peoples highlights Canada's failure in addressing social and economic determinants of health. Aboriginal peoples have the poorest health status of all Canadians. The federal government holds the primary responsibility to support Aboriginal communities in addressing the health gap. When basic needs such as safe water supplies and housing are not available to many communities, it is little wonder that health status is not significantly improving. To meet the challenge of administering and controlling their own health care, Aboriginal communities require adequate investment from the federal government to build their infrastructure. They also need continued support for initiatives that draw on traditional knowledge and culture to develop culturally relevant approaches to problems such as substance abuse and family violence. Although Canada's Aboriginal people have contributed a rich heritage to the country, they have not shared fully in its social and economic development. On June 11, 2008, the federal government publicly apologized to Aboriginal people for enduring generations of torment that saw the federal government strive to extinguish their language and eradicate their culture in residential schools. It was a historic moment when Canada's first peoples finally heard a prime minister say, "We are sorry." However, the insidious multigenerational damage to their people and communities cannot be undone, and moving forward requires much effort.

In the realities of day-to-day life, there are parents and families who require more than social supports, such as some parents with low incomes. Resourceful educators recognize and seek out respectful means to assist parents if they are willing. Along with discreetly sharing information on local food banks, clothing exchanges, and training and skills development opportunities, some educators actively advocate for universally accessible child care so that parents can engage in work, training, and other opportunities—a longer term strategy than food banks. However, the short-term reality often means that the small ways to support families are important for children and their families.

In conclusion, poverty, particularly as it affects children and families, must be addressed to improve health.

The federal government can make that happen with these initiatives (Campaign 2000, 2007, p. 7):

- Increase the National Child Benefit Supplement to create a full child benefit for low-income families of $5,100 per child per year.
- Increase federal work tax credits to $2,400 per year.
- Establish a federal minimum wage of $10 per hour (in 2007 dollars).
- Restore broad eligibility for Employment Insurance.
- Invest major federal funding in social housing.
- Invest major federal funding in early learning and child care.
- Establish a basic income system for persons with disabilities.
- Adopt specific poverty reduction targets, timelines, and indicators for Aboriginal families with intergovernmental coordination and accountability to First Nations on results.

Source: Reprinted with permission from Campaign 2000 (2007), *2007 Report Card on Child and Family Poverty in Canada: It Takes a Nation to Raise a Generation*, 7.

Five: Culture

Because families are so diverse, educators also recognize the importance of culture in people's health. "**Culture**" sounds like a simple word, but it can actually be a very complex term. It is probably best defined by each individual. "Inherited" culture can include one's race, ethnicity, language, and religion. "Personal" culture, on the other hand, is acquired and often reflects shared values and attitudes and similarities in ideology.

You may have become interested in environmental issues, and the way you live is based on a philosophy of care for the environment. Your philosophy may affect the way you eat, the clothes you wear, the way you travel, and so on.

You may define your personal culture primarily by your family structure, your race or ethnic background, the language you speak (e.g., Deaf culture), your religion, your sexual orientation (e.g., lesbian), and so on. People usually define their culture by the aspects of their lives that most affect their day-to-day living.

As noted by the Public Health Agency of Canada (2004), some people face additional health risks due to marginalization, stigmatization, and lack of access to culturally appropriate services. Culture-specific practices can also have an impact on the overall health of a population. The skilled educator respects and accommodates, as much as possible, the cultural preferences of a family— everything from respecting religious dietary restrictions to toilet learning preferences. Referring families to culturally relevant services and agencies in the community is one way to support their inclusivity and access.

CRITICAL THINKING

Your program's philosophy places a high value on helping children develop independence. However, one family in the program places a high value on interdependence (i.e., a long-term commitment to depending on one another, remaining close to family). How do the staff and parents compromise in the best interest of the child?

It is important to recognize that there are different ways of being and doing, and not all ways will be familiar to you. By asking parents informal questions such as "How do you handle this type of situation at home?" you can gain insight into why a child doesn't respond well to the educators' strategy, and you can also acquire another way of looking at the issue. In a program that has an open view to diversity, this would simply be viewed as a different way—a way to be respected. Children can be caught between two value systems. When issues about value differences arise, it is a priority to negotiate a cultural conflict so that neither way is devalued (see Table 1.2).

Educators have a responsibility to find out as much as possible about the child and family's culture and to be sensitive and responsive to differences. It is certainly possible for children to move comfortably between the early childhood setting and the home culture, where roles, expectations, and interactions may differ considerably, if there is mutual respect and interest by educators and parents. A climate of acceptance paves the way for understanding and learning for everyone involved.

If a child and his or her family believes that the early childhood environment supports the child's individuality and cultural values, beliefs, and practices, they will feel emotionally secure and comfortable contributing to others' awareness of their values and practices. Children are profoundly influenced by

TABLE 1.2   Suggestions for Approaching Cultural Conflicts

Here is a summary of hints to help you deal with the cultural conflicts that can arise in a child care setting:

1. *Take it slow.* Don't expect to resolve each conflict immediately. Building understanding and relationships takes time. Some conflicts won't be resolved; they'll just be managed. You have to learn to cope with differences when there is no common meeting ground or resolution. This coping sounds hard, but it's possible, if you're willing to accept the fact that resolution is not always the outcome of disputes.

2. *Understand yourself.* Become clear about your own values and goals. Know what you believe in. Have a bottom line, but leave space above it to be flexible.

3. *Become sensitive to your own discomfort.* Tune in to those times when something bothers you instead of just ignoring it and hoping it will go away. Work to identify what specific behaviours of others make you uncomfortable. Try to discover exactly what in yourself created this discomfort.

4. *Learn about other cultures.* Books, classes, and workshops help, but watch out for stereotypes and biased information. Your best source of information comes from the parents in your program. Check out what they believe about their cultures, and see if it fits with other information you receive. However, don't ever make one person a representative of his or her culture. Listen to individuals, take in the information they give you, but don't generalize to whole cultures. Keep your mind open as you learn. Check out your point of view. There's a difference between finding and celebrating diversity and explaining deficiencies.

5. *Find out what the parents in your program, individually, want for their children.* What are their goals? What are their caregiving practices? What concerns do they have about their child in your program? Encourage them to talk to you. Encourage them to ask questions. You may find out about cultures this way, or you may just find out about individual or familial differences. All are important.

6. *Be a risk taker.* If you are secure enough, you may feel you can afford to make mistakes. Mistakes are a part of cross-cultural communication. It helps to have a good support system behind you when you take risks and make mistakes.

7. *Communicate, dialogue, negotiate.* If you have a chance to build a relationship before getting into negotiations, you're more likely eventually to reach a mutually satisfying point.

8. *Share power.* Empowerment is an important factor in the dialogue-negotiation process. Although some see empowerment (allowing others to experience their own personal power) as threatening, in reality empowerment creates new forms of power. Some teachers and educators fear that empowerment means giving away their own power, but this is not true! No one can give personal power, and no one can take it away. We all have our personal power, though we can be discouraged or prevented from recognizing or using it. Sharing power, or empowerment, enhances everyone's power.

In conclusion, hard as it may be to take the risks involved in cross-cultural encounters, to learn what is needed to understand culturally different people, to gain skills in communication, and to cope when conflicts arise, exposure to more than one culture is a definite asset. As you care for children from various cultural backgrounds, everyone gains. You, the children, and the parents have the opportunity to learn more about and appreciate human diversity.

Source: *Diversity in Early Care and Education: Honoring Differences,* 5/E © 2008 by Janet Gonzalez-Mena. Reprinted with permission from The McGraw-Hill Companies, 55–57.

the attitudes of their adult community. The term "**cultural safety**" refers to the outcome of interactions in which individuals experience their cultural identity and way of being as having been respected or, at least, not challenged or harmed (Ball, 2007). It is essential for educators to remember the importance of this outcome in their relationships with families and coworkers.

People from common ethnic backgrounds may have shared traits (e.g., skin colour, language), customs, and behaviour. How people view health and illness, doctors, medicine, and approaches to healing may be influenced by their ethnicity. In addition to finding out about these beliefs directly from parents, you can contact agencies that are aware of an ethnoculture's health beliefs and practices. However, we can't assume from general information that a family has particular health beliefs or practices. Individuals and families are unique in their situations and beliefs—ethnicity is just one aspect of many that shape people's lives.

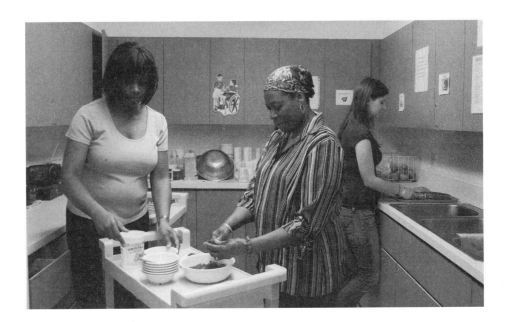

CRITICAL THINKING

The community centre that houses your early childhood program is offering a community kitchen on Saturday afternoons. All families are welcome. The children will be cared for by paid staff while the adults will cook together and bring home enough food for two evening family meals. Use Appendix 1.1 as a guide to identify the determinants of health being addressed and provide an example for how each of the features and values of a health promotion philosophy can be met in this scenario.

High-Quality Early Childhood Programs

Tens of thousands of children in Canada are enrolled in licensed early childhood programs, and many more thousands of children would benefit from the opportunity. High-quality programs support children's lifelong learning and families' social needs. Consequently, society must acknowledge that early childhood education programs are essential services for families, recognize the indicators of high-quality programs, and support the delivery of service through legislative and financial changes. If parents have access to high-quality early childhood programs, they can participate fully in their work or education, which enhances the quality of their lives and the lives of their children.

Early childhood programs support parents in their role as their children's primary educators. High-quality early childhood programs have positive long-term health effects for children. "The positive relationship between child care quality and virtually every facet of children's development . . . is one of the most consistent findings in developmental science" (Shonkoff & Phillips, 2001, p. 313).

A baseline for quality is found in the legislation in each province and territory. Regulations for licensed early childhood programs include specifications for the following matters, among others:

- early childhood education training requirements
- group size
- staff–child ratios
- space requirements
- program planning
- nutrition requirements
- management of ill children

Every licensed early childhood program has a copy of its provincial or territorial regulations. It is important to understand that these regulations ensure a minimum standard. A minimum level of care is not high-quality early childhood education. Because licensing early childhood settings is a provincial and territorial

responsibility, regulations vary greatly across Canada. An area of particular concern is the wide variation in levels of early childhood education training required for staff working in the field.

Your role as a student and entry-level educator in providing quality care is crucial in promoting the physical, emotional, and social well-being of the children and families you serve.

Early Childhood Program Policies

An early childhood program can ensure that high-quality early childhood education is implemented by having

- a written philosophy that states its ideology about children's care and learning;
- policies that guide decisions and plans of action;
- procedures that answer the who, what, when, where, and why for each policy; and
- educators who consistently implement the policies and procedures. Educators and parents need to understand the rationale behind the policies before they can see the big picture in procedures.

Early childhood education is a cooperative effort shared by staff and parents. Preparing a policy manual is one way to demonstrate that shared commitment. Writing, reviewing, and revising the manual annually draws on the expertise of

TABLE 1.3   The Elements of Quality Child Care

Children can experience high-quality child care in any type of child-care setting: at home, in a child-care centre or a family child-care home. High-quality child care begins by protecting a child's health and safety, but goes much further to provide an experience that actively supports the child's development. Research tells us that the following characteristics are fundamental to high-quality care:

■ **A high adult-child ratio.**

The fewer children under one adult's care, the better. A high adult-child ratio is associated with closer attachment between the child and the caregiver, and to children who are more considerate and less aggressive towards other children. A high adult-child ratio—ideally, 1:3 for children under two years, 1:6 for children aged two to three and 1:8 for preschoolers—is also linked with children being more independent when they reach grade one, with better cognitive development, communication and social skills. Children who attend child-care centres with higher adult-child ratios also see themselves as more competent.

Responsive Care

Responsive care recognizes both a child's physical and emotional needs (for food, sleep, attention, for example), and a child's limits (how many new experiences the child can take in or cope with at a particular time).

Responsive care responds to a child's own needs and signals—verbal and non-verbal—and helps to build the child's tolerance for stimulation and new experiences gradually. It does not over-stimulate or force the child into dealing with more than he or she is ready for.

■ **Small group sizes.**

Small group sizes are associated with children who are more cooperative, less hostile and better behaved than children in larger groups. The children in small groups also talk and play more with other children and score higher on tests of social ability and readiness to read.

■ **Post-secondary training/education.**

Child-care providers with college diplomas or university degrees in early-childhood education are more responsive to the needs of the children in their care. Their training helps them to provide the children in their care with activities that are both stimulating and appropriate to their levels of development; as a result, the children under their care score higher than others of the same age on standard tests of language development.

■ **A positive care provider–child relationship.**

When child-care providers spend a lot of time with the children, are sensitive and responsive and actively interested in them and encourage them to talk, the children:

• are more engaged with the world around them;
• spend less time in aimless wandering; and
• have higher levels of language development and play.

■ **Well-defined spaces.**

Children thrive in settings where there are clear boundaries between group space and activity areas, whether indoors or outside. Well-defined spaces are associated with positive interactions among children and between adults and children, and are associated with more time spent exploring the environment.

■ **Well-structured, well-planned curricula.**

Children like routine and respond well to a familiar daily schedule. Children who attend child care that provides organized and age-appropriate activities—while offering children the chance to pick and choose what they want to do—score higher on cognitive and language tests and show greater levels of creativity. Children who are asked to do things that are not appropriate to their age or stage of development are likely to show higher levels of stress.

(continued)

TABLE 1.3 The Elements of Quality Child Care *(continued)*

■ **Significant parental involvement.**
A good relationship between a child-care provider and a parent—where each respects the other, there is good two-way communication and the parent is involved as a partner in the child's care—helps the child-care provider to interact more with the child and the child to interact better with other children.

Source: Reprinted with permission from Canadian Council on Learning (2006), *Why Is High-Quality Child Care Essential? The Link between Quality Child Care and Early Learning*, 2-4. <http://www.ccl-cca.ca/CCL/Reports/LessonsInLearning/20060530LinL.htm> (June 2008).

the staff, parents, and professionals in the community (e.g., public health, child abuse prevention, social services). The reviewers evaluate the effectiveness and relevance of the policies and procedures. Health information, circumstances, and priorities change. Staff or parents may raise new issues and concerns.

Health Policies

Policy manuals are legal documents that outline the program's philosophy, its goals and objectives, and how the educators intend to meet the regulations and implement the procedures. Well-written policies combine the child care regulations, early childhood education training, the expertise of other professionals and parents, and the most current health information available, in addition to drawing upon what staff have learned from managing previous health and safety issues. However, regulations are only minimum requirements based on legislation. High-quality early childhood programs build on that foundation to develop fuller, broader, inclusive policies that reflect their knowledge and skills in caring for children daily. When a policy is well written, its rationale is clearly understood and the stated procedures obviously promote the well-being of children, staff, and families.

Policy manuals are living documents. Our knowledge of children's well-being, including health, nutrition, hygiene, safety, growth and development, illness, medical conditions, and physical or emotional challenges, evolves more quickly than legislators make or change regulations. Furthermore, educators use past experiences to identify additional policy issues. Policy manuals incorporate the unexpected—"What will we do if this happens?" (The manual outlines the steps to follow if, for example, a child's noncustodial parent arrives to take the child from the centre, as well as what to do when a child vomits medication.) An effective policy manual adapts to the changing needs of individual early childhood settings.

An infant program has an outbreak of diarrhea. Hand-washing and diapering routines should be suspected of causing the spread of the virus or bacteria responsible for the gastrointestinal infection. Without the policy manual setting out the steps for diapering and hand washing, staff are not able to evaluate the educators' compliance with the routines that would have prevented the spread. Perhaps the policy and procedures are not effective. Perhaps educators need retraining in the routines and closer supervision.

Beyond the legal licensing requirement for having a manual, policies have a variety of purposes. They can explain how to

- conduct staff orientation, in-service training, and job performance appraisals;
- extract the most relevant policies to be developed into parent handbooks; and
- define lines of communication and confidentiality.

They also

- contain the administrative and medical/health forms and specify who has access to that information;
- contain information sheets and handouts and routines that can be used for posters on such topics as diapering, toileting, hand washing, and exclusion criteria; and
- identify the names and associations related to early childhood programs so that staff stay current with related research.

Each regulation provides directors, educators, their boards, and parents with the basis for developing policies and procedures for the individual day-to-day program, the ages of the children, and their location. The following illustrates a few of the issues that may be included in discussions about policies and procedures:

- The medication policy indicates what medications are permitted and why. Procedures are clearly spelled out and cover administration, storage, and record keeping; identification and reporting of side effects and medication errors; and the management of emergency situations. The program's expectations of parents regarding medications would also be included. In the event of a medication incident, comparing the procedures with the actions of the educator will determine whether precautions were in place and carried out to the best of the person's ability to prevent the error. Perhaps such a review would determine that the current medication procedures require revision.
- A child falls from a climbing structure in the winter and breaks his arm. On examination, the impact-absorbing surface is found to be covered with a sheet of ice. Does the program have an outdoor play policy and procedures in place that, when implemented, would prevent children from using a climber when the surface does not meet safety requirements?
- A school-age program located in an elementary school establishes clear lines of communication with the principal and the children's teachers to ensure the consistent coordination of health policies.

. . . .

- When a child gets sick during the day, does the school notify the parents, or is doing so the program's responsibility?
- Are the regular safety checks of the playground and equipment a shared responsibility of the early childhood program staff and the school, or are they solely the school's responsibility? Are the expectations about the use

of the playground equipment consistent between the program and school? When issues arise, how are they reported and recorded? Who is responsible for record keeping?

- Do the educators and teachers consistently teach and model healthy habits?
- When concerns are raised about a child or family by either the educators or a teacher, do both parties work together to address the concerns?

Advocating for High-Quality Early Childhood Programs

Although many regard licensed early childhood programs as social welfare programs rather than health promotion programs, early childhood education has significant implications for children's development and health. In the 1980s, advocates for a national child care plan agreed on three fundamental principles for a child care system: universal accessibility, comprehensiveness, and high quality. Their continued advocacy for child care indirectly promotes children's health. Early childhood education benefits all children. "There is much to support the premise that a universally accessible set of ECEC [early childhood education and care] services should be available for all children rather than a fragmented set of targeted services for special populations" (Doherty, 2001, pp. 1–2).

> Access to affordable, high quality early learning and child care programs promote children's well being while enabling their parents to work or receive training. A universally accessible system of early learning and child care services is a critical element in a comprehensive poverty reduction strategy. The federal government must continue to play a role to ensure a national universal system is put in place. In 2006 there were only enough regulated child care spaces for 17.2% of children aged 0–12 in Canada—about 1 in 6 children. Almost 45% of these spaces are in Quebec, the only province with a universal type of child care program. The cancellation of federal funding agreements in 2007 has slowed the expansion of child care spaces in many provinces. It is reported that parent fees can range up to $12,000 a year. Out of 14 OECD countries, Canada spends the least amount per capita on early learning and child care programs. Canadian families continue to need a system of child care that is high-quality, publicly funded and accessible to all. (Campaign 2000, 2007, p. 5)

Source: Reprinted with permission from Campaign 2000 (2007), 2007 Report Card on Child and Family Poverty in Canada: It Takes a Nation to Raise a Generation, 5.

> The evidence is compelling and overwhelming: well-funded, integrated, early childhood programs improve the cognitive and social functioning of all children and affect education, health, the social capital, and the overall equity within populations. This is key for stable, cohesive societies and economic growth. Early childhood programs have the capacity to support pluralism and reduce inequities. If properly linked to labour, health and social services, early childhood programs can deliver additional outcomes, such as enhanced maternal employment, less family poverty; better parenting skills and greater family and community cohesion. Quality early childhood programs are not only good for children and families, they are good for the bottom line. Focused public spending on young children provides returns that outstrip any other type of human capital investment. (McCain, Mustard, and Shanker 2007, p. 135)

Advocacy doesn't occur only at the national level. Advocates for high-quality early childhood education are working to improve standards of care in each province and territory by ensuring that revisions made to legislation reflect the indicators of high-quality early childhood education.

How can early childhood educators and students deliver high-quality early childhood education that support health promotion? Your training provides you with the entry-level knowledge and skills to provide a level of care higher than the minimum set out in the legislation. Your training also helps you recognize the importance of delivering a high-quality early childhood program. This commitment to ongoing learning and professional behaviour makes you a "personal" advocate. To be a public policy advocate, you can be involved in local, provincial/territorial, or federal early childhood education organizations that address issues of quality, accessibility, and compensation for educators. "Policies that cannot measure up in addressing all three issues are not solutions and may become part of the problem" (Gestwicki & Bertrand, 2008, p. 252). We need to speak with one voice to safeguard accomplishments and move forward.

HEALTH PROMOTION ACTION PLAN

Health promotion, in a broad sense, enables individuals, the community, and levels of government to identify health risks and make positive changes at the individual, community, and societal (population) levels. However, not all of health promotion can happen at the macro level. A population health approach will affect social change, but the day-to-day realities of life necessitate action on a range of scales—from the individual to societal change.

Action Plan

Health promotion activities enable us to take action to improve our own health and that of all Canadians. A **health promotion action plan** establishes a set of strategies that can be divided into four components:

- individual problem-solving and self-reliance
- collective self-help
- community action
- societal change

Optimally, when all four components are at work, the likelihood of significant change is high. At the individual and collective self-help levels, small numbers of people are benefiting from the action, either in the short or long term. But all health promotion is positive and should not be underestimated. At the community level, larger numbers and groups of people are involved, and, of course, societal change is at the level of population health, improving outcomes locally, provincially, or territorially and sometimes improving outcomes for all Canadians. Realistically, however, we are not always successful in achieving our original goals. During the process, we may need to adjust the vision. Barriers may be impossible to overcome. But even these situations usually have outcomes that contribute to good health, such as developing coping skills, increased social supports, networking, and a long-term commitment to work for change.

Individual Problem Solving and Self-Reliance

As individuals, we solve problems all the time, and many of our behavioural changes occur when we focus on improvements or solutions. However, changing our behaviour is easier when we do not have to overcome barriers or when we have the resources to effect change.

- Because Alyssa's parents provide a variety of nutritious foods, she has learned to make healthy food choices. They guide their daughter's development of healthy eating habits by modelling. By the time she is of school age, she will have developed the knowledge and decision-making skills to make choices. Then when she becomes influenced by peers and the media and may not always make the healthiest choices, she will at least be aware when she is eating less nutritious foods and can therefore balance her choices.
- You decide to add more physical activity to your life by regularly walking to work or school.

Societal barriers or influences can affect our ability to make healthy lifestyle decisions either positively or negatively. In the past, smoking was accepted by society. The media depicted it as fun, sophisticated, and elegant. Smokers could smoke almost anywhere, and no one was concerned about second-hand smoke or about pregnant women smoking. There were no barriers;

in fact, society encouraged people to smoke. Today, smoking is recognized as one of the most serious public health concerns, and this has resulted in public education on the risks of smoking, support and products to help stop smoking, legislation from all three levels of government on smoke-free environments, taxes on tobacco, strict limitations on advertising, and limitations on availability (e.g., pharmacies do not sell tobacco, and cigarette vending machines have been banned). Long-time smokers are quitting, supported and encouraged by society. People are more comfortable in asking smokers not to smoke in their cars or homes, and many smokers ask permission before lighting up. Smoking in public has been severely restricted. Public health officials remain concerned, however, about the number of teenagers (more girls than boys) who are first-time smokers. From a developmental perspective, it's not surprising that adolescents are exerting control over their lives and may, in fact, make decisions counter to parental or public opinion. This is complicated by the fact that teenagers and young adults view themselves as invincible.

Collective Self-Help

When individuals come together as a collective, they pool skills, knowledge, and resources to support one another and work toward change.

A group of tenants in an apartment building has recognized that grocery shopping is difficult because of issues such as

- their low income,
- the lack of public transportation to affordable stores, and
- the many single-parent families who have no one to care for their children while the parents are grocery shopping.

As a collective, the tenants organize a food depot that is open once a week and sells fresh fruit and vegetables. A food produce supplier provides the produce at a reasonable cost.

Collectives don't always have to be large groups of people.

Several neighbours organize an informal baby-sitting system that lets one parent shop for groceries while another cares for the children. This allows the parents to shop without taking tired, bored, or hungry children with them, which often results in impulse buying and angry parents or frustrated children.

Although this example reflects cooperation, the group is somewhat self-reliant. Often, once groups have worked together in this way, they begin to identify broader social and health issues or concerns (e.g., causes of ill health) and may move toward more of a community action model.

A group of directors that meets regularly as a network shares a concern about the food that parents are providing for their school-age children. The directors organize a parent meeting, invite a dietitian-nutritionist and social worker, and provide child care and dinner. At the meeting, participants identify a number of issues:

- lack of affordable food
- lack of nutrition resources that fit the literacy and interest levels of a number of the parents
- time constraints for parents and their need for ideas for nutritious lunches that can be easily prepared
- children's practice of trading lunch items with peers and a concern that nutritious foods won't be desirable
- children's beliefs that foods from their ethnocultural backgrounds will not be accepted by their peers

These issues call on the resources and agencies in the community. They highlight the importance of looking beyond self-help to a much broader health promotion action.

Community Action

A health promotion strategy oriented toward community action is increasingly viewed as an effective way to make change to meet the health needs of the community, particularly where barriers are present. It aims for changes that will involve and have an impact on the whole group, a process known as community capacity building. Those changes can happen when groups of people

- work together to identify issues and priorities that reflect their needs;
- develop and implement an action plan, which usually involves communication with a number of agencies and resources; and
- evaluate the strengths and deficiencies of their actions and the extent to which they have realized their goals.

In the example about nutrition for school-age children, the collective's work led the participants to develop an action plan that included reaching out into the community for resources. This had benefits not only for the immediate issue but also for long-term well-being. Regular links with the broader community tend to foster an active problem-solving approach to life.

All participants involved have some role in the process, including evaluating whether goals have been met. Parents and staff may have different responsibilities and perspectives, but everyone works toward the same goal. Depending on the ages of the children and the actions being taken, some or all of the children may be involved in the process (e.g., if a community vegetable garden is part of the solution).

A few people in a neighbourhood are concerned about the quality of the air due to smokestack emissions at a local factory. Together, they go door to door to gain citizen support and they meet with public health officials, governmental officials, and the factory management. Then they develop a plan of action to reduce the emissions.

Depending on the extent of the issue and who is involved, community action can lead to legislative changes—locally, provincially, or federally—that affect everyone. If we take this example a step further, stricter government regulations for companies to reduce air pollution levels may emerge from what began as a small community action (see Appendix 1.1, page 53).

Societal Change

Issues can have a very broad impact on everyone through the work of community and lobby groups, agencies, and so on. Societal changes often result from changes in legislation or public health policy, the mandate of a population health approach. Here are some examples:

- air pollution controls
- no-smoking policies in public places
- banning the use of trans fats in our food
- drinking-and-driving legislation
- legislative bans on manufacturing and selling equipment that doesn't conform to safety regulations

Of course, even more sweeping changes than public health policy are the social policy changes that can come about when the social determinants of health are addressed. *For example, if the provincial minimum wage was legislated to increase substantially, a significant decline in poverty rates for families could mean improved health for many.*

Let's take one last look at the example of staff and parents and their concerns about children's nutrition. As a group, they recognize that their experience is not isolated, that the issue and solutions go beyond their own community and into society at large. Consequently, some participants join a lobby group that is trying to ban television advertising of junk food aimed at children, whereas others work with a national antipoverty group advocating a federal policy for a national child nutrition program. As discussed earlier in this unit, a focus on the bigger issue of reducing and eliminating poverty is, ultimately, the most effective health promotion approach. A collective vote is a powerful tool for effecting change. Find out where political candidates stand on various issues and cast your vote accordingly.

Health Promotion Action Plan in the Early Childhood Program

An action approach to promoting health in programs is positive for a number of reasons:

1. *It fosters partnerships with parents and other family members.* Working together for common goals recognizes and builds on people's knowledge and

strengths. In addition to getting the job done, you develop relationships with the families—a benefit to everyone involved.

2. *An action approach helps people learn to solve problems and experience the value of working cooperatively.* When individuals see results, they are more likely to view themselves as having enough personal and collective power to effect change. When all the players are committed to the issue, there are fewer barriers. Of course, there are times when interactions among employers, administrators, and boards or budget restraints result in insurmountable obstacles. Although this will be disappointing, it is helpful to view what has been gained through the process. Obviously, in addition to the benefits from the action itself, working cooperatively also models a cooperative approach for children that is crucial for adapting in our ever-changing world.

3. *An action approach increases the individual's and group's awareness of community resources, knowledge of community need, and community capacity building.* An action plan will probably include communication with the public health and other municipal departments, community health centres, social service agencies, and so on. An active approach to promoting health in early childhood settings can lead to improved accessibility for children and families to the larger community as information is shared through family and friends. This leads to community capacity building, whereby groups share common needs and a commitment to turning their ideas into reality.

OBJECTIVES

List ways that educators and early childhood programs benefit from networking with the community

Describe strategies to handle "mixed messages" that families and educators are faced with around health issues.

NETWORKING WITH THE COMMUNITY

Networking within the community contributes to the well-being of children, families, educators, and the overall early childhood program. Educators working effectively as a team contribute significantly to the level of quality provided by the program. No one works in isolation, and early childhood settings are no exception. Staff cannot and should not try to be all things to all people. Staff must establish a network with professionals, agencies, and associations in their community (see Figure 1.3). This network allows the staff to grow both personally and professionally, resulting in higher quality early childhood programs. Your early childhood education training and skills equip you to work as an effective member of the network of professionals concerned with the growth, development, and health of children (e.g., public health departments, child abuse prevention teams, school boards, community health centres). Collaboration with others should have the additional benefit of drawing a number of services together, thus reducing duplication, improving the delivery of service, and lowering costs.

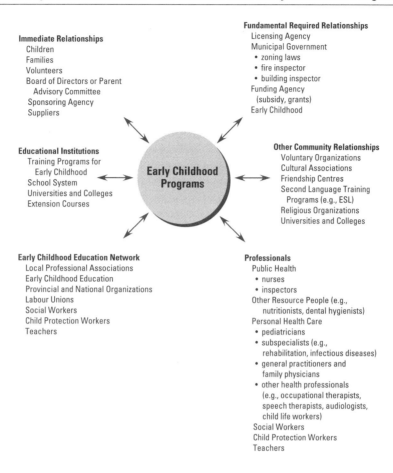

Immediate Relationships
Children
Families
Volunteers
Board of Directors or Parent
    Advisory Committee
Sponsoring Agency
Suppliers

Fundamental Required Relationships
Licensing Agency
Municipal Government
    • zoning laws
    • fire inspector
    • building inspector
Funding Agency
    (subsidy, grants)
Early Childhood

Educational Institutions
Training Programs for
    Early Childhood
School System
Universities and Colleges
Extension Courses

Early Childhood Programs

Other Community Relationships
Voluntary Organizations
Cultural Associations
Friendship Centres
Second Language Training
    Programs (e.g., ESL)
Religious Organizations
Universities and Colleges

Early Childhood Education Network
Local Professional Associations
Early Childhood Education
Provincial and National Organizations
Labour Unions
Social Workers
Child Protection Workers
Teachers

Professionals
Public Health
    • nurses
    • inspectors
Other Resource People (e.g.,
    nutritionists, dental hygienists)
Personal Health Care
    • pediatricians
    • subspecialists (e.g.,
        rehabilitation, infectious diseases)
    • general practitioners and
        family physicians
    • other health professionals
        (e.g., occupational therapists,
        speech therapists, audiologists,
        child life workers)
Social Workers
Child Protection Workers
Teachers

As students in an early childhood education program, you may be overwhelmed when you think about developing relationships with individuals and groups, but be assured that it doesn't happen overnight. It is important that you see the benefits of working cooperatively, learning from others, and sharing your expertise. In early childhood settings where staff and the director do not work cooperatively, children, families, and staff are at a real disadvantage. No one person or agency can do it all or know it all. Networking increases resources and decreases educator stress levels (see Figure 1.3).

As you can see from our discussion on health promotion, your approach to your work can affect the health and well-being of children and families. For those educators who are committed to their profession, what you think (attitude), what you know (knowledge), and what you do (behaviour) are evolving positively through education and experience. We must recognize our strengths and limitations throughout this lifelong learning process and make responsible decisions accordingly. All educators and directors need access to resources; a student or recent graduate of an early childhood education program needs to have increased support that is readily available.

Voices on Health and Learning Project

The Early Childhood Work Group of the Canadian Council on Learning's Health and Learning Knowledge Centre conducted a consultation in 2007 called the *Voices on Health and Learning Project* (Canadian Council on Learning, 2008, p. 1):

> Participants included parents, health-care professionals, early childhood educators and faculty from early childhood education post-secondary programs. This consultation asked participants to identify:
>
> ■ health and learning issues and concerns
>
> ■ sources of health information
>
> ■ barriers to accessing information
>
> ■ information gaps and needs
>
> Five themes resonated with all participant groups throughout this project as laying the basis for supportive health information to families:
>
> 1. Relationships between parents and professionals are "key" for health information.
> 2. Income security is a determinant of health. Poverty impacts all levels of health and learning.
> 3. Mixed messages about health abound: on the internet, media and agencies/departments.
> 4. Understanding health literacy with sensitivity to cultural practices is essential.
> 5. Communities and context matter.
>
> In addition to these themes, distinctions emerged between the sources that parents use for health information and the role of early childhood educators. Parents view health-care professionals, the internet and articles as key sources of health information for their young children and family. The role for early childhood educators in their work with families includes supportive relationships with parents, children and other professionals, referrals to reliable sources of health information, providing healthy early learning settings and acting as healthy role models. (Canadian Council on Learning, 2008, pp. 3–4)

Mixed Messages

One of the key findings from the *Voices on Health and Learning Project* was that parents of young children and early childhood educators are inundated with many mixed and competing messages about health issues as they try to determine how best to promote children's optimal well-being. These messages come from the media, the Internet, printed materials, family members, public health departments, and other sources. An everyday strategy is communication. When parents and educators connect about the health and well-being of children, they are creating social support networks, one of the Public Health Agency of Canada's 12 social determinants of health (see Table 1.1, page 6).

Educators need to view themselves as health promoters, supporting children and families in healthy ways (Best Start Resource Centre, 2006). Educators know, for example, that several opportunities a day for preschoolers to be physically active for short periods, especially outdoors, are an integral part of a quality program (Timmons, Naylor, & Pfeiffer, 2007). They need to ensure that this happens, through policy and practice, and share these experiences with families. If parents are confident that their children are getting the physical activity they need during the day, it helps them view the educators as partners in their child's healthy living. Educators and families may be able to share suggestions for enjoyable but simple physical activity ideas.

On the flip side, educators are responsive to families' concerns, creating an environment of mutual respect. As discussed earlier, educators take care not to abandon important cultural values but to make adjustments when it seems reasonable and recognize that collaborative relationships are key to effective decision making. An ongoing dialogue among parents, educators, and health practitioners can avoid confusion and mixed messages (e.g., fear of germs) that can result from one perspective that is not tempered by other points of view. This dialogue is also more likely to lead to healthy policy at the program level and possibly advocacy at community levels and beyond, which can contribute to health improvements for greater numbers of children.

Many, if not most, Canadian households now have Internet access. Among parents who were interviewed at a large Canadian children's hospital's emergency department, over 90% reported home Internet access and over 50% use the Internet for health-related information (Goldman & Macpherson, 2006). The sheer quantity of information accessible through the Internet, television, and other media sources can be overwhelming and difficult to evaluate for reliability. Health literacy is an essential tool for parents and educators. Invaluable tools such as *Guiding Parents in Their Search for High-Quality Health Information on the Internet* by the Canadian Paediatric Society (2007) need to be accessible for parents and educators (see Resource Materials, page 49). The Canadian Paediatric Society's Caring for Kids website is designed for parents and educators, and educators can include the site in communication tools such as parent or policy handbooks or newsletters (see Resource Materials, page 50).

CONCLUSION

As educators, we can contribute to the health promotion plan. In our daily work with children and families, we can put into practice a health promotion philosophy by

- developing and following healthy policies and procedures;
- modelling healthy habits ourselves;
- communicating in an ongoing way with the families, demonstrating sensitivity and openness to their health beliefs and practices; and
- networking with the community, realizing that we all benefit through sharing resources.

Each of the following units in this book discusses health-related practices in the early childhood program.

Healthy lifestyles, the physical environment, and genetics are significant determinants of health. To improve the quality of life for all Canadians, however, action needs to be taken on the social and economic determinants of health in particular, giving priority to the serious problem of income inequity. Generally, the wider the gap in population income, the poorer the population health. "Those with the lowest incomes have the worst health outcomes, but the negative impact of inequity is felt among all Canadians" (Canadian Institute of Child Health, 2000,p. 178). As Nelson Mandela said, "Security for a few is insecurity for us all."

What's Your Opinion?

HEALTH PROMOTER OR NOT?

Health promotion is the process of enabling people to increase control over, and to improve, their health. Health promoters include those who work to promote health regardless of professional designation, including people, organizations, and groups from various sectors. After reading this unit, do you recognize the role educators have as health promoters? Health promotion has been discussed in general terms in this unit. The upcoming units focus on specific content areas: occupational health, preventing illness, managing illness, nutrition, safety, healthy active living, preventing child maltreatment, and supporting children's development. *Before* you delve into these units, identify at least one specific way educators can be health promoters in each of these areas. *After* you complete these units, revisit your response to this question and compare it with what you have learned throughout the course.

ASSESS YOUR LEARNING

Define terms or describe concepts used in this unit.

- complementary (or traditional) medicine
- culture
- developmental health
- health policies
- health promotion action plan
- networking
- population health
- principles of medicare
- social capital

- cultural safety
- health
- health promotion
- natural health products
- personal health care system
- prevention
- public health system
- social determinants

Evaluate your options in each situation.

1.   Your doctor hands you a prescription. When you ask him what it's for and whether there are side effects, he replies, "Don't worry about it. Just take these pills and you'll feel better."

2.   Classes have been cancelled for the day to allow students to attend a child care rally at the legislature. You are tempted to skip it because you have to study for a test.

3.   A parent is angry at pickup time because his daughter's sleeves are damp from water play even though she was wearing a smock. He believes that this

is how someone gets a cold. He asks that his daughter never play at the water table again.

4. One of the parents of a child in the infant room says she doesn't know what to do because she gets different messages at every turn. The information in her magazines and what she finds on the Internet differs from what her husband's family tells her, and that differs from what the educators say and do in the early childhood program.

5. A safety issue arises at the centre. None of the staff can think of a suitable response, and you suggest that consulting with another centre may provide options. The director insists, "We can work this out ourselves," and does not want outside interference

RESOURCE MATERIALS

Organizations

Campaign 2000, c/o Family Service Association of Toronto, 355 Church Street, Toronto, ON M5B 1Z8. Tel: 416-595-9230, ext. 244; fax: 416-595-0242; http://www. campaign2000.ca

Canadian Association of Family Resource Programs (FRP Canada), 707–331 Cooper Street, Ottawa, ON K2P 0G5. Tel: 613-237-7667 or national toll-free 1-866-637-7226; fax: 613-237-8515; http://www.frp.ca

Canadian Child Care Federation, 201–383 Parkdale Avenue, Ottawa, ON K1Y 4R4. Tel: 613-729-5289 or national toll-free 1-800-858-1412; fax: 613-729-3159; http://www. cccf-fcsge.ca

Canadian Paediatric Society, 2305 St. Laurent Blvd, Ottawa, ON K1G 4J8. Tel: 613-526-9397; fax: 613-526-3332; http://www.cps.ca

Child Care Advocacy Association of Canada, 714–151 Slater Street, Ottawa, ON K1P 5H3. Tel: 613-594-3196 or national toll-free 1-877-261-1342; fax: 613-594-9375; http://www.ccaac.ca

Family Service Canada, 312 Parkdale Avenue, Ottawa, ON K1Y 4X5. http://www. familyservicecanada.org

Other Websites of Interest

Canadian Paediatric Society's site for parents: http://www.caringforkids.cps.ca/index. htm

Caring for Kids by the Canadian Paediatric Society. To subscribe to this electronic newsletter, visit http://www.caringforkids.cps.ca/index.htm (June 2008).

Centre for Families, Work and Well-being, University of Guelph: http://www.uoguelph. ca/cfww

Childcare Resource and Research Unit (CRRU): http://www.childcarecanada.org

Health Promotion On-line Course (HP-101) by the Ontario Health Promotion Resource System. To learn more about this free course and how to complete it, visit http:// www.ohprs.ca/hp101/main.htm (June 2008).

Invest in Kids site for parents and professionals: http://www.investinkids.ca

Public Health Agency of Canada: http://www.phac-aspc.gc.ca/chn-rcs/index.html

Printed Matter

The Integrated Pan-Canadian Healthy Living Strategy (2005) by The Secretariat for the Intersectoral Healthy Living Network in partnership with the F/P/T Healthy Living Task Group and the F/P/T Advisory Committee on Population Health and Health Security (ACPHHS). To download a copy, visit http://www.phac-aspc.gc.ca/hl-vs-strat/pdf/hls_e.pdf (June 2008).

A parent's guide to health information on the Internet by the Canadian Paediatric Society. To print a copy, visit http://www.caringforkids.cps.ca/healthybodies/InternetInfo.htm (June 2008).

BIBLIOGRAPHY

Ball, J. (2007). *Cultural safety in practice with children, families and communities.* Retrieved June 2008 from the Early Childhood Development Intercultural Partnerships, University of Victoria, website: http://www.ecdip.org/docs/pdf/Cultural%20Safety%20Poster.pdf

Best Start Resource Centre. (2006). *Putting health promotion into action: A resource for early learning and child care settings.* Retrieved June 2008 from http://www.beststart.org/resources/hlthy_chld_dev/pdf/hpaction.pdf

British Columbia Perinatal Health Program. (2008, February). *Caesarean birth task force report 2008.* Retrieved June 2008 from http://www.canadianmidwives.org/pdf/CBTF_FinalApril08.pdf

Brown, I., Raphael, D., & Renwick R. (1998). *Quality of life profile.* Toronto: Centre for Health Promotion, University of Toronto.

Campaign 2000. (2002). *Diversity or disparity? Early childhood education and care in Canada.* Toronto: Family Service Association of Canada.

Campaign 2000. (2007). *2007 report card on child and family poverty in Canada: It takes a nation to raise a generation.* Toronto: Family Service Association of Canada. Retrieved June 2008 from http://www.campaign2000.ca/rc/rc07/2007_C2000_NationalReportCard.pdf

Canadian Broadcasting Corporation. (2007, November 28). *Women happier when babies delivered by midwives: Statscan survey.* Retrieved June 2008 from http://www.cbc.ca/health/story/2007/11/27/statscan-babies.html

Canadian Council on Learning. (2006). *Why is high-quality child care essential? The link between quality child care and early learning.* Retrieved June 2008 from <http://www.cclcca.ca/CCL/Reports/LessonsInLearning/20060530LinL.htm

Canadian Council on Learning. (2008). *Target audience project report summary.* Voices on Health and Learning: Early Childhood Work Group, Health and Learning Knowledge Centre. Retrieved June 2008 from http://www.ccl-cca.ca/NR/rdonlyres/3C4FB36C-1977-485D-870F-00205A8D5310/0/HLKCWG1voicesonhealth_summary_EN.pdf

Canadian Council on Social Development. (2002 November 28). *Response of the CCSD to the final report by the Commission on the Future of Health Care in Canada.* Ottawa: Author.

Canadian Council on Social Development. (2006). Family life. In *The progress of Canada's children and youth.* Ottawa: Author. Retrieved June 2008 from http://www.ccsd.ca/pccy/2006/pdf/pccy_familylife.pdf

Canadian Institute of Child Health. (2000). *The health of Canada's children: A CICH profile* (3rd ed.). Ottawa: Author.

Canadian Paediatric Society. (2007). Guiding parents in their search for high-quality health information on the Internet. *Paediatrics & Child Health, 12,* 239–240. Retrieved June 2008 from http://www.cps.ca/english/statements/cp/practicepoint.htm

Doherty, G. (2001). *Targeting early childhood care and education: Myths and realities.* (Occasional Paper No. 15). Toronto: Childcare Resource and Research Unit.

Epp, J. (1986). *Achieving health for all: A framework for health promotion.* Ottawa: Supply and Services Canada.

Federal, Provincial and Territorial Advisory Committee on Population Health. (1999). *Toward a healthy future: Second report on the health of Canadians* (Catalogue No. H39-468/1999E). Ottawa: Minister of Public Works and Government Services of Canada. Retrieved June 2008 from http://www. phacaspc.gc.ca/ph-sp/phdd/pdf/toward/toward_a_healthy_english.PDF

Gestwicki, C., & Bertrand, J. (2008). *The essentials of early education* (3rd Canadian ed.). Toronto: ITP Nelson.

Goldman, R. D., & Macpherson, A. (2006). Internet health information use and e-mail access by parents attending a paediatric emergency department. *Emergency Medical Journal, 23,* 345–348.

Gonzalez-Mena, J. (2005). *Diversity in early care and education: Honoring differences* (4th ed.). New York: McGraw-Hill Publishing.

Health Canada. (2005a). *Canada's health care system* (Catalogue No. H21-231/2005E-PDF). Ottawa: Health Canada. Retrieved June 2008 from http://www.hc-sc.gc.ca/hcs-sss/alt_formats/hpb-dgps/pdf/ pubs/2005-hcs-sss/2005-hcs-sss-eng.pdf

Health Canada. (2005b). *Drugs and health products: Baseline natural products survey among consumers, March 2005.* Retrieved June 2008 from http://www.hc-sc.gc.ca/dhp-mps/pubs/natur/eng_cons_ survey-eng.php

Health Canada. (2007, June 8). *Drugs and health products: Natural health products.* Retrieved June 2008 from http://www.hc-sc.gc.ca/dhp-mps/prodnatur/index-eng.php

Health Council of Canada. (2006). *Their future is now: Healthy choices for Canada's children and youth June 2006.* Toronto: Author.

Hertzman, C. (1997). In K. Guy (Ed.), *Our promise to children.* Ottawa: Health Canada.

Hertzman, C. (1998). The case for child development as a determinant of health. *Canadian Journal of Public Health, 89*(Suppl. 1), S14–S19.

Hertzman, C., & Power, C. (2004). Child development as a determinant of health across the life course. *Current Paediatric, 14,* 438–443.

Institute of Population and Public Health. (2003). *The future of public health in Canada: Developing a public health system for the 21st century: June 2003.* Ottawa: Canadian Institute of Health Research. Retrieved June 2008 from http://www.cihr-irsc.gc.ca/e/19573.html

Invest in Kids. (2008). *About us: Our history.* Retrieved June 2008 from http://www.investinkids.ca/ ContentPage.aspx?name=Newsroom_OurStory

Keating, D. P., & Miller, F. K. (1999). Individual pathways in competence and coping: From regulatory systems to habits of mind. In D. P. Keating & C. Hertzmann (Eds.), *Developmental health and the wealth of nations: Social, biological, and educational dynamics* (pp. 220–234). New York: Guilford Press.

Labonté, R. (1993). *Health promotion: Theory and practice background material 1.* Toronto: Centre for Health Promotion, University of Toronto.

Leitch, K. K. (2007). *Reaching for the top: A report by the Advisor on Healthy Children and Youth* (Catalogue No. H21-296/2007E). Ottawa: Health Canada.

McCain, M. N., Mustard, J. F., & Shanker, S. (2007). *Early Years Study 2: Putting science into action.* Toronto: Council for Early Child Development.

Michalski, J. H. (2002). *Quality of life in Canada: A citizens' report card (background report).* Ottawa: Canadian Policy Research Networks.

Ontario Women's Health Council, Ontario Maternity Care Expert Panel. (2006). *Maternity care in Ontario 2006: Emerging crisis, emerging solutions.* Retrieved June 2008 from http://meds.queensu.ca/ prn/downloads/OMCEP_Final_Report_1.pdf

Picard, A. (2008, March 27). Children are the future - why can't we protect them? *The Globe and Mail,* p. L6.

Public Health Agency of Canada. (2002). What is the population health approach? *Population Health.* Retrieved June 2008 from http://www.phac-aspc.gc.ca/ph-sp/approach-approche/index.html AU

Public Health Agency of Canada. (2004). What determines health? *Population Health.* Retrieved June 2008 from http://www.phac-aspc.gc.ca/ph-sp/phdd/determinants/determinants.html#income

Red River College. (n.d.). Developmental health. In *Science of early child development.* Retrieved June 2008 from http://courses.scienceofecd.com/course/view.php?id=53

Ross, D. P., Scott, K. J., & Smith, P. J. (2000). *The Canadian fact book on poverty 2000.* Ottawa: Canadian Council on Social Development.

Shonkoff, J., & Phillips, D. (2001). *From neurons to neighbourhoods: The science of early childhood development.* Ottawa: National Academy of Sciences.

Statistics Canada. (2005). *Literacy rate fails to budge. Infomat. Retrieved June 2008 from http://www. statcan.ca/english/freepub/11-002-XIE/2005/05/13705/13705_04.htm*

Timmons, B. W., Naylor, P. J., & Pfeiffer, K. A. (2007). Physical activity for preschool children – how much and how? *Applied Physiology, Nutrition, and Metabolism, 32,* s122–s134.

Tzu Chi Institute for Complementary and Alternative Medicine (Canadian Health Network Affiliate). (2002). *Natural doesn't mean safe.* Retrieved July 2003 from http://www.canadian-health-network. ca/html/newnotable/jan1a_2002e.html

Wilkinson, R., & Marmot, M. (2003). *Social determinants of health: The solid facts* (2nd ed.). Copenhagen: WHO Regional Office for Europe.

World Health Organization. (1948). Preamble to the Constitution of the World Health Organization as adopted by the International Health Conference, New York, 19 June –22 July 1946; signed on 22 July 1946 by the representatives of 61 States (Official Records of the World Health Organization, no. 2, p. 100) and entered into force on 7 April 1948. Retrieved August 2008 from http://www.who.int/ suggestions/faq/en/

World Health Organization, Health and Welfare Canada, and Canadian Public Health Association. (1986). *Ottawa Charter for Health Promotion.* Ottawa: Health and Welfare Canada.

World Health Organization. (2005). *Health Impact Assessment Toolkit for Cities. Document 1. Background document: concepts, processes, methods. Vision to Action.* Retrieved June 2008 from http://www.euro.who.int/ Document/Hcp/HIA_toolkit_1.pdf

Health Promotion: Getting Started Checklist

APPENDIX 1.1

This checklist may help you determine where your program currently practises health promotion and where it might be possible to include or address health promotion more. Use the checklist as a launching point to identify if your program is aware of the determinants of health and the features and values of health promotion. It may help you see what you are already doing and in what areas you may need to take more action. In the last column, you can briefly note what next steps you can take.

HEALTH PROMOTION	ARE WE AWARE OF THE DETERMINANTS OF HEALTH AND THE FEATURES AND VALUES OF HEALTH PROMOTION?	IN WHAT AREAS ARE WE TAKING ACTION?	IN WHAT AREAS DO WE NEED STRENGTHENING?	WHAT ARE THE NEXT STEPS TO CONSIDER?
DETERMINANTS OF HEALTH				
Income & Social Status				
Social Support Networks				
Employment & Working Conditions				
Education & Literacy				
Social Environments				
Physical Environments				
Personal Health Practices & Coping Skills				
Healthy Child Development				
Biology & Genetic Endowment				
Health Services				
Gender				
Culture				
FEATURES OF HEALTH PROMOTION				
Taking a Holistic View of Health				
Taking Participatory Approaches				
Building on Strengths				
Addressing the Determinants of Health				
Using Multiple, Complementary Approaches				
VALUES OF HEALTH PROMOTION				
Empowerment				
Respect				
Inclusion				
Social Justice & Equality				

Source: Used with permission from Best Start: Ontario's Maternal, Newborn and Early Child Development Resource Centre (2006) *Putting Health Promotion into Action: A Resource for Early Learning and Child Care Settings*, 46–47.

Occupational Health

CONTENTS

S tudents in community colleges and universities are not a homogeneous group but reflect the communities in which they live. Many students are right out of high school; others are mature students returning to school after time spent in the workforce. Some are parents. Some are in their first educational program since arriving in Canada. Many are juggling school and part-time jobs or other commitments. You, too, are entering the early childhood education (ECE) program with experiences different from those of your classmates, and you have responsibilities beyond the classroom and placements in early childhood settings.

Even at the best of times, school is stressful. It is a period of transition: establishing new friendships and study habits, trying to budget your time and money. There can be additional adjustments to make, such as moving away from home for the first time or to a new community. It's not surprising if you are experiencing stressors, suffering emotional ups and downs, feeling tired and at times discouraged, feeling pulled in different directions. Recognizing and managing stress in your life are essential now and on graduation, when you will be working in an early childhood program. There is growing recognition that employees' overall health plays a significant role in job satisfaction, productivity, and turnover rates. Occupations that we tend to think of as stressful are those that are inherently dangerous, such as mining, operating heavy machinery, firefighting, and police work. Yet every occupation presents potential risks to its employees' physical and emotional health. Store clerks who repeatedly drag groceries over the scanner at the checkout counter can develop severe wrist pain as well as sore legs or varicose veins from standing. People who work at computer terminals all day may suffer from eyestrain, lower back pain, and carpal tunnel syndrome. Employees who perform repetitive tasks and work that permits them little control over their jobs experience a low level of autonomy, which leads to low job satisfaction. Every profession has stressors; ECE is no exception. Thankfully, it also includes many benefits and opportunities. In this unit, the focus is on the challenges, in order to impress upon you the importance of managing stressors over which you have control, while joining those who advocate to build a national system that will benefit children, families, and early childhood educators.

ECE is *not* babysitting! Many still believe that working in early childhood education is just an extension of minding other people's children. In addition, the fact that ECE is a predominantly female profession has historically accorded it low status, and many people believe that women naturally have the aptitude, knowledge, and skills needed to care for groups of children. In other words, the popular myth is that anyone can look after children. The reality is that, as discussed in Unit 1, one of the key determinants of health is child development, which highlights the essential role of increasing and retaining qualified and skilled professionals in the early childhood workforce. Many people also don't believe that ECE (unlike education and health care) constitutes an essential service to families. These attitudes contribute to the low status, low salaries, and lack of respect accorded to early childhood educators. There is a wide discrepancy in wage rates for centre-based staff, even within the same province or territory.

To address this reality, a number of provinces (Manitoba, Saskatchewan, and Nova Scotia) have taken specific steps to improve the income levels of early childhood educators. In addition, the Quebec government made $152 million available in wage enhancements to early childhood staff from 1999 to 2003. The result is improved staff morale and retention, as well as an increased interest in ECE as a career (Tougas, 2002, p. 15).

The Shedding New Light Study responded to the retention and recruitment issues in the ECE sector:

> The report concludes that the recruitment and retention challenges faced by child care centres result from a complex and dynamic interaction of several contributors . . . Solving recruitment and retention problems in child care requires a comprehensive, multi-pronged approach. This approach must take into account and simultaneously address: (1) the need to moderate the stress in the job; (2) compensation (wages, benefits and working conditions); (3) the accessibility of ECCE training; and (4) the current low level of public respect for the job. (Doherty & Forer, 2007, p. 5)

Staff turnover has a detrimental effect on everyone involved—children, families, and remaining educators—and is a very significant issue.

Fortunately, change is happening, however slowly. "Now more than ever, there is a serious need to reevaluate Canada's approach to child care. The answer to meeting child care needs rests in improved policy, funding, and support for the workforce. This can only be accomplished through the development of a well supported and publicly funded child care system" (Doherty & Forer, 2007, p. i). The early childhood community and its professional associations tirelessly advocate at all levels of government.Most parents recognize that early childhood programs are an essential service and that children's early experiences are critical to their overall development.

As in any other occupation, not everyone is suited to the work. Yes, children are amazing, energetic, curious, active learners. Yes, it can be exciting and rewarding to be involved in their lives and development. But contrary to the stereotype addressed earlier, educators must develop the attitudes, knowledge, and skills necessary to be competent in their career. In addition, ECE is physical and emotional work. Always having to be "on" with children can be emotionally tiring. Combine this with the working dynamics of coworkers, administration, and management styles of supervisors and directors, and educators can experience job stress and, possibly, burnout.

Most of those who work in early childhood settings do not belong to ECE organizations and, as a result, have little access to supports such as collegial networking, topical and timely sector information, and professional development opportunities. Educators working in smaller centres are often isolated and have limited interaction with colleagues. Those who provide family home child care usually work alone. Professional affiliation is a critical support to individuals and the workforce. Unlike many established and growing professions, professional affiliation in this sector is typically voluntary (Beach et al., 2004). An exception is in Ontario, where educators' membership in the College of Early Childhood Educators is legislated.

However, you can control many aspects of the work to increase your job satisfaction. In recent decades, a holistic approach to health has often been translated into dimensions of wellness to facilitate self-awareness and enhance individual goal setting. Although dimensions are listed separately in the accompanying table, there is recognition that all aspects of wellness are interrelated (Hoeger & Hoeger, 2000, p. 4). Table 2.1 provides descriptions of eight commonly identified dimensions of wellness.

TABLE 2.1	**Dimensions of Personal Wellness**
Physical: awareness of and respect for the body—nutrition, physical activity, relaxation, sleep, use of tobacco, health habits	
Emotional: level of self-esteem, security, flexibility, ability to express feelings, recognition of strengths and weaknesses	
Social: level of involvement with others; sense of belonging, membership, or affiliation	
Intellectual: active mind, inquiring, curious, seeking new information and ideas	
Occupational: clarity of direction; satisfaction with development of skills and potential, as well as autonomy; motivation to investigate options	
Spiritual: ability to achieve a sense of renewal, see purpose in life, find things that nourish the soul	
Environmental: level to which external environment contributes to or detracts from wellness; commitment to improving the environment	
Financial: becoming financially literate; learning to take control over money; ability to meet basic needs	

Goals can be short term (usually accomplished within a year), long term, or ongoing (e.g., lifelong inclusion of daily physical activity). You're more likely to achieve success in lifestyle changes if your goals are

- specific—Identify in exact terms what you hope to achieve and set out a detailed action plan.
- personalized—Set your own goals rather than having someone set them for you.
- written—Write down your goals and keep a journal of your progress and setbacks; make a contract with yourself.
- realistic—Be realistic. Unattainable goals will discourage you.
- measurable—Ensure that you can measure your goals, for example, "To be able to climb stairs to my apartment (six floors) without being out of breath within eight weeks." Goals such as "I'm going to get fit" or "I'm going to lose weight" are not measurable.
- time specific—Establish target dates for your goals. Deadlines are motivational; however, keep in mind that adjustments may be necessary. Behaviour change is always possible but may take a little longer than you predict. Remember to always acknowledge your accomplishments and keep moving forward.
- evaluated—Monitor your progress. This will help you keep on track and determine when a goal may be unrealistic or too easy. Make the necessary goal adjustments to support you in moving forward (Hoeger & Hoeger, 2000, pp. 35–37).

This unit begins with an exploration of the physical dimension of early childhood work for educators and students. The second section explores the social and emotional dimensions. Although the topics are organized in sections, they are all interrelated. To explore other dimensions (e.g., spiritual, environmental) more specifically, you may want to refer to wellness manuals such as the one by Hales and Lauzon (2007). (See also Resource Materials, page 103.) It is also important to acknowledge that a common source for health information is the Internet. If this is a significant vehicle of health information for you, ensure that the site is credible (see Appendix 2.1, page 107).

PROMOTING YOUR PHYSICAL WELL-BEING

What are your health concerns about working with children? When instructors ask new ECE students this question, many students worry about catching chickenpox, head lice, colds, and the flu. We know that when children are first enrolled in programs, they get sick more often, but as time passes, the rate of illness declines. This pattern applies to students as well. Adults benefit from a mature immune system; they are fully immunized, one hopes, and most have already experienced the common childhood diseases (e.g., chickenpox). Adults can also implement hygiene practices that protect them and reduce the opportunities for illness to spread among children and adults. Even so, you

OBJECTIVES

To identify and evaluate a personally balanced lifestyle.

To identify physical risks to educators working in programs (infectious diseases, musculoskeletal injuries).

To discuss prevention strategies for physical risks.

To list the three rights of the worker.

To identify workplace environmental issues and possible solutions.

may experience a few viral infections when you begin your early childhood program placements.

It probably will take only a couple of days of work in a program to experience firsthand how physically demanding caring for children can be. It's a strain for educators to lift and carry infants and toddlers; move play equipment; sit on the floor; lean over child-sized tables, sinks, and toilets; and be constantly on the move in the playground to supervise children or take part in a physical activity. The positive side is that this constant and varied movement, when performed correctly, contributes to physical fitness. It is also rewarding to care for children, both in terms of the close relationships you begin to develop and the role modelling that patient, empathic care is for children and families.

Achieving a Balance in Your Lifestyle

As adults, we make individual lifestyle choices that can have positive or negative effects on our health.

Nutrition

One of our basic needs is food. However, the amount of emphasis placed on food and our health varies among individuals and throughout society. The bottom line—nutrition has a significant impact on our health. The principles of nutrition discussed in Unit 5 apply to children's nutritional status and to your own. As well, factors that shape eating habits are discussed; these can assist you in developing insight into why, what, and when you eat. Some people's habits fall far short of the recommended principles of nutrition. Others know what good nutrition includes and put these principles into practice every day. Of course, there are times when nutrition is less of a priority—especially to someone experiencing a great deal of stress. There is concern, however, that this becomes a pattern of behaviour or a vicious circle because our bodies have increased nutrient needs at times of emotional or physical stress.

Lynn, an ECE student, is studying frantically for midterm tests and is trying to stay awake by drinking a lot of coffee. Not surprisingly, the coffee keeps her awake even when she wants to sleep. Lynn doesn't believe she has time for sit-down meals and instead eats doughnuts and other low-nutritive foods in the cafeteria. By week's end, Lynn is snapping at everyone and can't imagine how she'll ever survive her weekend job at the mall.

This example highlights the interplay between nutrition and physical, social, and emotional well-being. Lynn's nutritional habits have raised her stress level rather than lowered it. How can she use nutrition in her favour when she is stressed out during test week? Recognizing the problem, Lynn makes it a point to learn more about nutrition and how nutrients (especially B and C vitamins) nourish the nervous system. As test week approaches, Lynn eats a variety of foods high in these vitamins—whole-grain breads and cereals, milk and yogurt, dark-green leafy vegetables, broccoli, tomatoes, oranges, and bananas. During that week, she brings in nutritious snacks such as whole-grain crackers with cheese or hummus and fruit that she can refuel on. She limits her coffee to a couple of cups during the morning. She is pleasantly surprised that by the end of the week she isn't a bear! Let us hope that this experience has a positive impact on Lynn and that she makes some permanent changes to her eating patterns that help her in the long term.

Eating nutritiously confers benefits daily and over time for all of us. Foods that are high in nutrients keep our minds and bodies in good working order, providing ongoing energy. Eating patterns that maximize the intake of wholesome foods while minimizing the intake of processing and additives contribute to the prevention of serious chronic diseases (e.g., a diet that is low in fat is thought to help prevent heart disease and some forms of cancer). In addition to feeling good and preventing disease, we also provide healthy role models for children. *Eating Well with Canada's Food Guide* (Health Canada, 2007a) is based on two principles: eat well and be active today and every day.

Health Canada does not recommend dieting, which is recognized as counterproductive. Canadians are urged to reject the popular myth that a healthy body size is narrowly defined. Realistically, a healthy body size is achieved and maintained through nutritious eating, without dieting, and through incorporating regular physical activity into one's lifestyle. Age, gender, body type, and other factors influence our body size. It is noteworthy, however, that the dramatic increase in the rate of obesity in Canada is of concern to our mortality and morbidity. Statistics Canada (2002) reported that 47.9% of Canadians were overweight in 1998. Currently, the World Health Organization's (2008) international classification guidelines for body mass index (BMI) and measures of fat distribution (waist-to-hip ratio) are used to define obesity. With regard to BMI,

- adults with less than 18.5% body fat may have risks associated with being underweight;
- 18.5 to 24.9% body fat is optimal for adults; and
- adults with 25% or higher body fat may have increased risks associated with being overweight.

By society's standards, Marsha is obese. She has spent years yo-yo dieting and trying to attain a body size that is acceptable to those around her. Whenever she loses weight, even under a physician's care, she quickly regains it. She feels like a failure because she realizes she will never be able to lose the weight that she wants to. Family and strangers joke about Marsha's size, which is hurtful and disrespectful and diminishes her self-esteem (e.g., "You would be so pretty if you would only lose weight"). Marsha's anger is understandable—prejudice against large persons, especially women and girls, is one of the last forms of discrimination in which disparaging attitudes and comments remain socially acceptable.

Hercilia, a friend of Marsha's, is a large woman yet is much more self-assured. She suggested that Marsha consult with her dietitian-nutritionist, who follows a health promotion model. This was the turning point for Marsha. Two years later, Marsha's body size still does not fit society's standard. However, she has become much more aware of what is important to her and has a quality of life that far surpasses that of her past, when she was always on hold until she lost weight. She consistently makes healthy food choices and incorporates physical activity into her daily routine. For the past year, Marsha and her counsellor have worked through her feelings of failure, and that work has improved her feelings of self-worth and body image (see Body Image, page 220). The self-help group that she attends provides mutual support in coping with society's prejudice against people who are fat, their putdowns, and intrusive questions (e.g., a taxi driver asks his passenger, "So how much do you weigh?"). Since Marsha has stopped focusing on weight loss and has incorporated a health promotion model into her approach, she has more energy than ever before and is slowly losing weight.

The fashion industry creates powerful images of beauty and desirability that particularly affect society's view of women. However, changes in societal attitudes are gradually taking place. Today, there is some recognition of a wide range of healthy body sizes. Fashionable and affordable clothes are more readily available in a range of sizes. Even fast-food restaurants have started to offer foods that help people make healthier choices. A physically active lifestyle is essential for the long-term well-being of all Canadians. Some physical activity programs are designed for larger people, which may help them feel less self-conscious about exercising in front of others.

Following *Eating Well with Canada's Food Guide* and putting consistent effort into normalizing routine physical activity will help adults who are considered overweight move into a healthier range. Individuals who may be considered obese will probably require guidance and supervision by a physician and a dietitian.

How does your eating pattern rate? Try recording what you eat for the next few days or, even better, for a week. Then use the *Make your choices count!* checklist to see how your choices compared with *Eating Well with Canada's Food Guide* recommendations (see Figure 2.1).

- You are doing everything right, and this review confirms and supports your healthy lifestyle.
- You have a low energy level and feel that your overall health (e.g., complexion, dullness of hair, frequency of colds, headaches) can be improved.
- If you are a woman, perhaps you have chronic premenstrual syndrome (PMS) and have heard that changes in diet, such as eliminating caffeine and alcohol, may help reduce the symptoms.
- You know that you overeat when you're bored or that you crave salty food when you study.

CANADA'S FOOD GUIDE SUGGESTS...

☑ Eat the recommended **amount** and **type** of food each day.

☑ Eat at least one dark green and one orange vegetable each day.

☑ Choose vegetables and fruit prepared with little or no added fat, sugar or salt.

☑ Have vegetables and fruit more often than juice.

☑ Make at least half of your grain products whole grain each day.

☑ Choose grain products that are lower in fat, sugar or salt.

☑ Drink skim, 1% or 2% milk each day.

☑ Select lower fat milk alternatives.

☑ Have meat alternatives such as beans, lentils and tofu often.

☑ Eat at least two Food Guide Servings of fish each week.

☑ Select lean meat and alternatives prepared with little or no added fat or salt.

☑ Include a small amount of unsaturated fat each day.

☑ Satisfy your thirst with water.

☑ Limit foods and beverages high in calories, fat, sugar or salt.

☑ Be active every day.

Source: *Canada's Food Guide: Make Your Choices Count*, Health Canada, 2007 Reproduced with the permission of the Minister of Public Works and Government Services Canada, 2008.

Any habit is hard to break or adjust, so don't expect change to happen overnight. The first step is to find out what influences your eating. As children, we develop positive and negative associations with food. Using examples, Table 5.1 illustrates what food can mean to someone (see page 218). Sometimes you eat food because you feel like it, whether it is nutritious or not! If we feel deprived of food we enjoy, we are more likely to abandon our progress in making changes. Here are a few additional suggestions:

- If you are not currently a breakfast eater, try gradually to make changes. Eating from at least three of the four food groups in the morning has short- and long-term benefits.

- Reduce the percentage of animal foods in your diet and eat some fish and soy foods (e.g., tofu). More specifically, the "unhealthy" fats are saturated (e.g., from meats and cheese) and trans fats (created when liquid oils are transformed into shortening and margarine) (Liebman, 2002, pp. 3–4). These raise our low-density lipoprotein (LDL; "bad" cholesterol). Better fats (which don't raise cholesterol) are mono- and polyunsaturated fats (e.g., olive, canola, soy, and sunflower oils). The best fats are the omega-3 fats (e.g., fish oils, particularly salmon, trout, and sardines, but there are some omega-3 fats in all fish). It seems that there is something in omega-3 and omega-6 fats that raises our high-density lipoprotein (HDL; "good" cholesterol) and protects the heart. Eating seafood at least two times a week or taking a supplement is recommended.

- Follow the age and stage recommendations in Health Canada's *Eating Well with Canada Food Guide*. For example, women who could become pregnant or are pregnant or breast-feeding should take a multivitamin daily containing 400 micrograms of folic acid (Health Canada, 2007b, p. 42). Folic acid is a B vitamin that is known to reduce the risk of a fetus developing a neural tube defect and also supports the growth of maternal and fetal tissue. Men and women over the age of 50 need more vitamin D than can be obtained from food to reduce the risk of osteoporosis and fractures. A supplement containing 400 IU of vitamin D in addition to consuming 500 mL of milk each day is recommended (Health Canada, 2007b, p. 43).

- Gradually reduce the number of processed foods you buy, although some convenience foods may be too convenient to give up! Most, but not all, processed foods have a lot of saturated or trans fat, salt, sugar, and additives. Read labels to determine nutrition content.

- Bring your own food to school or work as often as possible, or bring at least part of the meal, or bring snacks to ensure some high-nutritive foods.

- Share ideas with your friends. Potluck lunches or two or three friends taking turns bringing lunch may be enjoyable and save time. This idea can promote openness to try new foods.

My Food Guide (Health Canada, 2007c) is an interactive tool that helps you personalize the information found in *Eating Well with Canada's Food Guide*.

Physical Activity

Generally, physical activity includes any bodily movement caused by muscle contraction that results in using energy. Balancing healthy eating with daily physical activity is a winning combination. Health Canada's (2007a) proclamation to "Eat well and be active today and every day!" includes benefits such as better overall health, lower risk of disease, a healthy body weight, feeling and looking better, more energy, and stronger bones and muscles. These benefits have a positive impact on one's sense of well-being and enhance one's physical and intellectual abilities, now and as we get older.

The fitter you are, the better your body is able to deal with the everyday demands you put on it and to recover from any injury. Ratey (2008, pp. 37–38) highlights the important role exercise plays in elevating and balancing the three brain (neuro) transmitters that have a powerful influence in supporting mental health:

- Serotonin influences mood, impulsivity, anger, and aggressiveness
- Norepinephrine can amplify signals that influence attention, perception, motivation, and arousal
- Dopamine is thought of as the learning, satisfaction, attention, and movement transmitter

Research is finding that fitness, not low body weight, is the more significant predictor to a longer life. A recent study, for example, concluded that in older adults, those who are obese but physically fit have a lower risk of dying than those who are of normal weight but are physically inactive (Sui et al., 2007).

Some people don't give exercise a second thought because being active is just part of their lifestyle (e.g., they walk or ride a bicycle to work rather than drive). Those of us who have not incorporated regular physical activity into our lives may find it easier to start by taking small steps rather than big leaps. A drastic change can be motivating at first, but soon becomes discouraging if the work and effort don't bring quick results. It may be difficult to fit one more thing into an already crowded schedule, and exercise may seem to be expendable. Single parents of young children, for example, may not see how it is possible. Maybe riding a stationary bike while watching television with the children would be workable, or taking the stairs rather than an escalator whenever possible. Often making a conscious effort to be more active while at work or school is a possibility. While supervising on the playground, educators can keep moving as much as possible, or they can go for a brisk walk during the coffee break.

The Alberta Centre for Active Living (2007a, 2007b, 2007c) reminds employers that workplace physical activity programs can reduce sick leave by up to 32% and increase productivity by up to 52%. The centre offers ideas for each of the four levels of the health promotion action plan to make physical activity at work a reality. Here are a few examples for each of the four levels, focusing on how employers can support employee fitness:

Individual Level

- "Start a physical activity closet filled with low-cost sport and activity equipment (e.g., basketballs, fitness bands, pylons, skipping ropes, Frisbees)" (2007b, p. 1).
- Track your physical activity week by week.
- "Buy one or two bikes and helmets for employees to use at work to get fresh air and sunshine or run errands" (2007b, p. 1).
- "Produce or link to an active living screensaver with physical activity tips that employees can download" (2007b, p. 1).
- "Help employees develop time-management skills. These skills can help employees make time for physical activity" (2007b, p. 1).

Collective Self-Help

- "Post a sign-up board where staff can join a group or find a buddy to participate in activities of interest" (2007c, p. 1).
- "Arrange a company badminton [tennis, softball, soccer, golf, or other] tournament that lasts several months, with each employee playing once a week. Post the results as the tournament progresses" (2007c, p. 1).
- "Co-ordinate a stair climb challenge. Post a chart at the top of the stairwell, and encourage employees to track the number of flights of stairs they climb each workday" (2007c, p. 1). Organize teams and have a goal (e.g., to climb the equivalent of Mount Logan).
- "Post and promote a sign-up board for lunchtime walking groups" (2007c, p. 1).
- "Co-ordinate a walk to work club. Acknowledge employees who either walk to work or walk to public transit" (2007c, p. 1).

Community Action

- Extend the walking or stair-climbing programs to other workplaces or community groups.
- Plan a workplace health fair involving other early childhood programs in the community or plan a walking or biking marathon for a charitable cause.
- "Post a map showing several walking routes around the workplace, inside and/or out" (2007a, p. 1).

Societal Level

- "Participate in national campaigns such as Healthy Workplace Week, SummerActive, WinterActive, Commuter Challenge Week and Particip ACTION events" (2007a, p. 1).
- Lobby the municipal government for more bicycle lanes and green space for walking, and public transportation expansion.

Four components of physical fitness are universally recognized as promoting good health: aerobic (cardiovascular) fitness, flexibility, strength, and endurance.

Aerobic fitness is considered the most important component and refers to how well your heart is able to pump oxygen-rich blood to your cells and carry waste out of your cells. The term "aerobic" means "with oxygen." In aerobic activity, the body performs low- to moderate-intensity tasks over an extended period of time. By working our heart muscle at 60 to 80% of its capacity for a minimum of 10 minutes (progressing to 30 minutes) 4 days a week, we increase and maintain our aerobic fitness level. Walking, hiking, cross-country skiing, cycling, dance aerobics or water aerobics, rope skipping, in-line skating, rowing, and stair climbing are some possibilities.

Individuals need to choose activities and times that suit their life situations. Busy people often try to fit aerobic activity into their workday by walking or climbing stairs at lunch or getting off public transit a few kilometres from work or home and walking the rest of the way. A bonus is that we get outside and have a change of scenery, which is also good for stress management.

Flexibility refers to the ability of your joints to move through the full range of their motion. Proper stretching is the best way to increase flexibility. Good back health and the prevention of pulls and other muscle damage are important benefits of flexibility (see Preventing Musculoskeletal Injuries, page 74). Stretching each major muscle group after a few minutes of warm-up and before you begin vigorous aerobic or strength training is an important way to prevent strains and sprains. Some stretching exercises can be incorporated into your day, such as head tilts, side stretches, arm circles, and sit/reach stretches. Even stretching in the morning before getting out of bed can contribute to your flexibility and back health. You may also enjoy yoga or tai chi classes for many benefits, including flexibility.

Strength refers to the ability of one of your muscle groups to exert force in one motion (e.g., lifting a toddler or moving a table). Strength training in a gym usually involves a range of machines with weights, focusing on strengthening different muscles. To a certain extent, this can also be done with free weights. A *set* is the number of repetitions performed for a given exercise lifting a certain weight. It is important to build strength and endurance gradually, to prevent muscle fatigue and injury. Strength-training exercises without weights and using body resistance to build strength include activities such as pushups, sit-ups, step-ups (climbing stairs helps!), pull-ups, arm curls, and abdominal curl-ups.

Endurance refers to the ability of one of your muscle groups to perform muscular contractions of moderate force over an extended period (e.g., lifting half of your maximum capacity a few times a minute over five minutes). If you walk, ride a bike, dance, or climb a hill, you are working on your aerobic fitness, strength, and muscular endurance all at the same time. In the work environment, muscular endurance may translate into putting all the cots away after nap time or being able to lift 10 toddlers—one at a time—off the change table.

Both strength and endurance increase through activity involving resistance training because your muscles get stronger when you condition them to lift more weight and gain endurance when you gradually increase repetitions. It is essential that you learn and practise the proper techniques to prevent injury.

An active lifestyle should include all four fitness components, but your goals and the level of activity you want in your life will help determine how much of each component will be included. For example, someone who wants to improve overall well-being but doesn't have the time or interest in focusing a lot of attention on a program may place more emphasis on aerobic activities and some gentle stretching to improve flexibility. Regardless of the aerobic activity chosen, strength and endurance should be relatively easy to incorporate. Although programs such as yoga, Pilates, and tai chi do not focus on aerobic activity, they improve flexibility, strength, and endurance.

Recognizing the short- and long-term benefits of moderate physical activity for one's personal and professional lives is the first step toward fitness. Remember the following:

- Start your program gradually and choose activities you enjoy.
- Make sure you have the right equipment and clothing for the activity. If cost is a factor, choose an activity that has lower equipment costs.

- Learn and use the proper techniques to prevent injury and maximize fitness benefits.
- Stop if it hurts! Listen to your body. Pain means there is something your body is not ready for and you can injure yourself if you continue.

There are several methods to monitor intensity during physical activity, with the simplest one being the talk test. Ask yourself, "Can I talk or sing while doing the activity?" (Table 2.2).

TABLE 2.2	Testing the Intensity of Your Physical Activity
SIGNING & TALKING STATUS	**INTENSITY**
I can sing!	Light intensity
I can talk!	Moderate intensity
I can't carry on a conversation!	Vigorous intensity
	Very vigorous intensity

Source: Adapted with permission from the Physical Activity Resource Centre, (Making Active Choices Workshop Handout: "Am I going Fast Enough", 2003).

Optimal intensity tends to be at the moderate level. As you build your fitness level, such as walking further, more briskly, or up inclines more easily, you'll find that you are able to do more with less intensity. To build your fitness level, it is important to "step up" your workout and increase the challenge. The Heart and Stroke Foundation of Canada and many other agencies and resources are available to help you get started with suggestions for fitness activities.

Leisure and Rest

Balancing our need for meaningful work with our need for leisure contributes to well-being. Leisure means different things to different people. For example, most individuals have a need for solitude that can be fulfilled through a variety of activities, such as completing puzzles, doing crafts or artwork, or meditating. Many people use meditation to relax and manage stress. Although different techniques and philosophies are advocated, in general, meditation uses deep breathing, allowing tension to leave the body. Most forms of meditation involve sitting quietly for 15 to 20 minutes, focusing on a particular word or symbol (a mantra), controlling breathing, and becoming more in tune with the inner self. With meditation, as with other forms of coping with or managing stress, the individual determines how effective it is as a tool. To satisfy our need to relate to others, we may like going to a movie with a friend, talking on the phone, entertaining at home, fishing with others, or going camping. Religious or political meetings may also fulfill this need. We might satisfy our need to participate through organized sports or physical activity, a gardening club, or an ethnocultural group. Most individuals also need to observe at times. They may satisfy that need by visiting amusement parks, watching parades, sitting on the porch and watching passersby, or browsing in a bookstore.

These are but a few examples, but they highlight the fact that for most of us there is an overlap between physical activity and relaxation, because going to the gym or taking a brisk walk may achieve both ends. In the discussion on stress later in this unit, the topic of leisure activities—whether physically active and social or quiet and solitary—as a means to cope with stress appears again. Being aware of what is relaxing for you and finding regular opportunities to unwind are part of everyday health promotion.

Our bodies need time to rest and sleep to revitalize and to provide time for the bodily functions and organs to slow down. The duration of sleep that adults need varies, but most of us need seven to eight hours a night. Illness, pregnancy, or other factors may increase the amount of sleep needed.

Stress factors such as financial or personal problems, exam-time worry, or a colicky baby can affect the amount or quality of our sleep. Here are some common-sense suggestions for having a better sleep:

- Avoid alcohol (which can disrupt sleep patterns) or smoking (because nicotine makes you wakeful) before going to bed.
- Eliminate or reduce consumption of caffeinated drinks (e.g., coffee, cola drinks) starting in late afternoon.
- Do something relaxing before going to bed.
- Maintain a regular schedule and routine for going to bed and getting up.
- Get out of bed and do something (e.g., read a relaxing book, write a list to reduce worries) rather than watch the clock when you are unable to sleep.
- Stress coupled with sleep deprivation is very taxing on one's emotional and physical health, and talking with a friend or counsellor can help you find short- or long-term solutions.

Especially when we are young, and often as students, socializing in the evenings may take precedence over getting enough sleep every night. When lack of sleep affects our health or work/school performance, we are faced with making some decisions and establishing priorities. And when we work with children, we must be especially alert to our surroundings from the standpoint of safety. As well, sleep deprivation often makes us irritable—not an appropriate frame of mind when working with children and coworkers. These decisions are sometimes difficult, especially for young adults who are training for a career, but responsibility does involve setting priorities. Balancing our need to socialize (e.g., on the weekend) with our responsibilities is essential to becoming a professional.

Reducing Other Risk Factors

Health behaviour either promotes your health or undermines it. Here are important examples of health behaviour that contribute positively to our health:

- quitting smoking and avoiding passive (secondhand) smoking
- limiting your consumption of alcohol and refraining from drinking alcohol during pregnancy and breast-feeding
- avoiding illegal drugs and being careful about medication use
- practising safer sex to prevent sexually transmitted diseases (STDs), including human immunodeficiency virus (HIV) infection and hepatitis B

- maintaining a regular schedule of physical and dental checkups and monthly self-exams of breasts or testicles for early detection of breast or testicular cancer

In keeping with the health promotion philosophy discussed in Unit 1, the continuum of responsibility between individual and society depends very much on your circumstances.

Selecting health care professionals who best suit our health needs can play a significant role in health promotion. If you live in an area where there is more than one choice, choose the health professional or agency that

- answers your questions clearly and directly,
- gives you access to your medical file, should you choose to see it, and
- is linguistically and culturally relevant to you.

You may have additional criteria, and it is important that you feel like a partner in your health care. It's in your best interest to take an active role in decision making about your medical treatments. This is our individual responsibility. When in doubt, ask for a second or third opinion. Women in particular often feel uncomfortable with or even intimidated by physicians and do not ask them questions about their own health care. Even today, some physicians prescribe tranquilizers for women with complaints such as PMS or symptoms of menopause.

One of the best ways that people who smoke can improve their long-term health is by quitting, but that's not easy. It's especially difficult when other stress factors are present and beyond the smoker's control. Smoking may be relaxing or a stress reliever for that person in that situation. Pursuing ways to quit smoking, however, is well worth the effort, and many communities have support systems that can help. At a time when so many Canadians are quitting smoking, it is discouraging that teens and young women are the fastest-growing groups starting to smoke. Young people who have been smoking only a short time are strongly encouraged to quit before the addiction becomes stronger. What messages are educators and ECE students sending to children who see them smoking outside the building on breaks, who smell the smoke on their clothes and hair, who see them smoking in the mall or on the street?

The issue of partner abuse is included to raise awareness and sensitize readers to the possibility that fellow students, future coworkers, children's parents, or even you yourself may be a victim. Violence can take many forms, including physical, sexual, emotional, social, and financial. You will need to expand your knowledge in this area, since we are only touching the surface of abuse.

Lidia was a victim of spousal abuse. She felt powerless to escape. She believed that if she left her husband, he would find and possibly kill her. Her coworkers talked among themselves about how weak Lidia was for not leaving her husband. Yet it's too simple to say, "Just leave him!" Family violence is a very complicated situation. Lidia eventually found the support and legal assistance she needed at the local women's shelter, but not before years of violence had taken a great toll on her well-being.

The following list is a sampling of statistics compiled by the Canadian Centre for Justice Statistics (2005, pp. 8–10):

- An estimated 7% of Canadians over 15 years of age experienced spousal violence in the previous 5 years. The rates of violence have remained unchanged since 1999.
- Women were much more likely to report spousal violence than men. *For example,*
  - 21% of women versus 11% of men reported that they were the targets of more than 10 violent incidents at the hands of their partner.
  - 44% of women versus 18% of men reported that they were injured as a result of the violence.
- The rate of reporting for those who are gay or lesbian was twice that of those who are heterosexual (15% versus 7%).
- Women were three times more likely to
  - fear for their life than men (34% versus 10%) or
  - take time off from their daily activities as a result of the violence (29% versus 10%).
- The rate of spousal homicides is between 4 and 5 times higher for women as the victim than men.
- Of all the homicides in Canada between 1961 and 2003, 76% of them involved family members.

Intimate partners who are being abused stay in the relationship for a number of reasons: fear, low self-esteem, a lack of economic and social supports, cultural taboos, religion, obligation, and oppression. When a woman discloses abuse to you, listen and believe her. This is the first step for her, and the emotional support you provide may encourage her to take action, although the decisions should be her own. In the future, possibly with your support, she may seek options (e.g., shelters, legal advice, services sensitive to women's needs) and make a safety plan.

Familiarize yourself with your community's emergency shelters and the telephone hot line as well as any available long-term services. Partner abuse, date rape, and other forms of violence, particularly against women, are known to be prevalent in our society. For victims of intimate-partner abuse, the abuse "follows" them to work as the abuser may call and harass them or their coworkers, and the stress affects the quality of their work or the amount of time off work.

With support, many can escape the vicious circle of violent relationships. Stopping the violence is a complex task and requires a multifaceted societal response. Training programs for early childhood educators are important tools to support the nonoffending parent and children in these difficult circumstances (see Resource Materials, page 103). Shelters are available in most communities across Canada.

Infectious Diseases and You

When you start working in programs, you'll probably find that you get sick more often than usual. Although this is to be expected, there are things you can do to prevent being ill so frequently, including being immunized, implementing hygiene practices, and maintaining a well-balanced lifestyle.

ECE training programs should require students to have up-to-date immunizations before they do their first placement in a program. The training institution's health personnel collect and review students' immunization records and other related medical information.

Standard immunization requirements for prospective child care practitioners are as follows:

1. Proof that immunizations against diphtheria, tetanus, polio and pertussis are up-to-date, with tetanus–diphtheria (as Td or dTap) received within the last 10 years and at least one dose of dTap received in adulthood.

2. Documentation of one MMR (measles, mumps and rubella) vaccination if a prospective child care employee was born after 1970. A laboratory-confirmed proof of immunity against these diseases is also acceptable.

3. Documentation of two doses of chickenpox (varicella) vaccine or a doctor's documentation of the person having had chickenpox or laboratory-confirmed proof of immunity against chickenpox.

4. A documented negative tuberculosis (TB) skin test. Some child care centres require a two-step skin test, to screen out false negative results. Two tests are completed 1 to 4 weeks apart, with the second test being the true result. Before beginning work in child care, a person testing positive must undergo further assessment and present a doctor's note confirming that active TB has been ruled out.

5. Annual influenza vaccine if the child care practitioner will be caring for children under 24 months of age or children with chronic diseases. (Canadian Paediatric Society, 2008, p. 373)

In addition to routine immunizations, there are a number of optional but recommended vaccinations. It is recommended that child care practitioners receive the following:

- **Hepatitis A vaccine**, especially in programs serving vulnerable communities (e.g., in rural or remote areas with inadequate water or sewage purification systems). A child care practitioner would receive two doses of hepatitis A vaccine, given 6 to 12 months apart.

- **Hepatitis B vaccine**, especially in programs where children whose families have come from countries where hepatitis B is common are present, or in communities where hepatitis B is common. The usual adult schedule is three doses: one at the first visit, a second one month later, and a final dose 6 months after that. Follow-up testing for antibody response may also be necessary to verify immunity.

- **Booster shots for mumps and measles.** While vaccines protecting against both these illnesses are universally administered in early childhood under the routine schedule, a booster shot may be required for those who received only one dose. Local public health recommendations should be followed. Child care practitioners can ask their doctor for advice. (Canadian Paediatric Society, 2008, p. 374)

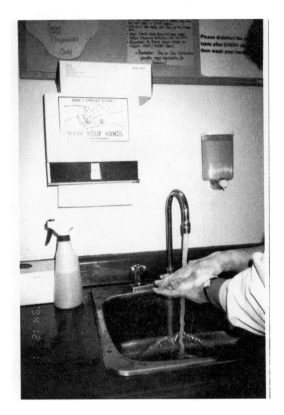

To reduce the spread of infectious diseases in programs, educators are responsible for implementing hygiene practices. Steps taken to reduce the spread of germs among children will have a positive effect on educators' health. On a daily basis, educators must pay particular attention to how and when they wash their hands. Unit 3 outlines what you need to know, including the ins and outs of hand washing and information on hygiene practices.

There will be times when educators who are ill should be excluded from work. An early childhood program's exclusion policy for educators and others working in the program should include the following conditions. The individual should be excluded when she or he

- cannot fulfill her [or his] responsibilities because her [or his] illness compromises the care of the children.
- is sick with a respiratory infection. Facility supervisors should encourage an ailing staff member to stay home to prevent the spread of illness.
- has a gastrointestinal infection with diarrhea or vomiting.
- has any of the specific conditions requiring exclusion [Appendix 4.1, page 197]. (Canadian Paediatric Society, 2008, p. 375)

Much of what we know about childhood infections applies also to adults, who can get the same infections. The more common childhood illnesses are discussed in Unit 4, which includes a table that summarizes the management of children's illnesses in the program (see Childhood Infections: Just the Basics, page 171).

Hepatitis B is a virus that causes infection of the liver and is spread by direct contact with blood or bloody body fluid. "The incidence of HBV transmission in child care settings is extremely low, and infection is preventable through routine practices" (Canadian Paediatric Society, 2008, p. 377). The hepatitis B virus immunization is part of the routine childhood immunization schedule in Canada. And as discussed earlier, the vaccination for educators is recommended where the prevalence of hepatitis B is higher. Where that is not the case, it may be beneficial because of educators' own personal health behaviour (e.g., sexual practices). Hepatitis C, like hepatitis B, is a virus that causes infection of the liver and is spread by direct contact with blood or bloody body fluid. "There have been no reports of HCV infection as a result of exposure in child care" (Canadian Paediatric Society, 2008, p. 377). Educators are not required to disclose their hepatitis B or C status (Canadian Paediatric Society, 2008, p. 378). Universal precautions are always important when cleaning blood and bodily fluids (see Universal Precautions, page 144).

Pregnancies are not always planned. Working with children increases your exposure to infections. Female ECE students and educators may have peace of mind if they talk with their physician. Five infections are particularly important to pregnant women: chickenpox, rubella, measles, mumps, and cytomegalovirus (CMV).

Chickenpox

Fortunately, most people have chickenpox when they are children. Although it is usually mild in children, it can cause severe illness in adults. Students and educators who can't recall whether they had chickenpox as children may wish to ask their doctor to do an antibody test, which will tell them whether they have had the disease. Working in programs puts you at risk of caring for children with chickenpox. Susceptible adults exposed to chickenpox or shingles should receive varicella-zoster immune globulin (VZIG) within 96 hours of exposure (Canadian Paediatric Society, 2008, p. 376). The chickenpox vaccine is part of the routine immunization schedule in Canada (see Table 3.3, page 126). The immunization of susceptible adults is recommended (National Advisory Committee on Immunization, 2006, p. 330). For more information about it, contact your physician.

For women who are susceptible to chickenpox and become infected during the first half of pregnancy, the fetus is at high risk of malformation. As soon as a woman knows that she has been exposed to chickenpox or shingles, she must contact her physician or the public health agency. When an infant is born to a mother who developed chickenpox a few days before or after delivery, the baby will likely develop a severe case of chickenpox.

Rubella (German Measles)

If your immunization schedule is up to date, you will know if you received your rubella vaccine. If not, ask your physician about the antibody test. If a pregnant woman is susceptible and has been exposed to rubella, she should talk to her physician immediately. Susceptible pregnant women who are infected with rubella during the first four months of pregnancy are at high risk of a miscarriage or, if the fetus goes to term, of delivering a baby with malformations.

Measles and Mumps

Most of us are immune to measles and mumps because we had the diseases or have received the MMR vaccine. Start by referring to your immunization schedule to see if it is up-to-date. If you have only received one dose of the vaccine, you may be susceptible to measles and mumps. If you are not sure, ask your physician about the antibody test, particularly if you are or want to become pregnant. Susceptible pregnant women who are infected with

- measles during the pregnancy have an increased risk of premature delivery (Canadian Paediatric Society, 2008, p. 377).
- mumps in the first three months of pregnancy may increase the risk of miscarriage (Canadian Paediatric Society, 2008, p. 376).

Cytomegalovirus

A person who is infected with CMV may not have any symptoms or may develop ones that are similar to those of mononucleosis (i.e., swollen glands, fatigue, fever). Usually, we aren't aware that we have been exposed to CMV because our bodies produce antibodies to protect us. In fact, we may have had CMV as children. Women pass their CMV antibodies to the fetus. After birth, children excrete the virus in the urine and saliva for a year or two and intermittently throughout life. Because of the relatively close contact between educators and children, some susceptible educators will probably become infected with CMV. Educators' best protection is effective hand washing, effective diapering and toileting routines, and cleaning and sanitizing surfaces that have been contaminated with body secretions (e.g., saliva, vomit, urine, or stool).

The only real concern about CMV is when women who are susceptible to CMV become infected during their pregnancy. "There is a risk that an infant will be infected *in utero*, and 5 to 15 per cent of affected infants will have serious disease at birth. There is also a small risk associated with re-exposure during pregnancy. Approximately 5 per cent of affected infants have mild but lasting effects, including moderate hearing loss and/or a developmental delay" (Canadian Paediatric Society, 2008, p. 380). A vaccine for CMV is not available, and an immune globulin that could be used for healthy individuals is only in the testing stage in the United States (American Academy of Pediatrics, 2006, p. 277). One's best defence is to pay particular attention to hand washing and adhering to the diapering and toileting routines with children.

Preventing Musculoskeletal Injuries

The most common injury experienced by early childhood educators is back injury. The injuries in a study of 54 early childhood settings in Quebec were predominantly due to excessive lifting, pulling, pushing, or carrying. The layout and design of the building, its furniture, the number of people, and available floor space all play a role in the likelihood of injury. Fortunately, more than half of the educators who were injured did not have to leave work as a result. Most of the injuries were strains and sprains—a muscle pulled when lifting a child awkwardly, for example, or an ankle sprained when tripping on a toy (Maxwell & Huot, 1994, p. 29). This study has not been replicated over the past 15 years in Canada, but the reality of musculoskeletal injury risk is still true for educators.

Ergonomics refers to the ways that the job can be altered to fit the person performing it, rather than the other way around. A survey of 258 early childhood educators in Wisconsin found that although most were aware of ergonomic interventions and were currently experiencing musculoskeletal pain while performing their jobs, they did not believe they needed to make ergonomic changes. The results of this study highlight the need for further analysis of specific child care tasks and identification of more effective methods to reduce the risk for musculoskeletal pain and injuries (King, Gratz, & Kleiner, 2006).

You don't have to go very far to find someone who has or is experiencing back pain. You may have had back pain too. Not all back pain or injury is preventable, but there are ways to reduce the risk of back injury and to manage back pain when it does occur:

- Maintain the three natural curves of your spine, to take undue pressure off your spine. In a healthy spine, the 33 vertebrae form a natural "S" curve.

- Change posture, even slightly, every few minutes because the disks, like the rest of the body, take in nutrients and get rid of waste products. When we remain in one position for too long, that process can't happen efficiently.

- Take part in regular physical activity, which helps increase the muscles' ability to support the back.

- Do stretching exercises to increase flexibility, decrease the risk of injury, and correct posture.

- Use proper lifting techniques, as described below.

When back pain does occur, individuals should

- consult with their family physician. Strained muscles and sprained ligaments are the most common causes of back pain and tend to heal within a few weeks.

- resume routines gradually but as soon as possible—it is now widely believed that bed rest for more than two or three days usually does more harm than good.

- pursue physiotherapy, chiropractic, acupuncture, massage, and yoga as more conservative therapy options. Surgery is not recommended as a therapeutic option in the vast majority of back problems.

In particular, improper lifting and carrying can result in back injuries, which may lead to long-term back problems, loss of wages, and even the need for a career change. Awareness of the potential problem and proper lifting techniques can help prevent back problems. Whether you are standing, walking, sitting on a chair or floor, or lifting or carrying something, your goal is to maintain the natural curves of your spine.

Some readers may think that the following list of preventive steps applies only to people who lift boxes in a warehouse, not to educators who lift infants off the floor. Granted, lifting a baby off the floor in the same way as you might bend to touch your toes may not hurt your back the first time, but using this technique repeatedly almost guarantees eventual back injury. You may lean over a table or reach down to pick up a piece of paper and then find you can't straighten up. A baby may not look as heavy as a large box or suitcase, but a 9-month-old could easily weigh 8 kilograms (18 lbs.) or more. When we lift something by using our back (by bending over) rather than our legs, that 8-kilogram baby puts 82 kilograms (180 lbs.) of pressure on our back. To prevent injury, follow the steps in Figure 2.2 when you are lifting infants from the floor.

FIGURE 2.2 | **Lifting Infants from the Floor**

Infant Lifting Technique – "Tripod Lift"

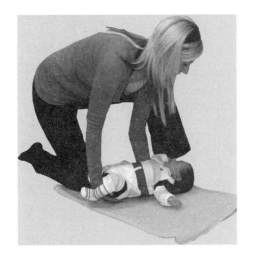

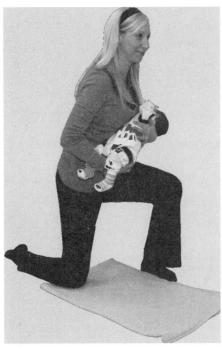

Source: Used with permission from the Occupation Health Clinics for Ontario Workers Inc. *Prevention through Intervention: Safe Lifting Techniques of Children*. <http://www.ohcow.on.ca/resources/handbooks/childlift/safeliftingbrochure.pdf> (July 2008).

1) Put one foot next to the infant. Keep your back straight, push your buttocks out and slowly lower yourself down onto one knee.
2) Position the infant close to your knee on the floor.
3) Slide the infant from your knee onto the floor to mid-thigh, keep your head forward, your back straight, your buttocks out, and lift the infant onto the opposite thigh.
4) Put both of your forearms under the infant with your palms facing upward and hug the infant close to you.
5) Prepare for the lift by looking forward.
6) Lift upwards following your head and shoulders. Hold the infant close to your body. Lift by extending your legs while keeping your back straight and buttocks out. Remember to breathe as you lift.

Learning how to lift children and objects properly and ensuring that you actually follow the steps each time helps prevent back injuries (see Figure 2.3).

| FIGURE 2.3 | Toddlers and Object Lifting Technique |

Toddler & Object Lifting Technique

- Avoid bending from the waist to reach children or objects located at ground level.
- Squat with feet shoulder width apart, keeping your back straight, and pushing your buttocks out to bring yourself as close to the child as possible, while holding the child securely.
- Tighten stomach muscles and look forward, and use your thigh muscles to raise yourself, while breathing out as you lift.

Wrong   **Right**

Source: Used with permission from the Occupational Health Clinics for Ontario Workers Inc. *Prevention through Intervention: Safe Lifting Techniques of Children.* <http://www.ohcow.on.ca/resources/handbooks/childlift/safeliftingbrochure.pdf> (July 2008).

When you are caring for toddlers, there will be many times when they need and want to be held. Figure 2.4 outlines the steps that will help protect you from a back injury.

Furnishings and Layout

The physical environment's design and the actual layout of space, including the height of counters and storage shelves, contribute to our health status. The equipment and furnishings in early childhood settings are designed for children's (not adults') comfort and accessibility. Many activities happen on the

FIGURE 2.4 | Holding Small Children

Holding Technique

- When holding toddlers, you should avoid placing them on one hip.
- When holding or rocking children, use chairs or furniture with upper back support.
- Keep children centered on your body and use both arms to hold.
- It is also helpful to teach the children to help you lift by holding onto your body rather than leaning away from you.
- When holding or rocking children, use chairs or furniture with upper back.

Source: Used with permission from the Occupation Health Clinics for Ontario Workers Inc. *Prevention through Intervention: Safe Lifting Techniques of Children.* <http://www.ohcow.on.ca/resources/handbooks/childlift/safeliftingbrochure.pdf> (July 2008).

floor. In addition, educators tend to put the children's safety before their own. Of course, this is necessary, but it may mean that unforeseen twists and turns are a reality. Of the many factors that create stress for educators, five relate to the physical workspace: noise, temperature, lack of rest areas, inadequate furnishings, and lack of equipment. As students, you have little or no control over the physical aspects of the space where you do placements. However, if you observe questionable or unsafe situations, you are obliged to report them to staff. Table 2.3 outlines some activities that educators are constantly involved in and provides suggestions for avoiding injury.

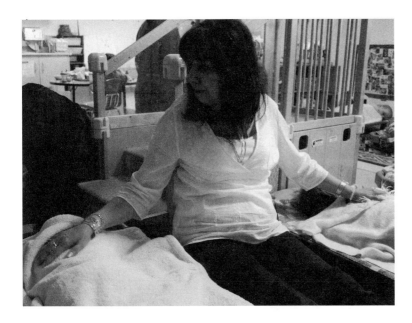

There are still centres that do not provide an adult-sized table, chair, or sofa to be used in rooms with children or adult-sized seating outside. Educators, like other employees, need to get away from their work for breaks and to do administrative work. A staff room provides an area in which educators can relax and socialize.

In the long term, ergonomic research will provide architects and early childhood licensing offices with vital information on designing settings that meet the physical needs of adults as well as children. Lack of funding and resources impedes needed improvements for adults in the early

TABLE 2.3   Worksite Analysis of the Child Care Work Environment

PROBLEM	RECOMMENDATIONS
1. Incorrect lifting of children, toys, supplies, equipment, etc.	1. Educate staff on proper lifting and carrying techniques 2. Promote task rotation where possible 3. Encourage independence in children whenever feasible
2. Inadequate work heights (e.g., child-sized tables and chairs)	1. Create a chair that allows the staff to slide their legs under the table 2. Use sit/kneel chairs 3. Educate staff on using proper body mechanics 4. Provide the staff with adult-sized chairs for occasional use
3. Difficulty lowering and lifting infants in and out of cribs	1. Modify crib sides to enable them to slide down or modify the legs of the cribs to accommodate the staff 2. Educate staff on using proper body mechanics 3. Have step stool available in sleep room
4. Frequent sitting on the floor with back unsupported	1. When possible, have staff sit up against a wall or furniture for back support 2. Perform stretching exercises 3. Educate staff on using proper body mechanics
5. Excessive reaching above shoulder height to obtain stored supplies	1. Redesign kitchen area, placing heaviest items at waist height, lightest above 2. Reorganize snacks and supplies to simplify snack preparation procedures 3. Use step stools when retrieving items that are above cupboard height
6. Frequent lifting of infants and toddlers on and off diaper-changing tables	1. Educate staff on using proper body mechanics 2. Encourage toddlers to use steps to decrease distance staff are lifting
7. Forceful motions combined with awkward posture required to open windows	1. Use step stool to allow for better leverage and reduce awkward posture 2. Have maintenance staff improve quality of window slide
8. Carrying garbage and diaper bags to dumpster	1. Provide staff with cart to transport garbage 2. Relocate garbage cart closer to work area 3. Reduce size and weight of loads 4. Educate staff on using proper body mechanics

Source: Reprinted from *Work: A Journal of Prevention, Assessment, and Rehabilitation*, 6(1): 25–32. From article entitled The Ergonomics of Child Care, Conducting Worksite Analyses by Phyllis M. King, Rene Gratz, Gina Scheuer, Ann Claffey (1996). With permission from IOS Press.

childhood environment. In the meantime, how can we improve workplace conditions? The most obvious answer is to purchase more adult-sized furniture and relatively inexpensive equipment to prevent musculoskeletal problems. For example, legless chairs are available that provide the educator with the necessary back support while sitting on the floor with the children. New tables and chairs purchased should be light and easy to move; mats and cots should be easy for staff to store (Markon, 1999, p. 3). When replacing worn equipment such as cribs, look for ones that meet Canadian Standards Association (CSA) safety standards and that have rails that can be lowered to mattress level.

A couch in a play area provides a comfortable spot for adults and children to sit and talk or read and for staff to bottle-feed infants. Perhaps a set of steps can be built that slide in and out under the diaper counter to give toddlers the opportunity to climb onto or down from the table rather than being lifted—an activity that most toddlers would prefer.

Educators should gather all the necessary diapering supplies before they bring the child to the change area. This eliminates the educator having to keep one hand on the child while reaching or turning to get supplies during the change.

Educators looking at their own workspace, talking about the issues, and referring to resources will undoubtedly come up with many more ideas. Directors and employers need to assess how work is organized to avoid excessive demands on staff. Work tasks should also be evaluated on the basis of physical demands. Of course, the primary obstacle in implementing improvements is accessing funds.

CRITICAL THINKING

While doing a field placement with toddlers, you notice that you are starting to get lower back pain and are concerned that, as a young adult, this is already bothering you. You realize that you need to make some changes immediately in both your personal and professional practices to ensure that you prevent further back pain.

Working with Art and Cleaning Products

Art supplies and cleaning products can be hazardous to educators and children. Educators must select play materials that are nontoxic and read labels for any special handling instructions. Pay particular attention to solvents, glues, dyes, and pottery products.

Painting is a desirable, ongoing experience for children. Rather than buying ready-to-use paints, staff often purchase powder paint and then mix colours as needed. Educators need to exercise caution when handling the powder. If inhaled, the powder can harm the lungs' airways. To protect themselves, educators should mix paint in a well-ventilated area away from children. Educators with asthma may need to avoid mixing powdered paint or wear a filter over their nose and mouth.

In terms of cleaning products, many programs choose soap and water for cleaning surfaces and objects. Many use a dilute solution of bleach and water for sanitizing. Facilities with automatic dishwashers will use the detergent recommended for the machine. All kinds of commercial products are on the market that we can use in our homes and in programs. Many companies advertise the product's sanitizing qualities and claim it makes things sparkling and fresh. For the most part, however, soap and water and good old elbow grease, which creates friction, remove most of the germs. Bleach kills any germs that may remain after cleaning. The recommended bleach dilution is strong enough to be effective yet dilute enough that it won't ruin clothes or make everything smell like bleach. It is also safe to use around children. An environmentally friendly alternative to bleach—one that falls within public health guidelines—will be welcomed when it arrives.

To protect themselves and others when using products, educators need to take precautions.

- Read and follow the product's instructions.
- Wear household rubber gloves to protect your hands from drying, if you prefer.
- Never mix two products (e.g., when ammonia and bleach are mixed, a poisonous gas is produced).
- Keep solutions in their original container and locked out of reach of children.
- Choose cleaners that are safe for our environment.

Workplace Hazardous Materials Information System

The legislation for the **Workplace Hazardous Materials Information System (WHMIS)** applies to all workplaces, which include early childhood settings. Employers are obliged to provide employees with information on the products they use at work. Certain controlled products have been defined as hazardous because they are compressed gas, flammable and combustible, oxidizing, poisonous, or infectious. These products must have labels that list their ingredients, their toxic effects, instructions on safe handling, and first-aid treatments. This legislation applies mainly to industries that use these types of products. Public health inspectors (PHIs) may be consulted to verify whether any of the cleaning and sanitizing products are controlled products. ECE programs frequently buy their cleaning products at grocery stores, and products for sale there would not be controlled.

Read the label for directions and the first-aid treatment on the container (e.g., "If splashed in eyes, flush thoroughly with water. If swallowed, give water or milk. Call a physician"). The first-aid treatment also includes the name of the hazardous ingredient (e.g., "contains sodium hypochlorite"). This information will be very helpful to your poison control centre, whose number is listed in the front of your phone book, if someone ingests the product.

The Rights of the Worker

Although every province and territory has its own legislation on worker health and safety, the Canadian *Occupational Health and Safety Act* (Canadian Centre for Occupational Health and Safety, 1999, p. 1) gives every worker in Canada three important rights:

- **Right to Know.** You have the right to know about actual and potential hazards in your workplace. Your employer or supervisor must inform you about anything in your job that can hurt you and ensure that you have the information or training that you need to work safely.

- **Right to Participate.** You have the right to take part in keeping your workplace healthy and safe. If your workplace agency has 19 employees or more, you can be part of the Joint Health and Safety Committee (JHSC) or be a Health and Safety Representative, which meets monthly and is comprised of employees and management. This committee deals with ongoing health and safety inspections, and any concerns by employees (e.g., in an early childhood program, it may be concern about heavy or awkward equipment that requires routine lifting, causing back injury). In a smaller centre, employees have the right to communicate their health and safety concerns, and must be aware of the process to do so, and be involved in the solutions.

- **Right to Refuse Unsafe Work.** If you believe that the requirements of your job are placing your health and safety in jeopardy, and that a mutually agreed upon solution has not been found to rectify the situation, you can refuse to do it in most situations. You will contact your Ministry of Labour.

Role of Public Health Agencies in Health Promotion

Public health nurses (PHNs) and PHIs work in **public health agencies**. PHNs may be available for consultation on staff illnesses, immunizations, and other concerns. PHIs conduct environmental sanitation inspections of early childhood settings. At least annually, PHIs inspect the building—its lighting, ventilation, kitchen facilities, garbage disposal, and so on. They submit a report to the licensing office (with a copy to the program) that includes any concerns and recommendations for improvement. As well, they may consult with the staff and answer questions about cleaning and sanitizing procedures and products. If the role of public health personnel in your community has been curtailed due to cutbacks, it is important for directors and staff to seek other consultants to perform this role. Keeping the physical environment up-to-date with current information and changes is essential for children's and adults' health in the early childhood program.

Workplace Environmental Issues

Comfortable environmental conditions are important for overall well-being; discomfort can result in stress, fatigue, and other conditions. Heating/air conditioning, ventilation, noise, and light levels all contribute to educators' and children's emotional and physical well-being. If it's too hot inside, we get drowsy and irritable and are more prone to making mistakes. Inadequate lighting causes eyestrain and headaches. The building's architectural design should allow as much natural light into the space as possible.

A well-ventilated space helps remove indoor air contamination. Indoor air is tainted by hair sprays, perfumes, cleaning products, and dust; odours from photocopiers and computer laser printers; formaldehyde (e.g., from unsealed plywood or particleboard, urea-formaldehyde insulation, fabrics, glues, carpets); germs from people's respiratory tracts; and outdoor pollutants. These pollutants are particularly irritating to people with asthma, respiratory illnesses, and contact lenses. Responding to the fact that more than one in four individuals suffers from respiratory disease, The Lung Association has published a document to outline how a company can go about incorporating a scent-free policy for the workplace if staff, parents, and children are affected by perfumes and other scents (see Resource Materials, page 103). Nova Scotia was the first province to promote scent-sensitive environments in 1999, and other jurisdictions are following suit.

Staff should suspect the quality of the air in the building when people are frequently experiencing symptoms such as headaches, fatigue, dizziness, or irritation in the eyes, nose, or throat. Temperature and relative humidity are two of several parameters that affect indoor comfort. Relative humidity levels under 25% can dry out the mucous membranes and skin, leading to chapping and irritation. Low relative humidity also increases static electricity, which can be irritating, and the static shocks can sting adults and children. High humidity levels can cause condensation within the building structure and on interior or exterior surfaces and the development of moulds and fungi (Health Canada, 2008). According to Health Canada (2008), the ideal indoor relative humidity levels are 35% in the winter and 50% in the summer in most Canadian cities. The most common ways to control humidity tend to be water spray or steam humidifiers in the winter and air conditioners in the summer.

Ideally, there are windows in every room that staff open every day for some time, year round. However, for programs located within larger buildings (e.g., in an office tower), the air is part of the building's ventilation system. Programs located in workplaces (e.g., in a manufacturing plant) should have a separate ventilation system to ensure that the children and staff are not breathing air from the plant. If staff or children frequently experience symptoms of illness, the ventilation system must be evaluated.

Of course, outdoor air quality can also have an effect on breathing, especially for those who have respiratory conditions such as asthma. Air Quality

Index levels, on days when there is concern about smog or other airborne contaminants, can always be confirmed by checking online with Environment Canada's air quality forecasts and advisories (see Resource Materials, page 103). This website also offers advice on whether to exercise indoors on days with air quality issues such as high smog.

Finally, the noise level can be an issue, considering the number of children and adults in the same place for extended periods. Although the noise level is never in a range that could potentially damage someone's hearing, a constant noise level can make people feel tired and irritable. Couches, curtains, carpets, pillows, carpeted areas, acoustic ceiling tiles, dress-up clothes, etc., all absorb sounds within the room.

Educators can manage noise by

- alternating quiet and active programs,
- guiding children to use their "indoor voice" indoors,
- alternating educators who supervise the playground, and
- taking staff breaks in a separate room.

In a broader environmental perspective, as citizens and professionals, we have much to be concerned about with regard to our own health and the health of our planet. North Americans are on a binge of consumption, at a rate that is clearly unsustainable for the planet. Many individuals have recognized the importance of taking action at all health promotion levels to reduce their own feelings of powerlessness and, of course, to make a difference. In particular for women, the increase in breast cancer rates is alarming, and environmental risks must be considered. For example, among other causes, radiation, pesticides, and some plastics have been linked to breast cancer. Although radiation and pesticides have long been an issue as powerful carcinogens, there is growing concern (and controversy) about the ingredients (nonylphenols) in some plastic wraps used to cover food, added to make the wraps more flexible. Nonylphenols, known carcinogens, are not chemically bound and can leach out of the plastic fairly easily. Other ingredients in plastics (e.g., phthalates, bisphenol A) are hormone disruptors. For more information on the environment, your health, and actions you can take to lessen your exposure to potentially hazardous products, refer to resources such as the National Network on Environments and Women's Health (see Resource Materials, page 103).

Injury Reports

When educators are injured at work, they must complete an injury report. Sometimes they are tempted to avoid the extra paperwork, especially if they believe that the injury is minor. However, a report is important for a number of reasons:

- to maintain adequate workplace injury records for liability
- to document any injury that seems minor at first but becomes serious later (e.g., a cut that becomes infected)
- to prevent further injuries, potentially

When staff can assess the conditions that caused or contributed to an injury, employers can implement preventive practices, review or provide training (e.g., in proper lifting), or modify the physical space to make it safer (e.g., by installing a handrail by the stairs or improving the lighting of the staff parking lot), which benefits everyone. Often the same injury report (or serious incident report) can be used for children and educators.

PROMOTING YOUR EMOTIONAL AND SOCIAL WELL-BEING

Workplaces don't present only physical risks and benefits; there are also emotional and social factors that can have positive and negative effects on employees' health. In general, **workplace stress** is the reaction from the combination of high demands in a job and a low level of control over the situation (Canadian Centre for Occupational Health and Safety, 2000). Although working with children and families is rewarding, no job is without elements that can create feelings of stress for employees. By recognizing potential stress factors, students take the first step in preventing or reducing the negative impact, resulting in richer professional and personal lives.

Creating a Supportive Early Childhood Environment

The single most important component of high-quality ECE, in terms of promoting healthy child development, is the nature of the daily relationship and interactions between educator and child. This relationship is, of course, affected by other quality factors. Although educators are the key component of quality, we have discussed the lack of recognition for the value of ECE as a profession. As stated earlier, most educators are relatively poorly paid, and many have few traditional occupational benefits and lack adequate professional development opportunities (Beach et al., 2004). For these issues to change, we need a coordinated policy approach and a new method of funding child care (Doherty, Friendly, & Forer, 2000, p. 172). These changes will take time and political will, but, in the meantime, the Doherty et al. study found that approximately 95% of educators and directors stated that the satisfaction of working with children and helping families keeps them in their jobs.

Educators who are content with their work conditions are much more likely to develop self-confidence and competence and are less likely to be dissatisfied and resign. Lower turnover rates mean more consistent care for children. Table 2.4 identifies 10 dimensions of the work climate that support professionalism. As you review those dimensions, you'll see the implied partnership between employee and employer.

OBJECTIVES

To discuss the major role that communication plays in educators' emotional and social well-being.

To identify possible sources of personal, professional, and societal stress and their impact on our well-being.

To list strategies to eliminate, reduce, or manage stress.

To understand the role and benefits of effective communication in the workplace and networking with community professionals and agencies.

A program emphasizes the personal and professional growth of the employees. The employer (e.g., director, board of directors, agency, college, or university) provides support and access to professional development activities (e.g., conferences, workshops). However, educators need to be motivated to attend, learn, and incorporate their learning into their work with children.

TABLE 2.4   The 10 Dimensions of Organizational Climate

DIMENSION	DEFINITION
Collegiality	the extent to which staff are friendly and supportive and trust one another
Professional Growth	the degree of emphasis placed on personal and professional growth
Supervisor Support	the degree of facilitative leadership that provides encouragement, support, and clear expectations
Clarity	the extent to which policies, procedures, and responsibilities are clearly defined and communicated
Reward System	the degree of fairness and equity in the distribution of pay, fringe benefits, and opportunities for advancement
Decision Making	the degree of autonomy given to the staff and the extent to which they are involved in program-wide decisions
Goal Consensus	the degree to which staff agree on the goals and objectives of the program
Task Orientation	the emphasis placed on good planning, efficiency, and getting the job done
Physical Setting	the extent to which the spatial arrangement of the physical environment helps or hinders staff in carrying out their responsibilities
Innovativeness	the extent to which the organization adapts to change and encourages staff to find creative ways to solve problems

Source: *Blueprint for Action: Achieving Center-Based Change through Staff Development* by Paula Jorde Bloom. © 2005 Published by New Horizons. Reprinted with permission from Copyright Clearance Center.

Role of Directors

How can directors promote staff health? Directors' philosophies and management styles play an integral role in supporting a healthy work environment. First, directors often set the tone in the program—if they are committed to employee health and ongoing training, their commitment will likely have a positive effect on educators. For those working in a nonprofit agency, the board of directors is the employer, and the director who speaks for the educators is a critical link in keeping the board informed about the needs of staff. These directors will advocate for proactive employee health policies that are clearly outlined in their policy manuals. These policies may include

- an interview and selection process that assists in hiring individuals who fit their specific program;
- job descriptions for all staff members;
- an orientation program and job performance appraisals;
- lines of communication and conflict resolution;

- an immunization schedule to ensure that all staff immunizations are up-to-date;

- techniques for staff to implement that reduce the physical hazards of the work, such as proper lifting techniques, methods for safely handling potentially hazardous products, and methods for cleaning up spills of those products and bloody body fluids;

- exclusion criteria for educators and pregnant women in relation to infectious diseases;

- reporting of **workplace injuries** and compensation for illness or injury;

- opportunities for professional development and in-service training; and

- role of substitutes, students, and volunteers in the program.

Regular job evaluations (at least annually) are acknowledged as a learning tool rather than a punitive device. A health-promoting director supports educators in goal setting and in achieving those goals. She implements measures to decrease stress for staff whenever possible. She serves as an advocate for educators with the board of directors and the outside community.

Directors also have the following responsibilities for educators' health:

- They conduct regular inspections of early childhood settings.

- They ensure that educator–child ratios and group sizes are maintained throughout each day.

- They regularly review the work assignments to assess whether the work is too demanding and how tasks can be modified.

- They review and discuss work-related injuries and determine what preventive steps are required.

Probably the director's most important role in promoting educators' emotional and social well-being is to establish clear lines of communication. Most of the dimensions in Table 2.4 (page 86) are directly related to communication. Educators who receive effective administrative support, encouragement, and clear expectations tend to experience job satisfaction. Directors can also provide opportunities for educators to participate in decision making and professional growth. The purpose of health promotion is to increase the amount of control that individuals and groups have over their lives. It makes sense that the more autonomy educators have at work, the more they feel in control. With the director's support, they feel free to express themselves on the job, especially when they view the director as an advocate. Directors help solve problems when they arise, such as inadequate opportunities for regular breaks or issues about communication with a family member. A director's role is also paramount in difficult issues such as supporting educators when they report suspected child maltreatment. Educators often need to relieve feelings of stress by talking frankly with the director without fear of repercussion, even if the educator feels compelled to follow a grievance process. Effective directors expect professional confidentiality from educators and also model this behaviour.

Occupational Standards for Child Care Administrators includes a standard on managing staff, with a section on motivating staff as an essential element (Child Care Human Resources Sector Council, 2006, p. 22). Required skills and abilities of administrators for motivating staff include the following:

a) establish a positive work environment;

b) listen and respond to staff concerns;

c) acknowledge staff's accomplishments;

d) empathize with and support staff;

e) model leadership skills;

f) involve staff in decision-making.

Role of Educators

It goes without saying that working with children has many rewards. It's probably the main reason you chose to enroll in an ECE program. You are also entering a profession that has occupational standards for child care practitioners that reflect the extensive range of skills and abilities, core knowledge, and standards of ethical practice expected of you (see Resource Materials, page 103).

The You Bet I Care! study asked educators and directors to list the most positive and most negative aspects of working in the ECE field. The results are summarized in Table 2.5.

Many educators prefer to work with a particular age group because their experience tells them that their aptitudes and interests fit best there; they usually find the stress factors manageable. Yet some educators may work with a particular age group because they have no choice. Others may have lacked prior experience or ECE training and assumed that they would fit well but didn't. Educators who don't have a "fit" with their work or the age group may find the nature of the work overwhelming. Working with infants is quite different from working with preschoolers, which is quite different from working with school-agers. During your placements, you will have opportunities to work with various age groups, gain realistic perceptions of working with children, and talk with educators about how they feel about their work and what they find rewarding and challenging (or stressful). You may have assumed, for example, that working with infants would not match your personality but, after your placement with infants, decided to begin your career working with this age group.

One thing is certain about work stress in early childhood settings: educators who develop and practise effective communication skills have lower stress levels. We have discussed the director's role in creating a supportive environment—let us not overlook the educators' attitudes, knowledge, and behaviour. Much of educators' work involves communicating with children, coworkers, and families. Educators who demonstrate collegiality with coworkers are likely to have it reciprocated. Fairness is an essential component of a healthy workplace. Recognition of each individual's rights and interests requires us to

TABLE 2.5 The Positives and Negatives of Working in Child Care

	% OF STAFF IDENTIFYING THIS AMONG THEIR TOP 3 CHOICES	% OF DIRECTORS IDENTIFYING THIS AMONG THEIR TOP 3 CHOICES
ON THE POSITIVE SIDE		
Nature of the work	94.6	93.7
For example: a people-oriented job; love from children; freedom to be creative; having my own group of children; a varied, stimulating job		
Fulfillment	32.6	37.6
For example: feel I am having an impact/helping; gives me a feeling of competence; enjoy the challenge		
Coworkers	20.1	22.7
For example: teamwork; working with other child care professionals; support from other staff		
Parents	11.9	23.8
For example: helping parents		
ON THE NEGATIVE SIDE		
Pay and promotion opportunities	75.5	73.5
For example: low salary; lack of wage increases; lack of benefits; unpaid overtime		
Lack of respect	45.8	43.1
For example: public's perception of the status of child care staff		
Working conditions	32.4	26.7
For example: hours; staffing ratio; lack of supplies; difficulty finding qualified substitutes		
Nature of the work	25.0	23.3
For example: doing cleaning and maintenance; lack of adult contact; insufficient planning time; collecting fees		
Dealing with society and government	20.7	25.2
For example: the attitude of government officials		
Note: Responses are not mutually exclusive.		

Source: Adapted with permission from *You Bet I Care! Study 1: A Canada-Wide Study on Wages, Working Conditions, and Practices in Child Care* by G. Doherty, D.S. Lero, H. Goelman, A. LaGrange, and J. Tougas, University of Guelph: The Centre for Families, Work, and Well Being (2000).

see one another as whole people rather than split us up into specific roles (e.g., director, educators).

The **Neighbour@Work** Centre™ (Shain, n.d., pp. 2–3) promotes a philosophy whereby a person makes every effort to

- Predict the effect of his/her own behaviour on others (particularly those under her/his supervision)

- Prevent and avoid foreseeable harm (psychosocial as well as physical)
- Recognize and accommodate the legitimate interests and rights of others
  And:
- Expects the same of others

Source: *The Neighbour@Work: Toward Optimal Health and Productivity (A Resource For Leaders-Part 1)* by M. Shain, 2-3. Reprinted with permission.

In other words, the Neighbour@Work <u>CHOOSES</u> to do the right thing, the thing that avoids harm, maybe even promotes health.

Directors who are appreciated for their efforts find it easier to support staff. The opportunity for autonomy assumes that the educator has the ability and motivation to make responsible decisions. In other words, communication is not a one-way street! However, communication skills are complex and require work, practice, and a willingness to learn. Cross-cultural communication, for example, assumes that you recognize that your usual way of communicating is only one way, not the best way.

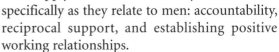

CRITICAL THINKING

You have been thinking about an issue that you are going to find stressful when you begin your career in early childhood education. To be proactive and feel as if you will be able to manage or eliminate this stressor, you come up with a "prevention plan."

Men Working in Early Childhood Settings

Historically, the overwhelming majority of educators in ECE have been female. The Labour Market Study found that over 96% of early childhood educators and assistants are women (Beach et al., 2004). If you are a male student, you probably have accepted that you will be working mainly with female colleagues. Although the following three criteria apply to all educators, they are discussed specifically as they relate to men: accountability, reciprocal support, and establishing positive working relationships.

Accountability

Male educators demonstrate professional behaviour such as open communication with parents and awareness of the need to be visible to another adult whenever possible when they are with any one child. In this way, they find that they are not likely to be considered suspect. Male educators may find it stressful that families (and sometimes female educators) place them under scrutiny. However, most men understand that this fear results from the fact that men commit the vast majority of crimes of sexual abuse. As each educator demonstrates his commitment and care for the children, these suspicions usually disappear.

Educators who take an active role in speaking with parents about the child's day help parents realize that educators are knowledgeable and care about their child. Parents can then get to know and trust the educators rather than simply view them as "male." Male educators who demonstrate professional behaviour avoid subtle and overt sexist remarks, jokes, and other such slights. One hopes that female educators also refrain from this type of behaviour, so that working relationships are not tainted with sexist overtones.

Men find ways to nurture children without placing themselves under suspicion. Early childhood staff should not, however, attempt to avoid suspicious circumstances for male educators by creating separate job responsibilities for males and females.

All educators are involved in diapering or toileting. A division of different responsibilities only serves to increase suspicion and animosity among educators.

Reciprocal Support

Men who connect with and support other male educators reduce their feelings of isolation, which is one of the most significant stressors for males in ECE and care. Often a male educator is the only male staff member, and he rarely, if ever, has the opportunity to talk with adult males at work other than with fathers at drop-off or pickup times. He will feel added stress from female educators or parents if he is stereotyped in particular roles:

- He may be expected to do all the heavy lifting or repairs or to take a lead role in disciplining children. Obviously, the assumption of roles or abilities on the basis of gender is inappropriate.
- Male educators often have to deal with the stereotype that they are not as masculine as other men. The stereotype is based on the traditional view of women taking responsibility for caring for children.

This stereotype is stressful to male educators, so it is beneficial to them if they can informally or formally network with others. It may be challenging to find out where other male educators work (your local ECE college faculty may know), but when you do, there are a number of ways to establish networks: a telephone buddy system, online chat or e-mail discussions, monthly meetings of a support group, or biannual sessions or workshops through the local ECE association. Opportunities to talk about issues that arise, and possible ways to handle them, can be helpful in managing stress and preventing problems. Male ECE students may be interested in pursuing some kind of support while in training, either informally, by talking with a male educator in placement, or by finding out if there is (or could be) a support system in which male educators serve as mentors to students and new graduates.

Establishing Positive Working Relationships

Emphasizing effective communication with the other educators reduces or avoids the "them and me" attitude.

Some female educators believe that men receive special treatment because of gender and are offered opportunities that female educators are not offered.

A key factor in reducing negative views is the experience of working with a male colleague in the early childhood setting. Obviously, then, energy put into communication is worth the effort. Male educators feel less isolated when they have positive working relationships. Camaraderie is fostered when all staff are included in social events after work or in lunchroom discussions.

The Juggle Struggle: Stress

Statistics Canada (2004, p. 11) reported that 26% of Canadians aged 18 or older characterized their life as "quite stressful" or "extremely stressful," and another 40% reported it to be "a bit stressful." A higher percentage of women than men in all age groups (except 18- to 19-year-olds) experience high life stress.

The most common forms of stress were chronic strains, especially trying to do too many things at once, which was cited by 44% of adults. Financial problems affected 38%, and 31% felt that others expected too much of them. One in five (21%) wanted to move but felt that this was not possible (Statistics Canada, 2004, p. 13). As Figure 2.5 depicts, balancing the many roles and needs in our

| FIGURE 2.5 | Juggling Roles and Needs |

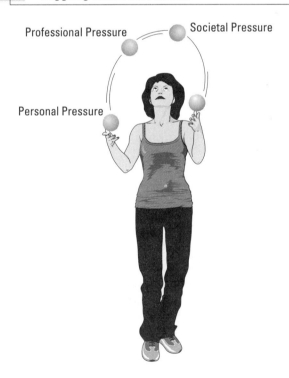

Professional Pressure

Societal Pressure

Personal Pressure

lives can be a juggling act. Students and educators are no exception and have very busy lives—juggling a number of roles that contribute to a time crunch and, ultimately, stress.

Stress is a fact of life. Both positive and negative events in our lives create stress. Stress is defined as "the wear and tear on our bodies that is produced by the very process of living" (Elkind, 1981, p. 142). Stress affects the mind and emotions as well as the physical self. In moderation, stress is positive: it motivates us to learn, develop, and cope with life's frustrations. But the way that stress is perceived and managed depends on the individual and the environment (e.g., family, work, school, socioeconomic class, community).

Coping refers to the ways that a person tries to decrease or eliminate a stress factor—a person's response to it. Stress management plays a major role in our wellness. If the individual is able to find ways to cope with stress, this has a positive impact on health. We all have had days when one thing after another goes wrong, usually minor things, and we feel "stressed out." We may stomp our feet, shout, slam a door, cry, or feel defeated. Eventually, those feelings pass. But when stress is severe or long term, the body and mind are weakened, making the person vulnerable to a number of physical and emotional conditions. This is especially true in individuals who have inadequate coping strategies or whose environment contains insurmountable barriers. These people may experience symptoms of stress overload, including headaches, insomnia, back or neck pain, repeated cold or canker sores, higher than usual susceptibility to illness, ulcers, addictions, anxiety, or depression. Stress overload is also a factor in heart disease and other chronic conditions.

Stress factors can result from a number of sources: our personal and professional lives and societal pressures.

Personal Stress Factors

Stress factors can be short term (e.g., an argument with a family member or friend, a minor injury, a busy week). Some stress factors are long term (e.g., separation or divorce, financial difficulties, death of a loved one).

How we perceive and cope with personal stress depends on our temperament, tolerance level, and experience. Our temperament plays a part in how we perceive the stress in our lives. People who prefer (innately) stability and predictability experience change as stressful.

The idea of moving to another city and beginning a new job is quite exciting and positive for some people. Yet for others, that change is perceived as anxiety producing and negative.

We all have individual tolerance levels for stress. When our tolerance level is reached and surpassed, we can experience feelings of distress. Past experiences with stress and the types of coping mechanisms that we have developed either help or hinder our ability to manage stress. An individual whose childhood was fraught with insecurity is likely to react differently to stressful events as an adult than a person whose childhood was happy and secure.

Our personal lifestyles can either magnify our feelings of stress or help us manage them. A **balanced lifestyle** contributes to our health; part of that lifestyle is helping our mind and body manage stress. Adequate sleep and leisure, physical activity, healthy eating, and meditation are effective body and mind defences against stress. We can help our body by avoiding certain substances that can trigger stress responses, such as caffeine and nicotine.

Professional Stress Factors

Employees who start to feel the "pressure to perform" can get caught in a downward spiral of increasing effort to meet rising expectations, with no increase in job satisfaction. The relentless requirement to work at optimum performance takes its toll in job dissatisfaction, employee turnover, reduced efficiency, illness, and even death. Absenteeism, illness, alcoholism, "petty internal politics," bad or snap decisions, indifference and apathy, and lack of motivation or creativity are all byproducts of an overstressed workplace (Canadian Mental Health Association, n.d.a).

Every profession and workplace has inherent stress factors; even people working from their homes experience stress. Identifying stress factors and eliminating them, or at least reducing them, fall into the domain of occupational health. Working with children, families, and staff is not a calm and tranquil experience. Although the majority of educators express high job satisfaction while working with young children and making a difference in their lives, the following stress factors are commonly experienced by educators:

- the increasing demands on and expectations of early childhood educators
- the need for further knowledge and skills in guiding children with behaviour challenges, in culturally sensitive practice, and in inclusive care for children with special needs
- the constant attention needed to ensure the safety and security of young children
- low compensation rates and benefits such as paid sick leave and extended health care, which seem to be more available in other professions
- the lack of resources needed to maintain an optimal environment
- the isolation from other adults, particularly in family home child care
- the perceived lack of opportunities for career advancement
- the communication issues with coworkers, directors, and parents, which can be stressful

Individuals may be managing their personal life very well but may experience feelings of stress at work. Without a resolution of, or at least a reduction in, the stress factors, one's personal life is affected, and burnout may creep up on the individual. One of the issues that affect many Canadians is difficulty in finding a work/life balance. In addition to the physical toll, chronic stress affects us emotionally and intellectually and can cause decreased concentration and memory, confusion, loss of sense of humour, anxiety, anger, and irritability. "The link between stress and mental illness has yet to be fully understood, but it is known that stress can negatively affect an episode of mental illness" (Canadian Mental Health Association, n.d.b, p. 1).

Chronic stress can result in higher risks for a number of ailments. Figure 2.6 depicts the costs of an unhealthy workplace. Individuals may respond to chronic stress with unhealthy lifestyle habits such as overeating, smoking, drinking excessively, or being physically inactive. Also, responding to stress with anger can contribute to increased blood pressure and other negative physiological changes. These habits increase the risk of many of the conditions included in Figure 2.6.

| FIGURE 2.6 | The Costs of an Unhealthy Workplace |

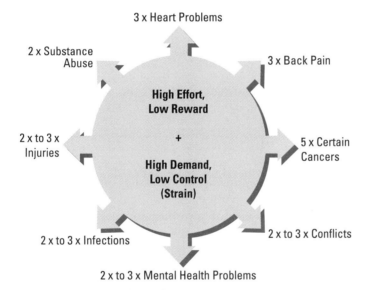

How to read the chart: For example, employees under sustained conditions of high effort/low reward and high pressure/low control are two to three times (2 x to 3 x) more likely to contract infections than other employees.

Source: *Best Advice On Stress Management in the Workplace*, Health Canada, 2008: Reproduced with the permission of the Minister of Public Works and Government Services Canada, 2008.

However, much of our stress comes from within us. How we interpret things – a conversation, a performance review, even a look – determines whether something becomes a stressor. Negative self-talk, where we focus on self-criticism and pessimistic over-analysis, can turn an innocent remark into a major source of stress.

Understanding where your stress originates can help you decide on a course of action. External stressors, like bereavement or career changes, can be managed over time and with the support of family and friends. Internal stressors, caused by our own negative interpretation, require changes in attitude and behaviour.

The goal of managing stress is to cue the "relaxation response". This is the physiological and psychological calming process our body goes through when we perceive that the danger, or stressful event, has passed. (Canadian Mental Health Association, n.d.b, p. 1)

Making changes involves identifying stress factors and, with the commitment of staff and management, working toward that change. Educators in all settings express considerable interest in additional training, education, and professional development (Beach et al., 2004). Evidence suggests that educators do take advantage of training opportunities available to them. Increased skills improve the quality of care that children experience and improve educators' work environments and recognition.

Workplace stressors vary greatly, as do the ways to reduce or prevent them. For workplace stressors that are physical in nature, it is best to control stress at its source. *For example, deal with noise through control measures such as adding carpeting to a noncarpeted surface or increasing insulation.* With regard to the expectations of the job, it should be reasonably challenging, but not what could be defined as "sheer endurance." As mentioned earlier in this unit, opportunities for learning and making decisions, a future career path, and a degree of social support and recognition in the workplace are all important components to prevent burnout (Canadian Centre for Occupational Health and Safety, 2000).

Societal Pressures

The quality of ECE across Canada and the issues of affordability, accessibility, and comprehensiveness for parents are national concerns. Many families are affected by governments' lack of commitment to ECE, and educators across Canada experience every day the effects of these societal attitudes. Other societal pressures affect everyone, educator and noneducator alike, such as the following:

- the expectation, especially for women, to have multiple roles and to perform them all well (e.g., to have two full-time jobs, one inside and one outside the home);
- issues of discrimination;
- the fast-paced, ever-changing world, particularly its technology, which makes many of us feel that we are being left behind;
- growing concern about violence in our communities and around the world; and
- serious concerns about other national and global issues, such as the economy and the environment (e.g., climate change).

Identifying sources of stress in our lives is the first step in managing them and avoiding stress overload. Some stress factors may be impossible to change. Fortunately, many can be addressed, with problem solving and commitment. There are a range of "stress-busters," depending on individual needs and interests: incorporating physical activity, eating well, meditating, sharing your feelings with trusted friends, taking time for yourself, and finding ways to laugh are just some of many possibilities.

The Heart and Stroke Foundation of Canada's website is an excellent resource that provides you with numerous tools to identify stressors in your life and ways to manage them (see Resource Materials, page 103).

Before deciding which coping strategy to use in a situation, ensure that you have determined whether it is

- an appropriate thing to do in a situation (e.g., chanting during a stressful interaction with a family member is not advisable),
- a positive way of coping (e.g., excessive alcohol or even excessive exercise is not positive), and
- is going to help in the long run (e.g., a short-term solution may not be enough).

- An early childhood program institutes a family responsibility leave for its staff, allowing educators whose own children are ill to be at home with them. This significantly reduces their overall stress level as working parents.
- All educators who belong to their provincial/territorial ECE association benefit from lower premiums for disability insurance.

Societal pressures can be complex, and we may feel that we have little or no control over them. Anxiety is often reduced through education—taking courses to enhance our understanding of issues or to build skills (e.g., computer, self-defence). Get involved in national, regional, or local organizations advocating for change in areas such as ECE and care and the environment. Participating in and working for positive change, even if it seems daunting, is one of the best ways to gain a sense of control over the world around you. It also tends to reduce isolation and expand your social support when you are involved with others.

Early Childhood Educational Experience: Setting the Stage

The process of becoming a professional begins the day you start your ECE training. You have chosen a career that requires a vast range of attitudes, knowledge, and skills. ECE students are on the road to lifelong learning that begins with recognizing their individual and social responsibilities and taking ownership of their responsibilities. Here are some examples of the professional behaviour that you can take ownership of now:

- promptness for classes and placements—behaviour that is not only expected throughout your professional life but is also appreciated in your personal life
- good personal hygiene
- communication skills that demonstrate respect for others' opinions, such as listening respectfully in class when the instructor or a classmate is speaking (as a matter not of authority but of respect) and using body language that conveys interest and learning (while recognizing a range of ways of

communicating that reflect ethnocultural diversity). Communication is a lifelong learning process and is obviously a critical skill for professionals. It is important to become aware of how you, as a student, communicate and to be open to learning new skills.

CRITICAL THINKING

As a student, you are frustrated by a clique of three students who sit together and regularly disrupt the class. What do you do?

Placements in early childhood settings provide you with opportunities to observe and analyze, which help you formulate your personal philosophy of education, which, in turn, is based on an integration of theory and practice. Placements also offer the advantage of starting your professional career with some experience working with educators already behind you. This experience helps you identify some of the attitudes, knowledge, and skills that either contribute to quality care or detract from it. Some examples of human qualities that are beneficial for educators include warmth, patience, high energy, openness to new ideas, flexibility, critical thinking, and maturity. Educators who possess these qualities are positive role models for students and graduates. With every placement experience, you meet a variety of educators who have their own styles yet fulfill these criteria. However, some educators demonstrate physical and emotional exhaustion through behaviour such as impatience and sarcasm with children, tension with others at work, and apathy toward their job. Unfortunately, these educators are modelling as much for students as are their positive coworkers.

Placements allow you to experience different management styles. The working environment is created by the educators' personal styles and the levels of education, how well they work together, the types of policies, and the style of the director. Some individuals like to work in an environment that is more laid-back; others like a structure with rules clearly laid out. Whatever administrative style you prefer, remember the 10 dimensions of organizational climate in Table 2.4 (page 86). As a student, you probably will not see the inner workings of the organization (e.g., salaries and fringe benefits, how promotions are handled, how the program implements change). Yet you can get a sense of how staff work together, the level and effectiveness of the supervision, and staff morale. Are you seeing a Neighbour@Work philosophy in practice? A list of statements accompanies the 10 dimensions of the organizational climate (see Table 2.6). As you work through the list, check off one of the three choices for each statement. You will see how healthy that work climate is and whether you would like to work in that environment on graduation.

Among the most important training opportunities that placements offer you as a student are self-evaluation and, of course, an evaluation of your progress by experienced professionals. Ongoing feedback of your demonstrated skills assists

TABLE 2.6 **List of Statements about Organizational Climate**

	SELDOM	SOMETIMES	ALMOST ALWAYS
Staff are friendly and trust one another.			
Morale is high. There is a good team spirit.			
Staff are encouraged to learn new skills and competencies.			
The program provides guidance for professional advancement.			
Supervisors are knowledgeable and competent.			
Supervisors provide helpful feedback.			
Communication on policies and procedures is clear.			
Teachers help make decisions about things that directly affect them.			
People feel free to express their opinions.			
Staff share a common vision of what the program should be like.			
The program is well planned and efficiently run.			
The work environment is attractive and well organized.			
There are sufficient supplies and equipment for staff to do their jobs.			
Staff are encouraged to be creative and innovative in their work.			

Source: *Blueprint for Action: Achieving Center-Based Change through Staff Development* by Paula Jorde Bloom. © 2005 Published by New Horizons. Reprinted with permission from Copyright Clearance Center.

you in identifying areas of strength and areas in which you need to make immediate or long-term changes. Students who view evaluation positively as a valuable learning tool can incorporate constructive criticism into their learning and make consistent progress in their skill levels. Self-evaluation and evaluation by others will be essential aspects of your career.

Graduates: Starting the Job Search

Your first position in an early childhood setting will probably leave a lasting impression on you. Starting in a program where you are treated with respect by educators who remember what it's like to be the new kid on the block, and who provide you with guidance and support, helps build your confidence and self-esteem. New graduates are influenced significantly by their first director. The kind of assistance, support, opportunities, and guidance that graduates receive contributes greatly to their ability to move forward. Therefore, during job interviews, it's in your best interest to consider the qualities of the director—will they fit with yours?

Graduates often bring a breath of fresh air, new ideas, and enthusiasm into programs. Graduates who demonstrate openness to learning from others—not an "I've learned everything I need to know" attitude—will start off on the right foot with their coworkers. A commitment to lifelong learning means that you recognize that your ECE training has set the stage for a career of future learning rather than being the final curtain.

REVISITING THE HEALTH PROMOTION ACTION PLAN

With reference to the health promotion action plan introduced in Unit 1, the following discussion illustrates this plan put into practice in terms of occupational health.

Individual Problem Solving and Self-Reliance

With the awareness of health issues that affect educators, each of us is able to identify our own health concerns and can be proactive in preventing or reducing the impact of our choices on our health. You, for example, may be making changes to include more whole foods and less fat in your diet and gradually becoming more physically active. You may also be cutting down on your smoking and getting support during this difficult transition. As a result of these changes, you're probably beginning to notice that you have more energy in working with children. You feel like a better role model. You are practising sensible lifting and bending techniques. Your commitment to lifelong learning through reading and attending workshops, seminars, and conferences on health issues enhances your ability to make choices in your personal life and professionally. All education plays a role in your ability to advance in your career.

Collective Self-Help

Together, the director and staff support each other, parents, and families. The Neighbour@Work philosophy is followed by all employees and administrators, demonstrating mutual respect regardless of the specific issue. Staff meetings are based on the premise that you can learn from one another through sharing resources and acknowledging each educator's expertise, experiences, and contribution. Stress relief comes in part from the knowledge that you can share concerns with a coworker or director and trust his or her professional confidentiality—and this contributes to a positive working environment. Conferring with professionals and agencies with expertise in occupational health, management, communication, and other areas also helps staff reduce stress and increase educators' knowledge and skills.

Community Action

Becoming involved in local organizations related to work with children and families (e.g., local breakfast clubs, joint health and safety committees) can enhance educators' understanding of issues and help effect change. As the early childhood profession is enhanced, so, too, are educators' feelings of self-worth and status as professionals. Representatives from your workplace and a few others in the community sponsor a full-day conference on the Mental Health Works initiative with the local chapter of the Canadian Mental Health Association. The morning focuses on awareness of workplace mental health and the afternoon on issues and solutions. Workplace representatives from across the community are invited to attend, broadening the knowledge and commitment to mental health in the community. Union stewards, managers, and workers are in attendance.

Societal Change

Advocacy at the provincial/territorial and federal levels can create change that affects occupational health on a broader level, such as a national ECE plan, family responsibility leave, or positive, supportive changes in legislation. The quality of the work environment in early childhood settings (including wages, benefits, working conditions, and the organization of the work) affects educators' performance and the program's quality (Bertrand et al., 2004, p. 6). Everyone benefits from a national child care plan.

As educators develop skills in the process of thinking about and addressing problems, they also develop increased pride in their work and growing confidence in their ability to communicate outside of the classroom. Passive acceptance of disheartening conditions in schools or programs, which leads to cynicism and burnout, can be replaced with optimistic attempts to improve situations whenever possible.

CONCLUSION

A proactive way to achieve job satisfaction and avoid burnout is to be aware of how well you are implementing healthy physical, emotional, and social practices. It is also important to examine your workplace—are the policies and practices contributing to staff well-being or to burnout? Appendix 2.2 (page 108) provides a checklist for this purpose. Can you identify practices that could be improved? Can you identify supports and barriers and possible solutions? Look back to the eight dimensions of wellness. Achieving balance in your life through setting achievable goals and action plans will contribute to your sense of control.

Where are we going in the future? The career ladder integrates education with career advancement, each a step further along in growth. Each step—based on education and training, job skills, and experience—broadens your role and responsibilities. With career advancement come increases in salary and job status.

Career advancement shouldn't mean that once you have worked with children for a certain period, the only place to go is the position of supervisor or director. Community colleges and some universities offer postdiploma certificates and degrees to ECE graduates who wish to continue their formal education. Educators may want to continue working with children and their families within a program but have more specialized skills and knowledge, such as infant and toddler care, special needs, child assessment, program evaluation, or health promotion advocacy. Here again, salaries must reflect the level of education and roles. Increased career opportunities in ECE depend in part on better bridges between levels of education and training and between different types of early childhood settings and related early childhood services (Beach et al., 2004). Recognizing that educators are the key component of quality ECE, *People, Programs and Practices: A Training Strategy for the Early Childhood Education and Care Sector in Canada* (Beach & Flanagan, 2007, p. 63) identifies the best practices and supports needed to refine mentoring and coaching approaches for new graduates as one of its strategic directions. New graduates are successful when they find ways to prevent or manage stressors that are within their control. When they feel supported in their new work environment and are members of at least one professional organization that helps them stay current and involved as advocates, they also tend to contribute to their profession.

TO TAKE A BREAK OR NOT TO BREAK?

Annie, a very enthusiastic student in her placement, insisted that she didn't need breaks during the day. Although the staff in the room pointed out opportune times to leave the floor for 10 or 15 minutes, Annie said she was fine and didn't want to miss a minute of learning opportunity. The educators appreciated her eagerness but were concerned that this was not a physically, emotionally, or socially healthy pattern to get into. What is your opinion?

ASSESS YOUR LEARNING

Define terms or describe concepts used in this unit.

- aerobic (cardiovascular) fitness
- balanced lifestyle
- endurance
- ergonomics
- flexibility
- Neighbour@Work
- personal stress factors
- public health agencies
- professional stress factors
- societal pressures
- strength
- stress factors
- workplace environmental issues
- Workplace Hazardous Materials Information System (WHMIS)
- workplace injuries
- workplace stress

Evaluate your options in each situation.

1. A colleague buys her lunch from the nearby fast-food restaurant almost every day. You can't resist having her pick up something for you too, even though you often feel full after eating the nourishing hot lunch with the children before you have your lunch break. The fries or burger tastes great, but you feel sluggish all afternoon.

2. You and a coworker rarely agree on program-related issues. As a result, your relationship deteriorates to the point where you speak as little as possible, and the tension is felt by the other staff, children, and families.

3. You and two coworkers have been injured over the past month from pinching fingers in a cupboard door while putting things away (out of children's reach). Each of you completed a detailed injury report and submitted it to the director, yet none of you have heard anything from her about this situation.

4. You enjoy talking with family members of the children in your program but are not confident trying to communicate with individuals whose first language is not English. You feel that you are being patronizing, speaking loudly and very slowly, and making hand gestures.

5. To the best of your parents' and your own knowledge, you never had chickenpox as a child. You are now pregnant, and three children who have chickenpox are in the program.

RESOURCE MATERIALS

Organizations

BOOST – Child Abuse Prevention and Intervention, 890 Yonge Street, 11th Floor, Toronto, ON M4W 3P4. Tel: 416-515-1100; fax: 416-515-1227; http://www.boostforkids.org

Canadian Centre for Occupational Health and Safety, 135 Hunter Street E., Hamilton, ON L8N 1M5. Tel: 905-572-2981 or national toll-free 1-800-668-4284; fax: 905-572-2206; http://www.ccohs.ca

Canadian Child Care Federation, 201–383 Parkdale Avenue, Ottawa, ON K1Y 4R4. Tel: 613-729-5289 or national toll-free 1-800-858-1412; fax: 613-729-3159; http://www.cccf-fcsge.ca

Canadian Paediatric Society, 2305 St. Laurent Blvd., Ottawa, ON K1G 4J8. Tel: 613-526-9397; fax: 613-526-3332; http://www.cps.ca

Canadian Mental Health Association, National Office, Phenix Professional Building, 595 Montreal Road, Suite 303, Ottawa, ON K1K 4L2. Tel: 613-745-7750; fax: 613-745-5522; http://www.cmha.ca

Child Care Advocacy Association of Canada, 323 Chapel Street, Ottawa, ON K1N 7Z2. Tel: 613-594-3196; fax: 613-594-9375; http://www.childcareadvocacy.ca

Dietitians of Canada, 480 University Avenue, Suite 604, Toronto, ON M5G 1V2. Tel: 416-596-0857; fax: 416-596-0603; http://www.dietitians.ca/healthystart/index.asp

National Network on Environments and Women's Health, 5021 TEL Building, York University, 4700 Keele Street, Toronto, ON M3J 1P3. Tel: 416-736-5941; fax: 416-736-5986; http://www.nnewh.org/index.php

Other Websites of Interest

Alberta Centre for Active Living: http://www.centre4activeliving.ca

Association of Early Childhood Educators Ontario (for information on the College of ECE): http://www.aeceo.ca

Canadian Centre for Occupational Health and Safety: http://www.ccohs.ca

Canadian Mental Health Association: http://cmha.ca

Centre for Children and Families in the Justice System (over 70 resources focusing on intimate-partner violence and training to support parents and children; most can be downloaded): http://www.lfcc.on.ca

Child Care Human Resources Sector Council (The council brings together national partners and other sector representatives to help develop a confident, skilled, and respected workforce valued for its contribution to early childhood care and education.): http://www.ccsc-cssge.ca

EATracker.ca: http://www.dietitians.ca/public/content/eat_well_live_well/english/eatracker

Environment Canada: Air Quality Forecasts and Advisories: http://www.smc.ec.gc.ca/aq_smog/aqforecasts_e.cfm

Government of Canada: Chemical Substances: http://www.chemicalsubstance-schimiques.gc.ca/en/index.html

Health Canada: http://www.hc-sc.gc.ca

Heart and Stroke Foundation of Canada: http://www.heartandstroke.com/site/c.ikIQLcMWJtE/b.2796497/k.F922/Heart_Disease_Stroke_and_Healthy_Living.htm

Mental Health Works (an initiative of the Canadian Mental Health Association): http://www.mentalhealthworks.ca

Neighbour@Work Centre™ (public service that provides research and educational resource materials related to Comprehensive Workplace Health Promotion): http://www.neighbouratwork.com

Physical Activity at Work: http://www.centre4activeliving.ca/workplace/

Physical Activity Resource Centre (PARC): http://www.ophea.net/parc

Shelternet: Making the Links for Abused Women: http://www.shelternet.ca/splashPage.htm

Sports Canada: http://www.pch.gc.ca/sportcanada

Statistics Canada: http://www.statcan.ca

Printed Matter

An Invitation to Health (2007), by D. Hales and L. Lauzon. (1st Canadian ed.) (Nelson Publishers).

Canada's Physical Activity Guide to Healthy Active Living, by Health Canada. To order a copy, visit http://www.phac-aspc.gc.ca/pau-uap/fitness/order.html

Making the Most of Meetings (2002), by Paula Jorde Bloom (New Horizons).

Occupational Standards for Child Care Practitioners (2004), by G. Doherty. Ottawa: Canadian Child Care Federation.

Policy for Developing a Scent-Free Workplace (n.d.), by The Lung Association. To download a copy, visit http://www.lung.ca/_resources/DevelopingaScentfreePolicyforaWorkplace.pdf

Our Bodies, Ourselves: A New Edition for a New Era (2005), by Boston Women's Health Book Collective (Simon & Schuster).

Our Bodies, Ourselves: Menopause (2006), by Boston Women's Health Book Collective (Simon & Schuster).

Reduce your stress (n.d.), by the Heart and Stroke Foundation of Canada. To review this information, visit http://www.heartandstroke.on.ca/site/c.pvI3IeNWJwE/b.3581755

Stress Test, by the Heart and Stroke Foundation of Canada. To download this test, visit http://www.heartandstroke.com/site/c.ikIQLcMWJtE/b.3977645/k.D87E/Stress_Test_How_fit_are_you_when_it_comes_to_managing_stress.htm

Video/DVD

A Guide to Workplace Health, Safety and Wellness, by Day Nursery Centre. To order a DVD, visit http://www.mflohc.mb.ca/temporary_folder.html/child_care/video_on_health_safety_wellness_for_child_care_workers.html

BIBLIOGRAPHY

Alberta Centre for Active Living. (2007a). *Physical activity @ work: Community level: Tapping into community physical activity resources.* Retrieved July 2008 from http://www.centre4activeliving.ca/workplace/ideas/community.html. Material on page 65 is reprinted with permission.

Alberta Centre for Active Living. (2007b). *Physical activity @ work: Individual level: Ideas for you.* Retrieved July 2008 from http://www.centre4activeliving.ca/workplace/ideas/individual.html. Material on page 64 is reprinted with permission.

Alberta Centre for Active Living. (2007c). *Physical activity @ work: Social level: Being active with your co-workers.* Retrieved July 2008 from http://www.centre4activeliving.ca/workplace/ideas/social.html. Material on page 65 is reprinted with permission.

American Academy of Pediatrics. (2006). *Red Book 2006: Report of the Committee on Infectious Diseases.* Elk Grove Village, IL: American Academy of Pediatrics.

Beach, J., & Flanagan, K. (2007). *People, programs and practices: A training strategy for the early childhood education and care sector in Canada.* Toronto: Child Care Human Resources Sector Council.

Beach, J., et al. (2004). *Working for change: Canada's child care workforce.* Toronto: Child Care Human Resources Sector Council.

Bertrand, J., et al. (2004). *Working for change: Canada's child care workforce: Literature review.* Toronto: Child Care Human Resources Sector Council.

Bloom, P. J., Sheerer, M., & Britz, J. (1991). *Blueprint for action: Achieving center-based change through staff development.* Lake Forest, IL: New Horizons.

Canadian Centre for Justice Statistics. (2005). *Family violence in Canada: A statistical profile 2005* (Catalogue No. 85-224-XIE). Ottawa: Minister of Industry. Retrieved July 2008 from http://www.statcan.ca/english/freepub/85-224-XIE/85-224-XIE2005000.pdf

Canadian Centre for Occupational Health and Safety. (1999, January 20). *OH&S legislation in Canada: Basic responsibilities.* Retrieved July 2008 from http://www.ccohs.ca/oshanswers/legisl/responsi.html#_1_3

Canadian Centre for Occupational Health and Safety. (2000). *Workplace stress: General.* Retrieved July 2008 from http://www.ccohs.ca/oshanswers/psychosocial/stress.html

Canadian Mental Health Association. (n.d.b). *Take control of stress.* Retrieved July 2008 from http://www.cmha.ca/bins/content_page.asp?cid=2-267-1320-1324

Canadian Mental Health Association. (n.d.a). *Sources of workplace stress.* Retrieved July 2008 from http://www.vcn.bc.ca/rmdcmha/sources.html

Canadian Paediatric Society. (2008). *Well beings: A guide to health in child care* (3rd ed.). Ottawa: Canadian Paediatric Society. Material on page 71 is reprinted with permission.

Child Care Human Resources Sector Council. (2006). *Occupational standards for child care administrators.* Ottawa: Government of Canada's Sector Council Program.

Doherty, G., & Forer, B. (2007). *Shedding new light on staff recruitment and retention challenges in child care.* Ottawa: The Child Care Human Resources Sector Council.

Doherty, G., Friendly, M., & Forer, B. (2000). *You bet I care! Study 1: A Canada-wide study on wages, working conditions, and practices in child care.* Guelph, ON: University of Guelph, Centre for Families, Work, and Well Being.

Elkind, D. (1981). *The hurried child.* Don Mills, ON: Addison-Wesley Publishers.

King, P. M., Gratz, R., & Kleiner, K. (2006). Ergonomic recommendations and their impact on child care workers' health. *Work: A Journal of Prevention, Assessment and Rehabilitation, 26,* 13–17.

Hales, D., & Lauzon, L. (2007). *An invitation to health* (1st Canadian ed.). Toronto: Nelson.

Health Canada. (2000). *Best advice on stress risk management in the workplace. Part 1 of 2* (Catalogue No. H39-546/2000E). Ottawa: Minister of Public Works and Government Services Canada. Retrieved July 2008 from http://www.hc-sc.gc.ca/ewh-semt/alt_formats/hecs-sesc/pdf/pubs/occup-travail/stress-part-1/stress-part-1-eng.pdf

Health Canada. (2007a). *Eating well with Canada's Food Guide.*

Health Canada. (2007b). *Eating well with Canada's Food Guide: A resource for educators and communicators.*

Health Canada. (2007c). *My food guide.* Retrieved March 2007 from http://www.hc-sc.gc.ca/fn-an/food-guide-aliment/myguide-monguide/index_e.html

Health Canada. (2008). *Indoor air quality in Canada: A technical guide.* Retrieved July 2008 from http://www.hc-sc.gc.ca/ewh-semt/alt_formats/hecs-sesc/pdf/pubs/air/office_building-immeubles_bureaux/93ehd-dhm166-eng.pdf

Hoeger, W. K., & Hoeger, S. A. (2000). *Lifetime physical fitness and wellness* (6th ed.). Englewood, CO: Morton Publishing.

Liebman, B. (2002, July–August). Face the fats. *Nutrition Action Health Letter, 29*(6), 3–12.

Markon, P. (1999). Safety in the child care center is also for the early childhood staff. *Child Care Connection,* 2.3.

Maxwell, A., Huot, G. (1994). Health and occupational safety for child care educators. *FOCUS,* January, 29–34.

National Advisory Committee on Immunization. (2006). *Canadian immunization guide* (7th ed.). Ottawa: Public Works and Government Services Canada.

Occupation Health Clinics for Ontario Workers Inc. (n.d). *Prevention through intervention: Safe lifting techniques of children.* Retrieved July 2008 from http://www.ohcow.on.ca/resources/handbooks/childlift/safeliftingbrochure.pdf

Physical Activity Resource Centre. (2003). *Am I going fast enough?* Retrieved July 2008 from http://www.ophea.net/parc/Workshops/MakingActiveChoices/Am%20I%20going%20fast%20enough.pdf

Ratey, J. J. (2008). *SPARK: The revolutionary new science of exercise and the brain.* New York: Little, Brown & Company.

Shain, M. (n.d.). *The Neighbour@Work: Toward optimal health and productivity (a resource for leaders-part 1).* Retrieved July 2008 from http://www.neighbouratwork.com/84/files/Example%20Folder%20A/The%20N%40W%20Leaders%27Resource%20Part%20%232.pdf

Statistics Canada. (2002). *Health indicators highlights: Life stress,* vol. 2002, no. 2. Ottawa: Ministry of Health.

Statistics Canada. (2004). Stress, health and the benefit of social support. *Health Reports,* 15(1) (Catalogue No. 82-003). Retrieved July 2008 from http://www.statcan.ca/english/studies/82-003/archive/2004/15-1-a.pdf

Sui X., LaMonte MJ, Laditka JN, et al. (2007). Cardiorespiratory fitness and adiposity as mortality predictors in older adults. *Journal of the American Medical Association, 298,* 2507-16 December 5.

The Lung Association. (2008). *Policy for developing a scent-free workplace.* Retrieved July 2008 from http://www.lung.ca/_resources/DevelopingaScentfreePolicyforaWorkplace.pdf

Tougas, J. (2002). *Reforming Québec's early childhood care and education: The first five years.* Toronto: Childcare Resource and Research Unit, University of Toronto.

Vary, C. P. H., Carmody, M., & LeBlanc, R., et al. (1996). The ergonomics of child care: Connecting worksite analyses. *Work: A Journal of Prevention, Assessment, and Rehabilitation, 6*(1), 25–32.

World Health Organization. (1998). *Obesity: Preventing and managing the global epidemic. Report of a WHO consultation on obesity.* Geneva: World Health Organization.

World Health Organization. (2008, January 9). *BMI classification.* Retrieved August 2008 from http://www.who.int/bmi/index.jsp?introPage=intro_3.html

Evaluating Health Information on the Internet

Here are some specific guidelines for evaluating online health sites:

Check the creator. Websites are produced by health agencies, health-support groups, health-product advertisers, health educators, health-education organizations, and provincial and federal governments. Read site headers and footers carefully to distinguish biased commercial advertisements from unbiased sites created by scientists and health agencies.

Look for possible bias. Websites may be attempting to provide healthful information to consumers, but they may also be attempting to sell a product. Many sites are merely disguised advertisements.

Check the date. If you are looking for the most recent research, check the date the page was created and last updated, as well as the links. Several non-working links signal that the site isn't carefully maintained.

Check the references. As with other health-education materials, Web documents should provide the reader with references. Unreferenced suggestions may be unwarranted, scientifically unsound, and possibly unsafe.

Consider the author. Is he or she recognized in the field of health education or otherwise qualified to publish a health-information Web document? Does the author list his or her occupation, experience, and education?"

Source: From HALES/LAUZON. *Invitation to Health Brief.* © 2007 Nelson Education Ltd. Reproduced by permission. www.cengage.com/permissions

APPENDIX

Health Practices: You and Your Employer

2.2

The following checklist summarizes the aspects of occupational health discussed in this unit. How do you rate yourself and a centre where you've done a placement? You may find it enlightening to check again after you've been working in an early childhood program for a year.

DO YOU . . .	YES	NO	SOMETIMES
maintain healthy eating habits by			
❏ being aware of your eating pattern	o	o	o
❏ setting reasonable goals to improve eating pattern (if needed)	o	o	o
❏ lowering fat intake	o	o	o
❏ drinking water every day	o	o	o
❏ increasing fibre	o	o	o
❏ decreasing processed foods	o	o	o
balance work, rest, and exercise by			
❏ taking time for regular physical activity	o	o	o
❏ setting goals and keeping track of fitness progress	o	o	o
❏ ensuring you get adequate sleep	o	o	o
❏ finding ways for leisure daily	o	o	o
❏ spending time with friends and family	o	o	o
prevent the spread of illness by			
❏ keeping your immunization up-to-date	o	o	o
❏ washing your hands effectively and consistently	o	o	o
❏ implementing cleaning and sanitizing routines	o	o	o
prevent workplace injuries by			
❏ using proper lifting techniques	o	o	o
❏ identifying and reporting required adjustments to workspace, equipment, and furnishings	o	o	o

(appendix continues on next page)

DO YOU . . .	YES	NO	SOMETIMES
❑ following products' safety recommendations	o	o	o
❑ using environmentally friendly products	o	o	o
❑ implementing the principles of WHMIS	o	o	o
❑ reporting workplace injuries	o	o	o
❑ keeping your first-aid and CPR certificates up-to-date	o	o	o

promote your social and emotional well-being by

	YES	NO	SOMETIMES
❑ demonstrating respect for self and others through professional behaviour such as promptness and confidentiality	o	o	o
❑ following the Neighbour@Work philosophy	o	o	o
❑ developing and practising effective communication skills	o	o	o
❑ knowing and using designated lines of communication to share concerns	o	o	o
❑ being actively involved in your self-evaluation and evaluation by others	o	o	o
❑ being flexible and open to learning new ideas	o	o	o
❑ identifying your stress factors and developing coping mechanisms that eliminate or reduce them	o	o	o
❑ seeking further professional development	o	o	o
❑ being a member of an early childhood association	o	o	o

lower other risk factors by

	YES	NO	SOMETIMES
❑ stopping smoking	o	o	o
❑ conducting monthly breast or testicular self-examinations	o	o	o
❑ limiting regular consumption of alcohol	o	o	o
❑ practising safer sex	o	o	o
❑ having an annual checkup with a health care professional	o	o	o
❑ keeping up-to-date on health issues	o	o	o

CAN YOU . . .			

evaluate balance in your life through awareness of wellness dimensions:

	YES	NO	SOMETIMES
❑ physical	o	o	o
❑ emotional	o	o	o
❑ social	o	o	o
❑ intellectual	o	o	o
❑ occupational	o	o	o
❑ spiritual	o	o	o
❑ environmental	o	o	o
❑ financial	o	o	o

(appendix continues on next page)

goal statement (specific and measurable)

action steps: 1.

           2.

           3.

           4.

target date:
Resources available to help you:
Barriers and how to deal with them:

DOES YOUR EMPLOYER . . .	YES	NO	SOMETIMES
support educators' healthy eating habits by			
❏ ensuring adequate break times	o	o	o
❏ providing a relaxing place to eat and relax	o	o	o
recognize the importance of staff balancing work, rest, and physical activity by			
❏ maintaining adequate educator–child ratios	o	.o	o
❏ ensuring all staff take regular breaks each day	o	o	o
❏ enabling physical activity opportunities by identifying staff needs and matching these with reasonable employer provisions (e.g., strategies in *Physical Activity at Work*; see Resource Materials, page 103)	o	o	o
❏ incorporating sufficient time in the daily schedule for program planning and documenting	o	o	o
❏ curtailing overtime and discouraging staff from taking work home	o	o	o
prevent the spread of illness by			
❏ keeping track of staff's immunization records	o	o	o
❏ providing orientation and regular in-service updating in			
• infection control strategy	o	o	o
• food handling and preparation	o	o	o
❏ providing adequate supplies and posters for hand washing, diapering, toileting	o	o	o
❏ developing and posting cleaning and sanitizing routines	o	o	o
prevent workplace injuries by			
❏ providing orientation and regular in-service training in			
• proper lifting techniques	o	o	o
• WHMIS and product safety	o	o	o
• other training, as needed	o	o	o
❏ responding to inadequacies in workspaces, equipment, and furnishings	o	o	o
❏ purchasing environmentally friendly products	o	o	o
❏ completing workplace injury reports and responding to injuries	o	o	o

(appendix continues on next page)

DOES YOUR EMPLOYER . . .	YES	NO	SOMETIMES
❏ requiring evidence that staff's first-aid and CPR certificates are up-to-date and arranging for staff to renew as a group	o	o	o
promote staff's collegiality and emotional well-being by			
❏ leading the way by implementing and following the Neighbour@Work philosophy	o	o	o
❏ providing job descriptions for each position and ensuring that all understand one another's role	o	o	o
❏ outlining lines of communication	o	o	o
❏ providing adequate supervision	o	o	o
❏ conducting regular performance evaluations	o	o	o
❏ organizing staff meetings and in-services on communication, conflict resolution, etc.	o	o	o
❏ providing a comprehensive employee benefit package that includes family responsibility leave	o	o	o
❏ providing time and possibly financial support for professional development	o	o	o
❏ actively participating as a centre member in a regional or national child care association	o	o	o
❏ encouraging opportunities for staff to socialize	o	o	o

DOES YOUR EARLY CHILDHOOD PROGRAM . . .

	YES	NO	SOMETIMES
lower other risk factors by			
❏ networking with community health resources	o	o	o
❏ providing current health literature for staff (e.g., public health pamphlets)	o	o	o

CAN YOU ARTICULATE YOUR PROGRAM'S

goal statement (specific and measurable)
action steps: 1.

       2.

       3.

       4.

target date:
Resources available to help you:
Barriers and how to deal with them:

Illness Prevention

CONTENTS

Young children get sick whether they are cared for at home or in an early childhood program, but the estimated rates of common illness are two to three times higher for children enrolled in centres. You only have to talk to a parent whose child has started in an early childhood program to hear the stories of the illnesses. Typically, while children are at home, their exposure to illnesses is limited. So when they start in a program, their potential exposure increases dramatically; as a result, they get sick. However, the longer children are in a program's care, the less often they are sick, and, in fact, they aren't sick much more often than children in family daycare. This information is reassuring for parents who choose centre care.

Among the reasons for higher rates of childhood infections are the following:

- The children enrolled in an early childhood program are from different families, which increases the number of infections that could be spread. Each child may be exposed to germs or infections from his or her parents, siblings, friends, or even strangers riding on the bus in the morning. So every day, it is likely that children spread germs among themselves and staff.

- Preschool children are still learning good personal hygiene habits.

- Infants and young children are more susceptible to illness because their immune systems are still developing.

In the past, most infants, toddlers, and preschoolers remained at home with their mothers. It was not until the children were in kindergarten or grade 1 that they frequently experienced common childhood illnesses during the first few months of starting school, for the reasons outlined above. But by the time children are five or six years old, they are better able to fight infections. Their immune system has matured, and they have almost completed their series of immunizations. Obviously, every child must eventually become part of a group, so the concerns lie in the age at which this occurs and in what can be done to reduce the number of infections that each child experiences as a result of that participation.

The opportunities for illnesses to spread are even higher among infants and toddlers than among preschoolers. Young children wear diapers, may be learning to use the toilet, require a great deal of hands-on care, crawl on the floor, and put hands, toys, and objects in their mouths and then share these wet objects with others. They are only beginning to learn how to wash their hands. They are also quite affectionate with each other (e.g., kissing, hugging, touching). Although this physical contact can contribute to the spread of respiratory infections, the emotional and social benefits of physical affection far outweigh the risk of illness. Rather than discourage this social behaviour, educators implement hygiene practices that reduce the spread of germs among infants and toddlers (e.g., hand washing, cleaning and sanitizing mouthing toys, diapering and toileting routines).

Early childhood educators' understanding of how infections are spread and the ability to implement health practices reduce the incidence of infections in children. The less often children are ill, the less often parents and staff need to manage illness. In other words, the discomfort and stress experienced by children, parents, and staff are reduced. Also, the fewer visits that children make to their physicians, the less money government is obliged to spend on physicians' fees, laboratory tests, and prescriptions, thus reducing health costs.

Most common childhood illnesses are minor and don't last more than a few days. The most typical childhood illnesses are the common cold, ear infections, other respiratory infections, and diarrhea. There are also several more serious communicable diseases that children and adults are susceptible to if they have not developed immunity either through immunizations or by having had the disease (see Immunity, page 115, and Immunization, page 123).

(see Immunity, page 115, and Immunization, page 123).

<table>
<tr><td>OBJECTIVE</td></tr>
</table>

To identify and describe our body's natural defence mechanisms.

OUR BODY'S NATURAL DEFENCE MECHANISMS

Because germs are everywhere, we are fortunate that our body has a built-in defence system; otherwise, we would have some kind of infection all the time. Our skin is our body's first defence, and one of the most important defence mechanisms, against the germs that we contact every day. The oily substance excreted by glands in the walls of the hair follicles is acidic; it kills germs that would otherwise grow on our skin. Normal intact skin is impermeable to germs and to fluids such as water and blood. Where the skin is nonintact (because of cuts, scrapes, sores, or burns, for example), germs can enter. Some chemical agents, such as some pesticides, can enter our body through the hair follicles.

Many germs enter our body through the nose. The nasal hair that you can see and the cilia that cover the mucous membranes in our nose and throat filter and collect air particles such as dust and germs. The mucus produced by the mucous membranes traps the particles, which are then swallowed and destroyed by gastric and acidic secretions in the stomach. We also expel mucus by coughing or sneezing, which rids our body of germs. As well, the mucous membranes in the gastrointestinal and urinary tracts can inactivate or destroy germs, which the bloodstream then clears out of our body. The urine's bacteriostatic (bacteria-destroying) action keeps the urinary tract sterile. Tear secretions destroy bacteria in our eyes. Wax protects our ears.

You have probably heard the sayings "You'll catch a cold if you go outside with wet hair" and "If you sit in a draft, you'll get a cold." In fact, the only way to catch a cold is through exposure to a cold virus that infects our body. Therefore, neither saying is true. But both remind us to think about vulnerability to viruses and bacteria. *For example, when you are rundown or "running on empty," your body will be more vulnerable to a virus or bacteria.* Every day we can provide our body with the nutrients and energy to fight off an infection or to get better. Our body needs these essential elements:

- nutritious food and water and a well-balanced diet
- adequate sleep
- adequate physical activity
- fresh air
- coping strategies to keep stress under control

And, of course, we need to live in a home that provides us with the basic needs of clean water, sewage disposal, and comfortable temperature, and we need warm clothes, coats, shoes, and boots in the winter. If we were always using our energy to keep warm in the winter, our body wouldn't have energy left for everything else we must do to keep healthy.

Immunity

Immunity provides us with protection from specific infections. Each time a germ enters your body, your immunity increases. When a specific germ multiplies in your body, it produces large numbers of its specific protein (antigen), which enter the bloodstream. The immune system responds by producing specific antibodies. Even when an infection is over, your body may continue to make antibodies for long periods, sometimes even for life.

But after many infections, the antibodies disappear from your body over time. Despite this disappearance, cells in your immune system remember the germ, so that if it is contracted again, the immune system makes antibodies very rapidly. Most people who have had chickenpox have a lifelong immunity to it. It is rare to get it again, even after being exposed to a person who has it. The body has a harder time warding off the common cold, however. There are approximately 200 different viruses that cause the common cold. The same cold virus can cause a cold more than once. Our body does not build immunity to these cold viruses which is why some of us get so many colds over our lifetime.

We develop immunity to a disease in one of two ways:

- naturally or actively
- passively (see Immune Globulin, page 128).

For the first few months of life, infants are resistant to some diseases. This naturally acquired immunity is passed on to babies from their mother before birth. Breast milk contains antibodies, which help protect infants from some bowel, ear, and respiratory infections. However, this natural immunity is short-lived. The immune systems of infants and young children mature through actively acquired immunity. Children develop different antibodies in two ways: either by actually having an infection or through immunizations (see Immunization, page 123).

OBJECTIVE

To explain how germs are spread.

HOW INFECTIONS SPREAD

Germs are everywhere. By understanding how germs are spread, you can break the chain of transmission and ultimately reduce or stop the spread of germs that cause illness.

The chain of transmission has four links, as illustrated in Figure 3.1:

- the germ
- the host (person who is ill)
- the vehicles of transmission
- the new host (next person who becomes ill)

FIGURE 3.1   **The Links in the Chain**

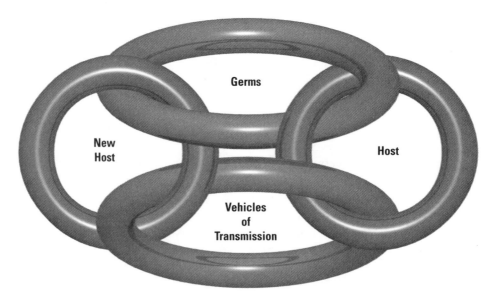

The Germ

The term "**germ**" is used generically to include viruses, bacteria, parasites, and fungi. Although most germs can't be seen by the naked eye (they are microscopic), they are capable of causing infections that range in severity from minor to fatal. The type of germ usually determines which part of the body develops the infection. This explains why we develop different infections, such as colds, strep throat, ear or chest infections, impetigo, urinary-tract (bladder) infections, or diarrhea.

We all have germs that live in our body and play an important role in keeping us healthy. Women, for example, have small numbers of bacteria and a fungus known as *Candida* living in the intestinal tract and the vagina. Let's use this example to see how the germs normally found in the body can cause infections in the following two scenarios.

In the first scenario, women may experience vaginal yeast infections while they are taking an antibiotic for a bacterial infection. While the antibiotic is destroying the bacteria that have caused the infection, it may also destroy the bacteria normally found in the vagina. Consequently, the fungus in the vagina multiplies, causing a yeast infection, because the natural balance of the vaginal bacteria and fungus has been altered by the antibiotic. *Candida* diaper rash can develop in young children in a similar way. An antibiotic given to an infant or toddler to treat a bacterial infection may also destroy bacteria normally found in the bowel, which then permits the fungus to multiply.

In the second scenario, you don't have to have diarrhea yourself to cause someone else to get diarrhea. We all have bacteria that live in our bowels and help keep us healthy. But when those bacteria contaminate an environment and someone else comes in contact with them, that person may develop diarrhea. *Effective hand washing is the key to preventing stool from contaminating an environment.*

Some germs, surprisingly enough, can live outside our body on countertops, toys, fabric, and other dry surfaces for several hours or even months and can still cause infection (see Table 3.1). Rotavirus and hepatitis A can live for weeks on objects such as toys, and germs that cause respiratory infections can live for several hours. This longevity contributes to the spread of infection. Germs thrive and multiply in food, causing intestinal infections that can, in rare cases, be fatal (see Through Food, page 121).

Furthermore, children and adults who have an infection are often infectious (or contagious) for a period of time, which fluctuates depending on the type of germ. Children with the common cold may be infectious for a day or two before the cold symptoms start and may remain so for the next seven days (see Appendix 4.1, page 197).

The Host

Health and medical professionals use the term "**host**" to describe the person with the infection. Think of the infected person as the host of a dinner party. The infected person's body provides the germs with the nourishment and warmth that they need to thrive. Germs may be spread to others during the three stages

TABLE 3.1	Life of Bacteria and Viruses on Surfaces
BACTERIA	**TIME RANGE**
Escherichia coli (*E. coli*)	1.5 hours to 16 months
Haemophilus influenzae	12 days
Shigella spp.	2 days to 5 months
VIRUS	**TIME RANGE**
Cytomegalovirus (CMV)	8 hours
Herpes simplex virus, type 1	4.5 hours to 8 weeks
Rhinovirus	2 hours to 7 days

From Kramer, Schwebke, & Kampf, (2006), pp. 3, 5.

of an infection: before we know we are ill, while we are ill, and in some cases even after we have recovered. A "carrier" is a host who does not actually have symptoms of an infection but has the germ living dormant in his or her body. Carriers can spread germs (e.g., hepatitis B) to others, and sometimes the germs may reactivate and cause an infection (e.g., shingles) in the carrier.

The Vehicles of Transmission

Hosts have germs in their body secretions (such as stool, saliva, blood) that can be transmitted (or spread) in a number of ways. The germs contaminate our environment and are spread directly from person to person through the air or by direct contact (e.g., touching, kissing, biting) or indirectly on vehicles (e.g., toys, hands, food, objects).

Through Direct or Indirect Contact

Infections are spread directly and indirectly from one host to another. The direct spread of infection takes place when we breathe in the germs that cause infections such as colds, chickenpox, and flu. Another way we come into contact with germs that cause skin infections is by touching the host's infected skin (e.g., impetigo, cold sores, scabies, the fluid in the blisters of chickenpox, the rash of shingles). Another example is when someone becomes infested with head lice after coming in contact with head lice.

Germs are spread indirectly on contaminated **vehicles**. Vehicles can be anything around us that germs can contaminate. The vehicles in early childhood programs that we need to pay particular attention to are hands, food and food-related objects, facial tissues, diapers, potties, mouthing toys, hairbrushes, toothbrushes, and blow toys/pipes/straws used in water tables. The germs on these vehicles can easily and frequently find their way into our body. If you watch TV, it is very likely that you have seen the frequently run TV commercials for different types of sanitizing products to use around your home. *Spray your phones*

Direct Contact   Indirect Contact

Source: Canadian Paediatric Society, *Well Beings: A Guide to Health in Child Care.* (Ottawa: Canadian Paediatric Society, 2008), 143. Reprinted with permission.

and door handles. Wipe down surfaces. Spray the inside of garbage cans. There are toilet cleaners that claim that they kill almost 100% of the germs way down at the curve in the pipe at the bottom of the bowl. Obviously, the toilet needs to be cleaned, but how, exactly, is sanitizing the toilet protecting us? Is there residue left in the toilet water for those who have dogs that drink from them? What is the environmental impact of these unnecessary chemicals being flushed into the sewage system? The first time someone uses the toilet there are germs in it again. We can't sterilize our homes or early childhood settings. We must remember that sanitizing an item is a temporary state. As soon as the item is used again, it becomes contaminated. This is why we assess what needs to be sanitized against its intended use and by whom. For this reason, hand washing is key: how you do it and when you do it.

Educators of toddlers and young preschoolers are often concerned about children biting. From the standpoint of infection control, the risk of children transmitting hepatitis B or C or human immunodeficiency virus (HIV) through biting is extremely unlikely. It is unusual for a child's bite to actually break (cut) the skin and cause bleeding, and, as such, none of these diseases would be spread. When the skin is broken, the risk of transmission continues to be very low. The spread of hepatitis B has occurred in early childhood settings but is rare (American Academy of Pediatrics, 2006, p. 139). It is important to remember that when the skin is not broken, hepatitis B is not spread in the saliva (Canadian Paediatric Society, 2008a). The number of children living with hepatitis C is very small. There has not been a case reported in which hepatitis C was spread from one child to another as the result of a bite (American Academy of Pediatrics, 2006, p. 141; Canadian Paediatric Society, 2008a). Saliva has not been shown to spread HIV. "The chance of transmitting HIV through a bite in the child care centre, even when the skin is broken, is extremely unlikely and has never been reported. Giving a child anti-HIV drugs after a bite is not recommended" (Canadian Paediatric Society, 2008a). In the rare occurrence that a bite does bleed, it is usually considered a serious incident or occurrence. Educators must follow the reporting process set out by their government licensing body,

which can include a report and contacting the local public health agency. Refer to *Well Beings* (2008) for the Canadian Paediatric Society's recommendations for administering first aid to the child who was bitten and the child who bit, as well as for communicating with the parents and health care providers.

Keep in mind that biting is a guidance issue for educators. Consideration may need to be given to children who are known to be biting and to the pain they inflict on others in the program. Biting is usually a short-term behaviour and reaches a peak in toddlerhood, when children do not as yet have the words to voice their anger and frustration. Parents and educators will need to discuss a consistent way to manage the biting.

Through the Air

Young children frequently experience colds and eye, nose, and throat infections. It is easy to understand why. The germs, both viruses and bacteria that cause minor or serious infections, are in the host's saliva and nasal secretions. The germs are spread by droplets of secretions that move through the air when we cough or sneeze. We can breathe in the droplets, or they can land in our eyes, nose, or mouth. Or the droplets, saliva, or nasal discharge lands on an object or our hands and the germs find their way into our mouth.

Droplet   Airborne

Source: Canadian Paediatric Society, *Well Beings: A Guide to Health in Child Care.* (Ottawa: Canadian Paediatric Society, 2008), 144. Reprinted with permission.

CRITICAL THINKING

When a tissue isn't immediately available when you or a child is going to cough or sneeze, a popular option is to turn your head into the crook of your elbow. The theory is that the germs and droplets will get trapped in the sleeve of your clothing. How do you think this recommended practice measures up when caring for young children?

Through Contact with Stool

Diarrhea can be caused by bacteria, parasites, or viruses found in the host's stool. As we have discussed, there are bacteria in our bowels that help keep us healthy. However, if those bacteria contaminate our environment, they can cause an intestinal infection in someone else. Whenever stool contaminates our hands, food, water, cooking surfaces, toys, taps on sinks, and other objects, the germs spread very easily among us. Germs enter our mouth from our hands and from toys or through food or water. This means of transmission is also known as the fecal-oral route.

Through Food

Food is an ideal medium for germs to grow on and multiply. Typically, food is contaminated in one of two ways: germs may be in or on the food before we buy it, or we can contaminate food when we handle or prepare it. Regardless of the way germs get into food, the way we prepare, cook, serve, and store food determines whether the germs multiply or are destroyed.

Although most food will have some germs in it, you don't get sick every time you eat because your body's defence mechanisms can destroy many germs. Only when germs multiply in numbers before you eat the food can they cause mild, serious, or, rarely, fatal infections. The severity of the infection depends on the type of germ or the number of germs that have entered the body. Breaking the chain of food transmission involves several safe food-handling practices: hand washing, purchasing, storing, preparing, cooking, and serving (see Food Safety Practices, page 273).

Through Contact with Blood and Bloody Body Fluids

Two serious infections, hepatitis B and HIV, are bloodborne diseases and in most cases spread to others through direct contact with blood or semen. These viruses are spread in three ways:

- by sexual intercourse
- by sharing needles used for illegal intravenous drug use
- by an infected woman to her fetus and, in the case of HIV, during breast-feeding

"In June 1981, scientists in the United States reported the first clinical evidence of a disease that would become known as Acquired Immune Deficiency Syndrome or AIDS" (World AIDS Day, 2007). At the start, we witnessed a high degree of anxiety about HIV in schools, early childhood programs, and hospitals, not to mention in our everyday work and personal lives. Over these many years, through public education and awareness, we have come to understand HIV and its transmission. For the majority of us, our anxiety has been alleviated, and we have come to accept and support people living with HIV/AIDS.

The routine screening of patients, students, employees, or children in early childhood programs, schools, and hospitals is not permitted under human rights legislation. Nor is it recommended or necessary under the guiding principle of universal precautions in infection control. It is important to understand that someone's HIV status is confidential medical information and that it is against human rights legislation either to insist on HIV testing or to demand that someone disclose her or his HIV status to program staff or to anyone else. If parents disclose their child's HIV-positive status to one educator, that educator must maintain confidentiality by not telling her or his coworkers, director, or other parents. This information can be shared only by the parents.

Working with children and coworkers does not put educators at risk of HIV transmission. We must focus instead on our personal lives to reduce our risks. Educators, like the general population, put themselves at risk if they participate in unprotected sexual intercourse or share needles and syringes. To learn more about HIV and hepatitis B transmission and about reducing your risk, contact your college/university resource or health centre, the public health agency, physicians, or the AIDS committee in your province or territory (see Resource Materials, page 153).

Hepatitis C is another bloodborne disease that has a very low infection rate among the general public. Its profile was raised, however, in recent years by those infected from tainted blood transfusions before 1989. But like HIV and hepatitis B, those at risk for the infection are intravenous drug users and those who participate in unprotected sexual intercourse.

The New Host

The term **"new host"** refers to the next person who gets the infection after the germs enter the body, whether through the mouth, eyes, nose, an open cut, or a rash or sore on the skin or by way of the gastrointestinal or genitourinary tract. The type of germ usually determines which part of the body develops the infection. This explains why we develop different infections such as colds, strep throat, ear or chest infections, impetigo, urinary-tract (bladder) infections, or diarrhea.

The incubation period begins when the germ first enters the new host's body. Then the germ multiplies in number. The body's natural defences try to destroy the germs, and if they are successful, we don't get sick. But if they are unsuccessful, we experience symptoms within hours, days, or weeks, depending on the germ and how much time it needs to multiply before it causes infection. By the time you feel that cold coming on, however, you have already been spreading the cold virus among others. This is relatively common for infections, including chickenpox, which makes controlling the spread of infection very difficult. Therefore, the control of infections is an ongoing job; you don't do it just when you know someone is ill.

TABLE 3.2	Summarizing the Links of the Chain
The Germ	• viruses
	• bacteria
	• parasites
	• fungi
The Host	• person who is ill (germs found in saliva, stool, and blood, on skin or hair, etc.)
The Vehicles of Transmission	• directly from person to person (e.g., through air, by touching, kissing, biting)
	• indirectly from person to person (e.g., on hands, toys, food, objects)
The New Host	• new person who becomes ill or a carrier

BREAKING THE CHAIN: DEVELOPING AN INFECTION CONTROL STRATEGY

Our initial defence against germs is understanding that although germs are everywhere, we neither want to, nor are we able to, produce a sterile environment (as in an operating room). Early childhood environments are designed to be friendly, nurturing, interesting, and child centred. Although children do become ill, our underlying assumption is that most people are healthy most of the time. Thus, we carefully choose where to focus our energy to prevent or reduce environmental contamination and the spread of germs. Maintaining our own health and that of the children in our care prevents the germs normally found in our bodies from causing infection and in many cases helps us resist germs from other sources. Thus, a program's infection control strategy demonstrates the staff's understanding of the chain of transmission by developing and implementing specific policies and procedures. To break the chain of transmission, programs' policy manuals will include infection control policies and procedures on the following:

- immunization
- hand washing and other hygiene practices
- cleaning and sanitizing routines
- daily observation of children
- documentation of health observations and sharing observations with parents and physicians
- exclusion criteria
- effective communication with parents
- pets and contact with animals (see Pets in Early Childhood Programs, page 145)

In addition to these policies, the manual will include policies and procedures that cover the following:

- safe food handling and storage (see Food Safety Practices, page 273)
- control of pests (see Controlling Insect and Rodent Infestation, page 278)

Immunization

Before vaccines were developed, epidemics caused thousands of people to die or, in the case of polio, to be left physically challenged. Currently, there are 12 serious infections—communicable diseases—that can be prevented through routine immunization, which can begin in infancy (see Table 3.3). The National Advisory Committee on Immunization (2006) also has schedules for children who were not immunized during infancy. The schedules vary depending on whether the vaccination program begins before or after the child is seven years old.

Immunization is one of the most important ways of promoting the health of children. Vaccines, however, have not eliminated these viruses. Although you may not have heard of a child in your community coming down with the measles or

OBJECTIVES

To explain the role that policies and procedures play in infection control.

To describe the principles and recommended practices for immunization.

To state the rationale for effective hand washing as the most important health practice in reducing the spread of infections.

To describe the when, what, and how of hand washing for educators and children.

To explain the rationale behind the steps in diaper-changing and toileting routines.

To understand why certain items must be cleaned and sanitized before and after use or on a daily or regular schedule.

To understand the goal of universal precautions and how to put them into practice.

FIGURE 3.2 | **Breaking the Chain**

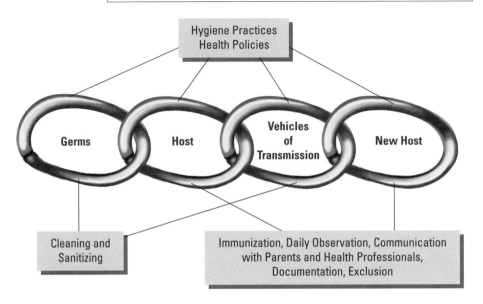

mumps, it does not mean that these and other serious infectious diseases don't exist in Canada and around the world. Without immunizations, children are susceptible to these infections. Canadian children are fortunate that routine vaccination costs are covered by medicare; this is not the case for millions of other children around the world. Your body responds to a vaccination by forming antibodies against specific diseases. The vaccination almost always results in lifelong immunity. In other words, the antibodies remain in your body, ready to destroy the virus every time it enters, whether you know you were exposed to it or not. There are other vaccinations that do require booster shots at regular intervals to maintain this immunity (e.g., tetanus).

Some parents in Canada, however, choose not to immunize their children for personal reasons. In addition, we live in a country that welcomes people from around the world. Many children born outside Canada may not have been vaccinated and could be carrying the virus for polio or diphtheria, which could put unimmunized persons at risk. In addition, Canadian families vacation in countries where immunization rates can be very low. As a result, these children may be exposed to serious infectious diseases and contract and spread them. As well, after reaching adulthood, these unvaccinated adults can travel and work in areas of the world where these diseases are prevalent. In fact, unvaccinated children and adults living in North America have a much greater chance of developing one of these vaccine-preventable diseases than those who are vaccinated (National Advisory Committee on Immunization, 2006, p. 31):

- In 2005, there was an outbreak of rubella in Ontario, and those who contracted it were unvaccinated.

- In the United States, in comparison with immunized children, those who are not immunized for

- the measles are 22 to 35 times more likely to get it.
- pertussis are 6 times more likely to get it.

The National Advisory Committee on Immunization (2006, p. 31) reports that when there has been a drop in vaccination coverage, there has been a return of vaccine-preventable diseases:

- As a result of two infant deaths following the diphtheria-pertussis-tetanus (DPT) immunization in Japan, the pertussis vaccine coverage dropped from 90% to 40%. Before the drop, there were 200 to 400 cases of whooping cough each year, but after the drop, there were 13,000 cases in three years, and 100 children died.

- As a result of allegations of a link between the measles vaccine and autism, measles vaccine coverage dropped to 76% in Ireland. The number of cases of measles jumped from 148 in 1999 to 1,200 a year later. Several children died from the complications of measles.

At home, in the spring 2008, there was an outbreak of measles in Toronto and other municipalities in Ontario. As part of the response, Toronto Public Health (2008) recommended that everyone ensure that their immunizations were up-to-date. Measles outbreaks were reported at the same time in the United States and Europe.

In the past several years, there has been more public discussion surrounding parents' concerns over the presumed correlation between a child receiving the measles-mumps-rubella (MMR) vaccine and the child developing autism. In 2007, the Canadian Paediatric Society published the position statement *Autistic Spectrum Disorder: No Causal Relationship with Vaccines*, which concludes that vaccines are not the cause of autism or autistic spectrum disorder (Canadian Paediatric Society, 2007, p. 3).

To ensure the health of Canadian children and those arriving in Canada, public health agencies must work toward 100% immunization.

Here are some important facts about immunization:

- For measles, mumps, and rubella, we require two doses of each vaccine?
- For the other diseases, we need a series of vaccinations to achieve immunity?
- For lifelong immunity against tetanus and diphtheria, adults require booster shots every 10 years?

    An exception is pertussis (whooping cough), whose vaccine protection wears off over time. As a result, previously immunized children and adults can develop pertussis, although the infection would not be as severe. Vaccinations against pertussis are not given to people over age seven because the risk of severe complications from pertussis is low in older children and adults. Moreover, adverse reactions from the vaccine, such as fever and pain, are common.

- A series of three doses of vaccine for hepatitis B is recommended for children in infancy or two doses for children between 9 and 13. This protects them before they might become sexually active or use intravenous drugs.

- Since 1999, Health Canada has recommended that children over 12 months of age be immunized against chickenpox.

- There are three vaccines against the three types of meningitis: *Haemophilus influenzae* type b, pneumococcal, and meningococcal.
- The polio vaccine is available in two forms: oral and injection. Other vaccines can be given as individual injections. Fortunately, they are commonly given in a combined solution, so children are given just one shot.

TABLE 3.3 **Routine Immunization Schedule for Infants and Children**

AGE AT VACCINATION	DTaP-IPV	HIB	MMR	VAR	HB	PNEU-C-7	MEN-C	TDAP	INF
Birth					Infancy				
2 months	●	◆			3 doses	⊠	◉		
4 months	●	◆			*	⊠	(◉)		
6 months	●	◆				⊠	◉		6–23 months
12 months			■	●	or	⊠ 12–15 months	or ◉ if not yet given		☻ 1–2 doses
18 months	●	◆	■ or ■						
4–6 years	●				Pre-teen/ teen 2-3 doses		◉ if not yet given	▲	
14–16 years									

DTaP Diphtheria, tetanus, pertussis (acellular) vaccine
IPV Inactivated poliovirus vaccine
Hib *Haemophilus influenzae* type b conjugate vaccine
MMR Measles, mumps, and rubella vaccine
Td Tetanus and diphtheria toxoid, adult type with reduced diphtheria toxoid
dTap Tetanus and diphtheria toxoid, acellular pertussis, adolescent/adult type with reduced diphtheria and pertussis components
Hep B Hepatitis B vaccine
V Varicella
PC Pneumococcal conjugate vaccine
MC Meningococcal C conjugate vaccine

Notes:
() Symbols with brackets around them imply that these doses may not be required, depending upon the age of the child or adult. Refer to the relevant chapter for that vaccine for further details.

● **Diphtheria, tetanus, acellular pertussis and inactivated polio virus vaccine (DTaP-IPV):** DTaP-IPV(=Hib) vaccine is the preferred vaccine for all doses in the vaccination series, including completion of the series in children who have received one or more doses of DPT (whole cell) vaccine (e.g., recent immigrants). In Tables 1 and 2, the 4–6 year dose can be omitted if the fourth dose was given after the fourth birthday.

◆ *Haemophilus influenzae* **type b conjugate vaccine (Hib):** the Hib schedule shown is for the Haemophilus b capsular polysaccharide-polyribo sylribitol phosphate (PRP) conjugated to tetanus toxoid (PRP-T). For catch up, the number of doses depends on the age at which the schedule is begun (see the *Canadian Immunization Guide, Seventh Edition, 2006,* Haemophilus Vaccine chapter). Not usually required past age 5 years.

■ **Measles, mumps and rubella vaccine (MHR):** a second dose of MMR is recommended for children at least 1 month after the first dose for the purpose of better measles protection. For convenience, options include giving it with the next scheduled vaccination at 18 months of age or at school entry (4–5 years) (depending on the provincial/territorial policy) or at any intervening age that is practical. In the catch-up schedule (Table 2), the first dose should not be given until the child is ≥ 12 months old. MMR should be given to all susceptible adolescents and adults.

◉ **Varicella vaccine (Var):** children aged 12 months to 12 years should receive one dose of varicella vaccine. Susceptible individuls ≥13 years of age should receive two doses at least 28 days apart.

- **Hepatitis B vaccine (HB):** hepatitis B vaccine can be routinely given to infants or preadolescents, depending on the provincial/territorial policy. For infants born to chronic carrier mothers, the first dose should be given at birth (with hepatitis B immunoglobulin), otherwise the first dose can be given at 2 months of age to fit more conveniently with other routine infant immunization visits. The second dose should be administered at least 1 month after the first dose, and the third at least 2 months after the second dose, but these may fit more conveniently into the 4 and 6 month immunization visits. A two dose schedule for adolescents is an option (see the *Canadian Immunization Guide, Seventh Edition, 2006, Hepatitis B Vaccine chapter*).

- **Pneumococcal conjugate vaccine - 7-valent (Pneu C-7):** recommended for all children under 2 years of age. The recommended schedule depends on the age of the child when vaccination is begun (see *Canadian Immunization Guide, Seventh Edition, 2006, Pneumococcal Vaccine* chapter).

- **Pneumococcal polysaccharide - 23-valent (Pneu-p-23):** recommended for all adults ⩾ 65 years of age (see the *Canadian Immunization Guide, Seventh Edition, 2006, Pneumococcal Vaccine* chapter).

- **Meningococcal C conjugate vaccine (Men-C):** recommended for children under 5 years of age, adolescents and young adults. The recommended schedule depends on the age of the individual (see the *Canadian Immunization Guide, Seventh Edition, 2006,* Meningococcal Vaccine chapter) and the conjugate vaccine used. At least one dose in the pimary infant series should be given after 5 months of age. If the provincial/territorial policy is to give Men-C to persons ⩾ 12 months of age, one dose is sufficient.

- **Diphtheria, tetanus, acellular pertussis vaccine - adult/adolescent formulation (Tdap):** a combined adsorbed "adult type" preparation for use in people ⩾ 7 years of age, contains less diphtheria toxoid and pertussis antigens than preparations given to younger children and is less likely to cause reactions in older people.

- **Diphtheira, tetanus vaccine (Td):** a combined adsorbed "adult type" preparation for use in people ⩾ 7 years of age, contains less diphtheria toxoid antigen than preparations given to younger children and is less likely to cause reactions in older people. It is given to adults not immunized in childhood as the second and third doses of their primary series and subsequent booster doses: Tdap is given only once under these circumstances as it is assumed that previously unimmunized adults will have encountered Bordetella pertussis and have some pre-existing immunity.

- **Influenza vaccine (Inf):** recommended for all children 6–23 months of age and all persons ⩾ 65 years of age. Previously unvaccinated children < 9 years of age require two doses of the current season's vaccine with an interval of at least 4 weeks. The second dose within the same season is not required if the child received one or more doses of Influenza vaccine during the previous Influenza season (see the *Canadian Immunization Guide, Seventh Edition, 2006, Influenza Vacccine* chapter).

- IPV Inactivated polio virus.

Source: Canadian Immunization Guide, 7th edition, Public Health Agency of Canada, (2006) 93, 95. Reproduced with the permission of the Minister of Public Works and Government Services Canada, 2008.

Immunization Records

Considering the importance of immunization, you may be surprised to learn that early childhood regulations on immunization at enrollment vary across Canada. But even in regions where immunization is not mandatory in the regulations, many programs require children to be immunized on enrollment and document it in their policy manual.

Although most parents agree that immunizing their children is important, many children's immunization schedules are not kept up-to-date. Depending on where children live, either individual physicians or a local public health clinic is responsible for immunizing them. As a result, there is often no systematic way of notifying parents of an upcoming appointment.

The physician or public health nurse usually gives parents an immunization record card for each child. The card is updated whenever the child is vaccinated. At the time of enrollment, parents provide the director with a copy of their child's record. Directors compare the information on these cards with the standard immunization schedule. If any discrepancy is found, the director asks the parents to discuss it with their physician or the director contacts the public health agency (see Children's Medical Examination at Enrollment, page 159).

Children's immunizations may not be up-to-date for many reasons, including

- families' hectic schedules,
- children of different ages in a family needing immunizations at different times, or
- the family's lack of a regular physician.

For most parents, a simple reminder that their child is due for an immunization prompts them to make an appointment with the doctor or clinic. Programs play an important role in ensuring that children are immunized at enrollment and by regularly reviewing these records to ensure that children don't miss a booster shot.

Some parents have decided not to immunize their children for religious, moral, or other reasons. Children cannot be denied access to programs if they are not immunized. In these cases, directors should have the parents provide a letter from the child's physician. If a child or educator develops a communicable disease, the public health agency then excludes all nonimmunized children and staff from the program for a certain period. This eliminates further contact with the infected child and attempts to protect the nonimmunized individuals (see Appendix 4.1, page 197).

If a child develops a serious disease, all susceptible children must be identified quickly and the illness managed properly. Consequently, the director and the public health staff must have immediate access to the current immunization record for every child and staff member in the program.

Adverse Reactions

Before children are immunized, the physician or public health nurse discusses the possible adverse reactions and contraindications of the vaccines with the parents. A day or two after a vaccination, children commonly experience mild side effects, ranging from redness, slight swelling, and tenderness at the injection site to a low-grade fever and irritability. Directors may suggest that parents arrange to have the vaccination appointment on a Friday. This way, children can spend the weekend getting the extra care they might need at home.

Children rarely experience serious allergic reactions following a vaccination. If one does occur, the child's physician and public health officials will determine whether the child receives further vaccinations.

Immune Globulin

Passively acquired immunity results when a susceptible individual is exposed to a certain disease and then given the immune globulin for it. Immune globulins are injections of antibodies that temporarily protect the individual from the disease or at least reduce the symptoms. In the case of chickenpox, within 72 hours of exposure, susceptible educators are given the varicella-zoster immune globulin (VZIG). Immune globulins are available for only a few diseases.

Hygiene Practices

You may initially feel overwhelmed by the number of health practices that you are expected to perform in a program. You may wonder, for example, why so many steps are involved in changing a diaper. Over time, effective hand-washing and diapering routines become second nature. And you will see that the time spent learning these steps reduces the number of ill children and educators. Remember: Infection control is an essential component of programs' disease prevention strategies.

Let's begin by examining the vital role **hand washing** plays in reducing the spread of infections in programs. This practice is important for everyone in the program: children, educators, and parents. The physical care of infants and toddlers poses challenges for infection control for educators. Without stringent adherence to diapering and toileting routines, outbreaks of diarrhea are inevitable.

Hand Washing

The most common and efficient way for germs to enter our body is through our mouth. Take a moment to think of everything that our hands touch each day: the number is staggering. Combine that with the number of times we put our hands or objects (e.g., pencils, toys, eating utensils) into our mouth.

Hand washing is the most important health practice that educators and children must implement to reduce the spread of infections. From the moment we wash our hands, we begin to collect germs all over again. Yet we can't spend the day with our hands in running water and soap. But if we pay particular attention to when and how we wash our hands, we accomplish the most significant practice in infection control.

When Do We Wash Our Hands?

While we care for children and carry out tasks in the program, we collect germs on our hands. By washing off germs before we begin particular activities, we greatly reduce the opportunity to spread germs to others. Washing our hands is important

- before preparing, serving, or eating food;
- before feeding infants and children;
- before giving a medication;
- before playing in the water table; and
- before carrying out first aid.

Certain activities expose our hands to large numbers of germs. To prevent contamination, it is important that we wash our hands immediately after completing the following activities. Washing our hands is important

- upon your arrival at work.

    Before we arrive at work, our hands can come into contact with a multitude of contaminated surfaces, including the hand rails on public transit, bicycle handles, and a vehicle's steering wheel, not to mention public doors that you have opened. Washing your hands before you start work helps limit the number of germs you begin to spread in the setting.

    In *Well Beings* (2008b), the Canadian Paediatric Society recommends that the hands of all children are washed upon arrival, too. This recommendation is ideal, but some programs may find it challenging to implement. At drop-off time, parents may be rushed, and educators are greeting parents and children, supervising children in the room, communicating with parents about the child's well-being, sharing relevant information, and settling the child for the parent's departure. Implementing this recommendation for infants, toddlers, and young preschoolers will depend largely on a centre's design and easy access to hand-washing sinks during this hectic part of the day. Perhaps for these younger children, ensuring that they wash their hands at the recommended times during the day is more practical. As for older preschoolers and school-agers, washing their hands upon arrival is a great hygiene habit

- after using the toilet or helping children at the toilet;
- after changing a diaper;
- after caring for ill children;
- after cleaning up spills of blood and body fluids;
- after wiping a child's nose (if possible);
- after cleaning or sanitizing routines, even if you wore disposable or rubber gloves;
- after preparing food;
- after handling animals;
- after playing outside or in sand tables; and
- after handling garbage.

What We Use for Effective Hand Washing

The five important components in the hand-washing routine are running water, soap, friction, drying the hands, and turning off the taps.

Running water is essential to rinse the germs off the hands and down the drain. A comfortable water temperature allows you to keep your hands in the running water for 10 to 15 seconds. Take disposable alcohol-based hand wipes or solution with you on field trips when you don't have access to running water.

Using running water may raise concerns over water conservation and our environment, but washing in a full sink or basin of water is *not* the solution. You defeat the purpose of hand washing by rinsing off the soap and germs in a pool of water. This practice recontaminates your hands with all the germs that are now in that pool of water. To conserve water, don't turn on the tap full blast.

All you need is plain, mild hand soap for hand washing, regardless of the activity you have just completed. Soaps with germ-killing ingredients are expensive and unnecessary and may kill "friendly" protective bacteria as well. Soaps with an alcohol base dry the skin. It is actually the friction that is created by rubbing hands and soap together that removes the germs from our skin.

Liquid hand soap is recommended for two reasons: the soap pump is convenient, and it's easier for children to use than a slippery bar of soap, which often falls on the floor. Also, germs, dirt, paint, and sand collect on the soap bar and in the soapy water at the bottom of the soap dish.

Educators wash their hands frequently, which may dry and chap their skin. Using mild soap and hand lotion helps prevent this. And, as discussed earlier, germs can enter our body through nonintact skin. As you'll see in Step 2 of the hand-washing routine, you wet your hands before adding the soap. This reduces soap's drying effect on your skin.

You have most likely seen advertisements for hand-sanitizing products as an acceptable replacement for running water. Alcohol is the cleaning ingredient; the hand sanitizer must have a minimum of 60% alcohol. But according to the Public Health Agency of Canada (2008, p. 3), "the alcohol kills both good and bad bacteria on your skin so use it sparingly. And keep in mind that [hand sanitizers] don't work well if you have a lot of dirt and grease on your hands." These products will not work when you have substances such as stool, urine, blood, or vomit on your hands either. You can purchase hand-sanitizing products in pump form or in containers small enough to keep in a purse or backpack. But are they a replacement for soap and water in an early childhood program? They are more expensive than soap, which is a consideration for programs operating on tight budgets. Although these products are used in health care facilities, they are not recommended for routine use in early childhood settings (Canadian Paediatric Society, 2008b). Following the instructions properly requires applying an adequate amount on the hands for 15 seconds, which is not much of a time-saver compared with the recommended hand-washing routine (see How We and Children Wash Our Hands, page 132). These products should be kept out of children's reach. Due to their high percentage of alcohol, care must be taken with children, as hand sanitizers can be harmful if swallowed and are flammable. They are convenient when activities such as field trips do not provide easy access to running water.

Soap and water are available everywhere in Canada. The single most important infection control practice and life skill that children learn is proper hand washing. During the course of the day, children observe educators washing their hands effectively. In addition, when the children's hand washing is supervised, this essential health practice is reinforced, which has a significant impact on the rates of infection in the program.

Many programs refill rather than replace empty soap pumps and hand lotion containers. Before you refill them, however, clean out the containers with soap and water and rinse them with water to remove the remnants and any germs that may have travelled down the pump during use. If the insides of the containers are not properly cleaned, these germs will contaminate the fresh liquid that is added.

Occasionally, educators' and children's fingernails need to be cleaned. Nailbrushes should not be used, for two reasons. First, the brushing action can cause very small cuts on the cuticles and under the nails, which can trap germs. Second, a communal nailbrush accumulates and transmits germs from everyone who has used it. Instead, ask parents to keep their children's nails trimmed (Canadian Paediatric Society, 2008b). When there is material under yours or a child's nails that won't come out with hand washing, use a disposable orange stick.

Drying our hands and turning off the taps are the final steps in hand washing. These steps can either remove further germs or recontaminate our hands before we leave the sink.

Towels can be either cloth or paper. Programs base their decision on cost, access to laundry facilities, storage space, and the number of staff and children. Rolling towel dispensers and electric hand dryers are not used in programs. We've all used rolling cloth towel dispensers that wouldn't let us pull out a clean towel or had run out of towelling, and we've all seen someone use a section of towel that someone else has used already. Electric hand dryers are not used for two reasons: they can break down, and they take a long time to dry hands thoroughly. It is not practical to expect groups of children and staff to wait in line to dry their hands.

Since we turn on taps with dirty hands, we don't want to wash and dry our hands and then turn off the taps with our clean hands. Some programs' sinks may have elbow taps, foot pedals, or sensors, which eliminate the need to use hands to turn the water on and off.

The scrubbing and rinsing during hand washing remove most of the germs. The drying action may remove even more. But reusing a wet or dry cloth towel increases the likelihood of recontaminating our hands with the germs that were left on the towel from the previous use. Single-use towels, however, whether cloth or paper, ensure that we dry our hands with a fresh towel each time. Then the towel can be used to turn off the taps before it is put into the laundry or the garbage.

Some programs may choose to use individual cloth towels, each one clearly marked with the child's or educator's name, hung to dry without touching, and changed at least daily. Individual cloth towels have disadvantages, however. They should not be used to turn off the water because the taps then contaminate the towels used throughout the day. As well, it is likely that the same towel will be used by more than one person during the day.

How We and Children Wash Our Hands

How, when, and what we use to wash our hands help ensure effective hand washing. The eight steps in the hand-washing routine ensure that as many germs as possible are removed. Remember, you are not trying to sterilize your hands, which is impossible, but rather to remove as many germs as you can.

Just as it is important for us to wash our hands, it is equally important for all children to wash their hands. Effective hand washing is one of the health habits we need to develop for a lifetime. Learning this habit begins in infancy (see Hand Washing for Infants and Toddlers, page 134).

For preschool and school-age children, the educator's role evolves from one of physically washing their hands to one of encouraging, supervising, and modelling effective hand washing. In school-age programs, children often need to be reminded to wash their hands, since their attention turns easily to more exciting activities. Basically, children should wash their hands before and after the same activities that were listed for educators. But children must be encouraged to focus especially on washing their hands after they use the toilet and before they eat or handle food (see Hand Washing and Germs, page 556).

Here are the essential steps in an effective hand-washing technique:

1. Use warm running water.
2. Wet your hands and add soap.
3. Rub your hands vigorously for 10 to 15 seconds.
4. Wash all surfaces, including the backs of hands and between fingers.
5. Rinse your hands well under running water for 5 to 10 seconds.
6. Dry your hands well with a towel. Turn off the taps with a single-use towel.
7. Dispose of the cloth or paper towel.
8. Apply hand lotion as needed.

This is particularly relevant to staff.

When using a hand sanitizing product, use the following steps:

1. Apply about 2.5 mL (1/2 tsp.) onto your palm. Rub your hands together over all surfaces—paying special attention to backs of hands, between fingers, fingernails, thumbs and wrists—until hands are dry, usually 10 to 15 seconds.
2. For young children, dispense the rub into your own hands, then rub the surfaces of a child's hands between yours.
3. Alcohol-based hand rubs are less effective than soap and water for cleaning hands that are visibly dirty, but they still kill micro-organisms, which makes them a good second choice if you don't have access to a sink. Use paper towels or disposable moist towelettes to remove as much dirt as possible, apply an alcohol-based hand-rub, then use a fresh hand wipe or paper towel to remove residue.
4. Wash hands with soap and water to remove dirt as soon as possible.

Source: Canadian Paediatric Society, *Well Beings: A Guide to Health in Child Care.* (Ottawa: Canadian Paediatric Society, 2008), 148. Reprinted with permission.

Monitoring Hand Washing

We have all been in public washrooms that didn't have soap or towels, have seen the tail end of the rolling towel lying on the floor, or have experienced electric hand dryers that don't blow hot air. The next time you are in a public washroom, compare the number of people who wash their hands thoroughly with the number who simply run one hand under the water or don't wash at all. How would you feel about sharing a box of popcorn at the theatre, being served at a restaurant, or having as a coworker someone who is so casual about hand washing?

Although we know the importance of the eight hand-washing steps, we may tend to skip steps or cut down on the time we spend at the sink because we are in a hurry. A poster close to the sink will act as a reminder to educators and parents. Regular monitoring of educators' hand-washing compliance is very important to maintain a high level of hygiene. Remember, this simple, inexpensive, low-tech routine is the most important health practice in the program's infection-control strategy.

Hygiene Practices for Infants and Toddlers

The rate of gastrointestinal infection is highest for infants and toddlers. The responsibility for infection control rests squarely on the educators' shoulders. This section highlights the hygiene practices that should be in place to reduce the opportunity for infection.

Hand Washing for Infants and Toddlers

Have you ever wondered why babies would need to have their hands washed during the day? Watch them to see what their hands touch as they explore and you will know the answer to this question. And remember, germs can be almost anywhere. Washing babies' hands is important

- after they have a diaper change or use the toilet/potty,
- before they eat or are bottle-fed, and
- after they play outside or with materials such as sand or paint.

To wash an infant's hands, use a warm, wet, soapy, single-use towel; rinse with a second wet towel; and dry with a third. When toddlers are able to stand at a sink, with careful supervision and help, they will follow the same steps for hand washing as the older children and educators.

Caring for Children in Diapers

Before we discuss the steps involved in changing a diaper, we examine other hygiene practices related to diapers. Either cloth or disposable diapers are used in programs. To prevent stool from contaminating the environment, diapers must

- absorb the urine and stool,
- fit snugly around the thighs and waist to contain the urine and stool,
- have a waterproof cover, and
- be covered with clothing.

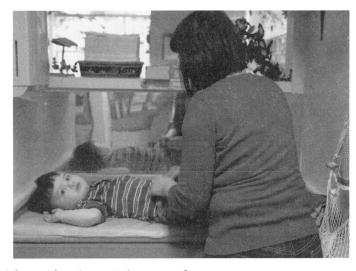

Researchers continue to compare the amount of fecal contamination in programs from disposable diapers with that from cloth diapers. Generally, disposable diapers are more absorbent and leak less than cloth diapers. However, the Canadian Paediatric Society and many public health officials do not recommend one type of diaper over another in programs. Programs and parents can choose the type of diaper that best meets their needs, based on financial considerations, environmental issues, access to a commercial diaper service, and laundry facilities.

If cloth diapers are chosen, care must be taken to ensure that the diaper covers ("pants") are laundered properly to ensure that urine and stool are removed. Many programs use a fresh diaper cover at each diaper change. The use of diaper covers that are pulled up and down the legs is discouraged. Problems arise if the leg elastics have stool on them because stool contaminates the child's legs when the pants are pulled off. Instead, diaper covers that fasten at the waist permit the educator to remove the cover and diaper in one step, reducing the risk of contaminating the program's environment. Obviously, if stool has leaked out of the diaper onto the legs, it will be washed off with soap and water during the change.

Studies have shown that the amount of fecal contamination is significantly reduced when children wear clothes over their cloth or disposable diapers. Clothing is an additional barrier between the diaper, its contents, and the room. Permitting children to wear just a T-shirt and diaper, or to eat in just a diaper and bib, to make cleanup easier is not acceptable practice for infection control. Babies soon figure out how to open a diaper and will learn even more quickly when there aren't any clothes to slow them down. Sitting beside another child provides another opportunity to gain easy access into another's diaper if that other child is wearing no outer clothing.

Second in importance only to hand washing, a strict diapering routine is essential in infant and toddler programs to control the incidence of gastrointestinal infection. Regardless of the type of diaper used, the educator's actions are crucial in determining the level of fecal contamination. Children learn to use the toilet at different ages; for many, this occurs after age two. Preschool programs may have children in diapers, and, if so, the diapering routine applies to preschool staff and parents.

The diaper-changing surface, the surrounding area, and diapering supplies should always be considered contaminated. The area should never be used for anything else, including putting a baby bottle down on the counter even for a minute.

Posting a diapering routine by the changing area acts as a reminder for educators and parents. However, regular monitoring of the educator's diapering technique helps ensure that the routine is properly implemented all the time.

You may be thinking, "I've changed a lot of diapers and it didn't take me 11 steps—or 10 minutes—to change a single diaper" or "There must be a ton of diapers to change during a day's work in an infant program!" However, if you were to write down everything you did during a diaper change, you may be surprised at just how many steps you did take. Furthermore, parents and others who change one child's diapers at home do not need to follow the same stringent guidelines because one baby at home is quite different from 8 or 12 infants and toddlers in a group setting. At home, every family member gets used to each other's germs. Older siblings are past the developmental stage at which they put everything in their mouth, and their own personal hygiene habits are improving.

Effective diapering involves the following steps:

1. Assemble all the necessary supplies.
2. Place the child on the changing surface and remove the soiled diaper. Fold the soiled surface inward and set it aside. If safety pins have been used to fasten the diaper, close them and put them out of the child's reach. Never put the pins in your mouth. Note: Keep one hand on the child at all times.
3. Clean and dry the child's skin. When necessary, use a facial tissue to apply ointments or creams. Put a fresh diaper on the child.
4. Wash the child's hands. Return the child to a supervised area.
5. Dispose of the diaper and, if used, the disposable paper covering.
When cloth diapers are used, bag the diaper without removing stool. The diapers are either sent home with the parents for laundry or placed in your laundry service's container.
6. Spray the sanitizing solution onto the entire surface of the changing surface. Leave for 30 seconds.
7. Put away all diapering supplies.
8. Wash your hands.
9. Dry the changing surface with a single-use towel. Dispose of the cloth or paper towel.
10. Wash your hands thoroughly.
11. Record skin condition and bowel movements, as necessary.

Educators' compliance depends on their understanding of the importance of and the rationale for the routine. The list below provides the rationale for a number of steps from the diapering routine:

Step 1: From the perspective of injury prevention, it is essential that you gather the diapering supplies before you bring the child to the diapering surface. Once you get started, you can't safely walk away from the child to retrieve supplies. It is not necessary to wash your hands before starting. We assume that educators have been washing their hands whenever necessary during the day. As well, the diapering area and supplies are always considered to be contaminated. So it doesn't make sense to wash your hands and then contaminate them immediately after taking off the soiled diaper or picking up a tube of ointment. After you take off the diaper and wash the child's skin, your hands are covered with germs.

Step 3: Using a facial tissue to scoop ointment out of the jar or to squeeze it from a tube onto the tissue has two purposes. First, the tissue provides a barrier between your hands and the ointment, which keeps the ointment in the jar or at the end of the tube from being contaminated by your hands. Second, the tissue is then used to spread the ointment onto the skin. This keeps the germs that are already on your hands off the child's washed skin. If you need more ointment, use a new tissue to get more from the jar or tube. This rule applies regardless of whether each child has her or his own jar of diaper cream or a communal container is used. From what you've read so far, you should be able to come up with the rationale for this last requirement.

The routine use of diaper creams and ointments on children's healthy skin is discouraged. Changing diapers frequently and cleaning the skin at each change prevent urine, stool, or ammonia from contacting the skin long enough to cause irritation. These preparations are also difficult to wash off thoroughly with every change, so urine and stool can be trapped under the cream and irritate the skin. When you do use these products, apply them sparingly. Do not use baby powders or talc because the infant's airways can be damaged by inhaling powder in the air when the container is shaken.

Step 4: Before children arrive at the diaper table, they may have already had their hands in their diaper. During diaper changes, children will likely touch the wet or soiled diapers, the changing surface, and the educator's hands. If children don't have their hands washed after the diaper change, they will immediately begin contaminating the environment with their hands.

Step 5: At home, parents who use cloth diapers often soak soiled diapers in the toilet, but educators must not do this in programs. The number of times the diaper is then handled increases by at least three times, and it is difficult not to splash and drip the water in the diaper over the toilet and onto the floor. The amount of fecal contamination would be excessive.

Step 8: Educators must wash their hands to prevent them from recontaminating the surface while they are drying off the sanitizing solution and remaining germs. But by drying the surface and then discarding the towel, they have now recontaminated their hands and need to wash their hands again (Step 10).

Step 9: During a diaper change, stool or urine can end up on the changing surface. Diapering surfaces need to be smooth, durable, and easy to clean, which allows educators to wipe up any visible urine or stool with toilet paper and then sanitize the surface. Cleaning first with soap and water is not necessary except in cases in which a large quantity of stool or urine is left on the diapering surface. Some programs use disposable change-table paper (the kind used in doctors' offices), which provides a barrier between the baby and the surface. Yet when urine or watery stool touches the paper, the liquid leaks through, which defeats the paper's purpose. Remember, even if the paper is still dry following a diaper change, the paper must be discarded and the surface sanitized. This, along with the cost and the extra garbage created by the paper, is why change paper is not recommended.

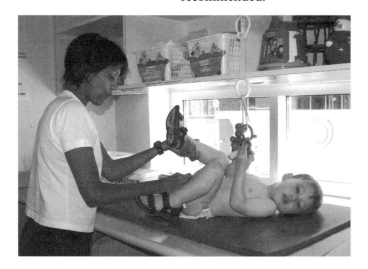

The routine use of disposable gloves is not recommended for changing diapers, even with stool. Gloves provide little protection in this situation beyond the natural protection of your skin. The toilet paper or facial tissue used to wipe stool off the skin and the disposable or cloth towel to wash and dry the child's skin provide the barrier between the stool and your hands. If stool gets on your hands, germs can't get into your body through your skin. If you are concerned about a cut or scrape, use a bandage and replace it when it is soiled or wet. If you have dermatitis or a cut or other broken skin and you must change diapers, use disposable gloves as a temporary means to keep stool off your open skin. Sometimes diapers are filled with loose or watery stools, which may have covered the child's front and back or run down the legs. Some educators find these diapers to be particularly difficult to stomach, and using disposable gloves makes them feel more comfortable.

Diaper changes provide ideal opportunities in your busy day for one-to-one interaction with the child. Wearing gloves puts plastic between your skin and the child's skin, which can't be comfortable for the child. And are we inadvertently sending children the message that bowel movements are somehow not a natural function of their body and that they are "dirty"?

The only time that disposable gloves are recommended for diaper changing is when blood is visible in the child's stool. Choosing disposable plastic gloves over latex gloves affords the program the same kind of protection without the increased cost. In addition, reducing exposure to latex (e.g., gloves and balloons) is a safer alternative for staff and children who are allergic to latex. Regardless of the reasons for wearing gloves, you must wash your hands after removing the gloves. If you don't wash your hands well after every diaper change, you contaminate objects, food, and the environment, and the germs can then enter children's and educators' bodies through the mouth.

Toileting Routine

The toileting routine is made up of the following 14 steps:

1. If the child wears a diaper, remove it. If the diaper is soiled, clean and dry the child's skin. Dispose of the cloth or disposable diaper.
2. Place the child on the toilet or potty. Stay with the child for a specific period of time. Five minutes is usually long enough.

3. Wipe the child.

4. Flush the toilet or let the child flush it. If a potty was used, empty its contents into the toilet and flush.

5. If necessary, diaper the child and help the child get dressed.

6. Assist the child in hand washing. Return the child to a supervised area.

7. Rinse out the potty and flush the water down the toilet.
   If any stool remains in the potty, you may want to wear disposable gloves and remove all the stool with toilet paper.

8. Put away all diapering supplies.

9. Wash your hands.

10. Dry the potty with a single-use towel. Dispose of the cloth or paper towel.

11. Dry the diaper-changing surface with a different towel. Dispose of the cloth or paper towel.

12. Return the potty to the storage area.

13. Wash your hands thoroughly.

14. Record the child's use of the potty, any bowel movements, and any skin condition, as necessary.

For many of the same reasons that apply to the diapering routine, educators need to take extra steps when cleaning a potty to prevent contamination of the surrounding area:

- Utility sinks should be available for staff to use for cleaning, including potties. The utility sink must be cleaned and sanitized after every use. Hand-washing sinks should not be used to rinse or clean potties.

- You may prefer to wear disposable gloves while you remove stool stuck to the potty. However, wearing gloves does not eliminate the need to wash your hands.

Cleaning and Sanitizing

You know that germs are everywhere. You know that germs can live on surfaces for hours, days, and even weeks. You've read about the vehicles of transmission and the important role they play in spreading infections. The rationale for the **cleaning and sanitizing routines** in programs is to have staff focus on objects and surfaces that pose the greatest risk to children and staff.

It can be overwhelming to think about all the objects and surfaces that children and staff come into contact with every day, as well as everything and everyone who has come into contact with germs that are spread through the air from coughing, sneezing, and talking. Where do I start? How often do I clean this and that? What do I clean with? How do I know that I am cleaning this object properly? These are just some of the questions that are answered in this section.

One of the infection control practices carried out by staff to break the chain of transmission is regular cleaning and sanitizing of objects, surfaces, and areas within programs. To implement this, educators need to

- identify what needs to be cleaned, sanitized, or both;
- use effective cleaning and sanitizing products and techniques; and
- understand how to protect themselves from **potentially hazardous substances**.

The purpose of *cleaning* is to remove dirt (organic material) and germs from objects and surfaces. But, as in hand washing, the cleaning solution must be combined with a scrubbing action to create the friction needed to remove dirt and germs. This is followed by rinsing with water and air-drying.

The purpose of *sanitizing* an object or surface is to ensure that as many germs as possible are eliminated. In most cases, objects and surfaces are cleaned and rinsed, then sanitized, and left to air-dry.

What Needs to Be Cleaned or Sanitized?

By establishing priorities, you can identify the items to be cleaned, sanitized, or both and how frequently. With the *Well Beings* publication, much of the organizational work has been done for program staff. Rather than repeating those recommendations, let's explore the rationale behind two of them.

Toys

Toys that have been in infants' and toddlers' mouths are obvious vehicles of germ transmission. Many toys for infants are designed to be safe for them to put in the mouth (e.g., plastic stacking rings on a cone, squeak toys, rattles). These toys are often referred to as mouthing toys. Of course, young children can put almost anything into their mouth (e.g., corners of books, puzzle pieces, plastic fruit and vegetables). For clarity, we will refer to any toy that children have chewed or sucked on as a mouthing toy. After one child has finished playing with a mouthing toy, it should be picked up by staff before a second child chews on it.

Toys that are mouthed should be cleaned and sanitized daily. Cleaning washes off organic materials, such as the children's saliva and any stool that may have been on a child's hands and transferred to the toys. Sanitizing is an added precaution that removes germs that may remain after cleaning, before the toys are air-dried and returned to the children. Plastic books can be cleaned and sanitized by hand; cloth ones can be put in the laundry.

The potential for spreading germs via toys used by preschoolers or school-agers is much lower than via mouthing toys, for three main reasons. Older children are not constantly putting their toys and hands into their mouth; they aren't touching, hugging, and kissing each other as frequently as babies and toddlers do; and their personal hygiene is improving. For these reasons, these toys can be cleaned weekly and when they are obviously soiled, but sanitizing is not necessary.

Water Tables

Although the water table is an important medium for learning, a pool of water can be easily contaminated and spread germs among the children using it. Germs enter the water from the children's hands and from everything they put in the water, such as toys, soap, and food colouring. Additional germs enter the water from blow toys and straws, as well as airborne germs that land in the water from laughing, talking, and coughing. Adding bleach or other sanitizing solutions is not necessary—saliva, soap, and sand in the water will reduce the bleach solution's effectiveness.

The Canadian Paediatric Society (2008, pp. 157) recommends the following hygiene practices for communal water tables:

- Fill the table with fresh water each morning.
- Empty the table at the end of every day:
    - Wash with detergent and rinse off with clean water.
    - Sanitize it and leave it to air-dry overnight.
- Sanitize and air-dry the water toys.
- Clean and sanitize blow toys, pipes, and straws after use. These toys, like mouthing toys, should not be shared among children.
- Encourage children and educators to wash their hands before playing in the table.
- Discourage children who are not feeling well (e.g., cold, diarrhea) or who have a skin infection from using the table.
- Close the table when the program has an outbreak of diarrhea.

Source: Canadian Paediatric Society, *Well Beings: A Guide to Health in Child Care.* (Ottawa: Canadian Paediatric Society, 2008), 157. Reprinted with permission.

Given how much infants and toddlers love to explore, not to mention their willingness to share toys, their affectionate nature, and their vulnerability to infections, it makes sense that infants and toddlers not use communal water tables. Instead, each child should have his or her own basin of water. The basins can be placed on the floor or on a table in a way that encourages social play. Individual basins permit children to use toys that can go between their own basin of water and their mouth and to splash and drool in the water and even drink it. In this way, the children do not share toys or come into direct contact with the contents of one another's basins. *Children must never be left alone with the basins of water, even for a second.* Children have drowned in as little as 4 cm (1½ in.) of water.

Products and Techniques

Household cleaning products and detergents that are safer for the environment are also effective cleaning products in programs. Cloth towels can be used for all cleaning and can be laundered after each use. When cleaning up blood and large amounts of stool, urine, and vomit, paper toweling is preferred because it can be safely discarded.

Household bleach is recommended for a number of reasons: it is highly effective, inexpensive, easy to use, readily available, and safe to use around children. When bleach is not used, programs usually consult their public health inspector before choosing sanitizing products. Other products are effective, and directors consider each product's cost and its safety around children and staff, as well as its environmental friendliness.

Using bleach may raise a few questions about chlorine in the environment, ruined clothes, and the smell of bleach in the air. You need add only a small amount of bleach to water to sanitize. The recommended dilution is 1 part bleach in 100 parts water—for example, 2.5 mL (½ tsp.) of bleach in 250 mL (1 cup) of water. When this proportion is used, the bleach solution is so diluted that problems with bleach odour and ruined clothing are eliminated. But the solution is still strong enough to be effective. In your practicum, you may find that a program uses different dilutions.

A dilution of 1 part bleach to 10 parts water is a common recommendation for cleaning up blood spills (e.g., 50 mL [¼ cup] of bleach in 500 mL [2 cups] of water).

Remember the following points when you use bleach:

- Objects and surfaces are usually cleaned first to remove visible organic material (e.g., dirt, food, saliva) because organic materials reduce the effectiveness of the bleach solution.

- The bleach solution is mixed fresh each morning for spray bottles used for diaper-changing surfaces. When the bleach solution is mixed in open containers and sinks, it should be prepared just before use. Otherwise, the bleach solution evaporates throughout the day, and anything that falls into the pail could reduce its effectiveness. From a safety perspective, containers of water should never be left within the reach of children.

- Use the dilutions that are recommended by your provincial or territorial child care office in conjunction with public health inspectors.

- The bleach solution needs to remain on the object or surface for two minutes to allow time for it to work.

- To protect your hands from the dryness that comes with using cleaning or sanitizing solution, you may wish to wear rubber gloves. Remember, take off your rings, watches, and bracelets to protect them from bleach.

Four Steps for Cleaning and Sanitizing

Having effective cleaning and sanitizing products, cloths, and rubber gloves—and being organized—takes some of the work out of cleaning.

Some objects, such as books and puzzles in infant and toddler programs, need to be sanitized only. Obviously, these and other objects are not placed in a container of bleach and water. Instead, they are wiped with a cloth that has been rinsed and wrung out in the bleach solution.

The dishwasher can be a timesaving device for cleaning and sanitizing smaller plastic toys. Make sure the toys can withstand the water temperature and the detergent.

Educators follow these four steps:

1. Fill one container (or sink) with soap (detergent) and water to scrub toys or objects and to wash surfaces.
2. Fill a second container with water to rinse what has been washed. (Soap needs to be rinsed off to ensure that sanitizing is effective.)
3. Fill a third container with the bleach solution. Bleach and water should be measured accurately. (To save time, the water level can be marked on the inside of plastic containers; then only the corresponding amount of bleach needs to be measured.)
4. The objects or surfaces are left to air-dry. The diaper-changing surface is the one exception. After the solution has been on the surface for 30 seconds, dry it off with a fresh towel.

Implementing the Routines throughout the Day

The number of times that educators wash their hands and the time spent on the routines discussed in this unit depend on the following factors: the size of the program, the number of children and staff, the ages of the children, and whether meals and snacks are prepared in the program or provided by parents.

Some programs, because of their location (e.g., workplace, office buildings, colleges, universities), have cleaning services that maintain bathrooms, floors, carpets, etc. In these programs, staff have more time for the remaining routines. However, it is important that staff monitor the external cleaning services to ensure that the quality is satisfactory, that the cleaning is done with the recommended frequency, and that the products used are safe around children.

A day in any program is busy, and fitting in all the routines takes some finesse. But the importance of implementing routines to break the chain of transmission means that there can't be shortcuts. We must ensure that the time spent on implementing routines is protected, because the work reduces the frequency of infection.

A written schedule for all routines is essential to ensure that they are implemented consistently. Programs may design a schedule based on the frequency of the routines (e.g., daily, twice a week, weekly) or by room. The schedule breaks down what can seem like an overwhelming task into more manageable routines. It includes instructions on how each item is to be cleaned or sanitized so that educators aren't left questioning the effectiveness of their work.

When there is an outbreak of an infection, a review of these written schedules can provide insight into the effectiveness of the cleaning and sanitizing routines and whether the schedule should be revised on a short- or long-term basis.

During an outbreak of diarrhea, it is advisable to close the water table. At the same time, staff's hand washing, diapering routines, and food-safety practices need to be evaluated.

Protecting Yourself from Potentially Hazardous Substances

In this section, we discuss the potential risks and steps to reduce educators' exposure to hazardous products related to infection control. These include the concept of universal precautions, the safe use of cleaning and sanitizing products, and the appropriate use of gloves.

Universal Precautions

Under normal conditions, when patients are admitted to a hospital, they are not routinely tested for any number of diseases. This practice would be expensive and time-consuming. In addition, such tests may not provide the hospital's infectious disease experts with reliable information. You have already read that a person can spread germs to others before she or he develops symptoms and that some of us carry infections even though we are not ill.

Universal precautions constitute the fundamental principle in protecting staff from the potential risks in the workplace. Hospital staff assume that everyone has the potential to expose them to germs, so safe medical and nursing procedures are developed specifically for the task or medical technique being implemented. Universal precautions, in turn, protect patients from hospital staff.

You may be wondering how anything in a hospital has any relevance to programs. Educators aren't changing bandages with blood, giving needles, routinely being exposed to blood, or caring for seriously ill patients. The fundamental principle on which hospitals build their infection control strategy is the same one as for programs. To reduce the spread of germs and to protect themselves from unnecessary exposure to potentially harmful organisms, educators must implement universal precautions in their daily work with children. All the procedures covered in this unit are based on universal precautions and, when implemented, protect not only the educators but also the children.

Cleaning and Sanitizing Products and Gloves

Cleaning products used in programs should be safe to use around children and staff and preferably be friendly to the environment. This does not eliminate the need for the products to be stored out of reach of children. Most products used in programs are household products purchased in grocery stores. It is advisable to read all product labels for safe handling directions and any first-aid information (see Workplace Hazardous Materials Information System, page 81).

Just as water and soap can dry our skin, cleaning and sanitizing products can be abrasive. Using rubber gloves while dishwashing and during cleaning and sanitizing routines helps protect our hands. Using differently coloured rubber gloves for the routine tasks and writing the task near the wrists of the gloves are two ways, in addition to separate storage areas, that help staff use the right gloves for the right task. *For example, pink rubber gloves are used only in the kitchen and are hung to dry in the kitchen. Yellow rubber gloves are used for cleaning and sanitizing toys and play equipment and are hung to dry in the utility area.*

There are times when disposable rather than rubber gloves are preferred. In addition to the occasional use during diapering and the toileting routine for toddlers, disposable (nonlatex) gloves are used when educators are at risk of exposure to blood or bloody body fluids. Once the gloves have been used, they can be disposed of carefully. Carefully remove one disposable glove at a time. While you are slowly peeling off a glove (starting at the wrist), turn the glove inside out. This method protects you from the germs on the gloves and also protects the immediate area. Wash your hands after disposing safely of the gloves.

Disposable gloves are just one way of providing a barrier between your hands and the blood. Facial tissue used to stop a nosebleed provides a barrier between your hand and the child's nose. Cotton balls or sterile gauze in first-aid kits, when used appropriately to clean cuts and scrapes, can be effective barriers between your hands and the source of the blood. It is not necessary for staff to keep disposable gloves in their pockets in case a child is injured or gets a nosebleed. Our skin's natural ability to protect us from germs—along with effective hand washing—is our best protection.

Regardless of which type of glove is used, there are two points to keep in mind:

- Gloves can provide a protective barrier against germs that cause infection. However they offer little protection beyond that achieved by good hand washing.
- You must always wash your hands after you remove the gloves.

After all, you are not the only person to wear those gloves. Your hands had germs on them before you put on the gloves, and so did the hands of the person who used the gloves before you. Therefore, these germs may be inside the gloves and may end up on the next person's hands. In addition, you get more germs on your hands when you put on and take off the gloves.

Pets in Early Childhood Programs

Pets provide children with the opportunity to learn to care for living things and add "life" to an early childhood program. Whether animals are permitted in a program or not is based on your provincial or territorial regulations and your public health regulations. When they are permitted, the regulations should cover the types of animals that are permitted and not permitted, vaccination requirements, and care of the animals and cages. Some programs are opting for a fish aquarium, which provides opportunities for relaxation, enjoyment, and responsible care for the fish. As well, discussions around the cycle of life and death inevitably become part of the experience. There are fewer daily responsibilities for the staff and none of the complexities of having a centre pet that must be cared for over the weekends.

In *Well Beings* (2008b), the Canadian Paediatric Society recommends that pets not be part of the early childhood program; rather, family or other community member pets could be brought in for visits. Reasons cited include the following: diseases can be passed from the animals to us and can pose issues for children, parents, and staff with allergies or weakened immune systems or pregnant staff or parents. The Canadian Paediatric Society does acknowledge that home-based (family day care) programs may have family pets in the house.

RECEIVING MIXED MESSAGES

On a regular basis, educators are inundated with messages and information from different agencies that come in contact with early childhood programs, including public health inspectors, public health nurses and other staff, the licensing office, health care providers, early childhood students and instructors, and newly hired graduates. In addition, TV and print ads are regularly "selling" us on products that aren't necessary.

Hand Sanitizers

There is an incredible marketing push surrounding the everyday use of hand sanitizers as an acceptable alternative to washing our hands with soap and water. Earlier in this unit, we discussed the occasional use of such products in early childhood settings. It has also been shown that these sanitizers do *not* offer any germ-killing advantage over soap and running water.

Yet there are public health departments across the country encouraging the use of sanitizers routinely in early childhood settings or giving the use of alcohol-based hand rubs equal status to hand washing with soap and running water. It is not uncommon to see a two- or three-year-old come to the setting with a personal-sized bottle of hand rub in a coat pocket. Some programs have been required to have the educators carry these products with them to the outdoor play areas. Why? We suggest that this is an unnecessary recommendation. First, those playing outside, typically, will have visible sand and soil on their hands, which render the sanitizer ineffective. Second, when educators help children blow their nose, tissue is the barrier between their hands and the child's nasal discharge. Third, no one is eating or drinking while they are playing. Fourth, alcohol is the sanitizing agent in such products, which is drying to the skin, and in the winter, this only adds to the dryness our hands experience. Fifth, if you have used such a product, you'll remember the smell and possible taste left on your hands. This is not the type of residue, no matter the amount, that you want to routinely expose young children to, particularly those who frequently put their hands and objects they touch in the mouth. Sixth, the outside of the bottle must always be considered contaminated, so if you use the product and then put the container back in your pocket, you have just contaminated your hands. Upon their return inside, everyone is expected to wash their hands because we know that their hands have become dirty while playing. Seventh, and most importantly, hand washing is still required even if you have used a sanitizer out in the playground.

Staff and parents in the programs may have conflicting opinions and practices around this issue and recommendations or requirements from their local public health agency that contradict this position. Children's use of these over-the-counter products for hygiene may undermine their development of healthy life skills, such as knowing when and how to wash hands.

Sanitizing or "Sterilizing" Our Physical Environment

As mentioned in the section on vehicles of transmission (page 118), TV commercials and the marketplace overwhelm us with a multitude of sanitizing products to kill every germ around the home—an unnecessary and impossible goal. These advertisements to "sterilize" our environments raise a number of questions:

- What about the residue left behind on the sprayed objects?
- What happens when the residue gets onto our hands and, in the case of a child, into the mouth? Aside from its effectiveness, another reason why a bleach solution is recommended for use in this unit is because it is safe to use around children in the dilutions recommended.
- What is the environmental impact of these unnecessary chemicals being sprayed in the air, dumped down the sink, and flushed into the sewage system?

Antibacterial Products

It seems as if the word "antibacterial" is appearing on more and more product labels. Considerable time and money are being spent on the promotion of the antibacterial ingredients in products to try to convince us that if we use the products, we will be protected from germs and, as a result, be healthier.

One such ingredient is **triclosan**, which is found in products such as soaps and cleansers. But it is also present in unexpected products, such as deodorants, toothpastes, and shaving creams. It has been reported that triclosan is added during the manufacturing process to items such as kitchen utensils, bedding, and even toys, socks, and trash bags. On Health Canada's website, triclosan is on the list of permitted cosmetic ingredients, but the manufacturers must meet specific conditions. When added to a product that will be going into the mouth (e.g., a mouthwash), the label must state the following: "The product is not to be used by children under the age of 12, in the case of mouthwashes, avoid swallowing. . . ." (Healthy Environments and Consumer Safety Branch, 2007, p. 18).

Antibacterial products play a significant contributory role in increasing the resistance of microbes (i.e., bacteria, viruses, and fungi) to **antimicrobials** used to either kill or inhibit the growth of these microorganisms. You are most familiar with antibiotics used to treat bacterial infections (see Antibiotic-Resistant Bacteria, page 178), but there are other medical applications to help us after being exposed to certain viruses. Sanitizing products fall under the antimicrobial heading. Health Canada (2003, p. 3) acknowledges the impact of antimicrobial (AMR) on our health: "The growth of undesirable microorganisms can outpace our ability to control and mitigate their effects on human health and the health of our environment. As a result, AMR has become a significant health issue. This result can and has had serious implications to our health."

There are also environmental concerns about triclosan. When triclosan is mixed with tap water that is chlorinated by your community's water treatment system, it is reported to create a gas classified as a "probable human carcinogen" (Marketplace, 2007a). You must ask yourself if you want to be exposed to an unnecessary risk by using products such as toothpaste, mouthwash, or shaving cream or by laundering bedding and clothing with this compound. After use, triclosan enters our water systems, where it is converted to dioxin when exposed to sunlight (Marketplace, 2007b).

The Canadian Paediatric Society (2006a) raised the concern that children who experience more infections in the early years are less likely to develop allergies and asthma. Or said another way, the more we "sterilize" the children's environment, the more we are understimulating the normal maturation of children's immune system. The fact that children who are not as "sanitized" with overuse of antimicrobial agents have better opportunities to strengthen their immune system was mentioned at the beginning of the unit. Researchers from the University of California summarized 14 studies and concluded that the risk of developing the most common type of childhood leukemia is reduced for those children attending early childhood education programs. The lowered risk, by as much as 30%, may be attributed to children's stronger immune systems from experiencing childhood infections (Science Daily, 2008).

The issue of **antimicrobial resistance** is not just a Canadian issue; it is a global issue. We all have a personal responsibility to limit the use of antimicrobial products. We must read the product's list of ingredients and not purchase products with ingredients of questionable or unnecessary use. *For example, we don't need an ingredient such as triclosan in our personal grooming products, clothing, and bed linens. Take a look at the products that you are already using at home. What is in your favourite brand of toothpaste? When you are at early childhood programs, take a look at the toothpaste used with the children.*

In early childhood settings, do the following:

- When sanitizing, we must limit the types of products used, follow the instructions, and use the products only where appropriate. Bleach is an antimicrobial product, and it is important to remember to measure the bleach and water each time you mix it and follow the recommendations for sanitizing surfaces and items in the program. Unnecessarily sanitizing items or using too strong a dilution can contribute to antimicrobial resistance.

- Manage the illnesses of children and staff responsibly (see Appendix 4.1, page 197).

PLANNING FOR A PANDEMIC

In 2003, Toronto and other Canadian cities and elsewhere were faced with an outbreak of severe acute respiratory syndrome (SARS), a severe form of pneumonia that can make people critically ill and can be fatal. This was the first large-scale outbreak of an infectious disease for many of us in our lifetime to have witnessed, at least through the extensive national news coverage. It took the cooperation of the municipal, provincial, and federal health authorities working together to coordinate the response by both health professionals and the public to curtail the spread of SARS within hospitals, personal care homes, and the general population. After the outbreak ended, Toronto was known worldwide for its response to and control of SARS.

What is a **pandemic**? The American Academy of Pediatrics defines it as "… the emergence and global spread of a new influenza A virus sub-type, leading to substantially increased morbidity and mortality rates" (2006, p. 403). In 1918, perhaps as many as 50 million people died during the worldwide flu pandemic.

Every fall, the annual flu vaccine program is launched. Health care workers in hospitals, personal care homes, and medical clinics and as emergency first responders should be vaccinated as a matter of course to lessen the spread to those they come in contact with in their work. Included in this recommendation are the following (National Advisory Committee on Immunization, 2006, pp. 213–214):

- Those working in early childhood programs (centre and home based) in which children under two years old are enrolled. Educators working with children who have chronic health issues should receive the flu shot regardless of the child's age.

- The household contacts of those people at high risk for the flu's complications. Parents of children under six months old. Families living with an elderly relative.

- Pregnant women

- Staff working in close proximity to and with those who are at high risk, such as the crews on cruise ships

Some groups in our population are more vulnerable to the complications of the flu. These groups include (National Advisory Committee on Immunization, 2006, p. 213):

- those living with chronic medical conditions,

- residents in personal care homes and other chronic care facilities,

- adults older than 65 years old, and

- healthy children between the ages of 6 and 23 months.

Planning for a pandemic is a multipronged approach. Your child care licensing agency and your public health agency have either already developed or are in the process of developing a plan for a pandemic. It isn't a question of if there will be a pandemic but when.

Once an influenza virus achieves the ability to be efficiently transmitted and sustain infection in humans, it is expected to spread around the world in a matter of months. The first peak of illness is expected to occur two to four months later, and the peak of mortality is expected within one month of the peak in illness. The Public Health Agency of Canada has estimated the impact of disease using published models that are based on the epidemiology of previous pandemics and interpandemic influenza. In these models, 15% to 35% of the Canadian population (4.5 to 10.6 million citizens) will become clinically ill, with between 2.1 and five million requiring outpatient care, between 34,000 and 138,000 requiring hospitalization, and between 11,000 and 58,000 deaths. (Canadian Paediatric Society, 2006b, p. 1)

Source: Canadian Paediatric Society, *Well Beings: A Guide to Health in Child Care.* (Ottawa: Canadian Paediatric Society, 2008), 1. Reprinted with permission.

As a result, planning for a pandemic is needed now rather than attempting to respond to it after its onset. It is not our intention to outline such a plan in this textbook. But prevention is key, year round, and not just during the annual flu season. In addition to the flu vaccine, hand washing and hygiene practices are paramount to prevent and limit the spread of infectious diseases, including the flu. When you are at your placements, ask the staff about their plan for a pandemic. Do they have a policy and procedures already in place? Are they aware of the work being done in your province or territory?

REVISITING THE HEALTH PROMOTION ACTION PLAN

Recall the Health Promotion Action Plan introduced in Unit 1. The following example illustrates this plan in practice in terms of preventing childhood illnesses, using immunization as the point of reference.

CRITICAL THINKING

After reading the health promotion action plan on immunization, identify an action for each of the four levels using the topic of antimicrobial resistance as the point of reference.

Individual Problem Solving and Self-Reliance

Due to the dynamic nature of immunization research, the list of diseases for which immunization is available is increasing. This reality makes it important for educators and parents to keep current through their family physician or local public health agency. As individuals, we are encouraged by public health agencies to recognize the importance of complying with recommended immunization schedules (see Table 3.3, page 126). Parents are encouraged to follow through with their children's immunization to contribute to their health and the public's health. An annual checkup with a family physician includes a review of each child's immunization history and future needs. As adults, you will want to keep track of when you are due for your diphtheria and tetanus boosters, which are recommended every 10 years. Parents who have made a decision for religious or other reasons not to follow through with immunization guidelines have an ethical responsibility to the early childhood program to submit a physician's letter for documentation. They must also follow public health guidelines in the event that these children are exposed to certain illnesses (see Appendix 4.1, page 197).

Collective Self-Help

Directors and educators can support the goal of 100% immunization by posting reminders for families on a parent bulletin board and by providing pamphlets that clarify the availability and benefits of specific immunizations. Directors need to keep immunization records up-to-date and contact parents if their child's immunization records have not yet been submitted. Directors can also help parents find a family physician by knowing which doctors in the community are taking new patients, as well as having information about community health clinics and drop-in clinics. An annual parent–staff meeting facilitated by a public health nurse could also promote awareness and education about immunization and other public health initiatives.

Community Action

In promoting 100% immunization in the community, it is important to know the issues that pose challenges or barriers to full participation in immunization compliance. *For example:*

- *In some remote communities, families may not have ongoing access to family physicians.*
- *In communities where few or no infectious disease outbreaks have occurred for over a generation, families may be more complacent and not see the need for immunization.*
- *Recent immigrants who have come from countries that do not have a universal immunization program, particularly those whose first language is neither English nor French, may not have the experience or access to our immunization information in their first language.*

We all must realize that immunization plays a significant role in continuing to prevent outbreaks. It is important to respond to specific community issues through effective action (see Appendix 1.1, page 53). Perhaps a community forum access to culturally relevant information, or other plans to build broad-based education and support, may lead to effective action.

Societal Change

A number of public challenges may present roadblocks to attaining the goal of 100% immunization. Provinces and territories may not make all immunizations recommended in the schedule available to everyone through medicare. In these situations, some children are possibly at a disadvantage if their families cannot afford to pay or have the costs covered through extended health benefits. Another barrier may be the lack of access to family physicians in nonurban areas. Government priorities placed on prevention involve advocacy, as stated earlier in this textbook. Hopefully, changes resulting from the Romanow Report (Romanow, 2002) will improve some of these realities— funds put into universally accessible preventive health care, incentives for physicians to practice in nonurban areas (and in Canada generally), and citizen advocacy groups.

CONCLUSION

One of the primary goals of high-quality early childhood programs is to maintain or improve the health status of children, which contributes to their growth and development and to their participation in the program and activities. Indicators of high quality include adequate educator–child ratios, small group sizes, staff trained in early childhood education, the provision of orientation and regular in-service training, and low staff turnover rates. These all need to be in place to control infectious diseases.

The consistent implementation of an infection control strategy is one of the best ways to prevent infections or at least reduce their spread in programs. Such a strategy includes effective hand washing as a priority for both educators and children, to break the chain of transmission. Adherence to a strict diapering and toileting policy (and procedures), regular cleaning and sanitizing, and, of course, hand washing are all essential to promote children's physical health in the early childhood setting. In addition, informal but routine daily health observations, beginning with an observation conducted when the child arrives at the program, ensures that staff connect with the child and usually the family. This initial health observation provides educators with a baseline reading of the child's health to use for comparison during the day. This process, which is discussed in more detail in Unit 4, ensures that adults take note of each child's health status so that changes in physical or behavioural status are recognized and responded to appropriately.

What's Your Opinion?

HAND SANITIZERS: ROUTINE OR NOT?

During the practicum, educators supervising the playground routinely use hand-sanitizing products, although they are not required to do so. When one of them asks you why you aren't using them, she suggests that it's easier than washing hands, and hospitals use them. She says, "Anyway, we know that we'll have to use them in an outbreak, so we may as well get used to it."

List the reasons for and against using them routinely. Which position wins and why?

ASSESS YOUR LEARNING

Define terms or describe concepts used in this unit.

- antimicrobial resistance
- cleaning and sanitizing routines
- hand sanitizers
- host
- immunity
- new host
- potentially hazardous substances
- universal precautions

- antimicrobials
- germs
- hand washing
- hygiene practices
- immunization
- pandemic
- triclosan
- vehicles of transmission

Evaluate your options in each situation.

1. One of the daily sanitizing routines in the program is to add a capful of bleach to the water table each morning. This practice saves water and time because staff empty the water only once a week.

2. While demonstrating the diaper-changing procedure, one of the educators tells you not to bother washing the infant's hands after diapering. She says it is a time-waster; instead, she wants you to ensure that the baby's hands are busy with a toy to prevent them from becoming contaminated during diapering.

3. You are in your first program placement. You are feeling nervous and, understandably, unsure of yourself. During your first few days at the program, you observe that all the educators wear disposable gloves whenever a child has stool in the diaper. When one of the educators runs through the diapering routine with you, she makes it clear that you are expected to wear gloves.

4. You have a close working relationship with a parent who discloses to you that her child is HIV positive. You are the only person in the program she has told, and she has asked you not to tell anyone else, including the director.

5. You believe in environmentally friendly cleaning products, so when your room partner suggests getting rid of the bleach and using vinegar and baking soda instead, you are thinking about it. After all, that's usually what you use at home to keep surfaces clean.

6. When a new child enrolls in your program, the parents let you know that he has an allergy to the program's pet guinea pig.

RESOURCE MATERIALS

Organizations

Canadian Institute of Child Health, 384 Bank Street, Suite 300, Ottawa, ON K2P 1Y4. Tel: 613-230-8838; fax: 613-230-6654; http://www.cich.ca

Canadian Paediatric Society, 2305 St. Laurent Blvd, Ottawa, ON K1G 4J8. Tel: 613-526-9397; fax: 613-526-3332; http://www.cps.ca

Other Websites of Interest

Canadian AIDS Treatment Information Exchange (CATIE): http://www.catie.ca

Canadian Coalition for Immunization Awareness & Promotion: http://www.immunize.cpha.ca

Centre for Health Information and Promotion, The Hospital for Sick Children: http://www.sickkids.ca/FamilyInformation/section.asp?s=Centre+for+Health+Information+%26+Promotion&sID=1124

The Hospital for Sick Children, Toronto: http://www.sickkids.ca

Public Health Agency of Canada (Health Canada), Immunization & Vaccines: http://www.phac-aspc.gc.ca/im/index-eng.php

Video

Gift Card Gotcha and The Dirt on Clean (aired January 31, 2007). Marketplace on CBC. To view, visit http://www.cbc.ca/marketplace/2007/01/triclosan.html

Printed Matter

Your Child's Best Shot: A Parent's Guide to Vaccination (2006), by Ronald Gold, M.D. 3rd ed. Ottawa: Canadian Paediatric Society. To purchase a copy, visit http://www.cps.ca

BIBLIOGRAPHY

American Academy of Pediatrics. (2006). *Red Book 2006: Report of the Committee on Infectious Diseases.* Elk Grove Village, IL: Author.

Canadian Paediatric Society. (2006a). Antimicrobial products in the home: The evolving problem of antibiotic resistance. *Paediatrics & Child Health, 11,* 169–173. Retrieved May 2008 from http://www.cps.ca/English/statements/ID/ID06-02.htm#Reallife

Canadian Paediatric Society. (2006b). Pandemic influenza and Canada's children. *Paediatrics & Child Health,* 11, 335–337. Retrieved May 2008 from http://www.cps.ca/english/statements/ID/PIDnote_Pandemic2006.htm

Canadian Paediatric Society. (2007). Autistic spectrum disorder: No causal relationship with vaccines. *Paediatrics & Child Health, 12,* 393–395. Retrieved May 2008 from http://www.cps.ca/english/statements/ID/PIDnote_Jun07.htm

Canadian Paediatric Society. (2008a). *Biting in child care: What are the risks?* Ottawa: Author. Retrieved April 2008 from http://www.cps.ca/caringforkids/keepingkidssafe/whenkidsbite.htm

Canadian Paediatric Society. (2008b). *Well beings: A guide to health in child care* (3rd ed.). Ottawa: Author.

Ford-Jones, E. L., & Gold, R. (2002). Pediatric immunization update. *Patient Care in Canada, 13*(4), 54–74.

Health Canada. (2003, June). Antimicrobial resistance: Keeping it in the box. *Health Policy Research Bulletin 6.* Retrieved May 2008 from http://www.hc-sc.gc.ca/sr-sr/pubs/hpr-rpms/bull/2003-6-antimicrob/intro-eng.php

Healthy Environments and Consumer Safety Branch. (2007). *List of prohibited and restricted cosmetic ingredients (the cosmetic ingredient "hotlist."* Ottawa: Health Canada. Retrieved May 2008 from http://www.hc-sc.gc.ca/cps-spc/alt_formats/hecs-sesc/pdf/person/cosmet/info-ind-prof/_hot-list-critique/hotlist-2007-liste_critique_e.pdf

Kramer, A., Schwebke, I., & Kampf, G. (2006). How long do nosocomial pathogens persist on inanimate surfaces? A systematic review. *BMC Infectious Diseases, 6,* 130 doi:10.1186/1471-2334-6-130. Retrieved August 2008 from http://www.biomedcentral.com/1471-2334/6/130

Marketplace. (2007a, January 31). *The dirt on clean: What is triclosan?* Retrieved May 2008 from http://www.cbc.ca/marketplace/webextras/triclosan/what_is_triclosan.html?triclosan

Marketplace. (2007b, January 31). *The dirt on clean: Health concerns & environmental damage.* Retrieved May 2008 from http://www.cbc.ca/marketplace/webextras/triclosan/health_concerns.html?triclosan

National Advisory Committee on Immunization. (2006). *Canadian immunization guide* (7th ed.). Ottawa: Public Works and Government Services Canada.

Public Health Agency of Canada. (2008). *Staying healthy is in your hands.* Retrieved May 2008 from http://www.phac-aspc.gc.ca/chn-rcs/handwash-eng.php

Romanow, R. (2002). Building on values: The future of health care in Canada. Ottawa: Commission on the Future of Health Care in Canada.

Science Daily. (2008, April 28). *Daycare attendance early in life cuts childhood leukemia risk by 30 percent, analysis finds.* Retrieved May 2008 from http://www.sciencedaily .com/releases/2008/04/080428084232. htm

Toronto Public Health. (2008). *Measles continue to circulate in Toronto.* Retrieved May 2008 from http:// wx.toronto.ca/inter/it/newsrel.nsf/9a3dd5e2596d27af85256de400452b9b/f14d53723466adc18525744 3006c912b?OpenDocument

World AIDS Day. (2007). *HIV/AIDS prevention is everybody's business: 27 years of HIV/AIDS.* Retrieved May 2008 from http://www.worldaidsday.org.au/internet/wad/publishing.nsf/Content/27-years

Illness Management

CHILDREN'S HEALTH CARE

This section focuses on the appropriate role that educators play in caring for children who are ill. In addition to implementing an infection control strategy, the educators' role includes

- working in partnership with parents;
- identifying possible signs and symptoms;
- implementing the early childhood program's policy for ill children, including
  - documenting observations in children's files and reports,
  - sharing relevant health information with parents,
  - communicating with health professionals, and
  - implementing the health care provider's recommendations (the term "health care provider" encompasses both physician and advanced practitioners); and

OBJECTIVES

To describe the why, how, and what of daily health observations.

To identify the signs and symptoms of illness and describe how to proceed with concerns.

To explain the principle of exclusion and consider the issues surrounding exclusion from the early childhood program.

To describe how to respond to the most common childhood infections.

To describe the safe administration of medication to children.

- helping children feel better, including
  - excluding children,
  - TLC (tender loving care), and
  - administering medication, if necessary.

Educators observe children throughout their daily activities. With experience, educators gain the expertise to differentiate between behaviour that is developmentally appropriate for children, behaviour that should be watched more closely, and behaviour that is cause for concern. If an educator is concerned about a child's behaviour or state of health, action is required on the part of educators and parents.

Educators' ability to articulate health concerns about children is an essential skill. As with any skill, experience and motivation on the part of the individual to continue learning assist educators in fine-tuning their skills for observation and documentation. The methods used for documenting health observations vary among early childhood programs. Regardless of the method, the key to effective documentation is that it is objective, systematic, and concise. Educators are trained professionals communicating with other educators, parents, and health or social service professionals in the community.

The quality of the relationships that staff have with parents in managing illness is paramount, since parents are the decision makers regarding their child's health. Establishing effective relationships with a child's parents begins at the time of enrollment, not the first time educators have concerns about the child. Because children will get sick and be unable to attend the program, the enrollment interview is the time for the director and parents to discuss the following issues: information sharing, program policies on health observations, childhood illnesses, communications with their health care provider, criteria for excluding children from the program, and administration of medication.

If the program's health policies and practices are realistic, logical, practical, and based on current health information, parents will likely understand their purpose and work cooperatively with staff. If, however, policies and practices seem unrealistic or unrelated to current health information, parents may be less willing to cooperate.

- Early childhood programs that take children's temperatures at the hint of a warm forehead and then use only the temperature's value to exclude children and send them to the health care provider
- Early childhood programs that exclude children with colds when the nasal discharge is yellow or green in colour

Neither example requires children to be excluded, nor do actions like these contribute to parents' viewing the program and educators positively. Partnerships with parents in managing children's illnesses mean that staff

- ensure that exclusion policies and practices are parent positive—respectful, realistic, and nonpunitive;
- demonstrate empathy for the parents' situation, balancing this with the needs of the ill child, other children in the group, and staff; and

- are supportive with regard to health information and resources but do *not* diagnose illness. Instead, educators document signs and symptoms that the parent can communicate to the health care provider.

Children's Medical Examination at Enrollment

Most early childhood programs in Canada require parents to have their children examined by a health care provider within a certain time period after starting in the program. These examinations result in a number of health promotion benefits:

- They provide the parents, health care provider, and educators with an overview of the child's current health status, which can be used as a measure in the future.
- They ensure that the child's immunizations are up-to-date.
- They advise health care providers that one of their patients is starting in group care, which gives health care providers the opportunity to talk with parents about the frequency of childhood illnesses.
- They include educators as participants in the care plan for children with specific health care needs by encouraging the health care provider and parents to share relevant information with the staff.

Daily Observation of Children

As educators get to know the infants and toddlers in their care, they become increasingly aware of behavioural changes and other signs and symptoms that may indicate possible infections. Preschool and school-age children are generally better able to tell educators if they aren't feeling well and answer questions that the educator asks for clarification. This assists educators in determining whether the parents should pick up their child early or whether the child is able to participate in the activities and can remain in the program. There are times when children are excluded because of a specific infection. When it comes to observing children for possible signs of illness, educators must first acknowledge the importance of daily health observations to identify ill children. Decisions regarding the care of children are based on the educators' observations, subsequent conversations with the parents, and health care providers' diagnoses.

Daily Baseline Health Observations

Programs that recognize the importance of baseline (starting point) **health observations** schedule enough staff at the start of the day to conduct them. Educators conduct baseline health observations of each child when he or she is dropped off so that educators can talk with the child and the parent. Staff encourage parents to take a few minutes at drop-off to ensure that parent, child, and educator have enough time to talk about

- how the child felt overnight and this morning,
- whether he or she ate breakfast,
- how well she or he slept, and
- whether the parents have any concerns about their child (e.g., "She had a sore tummy when she went to bed but seems to be feeling better this morning").

These conversations with parents, and the educator's familiarity with the children, establish a daily baseline to identify behavioural changes in a particular child for the rest of the day. The most reliable indicator of possible infection in children is a change in behaviour.

During the morning, there are times when the child just doesn't seem to be herself: she wants to lie down, turns down her snack, wants to be held a lot. Educators watch her more closely, taking into account the time of day and whether other children are sick. The director calls the parent to let him know that his daughter is feeling under the weather. Jointly, they decide whether she can remain in the program for the rest of the day or whether other steps should be taken.

Physical and Behavioural Signs and Symptoms

Using a checklist to evaluate children's signs of illness systematically assists educators in checking children. With practice, using the checklist quickly becomes second nature. Starting at the child's head and moving down to the toes, and in just a few moments, educators will have completed a baseline health observation.

Observing children calls on your senses of sight, hearing, touch, and smell. Educators should look for the following physical signs:

- Face: sad, tired, angry, upset, flushed
- Eyes: eyelids are puffy, whites of the eyes are red or yellow; eyes themselves are watery and clear or show thick (pus) discharge; sores or sties are present; child rubs eyes
- Ears: child rubs or pulls at ears; drainage seen in the outer ear
- Nose: runny; red or chafed from wiping or rubbing; child sneezes
- Mouth: bleeding; swollen gums; cold sores
- Neck: swelling along the jawline
- Breathing and/or voice: wheezing, congestion, coughing; child sounds stuffed up (nasal) or hoarse
- Skin: rashes or patches of irritated skin; cuts, scrapes or abrasions, bruises, bumps; skin has a yellow colour; child scratches the skin; skin feels hot, cold, sweaty, clammy, etc.

It is unnecessary and inappropriate for educators to examine children physically by using a flashlight to look into children's mouths and throats or by examining the skin for rashes or marks (e.g., bruises) on parts of the body that are covered by clothing. Even if a child complains of a sore throat, you are not responsible for examining the throat to determine whether the tissue is red or swollen or for concluding that he or she should be seen by a health care provider. Medical examinations are just that—medical—and can be intrusive to patients. Keep in mind that you are not expected or trained to be a health care provider or nurse.

During the day, educators will naturally see the bodies of infants and children while changing diapers, helping them on the toilet, or helping them change into swimsuits. These occasions provide opportunities to note the presence of skin rashes, bruises, and so on.

In most situations in which a child is injured or complains of itchiness or pain, it is appropriate for the educator to look at the child's skin and proceed accordingly. An exception is with preschoolers and school-agers when the genitals or buttocks are involved. In such cases, the child's health care provider or parents examine the child. However, in cases in which sexual abuse is suspected, educators should follow their suspected child maltreatment protocol.

The baseline health observation includes assessing children's hygiene, emotional health, and growth and developmental milestones. Early childhood courses in child development thoroughly cover the observation and documentation of children's milestone achievements. Concerns about the emotional, physical, or sexual abuse of children and issues of neglect are examined in Unit 8.

The terms "personal hygiene" and "cleanliness" are often used interchangeably. However, personal hygiene is a broader term. It includes hand washing, toileting practices, and dental care, along with the cleanliness of one's skin, hair, and clothing. In hygiene, as in many other things, there is a range of what each person finds to be an acceptable level. The food we eat (e.g., spices), the way foods are prepared (e.g., fried), the laundry products we use (e.g., scented or unscented), and whether we smoke, as well as whether we use perfumes or colognes, what shampoos or conditioners and deodorants or even incense we use, and whether we have pets—and so on—all contribute to our individual scent and the aroma in our homes. You may be aware of children's individual scents (e.g., the smell of fabric softener on a child's clothes). Some scents may be different from your own, and you may find particular scents unpleasant. In other cases, the scents may just be unfamiliar. Yet just because the scent is different doesn't mean the child is unclean. As in any other situation, educators' sensitivity to children and parents and respect for personal preferences are important to children's emotional well-being. Educators model appropriate comments and behaviour to children. There may be times when children have a distinctive odour because their skin, hair, or clothing is dirty from infrequent bathing or soiled clothes. Again, educators use their discretion in determining whether this is a common or infrequent occurrence. If it happens frequently, the child may be neglected.

If an educator observes more significant behavioural changes, the child should be seen by a health care provider as soon as possible. Parents or educators must seek medical attention for the child if the child shows any of the following behavioural changes or a combination of them:

- lethargy (or lacks energy)
- much sleepier than usual
- not alert
- uninterested in his or her environment (other children, toys, activities)
- unusually cranky, fussy, or irritable
- inconsolable
- refusal to eat or drink

Parents or educators must seek medical attention for the child if the child shows any of the following physical symptoms:

- change in breathing (rapid, shallow, or shortness of breath)
- pain or difficulty swallowing
- stiff neck
- rash with a fever
- rash with a change in behaviour

Fevers

A fever is just one of a number of signs of illness, like a runny nose, sore throat, cough, diarrhea, or vomiting. *Fever by itself is not dangerous. In fact, it is one of our body's defence mechanisms that helps us fight infection.* But when a child feels warm, many adults reach for the thermometer, give the child medication, and call the health care provider. Fever is unreliable as a sign in determining how sick a child is or whether to call the parents to pick up their child.

Even though children can be seriously ill and not have a fever, many people believe that a child with a fever is sicker than a child without a fever. But this is not necessarily the case. Children can have a very serious illness (e.g., meningitis) and have a fever of only 38.5°C (101.3°F). Very young infants can also have a temperature that is below normal even with a serious infection (Canadian Paediatric Society, 2008a, p. 171). A mild viral infection can cause a fever as high as 40°C (104°F). Most infections accompanied by a fever in children are minor (e.g., upper respiratory infections [URIs]). These are often caused by a virus, and the child usually gets better without medical treatment.

Another reason why parents become concerned about their child having a fever is the possibility of a febrile seizure. About 2% to 5% of children with a fever have one febrile seizure between 6 months and 5 years old. The seizure is likely the first signal that the child has a fever, and it can seem very serious to those observing it, but, in reality, febrile seizures are not harmful to children. The involuntary movements of the child are stiffening of the body, eyes rolling upward, and jerking movements of the head and limbs. The seizure lasts from 30 seconds to 2 minutes (Canadian Paediatric Society, 2008a, p. 173). There may be thrashing and drooling, which highlights the importance of ensuring that the child is in a place where he or she can be unrestricted to avoid injury. There is no treatment or preventive care for children with a history of febrile seizures. But if staff know that a child may have febrile seizures, that knowledge itself can alleviate some of the anxiety if one does occur. If a child has a seizure at the early childhood program, she or he should be seen by a doctor as soon as possible (Canadian Paediatric Society, 2008a, p. 173).

A fever is not caused by teething. A number of factors cause our body temperature to rise:

- overdressing
- strenuous exercise/play
- time of day (our normal temperature varies during the day, being highest in late afternoon)
- a vaccination
- an infection

By definition, a fever is a rise in body temperature, with a thermometer reading above 38°C (100.4°F) when taken rectally or by ear, above 37.3°C (99.1°F) when taken in the armpit (axillary), and above 37.5°C (99.5°F) when taken by mouth (Canadian Paediatric Society, 2008a, p. 171).

Staff often feel that they are in a Catch-22 situation—they observe a change in a child's behaviour and know that he or she is not feeling well. But when they call the parents, the parents want to know the child's temperature. And if the child does not have a fever, the parents may be reluctant or refuse to leave work. This situation causes the greatest concern. It could be dangerous to assume that because there is no fever, the child is not ill enough to be seen by a health care provider. More likely signs that a child may be running a fever are a flushed face or glassy-eyed look (Canadian Paediatric Society, 2008a, p. 171).

Observing a child's behaviour is much more important than taking a child's temperature. The child's behaviour is usually a much better indicator of illness (Canadian Paediatric Society, 2008). As educators become familiar with each child, they can identify behaviour changes. When children feel warm to the touch, you can first rule out the other possible reasons for the fever. If you think a child is ill and that is why she or he feels warm, watch closely for changes in behaviour. If the child feels warm but is playing and smiling, there is little to worry about. But if the behaviour changes, you must be concerned and take appropriate steps.

A child with any of the following behaviours or symptoms must be seen by a health care provider as soon as possible, regardless of whether the child has a fever or feels warm to the touch:

- unusual sleepiness, drowsiness
- lack of interest in toys, books, other children
- irritability, fussiness
- persistent crying, weak cry, inconsolable
- difficult or rapid breathing
- rash with a fever
- poor skin colour
- excessive drooling
- diminished appetite

The following are suggestions for managing children's fevers:

1. Share information with parents on fever and the importance of responding to children's behaviour. Encourage parents to discuss the issue of fever with their child's health care provider or invite a health care provider or public health nurse to speak to the staff and parents.

2. Post the list of signs and symptoms of illness that the staff will watch for in children at drop-off and throughout the day. Discuss this issue with each parent at the time of enrollment.

3. Taking children's temperature in early childhood programs on a regular basis is unnecessary. When staff notice a sign of fever (flushed face or glassy-eyed look), the Canadian Paediatric Society (2008a, p. 171) recommends that staff take temperatures. In these situations, refer to the Canadian Paediatric Society's *Well Beings* (2008) for the steps for taking temperatures. Parents should understand this policy and the rationale for it. When and how educators take children's temperatures should be outlined in the program's policy manual. Guidelines will ensure that taking temperatures is done safely and correctly. Note that although rectal temperatures are the most reliable, this method is *not* an appropriate method in early childhood programs.

4. Develop a medication policy related specifically to fevers that includes these practices:

   ■ Fever medication will be administered to a child only with a written recommendation by a health care provider (see Prescription and Over-the-Counter Medications, page 180).

   ■ If fever medication is administered, adhere to the following guidelines (Canadian Paediatric Society, 2008a, p. 173):

      – **Don't** give acetaminophen and ibuprofen at the same time, and don't give acetaminophen to a child who is already taking an OTC at home. Many OTCs already contain acetaminophen.

      – **Always** recheck the child's temperature before giving a second dose of medication.

      – **Never** exceed the recommended dose and schedule.

5. Parents should have children seen by a health care provider as soon as possible when educators observe any of the behaviours and symptoms listed earlier, regardless of the presence of a fever. Children who are younger than six months old and have a fever should be seen by a health care provider regardless of other symptoms or behaviours. However, when a child does have a fever and any of the following behaviours, call 911 *first* (or your 7-digit number) and then the parents (Canadian Paediatric Society, 2008a, p. 174):

   ■ seems limp, less responsive, or much more withdrawn than usual,

   ■ loses consciousness,

   ■ breathes rapidly or with significant difficulty,

   ■ has poor colour (i.e., skin that is bluish, purple, grayish or very pale),

   ■ has a stiff neck,

- cries inconsolably with high-pitched screams or cries, or cries very weakly,

- has a quickly spreading purple or deep red rash, or

- seems severely dehydrated (i.e., has sunken eyes or fontanel [the soft spot on the head of children younger than 18 months], absence of tears when crying, or dry skin, mouth and tongue).

6. Your program's exclusion policy should include the following:

- Children with a fever or who feel warm to the touch can continue to attend the program if they feel well enough to participate in the program.

- Infants under six months who feel warm to the touch, look flushed, or have a fever should be seen by a health care provider as soon as possible. This should be done regardless of whether the infant shows behavioural changes.

Health Observation throughout the Day

The health observations made when children begin their day provide educators and parents with a baseline against which to compare children throughout the remainder of the day. This baseline is particularly important when educators note a specific sign or symptom and monitor its progress. In other words, they watch to see if the sign or symptom gets worse, is resolving itself, or remains the same. Documenting health observations also assists educators and parents in identifying patterns in types of illnesses. Educators who observe the following early signs of allergies in children can assist parents and health care provider in the diagnosis: recurring colds and ear infections, nosebleeds, headaches, stomachaches, dark circles under the eyes, irritability (see Allergies, page 186).

Documenting Health Observations

Educators and parents of infants and toddlers in child care keep daily written records for each child. Some programs use a form and others a journal. Regardless of the style of documentation, it ensures that the parents share relevant health information with their child's educators at the time of drop-off. Educators document throughout the day and should include both

- "anecdotal" notes that elaborate on children's activities and their overall well-being and

- "health notes" that record their daily health observations (e.g., "Beginning to sound stuffed up" or "He didn't seem to be himself after his nap this afternoon").

Parents are interested in reading this information at pickup time.

Fewer educators are working with more children in preschool and school-age programs than in infant and toddler programs. Staff may not make daily entries in each child's file because children are older and because of time constraints. If nothing unusual happens, it may be unproductive for educators to write reports for the sake of it or for parents to read what they already know.

Documentation in Children's Files

Educators' careful and accurate documentation of each child's health provides parents and, ultimately, health professionals with valuable medical information in making diagnoses.

An educator would not phone a parent and simply say, "Max is not feeling well, and you need to pick him up right away." Rather, educators formulate their thoughts about their health observations before they write in a child's file or phone the parents. Their experience and training equip them with the skills needed to ask themselves the same questions that the parents will ask them. The answers to these questions guide educators in determining what to do for the child.

- How has the child's behaviour changed to lead you to believe that the child may be ill?
- What are the signs and symptoms that the child is experiencing? Describe the symptoms as clearly as possible.

In the case of a tummyache:

- Where is the pain in the abdomen, and does the pain move? (Depending on the child's age, the child may be able to point to where the pain is.)
- What kind of pain is it (sharp, throbbing, comes and goes, etc.)? (The answer will depend on the child's verbal ability.)
- Is the child feeling nauseated? Has he or she vomited or had diarrhea?
- What has the child eaten that day? Does he or she have allergies?
- When were the signs and symptoms first noticed, and how long have they lasted?
- Have the signs and symptoms changed? If so, how? Are they getting worse? Have they stayed constant, or are they coming and going (intermittent)?
- How is the child's appetite? Is he or she experiencing difficulty urinating or having a bowel movement?
- Has the child started eating a new food, taken a medication, been immunized in the past two weeks, or recently been injured?
- Does the child have any long-term medical conditions?
- Has the child had similar symptoms before?
- What have you done for the child so far? For example, have you continued to watch the child, administered a medication, or isolated him or her from the other children?
- What time was the parent called? What was said by both parties, and what is to be done next?
- Did you call the child's health care provider or an ambulance?

If one child is ill, educators take into account what has happened in the program over the past few days to consider factors that might be relevant to this child:

- Are any other children ill in the program? What are their signs and symptoms? What was the diagnosis (if they were seen by a health care provider)?
- What activities have the children been involved in over the past couple of days? Have they been on a field trip?

Coworkers or parents often say that their child always seems to be sick with something. Rather than searching through daily entries to find the ones that concern illness, educators may find it useful to maintain a flow sheet that lists each child's illnesses or symptoms. It takes only a few minutes to complete and can be conveniently kept in the front of each child's file. Such a sheet enables educators and parents to review the frequency and types of illness that the child experiences or to refer back to a specific entry within the body of the child's file. Directors may also wish to include a photocopy of the child's immunization schedule.

Early Childhood Program's Health Record

The frequency of illnesses is of concern to educators and parents. So, in addition to maintaining the flow sheet for each child, staff are encouraged to keep an ongoing health record that includes the suspected and diagnosed illnesses of all the children in the program on one form. Staff should include the following information in each notation:

- date
- child's first and last names
- brief description of the symptoms
- health care provider's diagnosis (if the child was seen)
- whether the child was excluded and, if so, for how many days

At the very minimum, use initials on the daily attendance form to indicate trends in absenteeism. *For example, use "D" for diarrhea, "URI" for respiratory illnesses, and "O" for other health reasons.*

Reviewing this form provides educators with valuable information:

- the frequency of specific illnesses
- which children are ill more often
- patterns in illnesses, because similarities begin to emerge in terms of the time of year, the age group of the children, and any one group of children experiencing more illnesses than other groups

Patterns in illnesses can help staff identify factors that might contribute to the spread of illness and what they can do to reduce that spread, such as improving the children's and educators' hygiene, cleaning and sanitizing routines, and food preparation practices.

Sharing Health Information with Health Care Providers

Staff network with a variety of professionals in their community and share information verbally and in written reports. Because of the frequency of young children's illnesses, educators may regularly communicate indirectly with health care providers through the child's parents. To protect confidentiality, educators do not communicate directly with health care providers. Before they do so, parents must give the educators permission to speak with their health care provider and let the health care provider know that an educator may call.

Educators' health observations are essential to assist health care providers or other health professionals in caring for children. As professionals, educators are encouraged to document their health observations on a report form, which the parents take to their child's health care provider. For the staff, this form is a direct line of communication with the health care provider. In addition, parents benefit from this documentation because it saves them from having to remember all of the details conveyed verbally by the educator.

Obviously, effective communication results when all parties share accurate information. Educators rely on the parents to share relevant medical information with them after the visit to the health care provider's office. The program can have a form that is given to the parents, that they ask the health care provider to complete. Ideally, the form includes a summary of the program's exclusion criteria. Parents return the completed form to the staff when their child returns to the program. This document provides staff with pertinent care information. Educators must keep in mind that health care professionals must act in accordance with the *Personal Health Information Act* (PHIA) and some medical information will not be shared with the educators. Providing the health care provider with the program's exclusion criteria reduces unnecessary conflicts between staff, parents, and the health care provider that can arise when the health care provider's recommendations are not consistent with those of the program.

Work experience familiarizes educators with the more common childhood illnesses. Educators may feel they know quite a bit about illness, especially if they are parents themselves. Once they have seen a few children with chickenpox or head lice, they are able to identify pox marks or lice eggs. Parents in the program, particularly those with infants or toddlers, often view individual educators as consultants on a range of topics, including their child's health. Of course, educators want to be helpful and can answer some health questions for parents. However, giving out medical information is overstepping their professional boundaries. Diagnosing illnesses and offering medical consultation are the roles of health professionals, not educators.

Excluding Children from Early Childhood Programs

If you ask educators to list the issues that they find to be the most challenging, ill children will probably be among the top three, perhaps even the first. If you are not a parent, you may have a hard time putting yourself into a parent's position. As discussed earlier, parents are in work or school situations and face a vast range of reactions and expectations from employers or teachers. Imagine yourself sitting in a board meeting, working on an assembly line, or writing an exam and being called away to take a phone call. Your child's educator tells you that your daughter is ill and you must pick her up as soon as possible to see the health care provider. Not only are you going to be worried about your child, but you are also faced with rescheduling your workday or class work, making a health care provider's appointment, and returning to work. As a student, are you able to concentrate on your exam when you know that your daughter may be ill?

Most employers do not provide family responsibility leave for their employees. This benefit entitles parents to paid leave to attend to a child who is ill, or for other family emergencies. Currently, most parents either use their personal sick-leave benefits, if eligible, or leave work without pay. Others may risk losing their job if they leave work. Few parents have jobs that afford them the flexibility to work from home during a child's illness. Families often do not live in the same community as their extended family, who may have been able to relieve the parents in a crisis. Travelling between work and the program and then to the health care provider's office may not be convenient, especially on public transportation in the middle of a Canadian winter! On the other hand, for many of the same reasons, parents may feel pressured to bring their children to the program in the morning, even if the child is not feeling well.

CRITICAL THINKING

Use the four levels of the health promotion action plan to identify at least one action for each level that would support families in the difficult dilemma of having a child who is too ill to participate in the program for one week, although not so ill that she or he needs to stay in bed. None of the adults in the family have paid time off.

Educators and parents are responsible for establishing a clear understanding of the program's **exclusion** criteria at the time of enrollment. Unnecessary exclusion of children is unacceptable. With the exception of certain infections, the primary reason for excluding children is that the child does not feel well enough to participate in the program's activities. Staff–child ratios in centres are such that it is seldom possible to give a great deal of individual care to a sick child and still have enough staff to meet the needs of the other children. Also, where would you rather be when you are sick—in a program with a group of energetic children and adults or at home with someone to bring you food and beverages and to care for your needs in quiet surroundings? Obviously, most children would prefer to be at home when they are ill.

Directors evaluate each situation individually. A director will think twice before he or she calls a parent to pick up a child if the parent works in a factory and has been warned about taking time off. However, a director is expected to give equal consideration before calling a parent who has a flexible work schedule. Who are the child care staff concerned about in managing illness?

- The ill child. Educators and the director want to ensure that the child is comfortable while in their care.

- Other children and staff. Educators may be concerned that the child's illness is contagious. Another concern may be the extent of one-to-one care that the ill child needs and how this affects the quality of supervision available to other children.
- The ill child's parents. Educators and the director consider the effects of the child's illness on the family.

The program's exclusion policy should stipulate that if the child presents with one of the following conditions (Canadian Paediatric Society, 2008a, pp. 174–175), the child will be excluded:

1. The illness prevents the child from participating comfortably in all program activities, including going outside.
2. The illness results in a greater need for care than the staff can provide without compromising the health, safety and care of other children.
3. The illness poses a serious health risk if it spreads to other children or staff, and/or local public health authorities require exclusion. (Consult your local public health unit for a list of these infections. . . .) [See Appendix 4.1, page 197.]

Erik and Anastasia in the preschool room have bad colds with runny noses and coughs and are irritable and lethargic. According to the third point in the exclusion policy, excluding children with colds is not recommended (see Appendix 4.1, page 197). However, both children's behaviour is affected, so the director needs to consider the first two points of the exclusion policy. She must decide if she will

- call both sets of parents to come immediately to pick up their children or
- call the parents and discuss what is in the best interests of each child. Erik's parents will be able to leave work in an hour and drop him off with his grandfather. Anastasia's mother is a single parent who recently moved to the city to attend university. She is in the middle of exams. She is already stressed and has no one to help care for her daughter. The director and mother discuss the issue and decide that Anastasia will rest in the director's office for the afternoon. If she is still feeling unwell tomorrow, the director will arrange for a volunteer to come to the program and care for her.

Each medical officer of health (MOH) in Canada is responsible for the health of children in centres within his or her geographic area. One of the responsibilities of the MOH is to establish the exclusion criteria for centres. These should be communicated to the health care providers as well. There are usually several MOHs working in one province or territory. Because they work independently of one another, centres in different regions may be provided with different exclusion criteria. In some cases, neither centres nor health care providers have received written criteria. So it is not surprising that there can be inconsistent expectations among everyone. In *Well Beings*, the Canadian Paediatric Society (2008) recommends exclusion criteria that centres, MOHs, and health care providers are encouraged to implement (see Appendix 4.1, page 197).

Programs are required to have space available to isolate ill children temporarily as a strategy to try to prevent or limit the spread of infection. The director's office is often used, or a cot is set up in a quiet, separate part of the play or nap area that allows educators to supervise the resting child. The decision to keep the child in the program until the end of the day is made by the director and educators. The decision is based on issues such as

- what the educators think is wrong with the child,
- the time of day, and
- whether they feel they can care for the child.

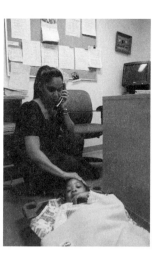

Alternative Care Arrangements

There are times when children must be excluded from the program. For some families, this is a minor glitch in their schedule. For others, it creates chaos. Programs require every family to have backup, or alternative, care available (e.g., relative, neighbour, friend) in the event that a child is ill. For parents who have neither job flexibility nor relatives or friends available as backup, **alternative care** arrangements can be makeshift, unreliable, or inconsistent. This latter situation often puts directors in an awkward position: they know the ill child's home situation but must balance the needs of the other children and staff. In some instances, the director may decide to keep the mildly ill child at the program. In other cases, the director may have to exclude the child, and the parents must deal with this decision.

Early Childhood Programs and Health Services for Ill Children

The pressure experienced by parents trying to continue to work or go to school while managing the care of ill children has led to the establishment of centres and health care services specifically for ill children. These services can range from a centre that cares only for ill children to private nursing or trained educators who go into the child's home. The parents pay the cost of these services. In addition, the parents continue to pay the centre for the days that the child is excluded.

These services are relatively few, and they raise questions about the best interests of the ill child. At best, these health services are feasible only for parents who can afford them. No one disagrees that an ill child at home with a loving parent is best. But parents who can't miss work, can't afford private care, and don't have access to alternative adults may be forced to leave a child at home alone—which may raise questions about neglect.

Caring for ill children is a political issue that has not been dealt with in any substantial way. Where does this situation leave children and families?

CHILDHOOD INFECTIONS: JUST THE BASICS

Fortunately, most common childhood infections are short-lived and minor. Children become ill regardless of the disease prevention practices implemented in programs, but these practices do reduce the spread of infection. There are far more childhood infections than we have included in this textbook. Our focus is on health promotion in children, not on cures. *As educators, your role is not to diagnose but to recognize potential signs of infection and refer children to health professionals.* Educators can refer to a number of books and resources describing childhood infections once a health care provider has made a diagnosis. *Well Beings* (2008) is the resource manual of preference for Canadian centres. The Canadian Paediatric Society's Caring for Kids website includes fact sheets on a variety of common childhood illnesses that can be downloaded and shared with parents (see Resource Materials, page 194). Therefore, we have included only the common childhood infections. Understanding the basics and how to manage them addresses the needs of the ill child, parents, other children, and staff. Refer to Appendix 4.1 (page 197) for additional information about managing illness.

The Common Cold

Children in centres can get as many as 8 to 10 colds a year. It may seem that at any one time at least one child has a runny nose or cough. Cold viruses, more than 100 of them, are spread easily through the air and on contaminated hands and objects. That's why preventing colds is nearly impossible. Another reason is that we spread the cold virus a day or two before we feel a cold coming on. Typically, colds last five to seven days. Symptoms include coughing, sneezing, a runny nose, a fever, fatigue, and lack of appetite. A child's runny nose may produce a clear discharge at first and then a yellow or green one.

Q. Should children with colds be excluded from the program?

A. No, not from the point of view of infection control. Imagine the havoc that would be created both in the program and for the families if every child and educator with a cold were excluded. Instead, educators can

- wash their hands and the child's hands carefully;
- model and encourage children to cover their mouth when they cough and sneeze;
- discard used tissues after use and never use the same tissue to wipe more than one child's nose, tempting as reuse might be when you are out in the playground in the winter;
- ensure that mouthing toys in infant and toddler areas are removed once a child has used them and that all of these used toys are cleaned and sanitized daily;
- observe those with colds to ensure that children are feeling well enough to take part in activities; and
- reassure parents that if their child feels well enough to be at the program, he or she is well enough to play outside, even in the winter (fresh air is good for the child).

Ear Infections

The eustachian tube, which runs between the middle ear and the back of the nose, is shorter and straighter in young children than in adults. The tube creates a path for fluid behind the middle ear to drain to the back of the throat. The straightness of the tube also permits fluid in the back of the throat and nose to travel into the ear. Ear infections often occur at the same time as colds, which seems logical because coughing, sneezing, and blowing the nose can force mucus from the nose or throat into the eustachian tube and the middle ear. The tube may become swollen, which prevents fluid from the middle ear from draining. In such cases, the trapped bacteria may cause infection. The Canadian Paediatric Society (2008a, pp. 178–79) estimates that "most children will have one or more [ear infections] before they are 3 years old, and these infections can occur with such frequency in child care settings that they seem to be contagious (even though they aren't)." Children with speaking skills can tell you whether they have an earache; for infants, you'll observe a change in behaviour—they often become cranky or unhappy. Parents and educators often comment that they see infants pulling or rubbing their ears, but this can be coincidental and shouldn't be relied on as a sign of infection.

Health care providers can usually confirm ear infection by looking into the child's ear. "Children younger than 2 years of age are usually treated with antibiotics because this infection can lead to other, more serious complications. For older children who don't experience too much discomfort from an ear infection, the doctor may suggest a painkiller, such as acetaminophen, and then re-examine the child 2 or 3 days later to see if antibiotics are needed" (Canadian Paediatric Society, 2008a, p. 179).

Q. Should children with ear infections be excluded from the program?
A. No. The infection is in the child's middle ear. The bacteria will not spread to other children or educators. Whether the child attends or not is based on how she or he is feeling and able to participate.

Gastrointestinal Infections: Diarrhea

Diarrhea is the most common symptom of gastrointestinal infection. Basically, diarrhea is a change in the consistency or frequency of an individual's bowel movements. The stool may be very loose or even watery. And—depending on the virus, bacteria, or parasite causing the infection—the stool may contain blood or mucus and be foul-smelling or mushy in consistency. In addition to the diarrhea, children may have abdominal cramps, fever, nausea, vomiting, or a loss of appetite. Others may just have a few loose stools and be otherwise fine.

Educators play an important role in preventing other children or staff from getting the infection. Diarrhea spreads easily among children, and if other children do come down with it, the hygienic practices in that program must be called into question. *Effective hand washing, strict diapering and toileting routines, and food safety every day, not just when someone is ill, are essential in reducing the spread of intestinal infection.*

As educators become familiar with the infants and toddlers, they are able to notice any change in a particular child's bowel movements. Educators should follow these steps when caring for children with diarrhea:

- Tell the other educators that the child has had one episode of diarrhea. All the educators should be extra vigilant when hand washing and diapering to ensure that stool does not contaminate the environment. The child can remain in the program as long as he or she feels well enough to participate and the stool is contained in the diaper (or the older child is able to get to the toilet in time). Parents appreciate being called so that they are aware of this situation.

- After the second episode of diarrhea, or when the diarrhea is accompanied with a fever, vomiting, or blood in the stool, call the parents to pick up the child. The parents should have the child seen by the health care provider as soon as possible. Advise the parents to *seek immediate medical attention* if the child

  - has bloody, mucousy or black stools,
  - is vomiting **and** showing any sign of dehydration:
    - no tears when crying,
    - dry skin, mouth and tongue,
    - fewer than 4 wet diapers in 24 hours,
    - sunken eyes or fontanel (the soft spot on the head of children younger than 18 months),
    - grayish skin, or
    - rapid breathing. (Canadian Paediatric Society, 2008a, p. 187)

- While waiting for the parents to arrive, prevent the child from becoming dehydrated. Children, especially infants and toddlers, can become dehydrated quickly because they lose more of their body fluids in diarrhea and vomit than they are able to drink. Paediatricians recommend that programs with infants and toddlers have oral rehydration solution (ORS) available for these situations and that you have the parents' written permission to give it to the child when warranted. ORS is available in liquid or powder (e.g., Lytren, Gastrolyte, Pedialyte) and is used to replenish the child's fluid and electrolytes even when the child is vomiting. "Give small amounts often, gradually increasing intake until the child can drink normally. If a child isn't vomiting, continue to offer breast milk, formula or regular foods in small, frequent feedings. If the child vomits, you may need to stop food and drink but continue to give ORS" (Canadian Paediatric Society, 2008a, p. 188).

- Notify the public health agency if two or more children have diarrhea within 48 hours of each other. These situations are called "outbreaks," and steps must be taken to control the gastrointestinal infection, including determining the cause.

Q. Should children with two or more episodes of diarrhea be excluded from the program?

A. Initially, the child should be separated from the other children while you are waiting for the parents to arrive. After the child has seen the health care provider, the child will be excluded from your program when

- diarrheal stool cannot be contained in a diaper or a toilet-trained child cannot control bowel movements,

- there's blood or mucus in the stool (unless bacterial infection has been ruled out by a doctor),
- the child is also vomiting (unless infection has been ruled out), or
- local public health authorities require it (e.g., if it is a symptomatic, confirmed *Giardia, E. coli, Shigella* or *Salmonella* infection). (Canadian Paediatric Society, 2008a, p. 188)

Refer to Appendix 4.1 (page 197) for the exclusion criteria that relate to the various types of gastrointestinal infections.

Pinkeye

Pinkeye (or conjunctivitis) is another childhood infection that is easily spread among children. The causes are viruses, commonly, and bacteria, occasionally. These infect the covering of the eyeball. However, children who have allergies or have been exposed to pollutants may develop pinkeye. Watch for the following symptoms in one or both eyes:

- The whites of the eye are pink or red.
- The child rubs the eye because it is itchy.
- The eye may be tearing a lot.
- There is a clear or pus (thick or yellow) discharge from the eye; the parents may tell you that the eyelid is stuck shut after sleeping.

Pinkeye is a good example of an infection caused by germs spread by indirect contact. A child with pinkeye touches or rubs his or her eyes; the eye discharge contaminates the fingers. In the course of play, the child touches other children's hands or objects, which, in turn, become contaminated. Now those children who have the eye discharge on their fingers and who touch their own eyes will get pinkeye. Sharing towels among children is another way that pinkeye is spread. The cycle continues until it is broken.

Q. Should children with pinkeye be excluded from the program?
A. Initially, the child should be excluded until being seen by the health care provider to diagnose the infection and determine the cause. After that appointment, whether the exclusion continues depends on whether the cause is viral or bacterial. When there is pus discharge, the child may be prescribed an antibiotic (eye drops or ointment) to treat the bacteria. If this is the case, children should be excluded until they have taken the medication for 24 hours. Otherwise, the child can return to the program. Regardless of the cause, educators must pay particular attention to hygiene practices to reduce the spread to other children and staff.

- Effective hand washing is critical, for both staff and the child, after wiping or touching the infected eye.
- Never share towels, facial tissues, and so on among children, regardless of whether someone has pinkeye.

Chickenpox

Chickenpox—a word that parents dread, although most of them want all the children in their family to get the illness at the same time and be done with it. For teens and adults who did not have chickenpox as children, it's usually a much more serious infection. The good news is that for children who haven't had chickenpox, a vaccine is available. When children begin in a program, checking whether or not they have been vaccinated is recommended. Children who did not receive the varicella vaccination at about 12 months of age can receive it at an older age. But even with the vaccine available, you will most likely care for a few children who have chickenpox.

Chickenpox is common in children because the varicella-zoster virus spreads easily through the air and by touching the liquid in the pox. By the time the red bumps appear, children may have already had a mild fever for a couple of days and have been spreading the virus through the air. Spots appear over two or three days. Gradually, the bumps turn into liquid-filled blisters (or pox) that crust over, at which time, the risk of the spread stops. Some children may be covered in pox; others may have just a few. For many children, the infection is mild, and the primary complaint is the itchiness of the pox. It takes 10 to 21 days to tell whether a susceptible person exposed to chickenpox is going to get it.

Never give the child acetylsalicylic acid (aspirin) to treat a fever or aches and pains from chickenpox. While the child is recovering, both educators and parents need to watch for signs of severe illness and seek immediate medical attention if any of the following signs are seen (Canadian Paediatric Society, 2008a, p. 199):

- the child's fever lasts longer than 48 hours and is 39°C [102°F] or higher,
- the fever subsides and then returns to 39°C [102°F] or higher in a day or two,
- any chickenpox spots become enlarged, red or very sore, or
- the child seems very ill.

Having chickenpox once provides most people with lifelong immunity to it, although some people get chickenpox twice. The virus can remain inactive in our bodies for life, but it can become reactivated and cause shingles. Children or adults with shingles can spread the virus to those susceptible to chickenpox. Shingles is a painful rash of itchy blisters, which often develop around the trunk of the body.

Q. Should someone with chickenpox or shingles be excluded from the program?
A. "Exclusion is not a very effective way to prevent the spread of chickenpox in child care facilities, because it is contagious 1 to 2 days before the rash appears" (Canadian Paediatric Society, 2008a, p. 199). Educators are advised to assess each child individually. What is in the best interests of this child? If the child feels well enough to take part in activities, or if you have enough staff available to provide more individualized care, the child can remain in the program.

Head Lice

Having head lice does not reflect a lack of parenting ability or cleanliness, despite popular belief to the contrary. As a matter of fact, lice like warm scalps and clean hair best! Yet some adults and children still make derogatory comments about people with lice, which can be very hurtful. Children who have head lice may already feel embarrassed, fearful, or ashamed, and educators need to be sensitive to these feelings. Know the facts and effective ways to treat head lice, listen to parents' concerns, and dispel stereotypes, and you can manage an outbreak.

Head lice are tiny, greyish insects that live on human hair. Usually, they lay their eggs (or nits) on hair behind the ears, on the crown, or at the back of the head. Nits look like dandruff but stick to the hair so that you can't pick or wash them off. You may first suspect head lice when you see a child scratching or complaining that his or her head is itchy. Check for nits on the hair, close to the scalp. The hatched lice shy away from light, so it is unlikely that you will actually see the lice. Although you may be scratching your head just thinking about lice, they actually don't hurt, spread disease, or jump between people. *Head lice spread quickly when children have their heads together or share items such as combs, brushes, hats and scarves, headphones, and play clothes.* Staff can reduce the opportunities for head lice to spread by

- providing space for each child to store his or her outerwear and a change of clothes without coming into contact with the next child's clothes (e.g., in a cubby/locker, in bins/baskets, or on hooks);
- stuffing hats and scarves down coat sleeves, especially when coats are hung on hooks;
- having parents provide a comb or brush for their child's personal use, to be kept in the child's space; and
- laundering dress-up clothes weekly. In the event of an outbreak of head lice, the clothes and accessories should be laundered and put away until the outbreak is over. The hats and wigs that can't be washed must be sealed in a plastic bag for 10 days. Dramatic play is an important element of child care programs, and wigs, hats, scarves, and dress-up clothes should be available for children despite the chance of head lice.

Basically, head lice are a nuisance that creates work for the staff and parents at home. If you find one child or educator with head lice, you must check everyone. Then educators must notify all parents, especially those whose children have the lice. Only the infected children and adults should be treated. Head lice are easily treated with special shampoos and conditioners containing a pediculicide. These products kill lice and nits and prevent re-infestation (if nits are not destroyed, they hatch in seven days). Parents can check with their health care provider or pharmacist about different brands. There is a range of other treatments used by parents, including putting an oil and vinegar mixture on the head overnight (covered with a shower cap). "Don't remove nits after treatment, as it is not necessary to prevent spread" (Canadian Paediatric Society, 2008a, p. 192). Parents need to check every person in the household for nits but treat only those who have them. A cautionary note: Some brands of shampoo contain an ingredient called lindane. This chemical is toxic and can be absorbed through the scalp, leading to poisoning (Burroughs Wellcome Inc., n.d.). Such products should not be used on children under two years old (Canadian Paediatric Society, 2008b, p. 2).

"Since lice don't live long off the scalp, there's no need for extensive cleaning. To get rid of lice or nits from specific items, like pillowcases or hats, wash them in hot water and dry them in a hot dryer. Dryclean items that cannot be washed, such as stuffed animals, or simply store them in an airtight plastic bag for 2 weeks" (Canadian Paediatric Society, 2008a, p. 192).

Q. Should someone with head lice be excluded from the program?
A. No. At the time of pickup, the parents of the infected child need to know about the treatment that should be done that day.

In the past, public health nurses were called into programs and schools to do "nit-picking" on every child. Nowadays, directors simply consult with their public health nurse and receive up-to-date information on prevention and treatment, perhaps in a number of languages. However, if a program has recurring outbreaks of head lice or a particular child's parents are not responding to the program's requests to use the treatment, the public health department should become directly involved.

ANTIBIOTIC-RESISTANT BACTERIA

The discovery of penicillin was a medical breakthrough. Since then, more and more antibiotics have been developed for the treatment of bacterial infections. As a result, lives have been saved and the quality of lives has improved. Ironically, pharmaceutical firms today are faced with the immediate challenge of discovering new, more potent antibiotics to be used to treat infections caused by bacteria resistant to previously effective antibiotics.

As you read earlier in this unit, bacteria live in our body and work to keep us healthy by fighting invading bacteria. When we take antibiotics, some of the beneficial bacteria are killed, which gives the disease-causing bacteria the opportunity to multiply and cause an infection. There is also the potential for the normal bacteria to become resistant to antibiotics. Such resistance would, if conditions are right, enable the bacteria to multiply, creating an infection that would be difficult to treat because of the resistance.

> Germs constantly adapt to their environment and have the ability to take on the characteristics of other germs. When antibiotics are used inappropriately, the weak bacteria are killed, while the stronger, more resistant ones survive and multiply. Germs that develop resistance to one antibiotic have the ability to develop resistance to another antibiotic. This is called cross-resistance. (Health Canada, 2006, p. 1)

Source: *It's Your Health—Antibiotic Resistence,* Health Canada, 2005. Reproduced with the permission of the Minister of Public Works and Government Services Canada, 2008.

Of course, antibiotics continue to be used effectively to treat many bacterial infections. But the soaring overuse of antibiotics must stop. They are often misused for nonbacterial infections (i.e., those caused by viruses) or automatically given for bacterial infections (e.g., ear infections) that may clear up on their own in a couple of days. Treating a cold with antibiotics does not work—period. Gonzales et al. (2005, p. 102) report that strategies are needed to reduce the inappropriate use of prescriptions for antibiotics to treat acute URIs. In fact, you may be shocked to hear that the vast majority of all antibiotic prescriptions written are to treat nonbacterial infections.

You may be asking yourself how this information relates to your work in early childhood programs. There is a direct correlation. We know

- that young children in groups are exposed to more illnesses,
- that the additional needs of ill children in attendance make it difficult for educators to provide quality care for all children in the group, and
- that the exclusion of children may prevent others from getting sick.

This last point is where educators should recognize the significant role they can play in decreasing the unnecessary use of antibiotics. These infections are common among young children; also, they are easily spread, and antibiotics are often used as a treatment for some URIs.

Appendix 4.1 (page 197) contains a table on the management of illness that lays out clearly the exclusion criteria and conditions recommended in *Well Beings* (2008a, pp. 225–234) for a child's return to a program. As you can see, few respiratory illnesses require that a child be excluded to prevent the spread to other children. The most common reason for a child's exclusion is that she or he is too ill to participate in the centre's activities.

How do these exclusion practices affect antibiotic use? If centres require parents to take their child to the health care provider because of green nasal discharge (a common symptom of the common cold) and exclude their child from the centre, one may assume that staff will request that the child be on antibiotics before he or she can return. In 2000, a study of the exclusion practices of early childhood centres in Toronto found that 38% of the directors surveyed believed that antibiotics were required in a child with a nonspecific URI to prevent bacterial infection, 26% believed that they prevent the spread of infection, and 21% believed that they hasten recovery (Skull et al., 2000, p. 182). Would these beliefs be the same or have changed if this study were to be repeated now? With so much more public attention being paid to superbugs and antibiotic-resistant bacteria, would we find that 18% (Skull et al., 2000, p. 182) of the directors still require that a child have an antibiotic prescribed for the URI before the child could return to the program? It is hoped that these misconceptions are currently not widespread.

There are other practices—in addition to having educators understand the principles behind exclusion—that staff can implement in the centre to reduce infections:

- proper hand washing
- proper diaper-changing routine
- proper food-handling practices. These include washing off bacterial and possible antibiotic residue from fruits and vegetables.
- the observation of children's behaviour as a key indicator of illness
- practising the principles of universal precautions
- the purchase and use of cleaning and hand-washing products that are not advertised to be antibacterial (see Antibacterial Products, page 147)
- strive to consume organic food and meat products.

  Links have also been made between giving drugs to animals and the development of resistance in humans. Drugs are often given to food-producing animals to treat and prevent infections in the agri-food industry and to promote growth. Products are also sprayed on fruit trees to prevent or control disease. These can then be transferred to humans in meat, milk, fruit or drinking water, adding to the resistance problem. An example of this is drug-resistant *Salmonella*, which can be transferred from animals to humans through the food chain. (Health Canada, 2006, p. 2)

Source: *It's Your Health—Antibiotic Resistence,* Health Canada, 2005. Reproduced with the permission of the Minister of Public Works and Government Services Canada, 2008.

We all need to understand when antibiotics are necessary and when they are not. When prescribed an antibiotic, follow the instructions and take the entire prescription. Do not stop taking a prescription once you start feeling better and then save the medication for later use, either by yourself or someone else.

ADMINISTERING MEDICATION

Fortunately, most healthy children need medication rarely or not at all. Moreover, most of the common childhood infections are caused by viruses (e.g., colds, other URIs, diarrhea) that are not cured by antibiotics. Strep throat and sometimes ear infections and pinkeye may be caused by bacteria that are treated with antibiotics. Occasionally, educators administer medication to children in programs. Educators have a legal and professional responsibility to be familiar with their child care regulations on administering medication. You must know which medications educators are permitted to give, what type of parental consent is required, and how medications are stored, administered, and documented. A program's medication policy should be accompanied by a list of procedures that all educators follow.

As an early childhood education student, you cannot administer medication to children when you are in program placements; that remains a staff responsibility. After graduation, you will eventually be assigned this role, however, so you need to be familiar with the fundamental principles of a medication policy and the rationale behind it.

Prescription and Over-the-Counter Medications

What is the difference between **prescription medication** and **over-the-counter (OTC) medication**? We are all familiar with health care providers prescribing medication when we have a short-term illness (e.g., urinary tract infection, yeast infection, strep throat). Anyone with a particular medical condition, such as asthma, diabetes, cystic fibrosis, or a seizure disorder, is prescribed medication that is taken at specific times each day. OTC medication, however, is purchased off a shelf in a pharmacy. These medications include cough and cold remedies, painkillers, fever medication, teething medication (e.g., Orajel), Ovol for flatulence in infants, and medicated creams and ointments.

Provincial and territorial child care regulations require that all medication administered in programs be prescribed or, for OTC medication, recommended in writing by health care providers. Some government child care regulations may include sunscreens, insect repellents, and diaper creams in their definition of medication and require that the child's health care provider recommend their use in writing. However, this is the exception rather than the rule across Canada.

Why do OTC drugs require the health care provider's recommendation in writing before they are administered in early childhood programs? OTC medications are medications nonetheless, despite their easy availability and should not be treated casually. Whenever you take more than one medication at the same time, you put yourself at risk of side effects because the ingredients from the different medications may interact. As well, drug interactions may influence the effectiveness of the medications.

Vitamins, including chewable ones, are medications. Eating well-balanced, nutritious food provides children with their daily requirement of essential nutrients. Health care providers discourage the routine use of vitamins; they are prescribed only when a child has a vitamin or mineral deficiency. Prescribed vitamins can be given at home by parents. Educators do not have to administer the vitamins during the day.

Naturopathic and homeopathic medicine have been practised for centuries in many cultures and are gaining popularity in Canada (see Natural Health Products, page 15). Herbal medicines, nutrition, vitamins, ointments, acupuncture, and hydra and physical therapies are used to treat various maladies. Herbal medicines consist of different combinations of herbs and plants that are available OTC or prescribed by naturopaths. As with any medication, they must be taken with care and knowledge. According to the child care regulations' definition, medications must be prescribed by health care providers or dentists—classifications that do not currently include naturopathic doctors. Consequently, parents who use herbal medicines for their children must give them to the children at home. Currently, staff can't give these medications to the child at the program.

OTC Medications: Effective?

"Don't give 'over-the-counter' (OTC) cough and cold medicines to children in your care. There is no proof that they work, and some side effects can make a child feel worse" (Canadian Paediatric Society, 2008, p. 176). Colds and coughs have to run their course. Children benefit from extra fluids, rest, and care but not from many of the OTC medications. Keep in mind that colds are caused by viruses and are not treated by antibiotics.

Over a 2-year period in the United States, more than 1,500 children under 2 years old were treated in emergency rooms for adverse reactions to cold or cough medications. In 2005, 3 children under 6 months old died after taking nasal decongestants. Tests showed that these 3 infants had drug levels 14 times higher than the recommended dose for children starting at 2 years old (Canadian Broadcasting Corporation, 2007). This is happening in Canada, too. Health Canada (2007a, p. 1) reported that "life-threatening adverse events, including unintentional overdose, have been reported to Health Canada in association with the use of these products in children under 2 years of age."

> Before using over-the-counter cough and cold remedies in children under 2 years of age, Health Canada urges caregivers to consult a healthcare practitioner to assure that their use is safe and appropriate. In addition, Health Canada strongly advises parents and caregivers to carefully read the labels and instructions for these products and to check the medicinal ingredients before giving them to any child, especially under the age of 2. Many of these products contain the same medicinal ingredient(s), and giving more than one product with the same ingredient or multiple doses of the same product could lead to an overdose. (Health Canada, 2007a, p. 1)

Children under 2 years of age

- Do not use cough and cold products, including drugs and natural health products, in children under 2 years of age unless instructed to do so by a healthcare practitioner.

- Even if the cough and cold products are labelled for use in children under 2 years of age (for example, they use the word "infant" in their name or have dosing instructions for infants) it is still preferable to discuss the use of these products with your healthcare practitioner before giving them to any young child. (Health Canada, 2007a, p. 1)

Source: *Recommendations for the Appropriate Use of Cough and Cold Products in Children,* Health Canada, 2007. Reproduced with the permission of the Minister of Public Works and Government Services Canada, 2008.

We also wonder whether children who are given an OTC medication for every sniffle, cough, ache, or pain could potentially develop a lifelong reliance on medication. These medications treat symptoms, not the cause of the illness. We should focus instead on preventive strategies and, when we are ill with a viral infection, let the illness run its course.

Acetaminophen (e.g., Tylenol, Tempra) is an analgesic (or painkiller) and may be recommended by health care providers for treating children's aches and pains from a cold and cough. Programs with infants and toddlers still commonly give acetaminophen whenever the child's temperature rises to a certain degree, although this practice is not routinely recommended. In these programs, parents are asked to sign a medication consent form, which is kept in the child's file and referred to each time the child's temperature is elevated. It is unlikely that each child's health care provider has provided the parents and educators with such a written recommendation. This practice shows how grey the interpretation of a specific child care regulation can be (see Fevers, page 162).

Ensuring the Safe Administration of Medication

Whether the medication is prescribed or recommended by the child's health care provider, the steps in its administration are identical to eliminate the chance of medication error. For an extensive discussion on medication administration, refer to Appendix 9.1: Administering Medication in *Well Beings* (Canadian Paediatric Society, 2008). The general principles and rationale for the administration of medication in programs are as follows:

■ Obtain the parents' written consent to administer any medication. A medication consent form must be completed for each medication, both prescribed and health care provider recommended. Consent forms should include at least the following information:

   – name of the child and date

   – name of the medication

   – reason why it is needed (e.g., strep throat)

   – amount to be given (dosage)

   – time(s) it is to be given during the day

   – time and date of the last dose in the program, which helps ensure that children don't continue to get medication longer than recommended by the health care provider and is particularly relevant to OTC medication (the bottle usually holds more medication than required for two or three days)

   – parent's signature

■ Before starting the medication at the program, ask parents whether the child has taken it at home for the past 24 hours. This period allows parents to watch for side effects or signs of allergic reaction to the medication, for the child to get used to the way it tastes or feels (e.g., eye ointment), and for the medication to begin its work. Parents may have a helpful hint or two to share.

- Keep all medication in a locked container out of reach of children. Liquid medications usually require refrigeration, which won't harm capsules, tablets, or creams either. All can be kept in a locked container in the fridge. Sunscreens, insect repellents, and diaper creams do not have to be kept locked but must be out of reach of children. Diaper creams are kept in the change area.

- Know who is responsible for giving the medication during the day. Programs usually assign this responsibility either to one educator who gives all the medications or to a number of educators who give medication to specific children. Any confusion over this responsibility can lead to a child either getting a double dose or missing the medication altogether.

- Compare the information on the medication label with the information the parent filled in on the consent form. Discrepancies must be verified and corrected.

- All medication, both prescription and OTC, must be kept in the original containers. It is not acceptable, for example, for a parent to put medication into a glass jar and label it with masking tape. When the medication must be administered while the child is at the program, encourage the parents to have the pharmacist split the medication into two containers so that one stays at home and the other at the program. This also eliminates parents forgetting to bring the container with them each morning. Prescription labels must include

  - the child's name (not a sibling's),
  - the name of the medication,
  - the dose (amount),
  - the number of times it is given each day, and
  - the route (oral, nasal, rectal, eye, ear).

Sometimes pharmacists place stickers on the container with additional information: "Shake well," "Take with meals," "May cause a photosensitive reaction."

- Follow the steps provided in the program's medication policy for preparing, giving, and recording medication. Know the procedure for reporting and responding to medication errors.

- When children have allergies to medicine, post the children's names and pictures and the names of the drugs at the place where medication is stored and prepared.

- For children who are prescribed an epinephrine auto-injector to treat allergic reactions, always have the medication in the same general area as the child. Epinephrine is the exception to the rule about keeping all medication in a locked container. Although it should be out of reach of children—perhaps in the first-aid kit in the play area—educators must be able to access and administer this medication on a moment's notice. If a child has a severe allergy to insect stings or other allergens found outside, you must take medication to the playground, on walks, and so on. For children with severe food allergies, take the medication outside only if the child might eat something there (e.g., a picnic lunch or snack, on a field trip). All educators must know how to use the auto-injector. It is an emergency when a child needs epinephrine, so educators don't have time to look for the educator responsible for giving medication. Ask the pharmacist for the manufacturer's poster that shows how to give the injection, to display it in the centre. Educators may also be required by the child care regulations to receive training on injections from a health professional or the parents. In any case, auto-injectors are simple to use (see Allergies, page 186). The same practice holds true for children who are prescribed an inhaler as a reliever medication during an asthma episode. The medication needs to move with the child.

- Remember the following tips when you give medication to a child:
  - Be honest with the child (e.g., if you don't know how the medication tastes, admit it).
  - Especially for young children, the child who receives the medication should know and be comfortable with the educator administering it.
  - Explain to the child what you are going to do and how he or she can cooperate.
  - Never call medicine "candy." Medicines are potentially hazardous products, and children must learn how to take medications safely.
  - Give the child the medication away from the other children.

Preventing Medication Errors

Medication errors—such as giving medication to a child who wasn't prescribed a drug, mixing up medications among children, giving an incorrect dosage, or putting ear drops in the wrong ear—can occur for a number of reasons. The consequences of such errors range from minor to very serious. However, you can go through your child care career without making any medication errors.

Medication errors result when one or more of the **"five rights" for administering medication** have not been verified:

- right child,
- right medication,
- right dose (amount),
- right time, or
- right route (oral, nasal, rectal, eye, ear, injection).

Safeguards:

- Always use a measuring spoon, dropper, or cup that is designed for medication.
- Check the sheet you use to record the administration of medication to ensure that no one has already given the drug to the child.
- Read the prescription label three times:

  1. when you take the medication out of the storage space,
  2. before you pour the medication from the bottle, and
  3. after you pour it and are putting the bottle back in storage.

During the three checks, compare the prescription label to the parents' medication consent form. Verify that all of the "five rights" are correct.

- If a child tells you that someone else has already given him or her the drug, or that he or she is no longer taking the medication, double-check with the other educators. Another educator could have given the drug and not recorded it, or the drug may have been stopped and the parent forgotten to tell you.
- Immediately record that you gave the medication on the parents' medication consent form.
- Document and report every medication error as soon as you are aware of it.

CRITICAL THINKING

During school hours, school-agers with asthma or life-threatening allergies are encouraged to be responsible for their own puffer or adrenaline kit and to carry it with them. However, while they are in the school-age program, educators are responsible for these medications. How do we help school-agers understand that expectations differ for them between the school and the child care program? And how do educators in school-age programs advocate for change in child care regulations to bring these programs into line with the school, to create the "seamless day"?

Parents should be encouraged to tell educators when their children are taking medication at home, even when staff don't need to give the drug during the day. Educators may notice that the child is experiencing side effects such as dizziness or fatigue and can notify the parents, who can then talk with their health care provider.

ALLERGIES AND ASTHMA

Perhaps you have allergies or asthma. Many of us do. In fact, experts estimate that about three million Canadians have asthma (Asthma Society of Canada, 2008). In Canada, one in five children are being diagnosed with asthma (Asthma Society of Canada, 2007, p. 2).

The number of children and adults with allergies and asthma is increasing. Environmental pollutants and sick-building syndrome are playing a significant role in this increase. We can assume that every program has at least one child with allergies or asthma. As such, educators must be aware of these health conditions and know how to avoid factors that trigger reactions and how to handle reactions when they occur. Depending on their age, children with allergies or asthma may wish to talk with other children about the condition, about how they feel when they get sick, about what they do to make themselves feel better, or about their hospital experiences. These opportunities are wonderful and natural times for children to learn about health.

OBJECTIVE

To understand the importance of working with parents in the daily management of asthma and allergies.

Allergies

Basically, **allergies** are the result of our body's hypersensitivity to a substance. These substances are not usually harmful to most people (e.g., pollen, peanuts, feathers, animal fur, perfume, latex), but for those with allergies, they can cause mild to severe allergic reactions.

Fortunately, most allergies are not life threatening. The substances that cause allergies, called allergens, enter our body through breathing, eating, touching, or being stung or bitten. Once the allergen is in the body, our immune system responds by producing antibodies that attack it. These antibodies remain in our body to protect us the next time we are exposed to that allergen, providing immunity. But for people with allergies, repeated exposure to an allergen results in their immune systems becoming overly sensitive to that particular allergen. An allergic reaction results when the person is exposed to the allergen and the body produces chemicals such as histamines, which cause various physical symptoms (or reactions), such as sneezing, a runny nose, vomiting, tightness in the chest, or hives. Table 4.1 lists allergens that are responsible for allergic reactions.

TABLE 4.1   Common Allergic Substances and Reactions

COMMON ALLERGIC SUBSTANCES	TYPICAL REACTIONS
Environmental dust, dust mites, mould, pollen	runny and itchy nose, itchy eyes or skin, red rash, breathing difficulties, coughing, wheezing, chest tightness
Pets pet dander, skin flakes, saliva, and urine	itchy eyes and nose, runny nose
Insects stings from bees and wasps	wheezing, dizziness, hives, swelling of upper airway with difficulty breathing and in extreme cases swelling of face and anaphylactic shock
Foods eggs, peanuts and other nuts, sesame seeds, soy, seafood (shellfish, crustaceans, fish), sulphites, milk, and wheat and other cereal products containing gluten (the latter two are common causes of infant allergies)	flushed face, hives or a rash, red and itchy skin; swelling of the eyes, face, lips, throat, and tongue; difficulty breathing, speaking, or swallowing; anxiety; cramps; diarrhea; vomiting; and in extreme cases anaphylactic shock
Drugs commonly seen with antibiotics such as penicillin and with aspirin and anti-inflammatory drugs	range from mild to severe skin rashes, swelling, difficulty breathing, and in extreme cases anaphylactic shock
Latex balloons, gloves, rubber toys, baby-bottle nipples, bandages, gloves, fabrics with elastic, sports equipment, condoms, dental dams	itchy, watery eyes, sneezing or runny nose, coughing, rash or hives, chest tightness, shortness of breath, and in extreme cases anaphylactic shock
Scents strong odours found in products such as perfumes, hair spray, soaps, fabric softeners	irritation of the nose and lungs

Sources: Allergy/Asthma Information Association (2004, 2006, n.d.); Canadian Allergy, Asthma and Immunology Foundation (n.d.); Health Canada (2007b); Ministry of Health and Long-Term Care (2006).

Allergic reactions can cause feelings of fear, discomfort, or anxiety in children and their parents. The goal should be to maintain as normal a lifestyle as possible. It is important to balance supporting a child's awareness of his or her allergens with knowing what to do if the child is exposed and avoiding overwhelming fear and excessive limits on the child's activities.

Most of the symptoms listed in Table 4.1 are from four of the body systems: upper and lower respiratory tract, skin, eyes, and gastrointestinal tract. The more body systems that are affected by an allergen, the more severe the allergic reaction. Severe allergic reactions are most commonly caused by peanuts and other nuts, eggs, shellfish, bee and wasp stings, penicillin, and aspirin. In a severe allergy to bee sting, for example, the first sting results in a significant reaction. Any subsequent sting, however, could be fatal. When children are diagnosed with severe allergies, the health care provider prescribes epinephrine (e.g., EpiPen® (epinephrine) Auto-Injector, Twinject® auto-injector) to be administered in the event of severe allergic reaction. In these instances, parents are required to provide the program with an adrenaline kit.

The most severe allergic reaction is called **anaphylactic shock**, which affects the entire body. *This reaction happens quickly.* Within seconds, the child's eyes, lips, and face begin to swell; he or she may get a headache; hives may appear all over the body; the throat may swell and cut off the breathing; and he or she may vomit and have diarrhea. Eventually, the child becomes unconscious. All of this can happen in less than 10 minutes. Educators must identify these symptoms immediately, administer the child's epinephrine, and call an ambulance. *To save the child's life, further emergency medical care is needed.* Even if you aren't sure about the child's allergic symptoms, always give epinephrine to the child and call an ambulance. Depending on the child and your accessibility to emergency personnel, the health care provider may prescribe the Twinject® auto-injector instead of the EpiPen® (epinephrine) Auto-Injector, which provides two doses of epinephrine. Here again, you must follow the instructions provided by the physician or pharmacist. Parents should be encouraged to obtain a medical alert bracelet for any child who has been diagnosed with severe allergies. The bracelet must be worn at all times. There is no cure for allergies. We try to prevent reactions by eliminating exposure to allergens whenever possible (e.g., peanuts, shellfish, animals) or at least limiting exposure to allergens (e.g., smoke, dust, pollen). The only treatment for allergies is to alleviate or reduce the effect of the symptoms (e.g., runny noses, itchy red eyes, nasal and sinus congestion) with medications such as antihistamines and decongestants. During hay fever season, children with hay fever may be more comfortable playing outside in the afternoon because most plants pollinate in the morning.

CRITICAL THINKING

A toddler who is allergic to wheat is mistakenly offered bread made with wheat by a substitute staff at morning snack. She has a tummyache at nap time, but it subsides, and upon awakening, she seems to feel back to normal. Your room partner is leaving her shift and advises you not to let the parent know about the incident at the end of day since the child is fine now. What would you do and why?

Preventing Allergic Reactions

First, effective communication is essential between educators and parents to prevent allergic reactions. At the time of enrollment, parents must be asked for the following information about their children's allergies: the name of the allergen(s) and the specific symptoms, steps to prevent exposure to the allergen, what actions the educators should take when a child has symptoms, and what medication the health care provider has prescribed or recommended. Educators and parents can then develop an allergy care plan that meets the child's needs.

The program's policy and preventive practices on allergies should include all of the following:

- a medical form completed by the child's health care provider outlining the management of the allergies, what educators need to be aware of, and any instructions on handling emergency situations
- the sharing of allergy information with all staff members by
  - posting a list of children with their allergies in the kitchen and eating areas. Adding photos of each child to the list ensures that children are not exposed to known allergens, especially when volunteers, students, and substitute educators enter the program. This is particularly important when the children are younger and when there are children with the same first names. There have been educators who raise concerns around medical confidentiality and the posting of such information. However, the health risk of not sharing this vital information surpasses any such concern and assists staff and volunteers in providing a safe environment for the children.

  - including the pertinent allergy information with the emergency information cards kept in the first-aid kits.
  - attaching an allergy list to the top of the first-aid kit used outdoors (i.e., on the playground, field trips, walks) that focuses on children who are allergic to substances found outside, such as bees, wasps, animal hair, and feathers. Educators can quickly refer to this list to prevent or respond to allergic reactions. Educators can also refer to the list before they leave, to make sure they take the epinephrine auto-injector outside for those children who have been prescribed one. The epinephrine auto-injector must always be in the same general area as the child. Educators do not have time to go back to the program and then return to the playground to give the injection. Remember, anaphylactic shock happens very quickly, and educators must administer the adrenaline immediately (see Ensuring the Safe Administration of Medication, page 182).
- an awareness of how food is purchased, prepared, and served. The cooks or educators responsible for snacks and meals must know which children have food allergies, read all the ingredients on labels, and so on. New food labelling regulations came into effect in 2003. Processed food labels now clearly list the ingredients so consumers can avoid foods that provoke allergic reactions. With

time, there will be further legislative changes to support the education of consumers in understanding what foods they are eating.

- Use extreme caution for children with allergies to peanuts and peanut products. Educators must take parents' concerns very seriously because for some children, even the smell of peanuts or a trace of grated nuts in a cookie can cause anaphylactic shock. Some early childhood programs have voluntarily banned peanut butter and nut products from their programs. In the province of Manitoba, for example, in *Best Practices Licensing Manual for Early Learning and Child Care Centres,* there is a guideline for Section 16(4) that states that "caregivers must not serve foods containing known peanut products to children under three years of age to reduce their risk of developing severe allergies. Caregivers who prepare and serve foods for children under three years of age should carefully read food labels to determine ingredients" (Manitoba Child Care Program, 2005, p. 113). Obviously, this regulation does not prevent parents from sending nut products in their child's meals, but educators strongly discourage parents from doing so.

- the posting of menus so parents can make substitutions for foods or food ingredients to which their child is allergic. When the program provides substitute foods, choose foods that look similar to those the other children are having. This can help normalize eating experiences for children with food allergies.

- the documenting of all allergic reactions in the child's file. The child's parents must be contacted.

Eighty percent of allergies develop before the age of five. To ensure children's safety, programs need to

- require all parents to give their children prescribed or OTC medication for 24 hours before educators administer it in the program so parents can determine whether their child has any side effects or allergic symptoms;

- outline how new foods are introduced to promote early awareness of allergies, which is particularly important for infants (see The Process of Introducing Semisolid Foods, page 255); and

- as a general practice, use unscented laundry and cleaning products and encourage staff not to wear perfumes and colognes, to which many people are sensitive.

Asthma

When someone has **asthma**, the mucous membrane that lines the airways is chronically inflamed, which narrows the airways (or bronchial tubes). The membranes produce more mucus, which is stickier than normal, resulting in less space in the airways for air to pass through. The cause of the tissue's chronic inflammation is not known.

Asthma varies in severity and is diagnosed when children have recurring episodes of wheezing, coughing, or shortness of breath. Wheezing has been considered the classic asthma symptom. Some people with asthma have a chronic dry cough rather than a wheeze, so their asthma may go undiagnosed because the wheezing can't be heard over the coughing. Severe asthma episodes can be life threatening because the airway completely closes and no air can get to the lungs.

The mucous membranes are more sensitive to allergens (e.g., dust mites, pollen, mould, grass, trees, and weed pollens), substances (e.g., air pollution, perfume, cologne, paint fumes, chemicals, tobacco smoke), cold weather, strenuous exercise (episodes in this connection are referred to as exercise-induced asthma [EIA]), URI, colds, emotional upset, sudden changes in the atmosphere or weather, and food additives and preservatives. Any of these may irritate the mucous membranes and trigger an asthma episode. The child has to work hard at breathing because the muscles around the airway tighten, and the lining swells further and produces more sticky mucus. The child may cough frequently, wheeze, breathe at a faster rate, and complain that the chest feels tight and may have behaviour changes (e.g., tiredness, restlessness, irritability).

"Respiratory illness accounted for the greatest proportion of hospital admissions for children aged 1 to 4 years (41%). . . . Hospital admissions are often recurrent and the result of chronic conditions such as asthma or neurological conditions" (Canadian Institute of Child Health, 2000, p. 72). "Six out of ten people with asthma do not have control of their disease. Their poorly controlled asthma may lead to a severe, life-threatening asthma attack and permanent lung damage" (Asthma Society of Canada, 2008, p. 1). Approximately 500 adults and 20 children per year die of asthma in Canada; many of these deaths could have been prevented through education and management (Asthma Society of Canada, 2007, p. 3) (see Table 4.2).

TABLE 4.2	How Do You Know If Your Asthma Is Well Managed?

THE 30 SECOND ASTHMA TEST®		
	YES	NO
1. Do you use your blue inhaler 4 or more times a week? (Except one dose/day for exercise)	☐	☐
2. Do you cough, wheeze, or have a tight chest because of your asthma? (4 or more days a week)	☐	☐
3. Do coughing, wheezing, or chest tightness wake you at night? (1 or more times a week)	☐	☐
4. Do you stop exercising because of your asthma? (In the past 3 months)	☐	☐
5. Do you ever miss work, school or social activities because of your asthma? (In the past 3 months)	☐	☐
EVEN ONE "YES" MEANS SEE YOUR DOCTOR. YOUR ASTHMA IS NOT UNDER CONTROL.		

®used under license by GlaxoSmithKline Inc. © 2005 GlaxoSmithKline Inc. All rights reserved.

Identifying and managing the **triggers of the child's asthma episodes** are the first line of prevention. Educators can work with the children's parents to identify triggers, to remove or at least reduce exposure to allergens, and to administer prescribed medications. Three of the most common allergens for children are dust mites' feces, pollen, and cat dander. For some children, even being around another child who comes to the program or school with cat or dog hair on his or her clothes can irritate the airways. Dust mites thrive in warm, humid places, live off human skin scales, and can be found on pillows and mattresses, carpets, cloth-covered furniture, and soft toys. Educators can reduce the number of dust mites in programs by regularly dusting, vacuuming, and laundering cloth toys. Many allergens and irritants are found outdoors (e.g., pollens, fumes, tobacco smoke) and in public places and are more difficult to reduce or alleviate.

Two types of medications can be prescribed for children to control and relieve symptoms of asthma. The controllers treat the airway's underlying inflammation. These medications are taken daily regardless of experiencing symptoms and may be in the form of an inhaler (e.g., Pulmicort®, Flovent®) or pill (e.g., PediaPred®, Decadron®). The reliever (or rescue) medications are bronchodilators, which, as the term suggests, are used to relieve the asthma symptoms by relaxing the bronchial tubes during an attack so that the child can breathe more easily. These medications are often administered in an aerosol inhaler (or puffer) (e.g., Ventolin®, Airomir®, Bricanyl®), Diskhaler, Diskus, or Turbuhaler; in a syrup; or in tablet form. (Asthma Society of Canada, 2007, p. 6; The Lung Association, 2008, pp. 2–3, 6).

Younger children often use an AeroChamber because they are not yet able to use a puffer, which requires exhaling completely and then pumping the puffer once and inhaling the puff of medication in one breath. Most individuals are prescribed two or three puffs. At one end of the AeroChamber is the hole where the mouthpiece of the puffer is inserted; the face mask is on the other end. The mask is placed over the child's mouth and nose, one puff of the medication is pumped into the chamber, and the child breathes in the medication over at least six breaths. Before the second puff, the child needs to wait one minute to allow the medication to travel through the air passages. This wait between puffs applies to all ages and all types of inhaler.

The program's policy and practices for the care of children with asthma should include

- providing parents with a medical form for the child's health care provider to complete, which outlines the management of the asthma, what educators must be aware of, and any instructions on medication and emergency situations. Have parents provide you with a copy of the child's asthma action plan.

- sharing this medical information with the child's educators.

- observing the child during strenuous play and in cold weather. If the child starts wheezing or coughing or is short of breath,

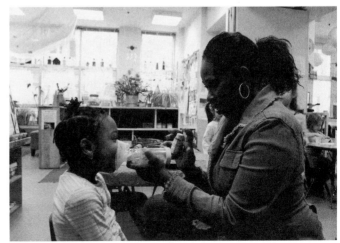

stop the activity. If the weather is cold or damp, bring the child inside. Have the child sit down to use the bronchodilator. Regular exercise is just as important for children with asthma as it is for other children; however, it is important to discuss the child's specific needs for exercise or being outside in the winter or in very hot weather.

■ documenting all asthmatic episodes in the child's file and contacting the child's parents. If an episode doesn't subside after two consecutive treatments of the bronchodilator medicine, the child should be seen by a health care provider as soon as possible.

REVISITING THE HEALTH PROMOTION ACTION PLAN

Recall the health promotion action plan introduced in Unit 1. The following example illustrates this plan in practice in terms of preventing and managing childhood illnesses.

Individual Problem Solving and Self-Reliance

Each day, educators have the opportunity to influence individual children's health positively by implementing the program's infection control strategy. Granted, children get sick, and even if they are ill for only a few days, the whole family's schedule can be disrupted. Health policies and practices should be supportive, empathetic, and respectful of parents' situations and should take into account the program's responsibility for the health of the other children. We often forget that programs are also employers, and, as such, the program's board can demonstrate a commitment to employees' families by providing family responsibility leave for staff and permitting staff to bank overtime hours.

Collective Self-Help

Directors can benefit from developing a pool of substitute educators and/or volunteers who can be called on when

■ a child is mildly ill but stays at the program and needs extra attention;

■ an educator is absent due to illness;

■ a program needs extra adults (volunteers or paid), who come in for a few hours each day to cover busier times (e.g., meals, staff break times); or

■ a field trip is planned or an activity needs additional supervisors.

Ideally, volunteers and substitutes are in the program often enough that the children and the adults get to know one another. When they are approached by staff, these trusted adults may be interested in providing care for the mildly ill child in the family's home or in their own home when the need arises. For parents who don't have access to alternative (or backup) care, this service could be extremely valuable. In communities where there is a cluster of programs in close proximity, directors could work collaboratively to support families and their staff.

Community Action

Staff have identified the need for a community service that provides care for mildly ill children. Either on an individual basis or with a collective of programs, educators could advocate to a local agency to develop such a service (e.g., Victorian Order of Nurses [VON]). In communities with only one or two main employers, most, if not all, of the parents who use the program work for the same company. The program's board could meet with the company's management to discuss establishing family responsibility leave for their employees. Perhaps the local public health agency would work cooperatively with the program and the company.

Societal Change

Provincial/territorial and national child care associations (e.g., Saskatchewan Child Care Association, Canadian Child Care Federation) lobby the government to legislate employers to provide family responsibility leave. These associations are made up of members like you. Individual educators can exercise their democratic right (and responsibility) to vote for political candidates who are committed to child care and the family.

CONCLUSION

Even when an early childhood program implements the infection control strategies covered in Unit 3, children do get sick. Fortunately, most of the illnesses are mild and short-lived. Most do not require exclusion or prescriptions. In cooperation with parents, educators address the needs of the ill child, yet consider the best interests of the other children and staff.

What's Your Opinion?

TO COLLABORATE OR NOT TO COLLABORATE?

The school-age program is located inside the elementary school. One part-time educator works in the afternoon and after school. Two full-time educators work in the program, preparing activities and planning the curriculum in the morning and working with children from the half-time kindergarten class in the afternoon. Classroom teachers often expect the educators to care for any mildly ill child who is also enrolled in the school-age program rather than call the parents or keep the child in the classroom until the end of class. At times, the educators manage to accommodate an older ill child in the afternoon. As a result, the teachers expect the educators to be responsible for ill children and to notify parents when the child becomes ill in the classroom. The educators feel resentment toward these teachers.

　　The teachers and educators need to work cooperatively and collaboratively. Debate both sides of the issue from the perspective of the teachers and the educators. How can this issue be resolved in a way that is in the best interests of the children? Design a policy and procedures for the management of ill school-agers that can be used by teachers and educators. Don't overlook the parents.

ASSESS YOUR LEARNING

Define terms or describe concepts used in this unit.

- allergic substances
- allergies
- alternative care
- "five rights" for administering medication
- health observations
- prescription medication

- anaphylactic shock
- asthma
- exclusion
- over-the-counter (OTC) medication
- signs and symptoms
- triggers of the child's asthma episodes

Evaluate your options in each situation.

1. One of the two-year-olds is listless and unhappy today. He is unable to participate in the program and needs to be held and comforted. When the director calls his mother, she asks that you take his temperature. You do so, and because the child does not have a fever, the mother refuses to pick him up early.

2. A preschooler has a number of food allergies, so she is often offered other foods at lunch and snack. She cries and says she wants only what the other children eat. Meanwhile, some of the other children only want to eat the same food she eats.

3. One of the families goes to a naturopath as their health practitioner. You also believe that naturopaths have a lot to offer in promoting health. The parents ask you to administer the homeopathic (i.e., not prescribed by a medical doctor or advanced practitioner) medicine to their child daily. They are willing to sign the medication form. Are you able to administer this medication?

4. One of the preschoolers who has asthma often needs her "reliever" (or rescue) medication (Ventolin inhaler) to prevent severe attacks. Today you are going on a field trip away from the centre but didn't notice until you are ready to leave that the inhaler is empty. The parent has already left for work. What do you do?

RESOURCE MATERIALS

Organizations

Allergy Asthma Information Association, Head Office, 111 Zenway Boulevard, Unit 1, Vaughan, ON L4H 3H9. Tel: 905-265-3322 or national toll-free 1-800-611-7011 (or contact regional office); fax: 905;850-2070; http://aaia.ca/

Asthma Society of Canada, 4950 Yonge Street, Suite 2306, Toronto, ON M2N 6K1. Tel: 416-787-4050 or national toll-free 1-800-787-3880 (or contact regional office); fax: 416-787-5807; http://www.asthma.ca

Canadian Institute of Child Health, 384 Bank Street, Suite 300, Ottawa, ON K2P 1Y4. Tel: 613-230-8838; fax: 613-230-6654; http://www.cich.ca

Canadian Paediatric Society, 2305 St. Laurent Blvd., Ottawa, ON K1G 4J8. Tel: 613-526-9397; fax: 613-526-3332; http://www.cps.ca

The Lung Association, National Office, 1750 Courtwood Crescent, Suite 300, Ottawa, ON K2C 2B5; Tel: 613-569-6411 or national toll-free 1-888-566-5864 (connects to regional Lung Associations) or contact regional offices directly; fax: 613-569-8860; http://www. lung.ca. (The association provides educational sessions on asthma for parents.)

Other Websites of Interest

Canadian Paediatric Society's site for parents: http://www.caringforkids.cps.ca/index. htm

EpiPen® (epinephrine) Auto-Injector: http://www.epipen.ca

The Hospital for Sick Children: https://www.aboutkidshealth.ca

Twinject® auto-injector: http://www.twinject.ca

Printed Matter

Asthma Handook Parent (n.d.), The Lung Association. To download a copy, visit http://www.lung.ca/diseases-maladies/asthma-asthme/manual-manuel/index_e.php

When Your Child Is Sick:

- *Colds in Children* (2005), by the Canadian Paediatric Society (updated October 2005). To download a copy, visit http://www.caringforkids.cps.ca/whensick/colds.htm

- *Fever and Temperature Taking* (2008), by the Canadian Paediatric Society (updated April 2008). To download a copy, visit http://www.caringforkids.cps.ca/whensick/Fever.htm

- *Using Over-the-Counter Drugs to Treat Cold Symptoms* (2007), by the Canadian Paediatric Society (updated October 2007). To download a copy, visit http://www.caringforkids.cps.ca/whensick/OTC_Drugs.htm

BIBLIOGRAPHY

Allergy/Asthma Information Association. (2004). *Scents in the workplace.* Retrieved August 2008 from http://aaia.ca/en/scents_in_the_workplace.htm

Allergy/Asthma Information Association. (2006). *Drug allergy: How you can help your allergist make the diagnosis.* Retrieved August 2008 from http://aaia.ca/en/drug_allergy.htm

Allergy/Asthma Information Association. (n.d.). *Dust, pet and mold: Allergies.* Retrieved August 2008 from http://www.aaia.ca/en/dust_brochure_en.pdf

Asthma Society of Canada. (2007). *Asthma allergy COPD: 2007 special information supplement.* Retrieved June 2008 from http://www.asthma.ca/adults/Asthma_Society_2007_Special_Information_Supplement.pdf

Asthma Society of Canada. (2008). *About asthma: Who gets asthma?* Retrieved June 2008 from http://www.asthma.ca/adults/about/whoGetsAsthma.php

Burroughs Wellcome Inc. (n.d.). *Head lice education program.* Montreal: Author.

Canadian Allergy, Asthma and Immunology Foundation. (n.d.). *Natural rubber latex allergy: A guideline for allergic patients.* Retrieved August 2008 from http://www.allergyfoundation.ca/latex_allergy_guidelines.htm

Canadian Broadcasting Corporation. (2007, January 12). *Cough syrup dangerous for babies, U.S. officials warn.* Retrieved June 2008 from http://www.cbc.ca/consumer/story/2007/01/12/cough-syrup.html

Canadian Institute of Child Health. (2000). *The health of Canada's children: A CICH profile* (3rd ed.). Ottawa: Author.

Canadian Paediatric Society. (2008). *Well beings: A guide to health in child care* (3rd ed.). Ottawa: Author. Material on pages 162, 163, 164, 170, 174, 175, 176, 177 is reprinted with permission.

Canadian Paediatric Society, (2008b). *When Your Child is Sick: Head lice.* Retrieved October 2008 from https://www.caringforkids.cps.ca/whensick/headlice.htm

Gonzales, R., et al. (2005). The 'Minimizing Antibiotic Resistance in Colorado' Project: Impact of patient education in improving antibiotic use in private office practices. *Health Services Research, 40*(1), 1001–1116.

Health Canada. (2006, December 15). *Healthy living: Antibiotic resistance.* Retrieved June 2008 from http://www.hc-sc.gc.ca/hl-vs/iyh-vsv/med/antibio-eng.php#is

Health Canada. (2007a, October 11). *Advisory: Recommendations for the Appropriate use of cough and cold products in children.* Retrieved June 2008 from http://www.hc-sc.gc.ca/ahc-asc/media/advisories-avis/_2007/2007_147-eng.php

Health Canada. (2007b, November 28). *Food and nutrition: Food allergies.* Retrieved June 2008 from http://www.hc-sc.gc.ca/fn-an/securit/allerg/fa-aa/index-eng.php

The Lung Association. (2008, March 6). *Asthma: Medications for asthma.* Retrieved June 2008 from http://www.lung.ca/diseases-maladies/asthma-asthme/medications-medicaments/index_e.php#inhaled

The Lung Association. (n.d.). *Asthma handbook.* Retrieved June 2008 from http://www.lung.ca/pdf/handbook_web.pdf

Manitoba Child Care Program. (2005). *Best practices licensing manual for early learning and child care centres.* Winnipeg: Manitoba Family Services and Housing, Province of Manitoba. Retrieved June 2008 from http://www.gov.mb.ca/fs/elccmanual/manual.pdf

Ministry of Health and Long-Term Care. (2006, December 6). *Public health: First aid for bee and insect stings.* Retrieved August 2008 from http://www.health.gov.on.ca/english/public/pub/pubhealth/bee_stings.html

Skull, S. A., et al. (2000). Child care centre staff contribute to physician visits and pressure for antibiotic prescription. *Archives of Pediatrics and Adolescent Medicine, 154,* 180–183.

Management of Illness

Requirements for reporting vary across Canada. Find out which infections are reportable in your province/territory by contacting your local public health unit.

ILLNESS	TRANSMISSION	SIGNS/ SYMPTOMS	INFECTIOUS PERIOD	EXCLUSION	REPORTING AND NOTIFICATION
Viral respiratory infections					
Viruses include: respiratory syncytial virus, parainfluenza virus, influenza, adenovirus, rhinovirus, coronavirus, metapneumovirus See page 175 for additional information	Viruses in the nose and throat spread by: **direct contact** with respiratory secretions or contaminated hands, **indirect contact** with toys, tissues, or other objects contaminated with respiratory secretions, or **droplets** from coughs and sneezes	**Common cold:** Runny nose, cough, sneezing, sore throat, headache, possibly fever **Bronchiolitis:** Cough, laboured breathing, wheezing, fever **Croup:** Hoarseness, barking cough, rapid, laboured or noisy breathing, fever **Influenza:** Fever, chills, cough, headache and muscle pains **Pneumonia:** Fever, cough, rapid or laboured breathing, poor skin colour	Depends on the virus but usually 3 to 8 days (longer for children with a weakened immune system) Most infectious while symptoms are present	**Common cold:** No, unless the child is too ill to participate in all program activities **Bronchiolitis, croup, influenza, pneumonia:** Yes, until the child is well enough to participate in all program activities	No No, unless you suspect an outbreak

(appendix continues on next page)

ILLNESS	TRANSMISSION	SIGNS/SYMPTOMS	INFECTIOUS PERIOD	EXCLUSION	REPORTING AND NOTIFICATION
Bacterial pneumonia Can be viral or bacterial. See page 186 for additional information.	Bacteria usually present in the nose and throat and can cause disease if they get into the lungs	Fever, cough, rapid or laboured breathing, poor skin colour	Usually not considered contagious	Yes, until the child is well enough to participate in all program activities	No, unless pneumococcus or *Haemophilus influenzae* type B is isolated during blood testing
Gastrointestinal infections	Germs in stool spread by: **direct contact** (hand to mouth), or **indirect contact** with toys, other objects or surfaces contaminated with stool				
Campylobacter	Bacteria usually ingested in contaminated **food** (e.g., improperly cooked poultry, unpasteurized milk) or water Person-to-person spread by **direct or indirect contact with stool** can occur, especially among young children	Fever, diarrhea (often with blood and/or mucus in stool), cramps	Bacteria excreted in stool for 2 to 3 weeks Most contagious during the acute illness	Yes, if a child's diarrhea can't be contained in a diaper, or a toilet-trained child can't control his bowel movements	Yes, by the testing laboratory Contact your local public health unit if a child at your facility is diagnosed with *Campylobacter* gastroenteritis
Clostridium difficile (*C. difficile*)	Bacteria are normally found in soil and in the intestinal tract. Antibiotic treatment permits overgrowth of *C. difficile* in the gut and may trigger disease. Person-to-person spread by **direct or indirect contact with stool** can occur	Diarrhea (sometimes with blood and/or mucus in stool), cramps, fever Most children under 1 year of age have no symptoms, and most older children have a very mild illness	Infectious as long as diarrhea lasts	Yes, if a child's diarrhea can't be contained in a diaper, or a toilet-trained child can't control his bowel movements	No

(appendix continues on next page)

Illness	How it is spread	Symptoms	Period of communicability	Exclusion	Reportable
Escherichia coli 0157 (E. coli)	Bacteria usually ingested in contaminated **food** (e.g., poultry, beef, milk, unpasteurized apple juice, raw vegetables), or **water** contaminated with animal or human feces Also spread from person-to-person by **direct or indirect contact with stool**	Starts as non-bloody diarrhea, usually progressing to visibly bloody stools, with severe abdominal pain	Bacteria excreted in stool for about a week Infectious as long as diarrhea lasts	Yes, until diarrhea subsides **and** 2 stool cultures (taken when the child is no longer receiving antibiotics) test negative	Yes, by the testing laboratory Contact your local public health unit if a child in your facility is diagnosed with *E. coli* 0157 gastroenteritis
Giardia For more information, see page 187	Parasites in the stool are spread from person to person by **direct or indirect contact with stool** or are ingested in **contaminated food or water**	Watery diarrhea, recurrent abdominal pain Some children experience chronic diarrhea with foul-smelling stools, a distended stomach and weight loss Many infected children have no symptoms.	Infectious as long as cysts are in the stool, which can be for months	Yes, until diarrhea subsides	Yes, by the testing laboratory Contact your local public health unit if a child at your facility is diagnosed with *Giardia* gastroenteritis. In the case of an outbreak, authorities may screen and/or treat all children and staff, with or without symptoms.
Rotavirus	Viruses in the stool spread easily from person to person by: **Direct or indirect contact with stool and contaminated toys**	High fever, vomiting, followed within 12 to 24 hours by profuse, watery diarrhea	Infectious just before onset of symptoms and as long as 3 weeks later	Yes, if a child's diarrhea can't be contained in a diaper or toilet-trained child can't control her bowel movements	No Contact your local public health unit if you suspect an outbreak (i.e., 2 to 3 or more children have diarrhea within 48 hours)

(appendix continues on next page)

ILLNESS	TRANSMISSION	SIGNS/SYMPTOMS	INFECTIOUS PERIOD	EXCLUSION	REPORTING AND NOTIFICATION
Salmonella typhi (gastroenteritis or typhoid fever)	Bacteria in the stool are spread from person to person by **direct or indirect contact with stool,** or are ingested in **contaminated food**	Diarrhea, cramps, fever	Infectious as long as bacteria are in the stool, which can be many weeks	Yes, until diarrhea subsides **and** 3 stool cultures (taken when the child is no longer receiving antibiotics) test negative	Yes, by the treating physician and testing laboratory Inform your local public health unit **immediately** if a child or adult at your facility is diagnosed with *S. typhi* infection. Stool cultures for other children and staff may be required.
Salmonella gastroenteritis (non-typhi)	Bacteria are usually ingested in **contaminated food** (e.g., meat, poultry, eggs, unpasteurized dairy products, vegetables and fruit) Person-to-person spread **may occur from direct or indirect contact with stool** **Reptiles and amphibians** are also sources of infection	Diarrhea, cramps, fever	Infectious as long as bacteria are in the stool, which can be many weeks	Yes, until the child is well enough to participate in all program activities	Yes, by the testing laboratory Contact your local public health unit if a child at your facility is diagnosed with *Salmonella* gastroenteritis
Shigella gastroenteritis	Bacteria in stool spread from person to person **by direct or indirect contact with stool**	Watery diarrhea, with or without blood and/or mucus, fever, cramps	Infectious as long as bacteria are in the stool, which can be up to 4 weeks	Yes, until diarrhea subsides **and** 2 stool cultures (taken when the child is no longer receiving antibiotics) test negative	Yes, by the testing laboratory Contact your local public health unit if a child at your facility is diagnosed with *Shigella* gastroenteritis. Other children, staff or household contacts with symptoms may need testing.

(appendix continues on next page)

Illness	How it is spread	Symptoms	Infectious period	Keep child at home?	Reportable/Notify
Yersinia gastroenteritis For more information and important requirements, see page 198–99 and 375	Bacteria are ingested in **contaminated food** (e.g., raw or undercooked pork, unpasteurized milk) or **water** Person-to-person spread is rare	Fever, diarrhea (often with blood and/or mucus in stool)	Infectious as long as bacteria are in the stool, which can be up to 2 to 3 weeks	Yes, if a child's diarrhea can't be contained in a diaper, or toilet-trained child can't control his bowel movements	Yes, by the testing laboratory Contact your public health unit if a child at your facility is diagnosed with *Yersinia* gastroenteritis

Other Illnesses

Illness	How it is spread	Symptoms	Infectious period	Keep child at home?	Reportable/Notify
Chickenpox (varicella) For more information, see page 193	Viruses in the throat and from skin lesions spread easily from person to person **through the air,** and can travel large distances Viruses in skin lesions spread **by contact with fluid from blisters** Virus persists in the body for life and may recur as shingles. Viruses can spread by contact with shingles if lesions are not covered.	Fever and itchy rash. Crops of small red spots turn into fluid-filled blisters that crust over within a few days and become itchy.	Infectious for 2 days before rash starts until all blisters have crusted over and dried (usually about 5 days after start of rash)	No. Children with mild chickenpox can attend child care regardless of the state of their rash, as long as they feel well enough to participate in all program activities.	Yes, in some jurisdictions, by the treating physician and testing laboratory Contact your local public health unit if there is an outbreak at your facility **Notify all parents and staff immediately.** Non-immune children and staff may need to see a doctor right away. Preventive treatment (vaccine or immune globulin) may be needed.
Cold sores (herpes simplex type 1 virus) For more information, see page 193	Viruses spread from person to person by **direct contact** of mucous membranes (mouth, nose, eyes) with cold sores or saliva Virus persists in the body for life and infections may recur	Range from no symptoms to a simple cold sore or many painful ulcers in mouth and a high fever	Infectious for at least a week during the first infection Recurrences are less contagious for a shorter time	No, for a child with simple cold sores Yes, for a child with mouth ulcers who is drooling, until she is well enough to eat and participate comfortably in all program activities	No

(appendix continues on next page)

ILLNESS	TRANSMISSION	SIGNS/ SYMPTOMS	INFECTIOUS PERIOD	EXCLUSION	REPORTING AND NOTIFICATION
Conjunctivitis (pinkeye) See page 180 for additional information	Bacterial or viral. Germs spread easily by: **direct or indirect contact with eye secretions, or droplets** from coughs and sneezes when associated with a respiratory virus. It can also be caused by an allergy or eye irritation	Scratchy, painful or itchy red eyes, light sensitivity, tearing with purulent (pus) or mucousy discharge	**Bacterial:** Infectious until 24 hours of appropriate anti-biotic treatment received **Viral:** Infectious as long as there is eye discharge	Yes, until seen by a doctor If bacteria, child can return to program after 24 hours of appropriate antibiotic treatment If viral, child can return with doctor's approval No need to exclude if there is no eye discharge, unless there is an outbreak	No Contact your local public health unit if you suspect an outbreak
Cytomegalovirus (CMV infection) See pages 184 and 380 for additional information	Viruses in saliva and urine spread by **direct contact** Virus persists in the body for life and infec-tions may recur	Children usually have no symptoms Can infect a fetus if the mother is infected or re-exposed during pregnancy	Infectious as long as virus is in the urine and saliva, which can be for months in many healthy infants	No	No

(appendix continues on next page)

202   **UNIT 4**   ILLNESS MANAGEMENT

NEL

Group A Streptococcus (GAS) invasive diseases (e.g., toxic shock syndrome, necrotizing fasciitis [flesh-eating disease])	Some strains of GAS cause invasive disease. Bacteria spread from person to person by: **direct contact with skin lesions,** or **respiratory droplets.**	**Toxic shock syndrome:** Fever, dizziness, confusion and abdominal pain	Infectious until 24 hours of appropriate antibiotic treatment received	Yes. A child can return to the program once she has received **at least** 24 hours of appropriate antibiotic therapy, and a doctor has determined she is recovered and well enough to participate in all program activities.	Yes, by the treating physician and testing laboratory
		Necrotizing fasciitis: Fever, severe, painful localized swelling, and a rapidly spreading red rash			**Notify your local public health unit immediately if a child or adult at your facility is diagnosed with invasive GAS.**
For more information and important requirements, see page 211	Children are at highest risk of infection within 2 weeks of having chickenpox				Antibiotic treatment may be required for all exposed contacts, especially if chickenpox is also present.
					Inform public health authorities if a child or staff member in your program has had a non-invasive GAS infection (e.g., impetigo or pharyngitis) or chickenpox within the previous 2 weeks
Haemophilus influenzae type b (Hib) disease	Bacteria in mouth and nose are spread by: **direct contact** and respiratory droplets	Causes fever and pneumonia, meningitis, epiglottitis, blood, bone and joint infections. Symptoms develop rapidly.	Infectious until **at least** 24 hours of appropriate antibiotic therapy received	Yes. A child can return to the program once she has received at least 24 hours of appropriate antibiotic therapy, and a doctor has determined she is well enough to participate in all program activities.	Yes, by the treating physician and testing laboratory
For more information and important requirements, see page 206	Does not spread easily, and requires prolonged close contact				**Inform your local public health unit immediately if a child at your center is diagnosed with a Hib infection.** Antibiotic treatment or vaccine may be required for exposed children.
					Notify all parents

(appendix continues on next page)

ILLNESS	TRANSMISSION	SIGNS/ SYMPTOMS	INFECTIOUS PERIOD	EXCLUSION	REPORTING AND NOTIFICATION
Hand-foot-and-mouth disease See page 200 for additional information	Intestinal viruses spread from person to person by: **direct or indirect contact with stool or saliva**	Fever, headache, sore throat, small, painful mouth ulcers and a rash (small red spots or small blisters), usually on the hands and feet	Virus in saliva for a few days only but can remain in stool for 4 weeks after onset of illness	No. Children can attend child care as long as they feel well enough to participate in all program activities.	No
Head lice See pages 191–92 for additional information	Spread from person to person by: **direct contact** (head to head), **or indirect contact** (e.g., shared hats, hairbrushes, headphones)	Itchy scalp	Infectious as long as left untreated	No. Exclusion is ineffective and unnecessary.	No. Contact your local public health unit for guidance if an outbreak cannot be controlled.
Hepatitis A virus (HAV) For more information and important requirements, see pages 189–90 and 380–81	Virus in stool spreads from person to person by: **direct or indirect contact with stool,** or **contaminated food or water**	Tea-coloured urine, jaundice and fever. Most young children do not get sick but can still spread the virus to others. Older children and adults are more likely to have symptoms	Most infectious 1 to 2 weeks before onset of illness until 1 week after onset of jaundice	Yes, for one week after onset of illness (unless all other children and staff have received preventive treatment)	Yes, by the treating physician and testing laboratory. **Inform your local public health unit immediately if a child or adult at your facility is diagnosed with HAV.** Contacts may need vaccine or immune globulin **Notify all parents and staff**

(appendix continues on next page)

Hepatitis B virus (HBV) For more information and important requirements, see pages 212–14 and 377–78	Virus in blood and other body fluids (e.g., saliva, genital secretions). Mainly transmitted through sexual intercourse, from mother to newborn, by sharing contaminated injection equipment or by transfusion of unscreened blood. May be transmitted if an open cut or the mucous membranes (eyes or mouth) are exposed to blood	Young children almost always have no symptoms Older children and adults may have fever, fatigue, jaundice	Infectious as long as the virus is in the blood and body fluids May persist for life, especially in infants infected at birth	No. A child with HBV can participate in all program activities.	Yes, by the treating physician and testing laboratory Contact your local public health unit about **any** bite that breaks the skin. Blood tests may be required
Hepatitis C virus (HCV) For more information and important requirements, see pages 216 and 378	Virus in blood. Mainly transmitted from mother to newborn. Also by sharing contaminated injection equipment or by transfusion of unscreened blood. May be transmitted if an open cut or mucous membranes (eyes or mouth) are exposed to blood	Young children almost always have no symptoms Older children and adults may have fever, fatigue, jaundice	Infectious as long as the virus is in the blood May persist for life	No. A child with HCV can participate in all program activities.	Yes, by the treating physician and testing laboratory Contact your local public health unit about **any** bite that breaks the skin. Blood tests may be required.

(appendix continues on next page)

ILLNESS	TRANSMISSION	SIGNS/ SYMPTOMS	INFECTIOUS PERIOD	EXCLUSION	REPORTING AND NOTIFICATION
Human immuno-deficiency virus (HIV) For more information and important requirements, see pages 215–16 and 378–79	Virus in blood, genital secretions and breast milk. Children usually acquire HIV from mothers before, during or after birth (by breast-feeding). Otherwise, transmitted through sexual intercourse, by sharing contaminated injection equipment or by transfusion of unscreened blood. May be transmitted if an open cut or the the mucous membranes (eyes or mouth) are exposed to a large amount of blood	Children usually have no symptoms. If AIDS develops, they may have persistent thrush, *Candida* dermatitis, chronic diarrhea, and failure to gain weight.	Infectious as long as the virus is in the blood and body fluids, presumably for life	No. A child with HIV can partici-pate in all program activities.	Yes, by the treating physi-cian and testing laboratory Contact your local public health unit about **any bite** that breaks the skin. Blood tests may be required.
Impetigo For more information and important requirements, see pages 194–95	Caused by Group A *Streptococcus* or *Staphylococcus aureus* bacteria. Both spread from person to person by: **direct contact** (e.g., by touching skin lesions), or **indirect contact** (e.g., via con-taminated bed linens or clothing).	Fluid-filled blisters, usually around the mouth or nose, but may occur elsewhere. Blisters break, ooze, and become covered by a honey-coloured crust.	Infectious until lesions have dried up. If Group A *Streptococcus*, until 24 hours after first dose of an appropriate antibiotic.	Yes, if draining lesions cannot be kept covered. For Group A *Streptococcus* infec-tions, until 24 hours of appro-priate antibiotic treatment received.	No (but community-associated methicillin-resistant *S. aureus* [CA-MRSA] is reportable by the testing laboratory in some jurisdictions) Contact your local public health unit for advice if you suspect an outbreak (e.g., more than one child in the same room has impetigo within a month)

(appendix continues on next page)

Illness	Symptoms	How it is spread	Period when infectious	Can the child/staff return?	Reporting and notification
Measles For more information and important requirements, see pages 200–01 and 377	High fever, cough, runny nose and red eyes 2 to 4 days before a rash appears, first on the face, then over entire body	Viruses in respiratory secretions **spread easily from person to person through the air**	Highly infectious from 3 to 5 days before and up to 4 days after the rash appears	Yes. A child with measles cannot return to child care until **at least** 4 days after onset of rash. Non-immune children and staff must be excluded for 2 weeks after the onset of rash in the child diagnosed with measles, unless they have been vaccinated within 72 hours of first exposure	Yes, by the treating physician and testing laboratory **Measles exposure is a medical emergency** **Notify your local public health unit immediately if a child or adult at your facility is diagnosed with measles** Exposed susceptible children and staff may require vaccine or immune globulin within 72 hours of the first contact **Notify all staff and parents immediately**
Meningitis (bacterial or enteroviral) For more information and important requirements, see pages 204–06	**Bacterial:** Fever, lethargy, headache, extreme irritability, vomiting, stiff neck, seizures, a bulging fontanel in babies under 18 months old. Usually progresses rapidly. Child may have a rapidly spreading, bruise-like rash. **Viral:** Usually milder, often fever and irritability only	Not all forms of meningitis are contagious **Bacterial:** See Meningococcal disease and *Haemophilus influenzae* type b disease **Enteroviruses** in saliva and stool are spread by **direct or indirect contact**	**Bacterial** meningitis is infectious until 24 hours of appropriate antibiotic therapy received **Enteroviruses** are found in saliva for only a few days but can remain in stool for 4 weeks after onset of illness	Yes. A child can return to the program once she has received **at least** 24 hours of appropriate antibiotic therapy, and a doctor has determined she has recovered and feels well enough to participate in all program activities.	Bacterial meningitis: Yes, by the treating physician and testing laboratory **Notify your local public health unit immediately if a child or adult at your facility is diagnosed with bacterial meningitis** Antibiotic treatment or vaccine may be mandated for some or all exposed children and staff **Notify all parents and staff immediately**

(appendix continues on next page)

ILLNESS	TRANSMISSION	SIGNS/ SYMPTOMS	INFECTIOUS PERIOD	EXCLUSION	REPORTING AND NOTIFICATION
Meningococcal disease For more information and important requirements, see pages 207–09	Meningococcus is a bacterium found in the mouth and respiratory secretions. Does not spread easily but can be transmitted by: **close, direct contact** (e.g., with saliva), or **respiratory droplets.**	Usually causes sepsis or meningitis, with high fever and rapid progression to shock (decreased responsiveness, poor skin colour). Child may have a distinctive rash that starts as small red spots but rapidly progresses to large red-purple bruises.	Infectious until after 24 hours of appropriate antibiotic treatment received	Yes. A child can return to child care once he has received **at least** 24 hours of appropriate antibiotic therapy, and a doctor has determined he has recovered and feels well enough to participate in all program activities.	Yes, by the treating physician and testing laboratory. **Inform your local public health unit immediately if a child or adult at your facility is diagnosed with meningococcal disease.** Public health authorities may mandate antibiotic treatment and/or vaccination for exposed children and staff. **Notify all parents and staff immediately**
Molluscum contagiosum For more information, see page 197	Virus spreads from person to person by **direct (skin-to-skin) contact with lesions,** or **indirect contact** (e.g., **with bed linens contaminated with material from the lesions)**	Smooth, shiny pinkish-white bumps with a dip in the middle and a cheesy material inside, anywhere on the body	Unknown Molluscum disappears after several months without treatment	No	No
Mumps For more information and important requirements, see pages 184 and 376–77	Not very contagious Virus in saliva and respiratory secretions spreads easily from person to person by: **direct contact** (e.g., kissing), or **respiratory droplets**	Fever, swollen glands at the jaw line or on the face, headache	Infectious from 2 days before onset of swelling until 9 days after	Yes, for 9 days after onset of swelling	Yes, by treating physician and testing laboratory **Notify your local public health unit immediately if a child or adult at your facility is diagnosed with mumps.** The authorities may mandate vaccination for non-immune contacts. *(appendix continues on next page)*

Illness	How it spreads	Symptoms	Infectious period	Should the child be excluded from the program?	Is it reportable?
Otitis media (middle ear infections) For more information, see page 178	Viral or bacterial, usually a complication of the common cold. Non-contagious.	Earache, irritability, possibly fluid draining from ears. Child may have fever or cold symptoms.	Non-contagious	No, unless child is too ill to participate in program activities	No
Parvovirus B19 infection (fifth disease, erythema infectiosum, or "slapped cheek" syndrome) For more information and important requirements, see pages 201–02 and 379–80	Virus in respiratory secretions spreads by: **direct contact**, and (possibly) **respiratory droplets** Can also be transmitted from mother to child before birth	Red rash on the cheeks followed by a lace-like rash on the torso and arms that spreads to the rest of the body. Sometimes preceded by a low fever or cold symptoms 7 to 10 days before rash appears.	Infectious for several days before the rash, and non-infectious once rash appears	No. Once rash appears, a child is no longer contagious.	No Notify all parents and staff Advise exposed pregnant staff and parents to contact their doctor
Pertussis (whooping cough) For more information and important requirements, see pages 182–83 and 379	Bacteria in respiratory secretions spread easily from person to person by **droplets from coughs and sneezes**	Runny nose, frequent and severe coughing spells, sometimes followed by a whooping sound, gagging or vomiting. Babies may have serious difficulty breathing.	Infectious for up to 3 weeks from onset of illness if not treated, and for 5 days if appropriate antibiotic treatment is received	Not routine but exclusion may be mandated by public health authorities if high-risk persons are present Exclude until 5 days of appropriate antibiotic treatment received or for 3 weeks from onset of illness if not treated Exclusion may be mandated if high-risk persons are present	Yes, by the treating physician and testing laboratory **Inform your local public health unit immediately if a child or adult at your facility is diagnosed with pertussis.** Antibiotic treatment and/or vaccination may be mandated. **Notify all parents and staff immediately**

(appendix continues on next page)

ILLNESS	TRANSMISSION	SIGNS/SYMPTOMS	INFECTIOUS PERIOD	EXCLUSION	REPORTING AND NOTIFICATION
Pinworms See pages 190–91 for additional information	Worm eggs spread by: **direct contact** (e.g., contaminated fingers), or **indirect contact** (e.g., contaminated bed linens, clothing, toys).	Anal itching, disturbed sleep, irritability	Infectious as long as eggs are being laid on skin. Eggs are infective for 2 to 3 weeks indoors.	No	No
Pneumococcal disease See pages 209–10 for additional information	Bacteria are normally found in the nose and throat and usually do not cause infection Possible person-to-person spread by: **close, direct contact with mouth secretions** (e.g., kissing), or **respiratory droplets**	Usually an ear or sinus infection following a cold Invasive infections include fever and pneumonia, meningitis, blood, bone and joint infections. Symptoms develop rapidly.	Not usually considered infectious. Probably not transmissible after 24 hours of appropriate antibiotic therapy.	No, for minor illness (e.g., otitis, sinusitis) A child with serious illness can return to child care once a doctor has determined he is well enough to participate in all program activities	Yes (for invasive pneumococcal infections **only**), by the treating physician and testing laboratory
Ringworm See pages 195–96 for additional information	Fungus spreads from person to person by: **direct contact** (skin-to-skin), and **indirect contact** (e.g., shared combs, unwashed clothes, or shower or pool surfaces) Also acquired from **pets, especially cats**	Ring-shaped itchy, scaly lesions on scalp, body or feet (Athlete's foot). Bald spots on the scalp.	Transmissible as long as rash is untreated and/or uncovered	Yes, until the first treatment has been applied	No
Roseola For more information, see page 203	Virus probably spreads from person to person by **direct contact with saliva.** Often found in saliva of people with no symptoms.	High fever and crankiness for 3 to 5 days. When the fever subsides, a rash of small red spots appears on the face and body, lasting a few hours to 2 days.	Infectious while symptoms are present	No. A child with roseola can continue to attend child care as long as she is well enough to participate in all program activities.	No

(appendix continues on next page)

Illness	How it spreads	Symptoms	Infectious period	Exclude?	Report / Notify
Rubella (German measles) For more information and important requirements, see pages 203–04 and 376	Virus spreads from person to person by: **direct contact with nose/mouth secretions, or respiratory droplets**	Mild in children, with low fever, swollen glands in the neck and behind the ears, and a rash with small red spots. More severe in adults. If acquired in pregnancy, may seriously affect the fetus.	Infectious from 7 days before to 7 days after the rash appears	Yes, for 7 days after the rash is first noticed	Yes, by the treating physician and testing laboratory **Rubella exposure is a medical emergency. Notify your local public health unit immediately if a child or adult at your facility is diagnosed with rubella.** Non-immune children and staff may need immunization. **Notify all parents and staff immediately** Advise pregnant staff and parents who aren't sure of their immune status to see their doctor
Scabies See pages 192–93 for additional information	Mites spread from person to person by **direct (prolonged, close and intimate) contact**	Itchy red rash, usually between fingers and toes, or the wrists or in the groin, with thread-like lines and scratch marks. May be elsewhere on the body in children under 2 years of age.	Transmissible as long as infestation is untreated	Yes, until the first treatment has been applied	No. Contact your local public health unit for guidance if an outbreak cannot be controlled.

(appendix continues on next page)

ILLNESS	TRANSMISSION	SIGNS/ SYMPTOMS	INFECTIOUS PERIOD	EXCLUSION	REPORTING AND NOTIFICATION
Streptococcal pharyngitis (strep throat) and **scarlet fever** See pages 181–82 for additional information	Bacteria in throat spread from person to person by: **direct contact with saliva, or respiratory droplets**	Sore throat, fever, swollen tender neck glands Scarlet fever is strep throat with a red sunburn-like rash covering the entire body	Infectious from onset of illness until 24 hours of appropriate antibiotic treatment received	Yes. A child can return to the program once he has received at least 24 hours of appropriate antibiotic treatment, and the child is well enough to participate in all program activities.	Scarlet fever is reportable by the treating physician in some jurisdictions Contact your public health unit if you suspect an outbreak at your facility (more than 2 cases in a month)
Thrush and *Candida* diaper rash See pages 196–97 for additional information	Fungus is normally present in the body without causing illness, and rarely spreads from person to person Thrush can be transmitted to an infant by contact with contaminated bottle nipples or soothers	Thrush presents as whitish-gray patches on the inside of the cheek or on the tongue *Candida* diaper rash is a painful bright-red rash in the deepest creases of a baby's groin, on the buttocks or in moist neck folds	Usually not spread from person to person	No	No Make sure bottle nipples and soothers aren't shared between children
Tuberculosis (TB) For more information and important requirements, see pages 210–11 and 381	Bacteria from the lungs **spread through the air in particles produced by coughing**	For infectious TB: fever, cough, difficulty breathing Young children rarely have infectious TB	If infectious TB: As long as bacteria are in the respiratory secretions	If infectious TB: Yes, for at least 2 weeks after starting appropriate antibiotic treatment and until the treating physician or local public health unit states that the child is no longer infectious	Yes, by the treating physician and testing laboratory **Notify your local public health unit immediately if a child or adult at your facility is diagnosed with TB** Exposed children and adults may need testing and antibiotic treatment **Notify all parents and staff immediately**

Source: Canadian Paediatric Society, *Well Beings: A Guide to Health in Child Care*. (Ottawa: Canadian Paediatric Society, 2008), pp. 225–34. Reprinted with permission.

All page numbers cited above refer to Well Beings: A Guide to Health in Child Care

Nutrition

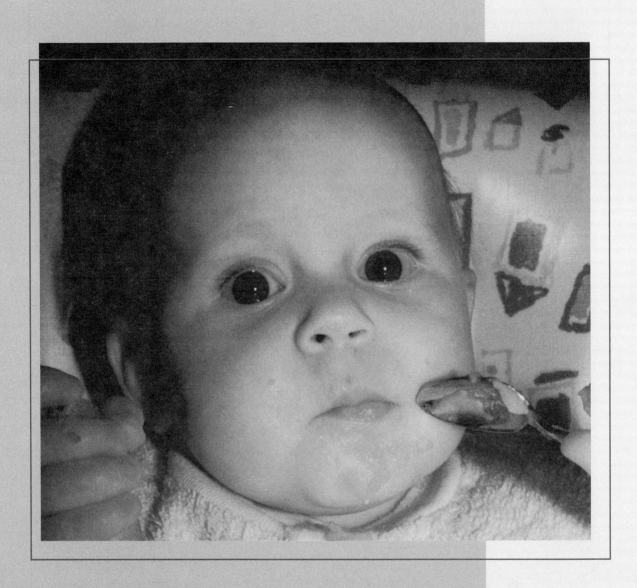

CONTENTS

Nutrition is the science of food and how it is used by the body. Discussion on nutrition includes these facts:

■ Food has different meanings for each individual.

■ Eating patterns are shaped by interrelated factors in our lives.

Nutritious food is essential for all dimensions of our health. This key factor is the cornerstone in developing and evolving nutrition programs for young children. Educators' motivation plays an essential role in promoting children's well-being. It is important to balance children's rights to have control over what and how much food they consume with adults' responsibility to provide

- enough food,
- a variety of wholesome foods, and
- an eating environment that promotes healthy eating.

When we recognize that healthy eating habits developed early tend to have life-long benefits, the influence that early childhood educators have in supporting eating habits cannot be understated.

OBJECTIVES

To list and discuss six factors that shape our eating habits.

To be aware of food insecurity in Canada.

FACTORS THAT SHAPE EATING HABITS

For most people, food usually means more than just relieving hunger and providing nourishment. The meaning that food carries can be positive and healthy and associated with celebrations, including special foods, holidays, social time with family and friends, and religious or ethnocultural events. Other meanings may be negative and not conducive to health or well-being; these may result in eating for the wrong reasons (see Emotional, page 217).

Think about how you view food generally, the food choices you make, and how you feel before, during, and after eating. Awareness of our emotions, attitudes, and behaviour toward food and eating is necessary to foster healthy eating habits in children. If we perpetuate myths or model poor eating habits—such as a focus on dieting—we are giving negative messages to children and may unwittingly influence lifelong eating problems.

Several Factors that Affect Eating Habits

Several factors must be considered when we look at nutrition: physical, emotional, social, cultural, body image, and economics. The interaction of these factors and others results in complex dynamics that educators need to be aware of to promote healthy attitudes toward nutrition and eating.

Physical

The first factor that comes to mind is our physical need for food. Nutrients in food provide the building blocks for cell and tissue growth, the regulators for many of the body's functions, and fuel for energy. Each nutrient can play a specific role or multiple roles. The way nutrients interact with the other factors is very complex. Nutrition affects a child's thinking and learning capacities, for example. A child who is weak from poor nutrition will have little energy to learn or socialize. Canadian nutritional guidelines have been established for the intake of nutrients (vitamins, minerals, proteins, fat, carbohydrates) for children and adults. The guidelines take into account that variations exist in the requirements for nutrients among individuals. Growth rates and body types vary because we all differ in our genetic makeup, even from our siblings. The human body's need for energy varies with age, body size, growth patterns, gender, level of physical activity, and basal metabolic rate (the rate at which your body uses energy for essential bodily functions).

Physical Activity

We know that physical activity goes hand in hand with nutrition as part of an active, healthy lifestyle, which is discussed in Unit 6. Individuals of all ages who maintain a moderate level of daily activity help their bodies work more efficiently, often by increasing their basal metabolic rate and bone density. It is hoped that children enjoy physical activity just for the fun of it, and it supports their physical fitness, brain development (Ratey, 2008), and positive self-image.

Sensory Experiences

Eating is a truly sensory experience. When you watch young children eat, they see, smell, taste, and touch the food. They hear the crispy, crunchy, and squishy sounds that food makes. From infancy, we begin to develop taste preferences. Several studies have shown that newborn babies innately prefer sweet tastes. This preference, however, may be altered early on by introducing other tastes. Older infants and young children often prefer a saltier taste. Children's love of dill pickles and salty broth sometimes surprises adults. There is interest in, but no conclusions yet on, some of the genetic links between taste preferences. Young children also react to texture, generally preferring soft, fluffy foods (e.g., pudding) and crisp vegetables. Meats are not favoured generally because they are difficult to chew with primary teeth.

Families' ethnocultural food habits are powerful, especially for children's developing tastes. A study was conducted in a Mexican community to see how the people developed a taste for chili peppers. This food is a daily staple in their community, and the gradual, respectful introduction of chili peppers from infancy resulted in a preference for this taste by preschool age. Lambert-Lagacé (2002) suggests that, using this approach, broccoli should be easy!

Emotional

The emotional component of nutrition is related to individual likes and dislikes. It may simply be a matter of taste differentiation or a desire for or aversion to food associated with a positive or negative experience. *For example, a child who is forced, rather than gently encouraged, to eat yams may develop an aversion to yams.* Table 5.1 shows ways in which children can develop positive or negative associations with food or affect their eating habits.

Children enter early childhood programs with their repertoire of familiar foods based mostly on what their families serve and the emotional and social status that these foods hold. Children quickly pick up messages that may make them more or less responsive to a new food.

If a two-year-old's parent has told her to eat all her vegetables before she can have dessert, it is no mystery that she will give the dessert a higher status than the vegetables, reinforcing her preference for dessert.

Social and Cultural

The social and cultural aspects of eating have a significant influence on our lives and are linked with physical and emotional forces; food often has deep personal

TABLE 5.1   What Food Can Mean

POSITIVE AND NEGATIVE ASSOCIATIONS WITH FOOD	
Security	When an infant cries from hunger, someone feeds and cuddles him or her, which contributes to a sense of security.
Insecurity	When a family is unable to provide enough food regularly (food insecurity), the child's ability to predict events may be jeopardized.
Pacifier	A child who is always given food whenever he or she cries, regardless of whether the child is hungry, views food as a pacifier rather than a means of nourishment.
Learning	A young child learns about the world by experiencing food through the five senses.
Punishment	Parents withdraw food, often dessert, because of inappropriate behaviour or may send the child to bed hungry.
Reward	Children are offered food, usually sweets, as a reward for success or "good" behaviour.
Individuality	A child uses food as a way to express individuality (i.e., food likes and dislikes).
Love	The child learns to give and eat food to show love (e.g., chocolates on Valentine's Day or a mother saying, "Don't you like mommy's dinner?" which equates rejection of the food with rejection of her).
Comforter	Food is used to relieve boredom or loneliness or to handle anxiety or disappointment (e.g., following rejection by a friend, a child is comforted with cookies or candy). The child learns to use food as a coping mechanism.
Fear	An unpleasant experience with food (e.g., choking) causes a child to fear eating that food in the future.
Approval	A child tries to win approval and acceptance through food by eating and refusing what his or her peers eat and refuse (e.g., a school-age child rejects foods from home that had been readily accepted until the child's friends commented negatively on it) or by "cleaning off the plate" for daddy.
Weapon	A child with little control over his or her environment uses food for revenge or to get attention (e.g., by refusing to eat, demanding food, throwing food).

meaning. It would be rare not to see food playing a significant role in any social gathering. Some foods are more likely to be served in certain social situations—such as hot dogs at ball games and popcorn at movies. Many food traditions in social gatherings are related to particular ethnocultural or religious holidays.

Cabbage rolls as one of the 12 meatless dishes prepared at Ukrainians' Christmas Eve. Chinese cake at Chinese New Year. Special baked goods at Passover or Easter. Turkey at Thanksgiving. Iftar (breaking fast) during Ramadan is often done as a community, starting with eating sweet dates.

Eating with other people tends to be viewed as a more enjoyable experience than eating alone. Do you, or someone you know who lives alone, eat in front of the television for company? Eating together can promote positive values, such as awareness of your needs and desires as well as those of others, sharing, learning respectful rhythms of talking and listening, and celebrating as a community (see Creating a Positive Eating Environment, page 248).

Young children who eat with positive adult companionship eat better than those who have no or negative adult intervention (Escobar, 1999, p. 54). The way foods are viewed by others in our midst affects the status of the food. If parents and educators treat all nutritious foods with equal respect, children are more likely to try a variety of them. If certain foods are given lower status, children are liable to share that view.

Traditional ethnocultural preferences for food are often strongest in families that have recently come to Canada. When ethnicity is an important aspect of family life, parents often continue to prepare traditional foods and perhaps combine them with contemporary foods of North America. We often associate North American foods with the highly processed, high-fat, and refined-sugar foods that are not as rich in nutrients as many of the more traditional, ethnocultural foods. *Eating Well with Canada's Food Guide* encourages Canadians to reduce their intake of highly processed, refined foods (Health Canada, 2007a) (see Appendix 5.1, page 287). The World Health Organization (2003, p. 16) has expressed alarm about the major change in peoples' diet around the world, first in industrial countries and more recently in developing countries. Chronic lifestyle diseases are the result of a myriad of factors, but they are undeniably linked to the energy-dense diets high in animal fat that are replacing traditional plant-based diets in much of the world. Educators should try to be aware of and reinforce traditional, ethnocultural food preferences, particularly those higher in nutrients (e.g., vegetables and fruit) and less refined (i.e., whole grains).

We are bombarded daily with information and pressure from the media— newspapers, magazines, radio, television, movies, videos/DVDs, the Internet, and video games. Young children are unable developmentally to discriminate between the commercials and the television show, which makes them vulnerable to advertisements for non-nutritious foods. Also, children notice that many shows depict "cool" children and adolescents regularly eating low-nutritive snack foods such as chips and cookies or complaining when they eat vegetables. Furthermore, the significant amount of sedentary screen time that children could be spending in physically challenging activities does not contribute to optimal health. Watching television is also associated with snacking on high-fat and high-sugar foods (see Impact of Screen Time on Healthy Active Living, page 336).

Parents, educators, and other adults in children's lives can have a significant influence on their acceptance of a variety of foods. The more someone experiences different foods, the more likely that child is to develop a taste for them. Children who have had less exposure to new foods are more likely to be labelled as "picky eaters" and unwilling to try new foods, which creates a vicious circle (Carruth et al., 2004).

Body Image

Maintaining weight within a normal range is conducive to health. However, the range that has been considered normal, particularly for women (although it is becoming more of an issue for men), has been narrowly defined by the fashion industry, the media, and some factions of the dance and sport domains. Society continues to focus too much on body weight. This preoccupation has, in fact, contributed to the dramatic overall rise in obesity (obesity in Canadian children has doubled in the past 20 years) and eating disorders in our society over the past few decades. How? Dieting can be the first step in the development of **disordered eating** (the behaviour) and **eating disorders** (a diagnosed illness) (National Eating Disorder Information Centre [NEDIC], 2008).

Dieting by restricting calories or food groups will almost certainly cause problems that are counterproductive:

- The metabolism will slow down as the body tries to fight the starvation process.
- The weight will return in a short time.
- A lowered sense of self-worth or depression is common due to feelings of failure.

The process and philosophy of dieting ignore the fact that healthy people come in all shapes and sizes and, instead, tie personal worth to physical thinness. Natural body weights, based on genetic predisposition and managed when we treat our bodies with respect through healthy eating and regular physical activity, do not come close to those of the runway models for the vast majority of women and men. The ideal body image is often portrayed as the unattainable "perfect" body (usually associated with thinness). Children, especially girls, from a very young age can become obsessed with their weight if they are surrounded by these dangerous messages. Early on, families and educators need to support young children to have a healthy lifestyle, become media literate, develop positive life skills such as assertiveness and problem solving, and learn how to handle harrassment or teasing based on appearance. (NEDIC, 2008). A study in 1961 in which 5th and 6th grade children ranked pictures of other children was replicated 40 years later (Latner & Stunkard, 2003). The prevalence of obesity had more than doubled between 1961 and 2001. The picture of the obese child was liked significantly less (by 40.8%) in the present study than in 1961—a disturbing conclusion that the stigmatization of obesity seems to have increased over the past 40 years (see Concerns about Childhood Obesity, page 298). Women receive ubiquitous messages from the fashion, media, and diet industries that they are never good enough and that they must deprive themselves to continually fight the natural size of their body. Young men are also expected to have muscular "six-pack" bodies. In addition, the "fear of fat" that pervades our society results in social prejudice and discrimination against individuals who weigh more than what is deemed acceptable. This can damage their feelings of self-worth and result in extreme dieting, creating a vicious circle. Another study (Latner, Rosewall, & Simmonds, 2007) that assessed how much time 10- to 13-year-olds spent weekly reading magazines and watching TV and video games revealed that a greater dislike of obese children was associated with more time in these activities, especially magazine reading.

According to a large school-based study in Ontario (Jones et al., 2001),

- more than 27% of girls aged 12 to 18 years had disordered eating attitudes and behaviour.
- dieting, binge eating, purging, and using diet pills were cited at all ages, including 12% of 12- to 14-year-old girls who reported binge eating in the previous month and 7% who self-induced vomiting.

Children gain some fat prior to puberty as part of the normal growth process. This gain often coincides with an increased concern with body image, and the cycle of dieting may begin. The Jones et al. (2007) study recommends interactive education that doesn't simply teach principles of healthy eating but also focuses on the positive aspects of the self to validate girls' experiences and feelings while providing them with the tools to understand the societal pressures that they face.

Many young children are eating less than the recommended amount of food and calories and are showing low muscle mass. This evidence suggests that lack of physical activity plays a role in their weight gain. The tendency in our society to diet adds to the problem rather than helps because lowering food intake tends to slow our metabolism rather than make it run more efficiently. *Eating Well with Canada's Food Guide*, on the other hand, focuses the message of eating well and being active today and every day (Health Canada, 2007a).

This issue is important in early childhood education because educators, like everyone else, are profoundly influenced by media messages. Remember the great impact you have on children and how they look up to you. It is important to be sensitive to the subtle messages (e.g., you are constantly on a diet) and the overt ones (e.g., you comment to a child that he or she is chubby or skinny) that you send to children.

Economics

In Canada, an exciting range of foods is available in many urban communities. However, this is not the case in all Canadian communities. Even when a vast range of foods is available, they may not be used due to cost or perhaps because many people are unsure of how to prepare them.

Family incomes and parents' awareness of nutrition directly influence the quality of the family's dietary intake. That is, higher levels of family incomes and parents who are knowledgeable about nutrition and cooking contribute to better dietary intake. Better-off parents can afford and prepare a wider variety of wholesome foods. Families with lower incomes not only have less money in their food budget but also may lack adequate transportation, which limits their access to bulk purchases, sales, or lower priced but more nutritious foods. Small neighbourhood convenience stores, for example, may not carry a variety of fresh fruit and vegetables or may charge higher prices.

Parents may choose to spend part of their food budget eating in restaurants. Eating out shapes eating habits because restaurant menus limit food choices and affect how foods are prepared. Even so, many families with young children eat in fast-food places that serve mainly high-fat, high-sodium fried food. Children's choices are influenced by marketing of children's "meal deals," comprising a hamburger, fries, pop, and a toy. Some ofthese fast-food restaurants offer to increase the portion sizes for a small increase in price, thus encouraging individuals to eat larger portions because they see the deal as a bargain (see Supporting Healthy Eating Habits, page 323).

Food Insecurity

Food is one of the most basic needs of every human being. However, in Canada and around the world, people do not have equal access to food.

Generally, **food insecurity** is determined by financial insecurity. In other words, when a family does not have the financial means to afford all the necessities

of a healthy life, their food and nutrition intake suffer. Fixed payments such as rent and power bills make it likely that the more "flexible" grocery budget is what bears a large burden of poverty. A sequence of events, starting with an illness, loss of a job, or another family member to take care of, can take families from anxiety about running out of food, to buying lower quality foods, to not even having enough to satisfy hunger (McIntyre, 2002). These families are more likely to have multiple chronic conditions, including heart disease, diabetes, high blood pressure, and food allergies (Che & Chen, 2001; Tarasuk, 2002).

Food costs have also been rising worldwide, partly due to changing fuel prices and commodity costs, weather concerns such as droughts, and other reasons, affecting long-term costs in the food industry. In 2007, grain-related products, such as corn, led the way in price jumps, but foods of all kinds are now being affected. (Magnan, 2008). In the news, there are reports of families in Canada buying rice in large quantities in grocery stores and shipping it back to their families living in developing countries where there is a rice shortage and what is available is very costly.

Another reason that food costs are rising is the use of available food for reasons other than for eating. The production of biofuels illustrates this

point. The global production of biofuels is booming as higher oil prices and technological breakthroughs have made it a more profitable business. Another reason for the demand is that governments in most industrialized countries are seeking a reliable source of energy to respond to concerns about fossil fuels and their affects on global warming. *For example, ethanol, an alcohol produced through fermentation of sugar sources such as plants, can be used as is or blended with regular gasoline. In Canada, ethanol is made from wheat in the western provinces and from corn in Ontario and Quebec. The Canadian government projects that ethanol production will increase to about 2.74 billion litres by the end of 2010 (Forge, 2007).*

Although biofuels, and ethanol in particular, have been used for over a century, they have only recently been recognized as playing a role in reducing greenhouse gas emissions. With less corn and wheat available for public consumption, the cost of these grains and their products (e.g., bread) is rising. Food banks are "Band-Aid" solutions to the poverty and food insecurity experienced by families in Canada. Food banks have become an institution in Canada for many families whose breadwinners work at low-paying jobs or depend on social assistance and who can't manage the cost of food on top of rent, utilities, clothing, and transportation. Many children are hungry day in and day out, which affects their short- and long-term physical, emotional, and social well-being. In a country as rich as Canada, it is atrocious that so many children and families go hungry. Poverty is a complex social issue that must be addressed by all levels of government and communities across Canada. "Sustainable solutions require a commitment to economic and social policy reform, not just to stop-gap measures such as food banks or targeted, short-term nutrition support programs" (McIntyre, 2002, p. 3).

To list the seven categories of nutrients and describe their main functions.

To explain the important aspects of *Eating Well with Canada's Food Guide* as it relates to children.

NUTS AND BOLTS OF NUTRITION

Understanding the basics of nutrition enables us to understand the important role that eating healthy food plays in promoting health.

Role of Nutrients

Nutrients are substances that are found in food. They are divided into seven categories: carbohydrates, proteins, fats, vitamins, minerals, fibre, and water (see Table 5.2).

TABLE 5.2   Functions of Nutrients

CATEGORIES	FUNCTIONS
Carbohydrates	primary nutrient for providing calories (or energy) needed for work and physical activity
Proteins	support bodily functions (e.g., proteins are needed for cell growth and repair); part of various enzymes, hormones, and antibodies; provide energy
Fats	all cell membranes are made of lipids (fats), including cells of the nervous system; omega-3 and -6 fats essential for brain and nerve function and healthy skin; transport fat-soluble vitamins; provide energy
Vitamins	organic substances (i.e., contain carbon) essential for helping the body regulate its functions (e.g., water-soluble vitamin C is an antioxidant that protects cells from damage and helps the body absorb iron, a mineral, from nonmeat sources as it is transported through the body)
Minerals	inorganic substances essential in differing amounts to help the body function properly and stay strong (e.g., magnesium is one of the minerals needed in the formation and maintenance of strong bones and teeth); transmission of nerve impulses; release of energy
Fibre	regular functioning of intestines and bowel; feeds the bacteria in the colon to sustain colonic health
Water	necessary to maintain normal hydration, blood pressure, and fluid balance; water makes up between 45 and 75% of body weight in humans; toddlers are generally around 70% water

Appendix 5.2 (page 289) expands on the description of nutrients, what foods they are found in, and their functions. Remember the following points about nutrients:

- All nutrients needed by the body are found in food. In addition to the seven categories listed above, hundreds of other chemicals are found in foods (e.g., phytochemicals found in fruit and vegetables). There is no such thing as the perfect food. Eating a varied diet usually provides our body with all the vitamins and minerals we need.

    There are some exceptions; for example, women who could become or are pregnant should take a multivitamin containing 0.4 mg (400 µg) of folic acid every day. Folic acid is required to reduce the risk of neural tube defects in developing babies.

    There are other situations in which people in particular life stages or who have certain lifestyles or a health condition that requires higher needs for specific nutrients should be under the care of a physician or dietitian to monitor needs for added supplements (Dietitians of Canada, 2008).

    However, parents who give their children daily vitamin or mineral supplements "for their health" should evaluate the short- and long-term safety of this practice. Keep in mind that these supplements are not a substitute for food. "Real food is complex and offers many substances including antioxidants and phytochemicals in desirable proportions" (Deverell, 1998, p. E5).

- Many nutrients work best when combined with one or more other nutrients.

Our body absorbs iron better in the presence of vitamin C, and calcium needs phosphorus, magnesium, and vitamin D to build bones and teeth.

- Many foods are not simply a carbohydrate, protein, or fat but are a combination of two or three nutrients.

The yolk of an egg is high in fat, but the white is high in protein. Most cheeses and meats are a combination of protein and fat. The energy from whole-grain bread comes mostly from carbohydrates with a little from protein and fat.

- We all need the same nutrients, but how much we need of each nutrient varies with age, size, activity level, and other factors.

Children need more calcium because of bone and tooth formation. A very physically active teenager needs more food energy than a less active one.

- The quality of nutrients is affected by how food is grown, harvested, stored, and prepared.

Broccoli provides more vitamin C and the B vitamins, especially folate, when it is raw than when it is boiled until soft because most of the B and C vitamins are lost in the water—they are water soluble.

- Rinsing fresh fruit and vegetables under running water with a mild soap removes soil and pesticide residue. Although peeling produce (e.g., apples, cucumbers) results in a loss of fibre, vitamins, and minerals, peeling may be advisable if there is concern about pesticide use. Other ways to avoid vitamin and mineral loss are to
  - cut, tear, or chop produce just before use to reduce the loss of vitamin C;
  - microwave, pressure cook, steam, or stir-fry vegetables just until tender;
  - avoid boiling vegetables; and
  - save cooking water for soups or stews.

- Eating too much or too little of any nutrient can contribute to or cause disease. Reduce the amount of fat, sugar, and salt you eat by using less or none at all in cooking and at the table. The taste for salt is learned, and the excess salt (sodium) intake of Canadians is of concern.

  Research shows that sodium causes high blood pressure and damage to blood vessels even in children, setting them up for an increased risk of stroke and heart disease (Kirkey, 2007) (see Appendix 5.2, page 289).

  According to the Heart and Stroke Foundation of Canada (2008), most Canadians consume about 15 mL (3 tsp.) of salt every day, which is three times the recommended daily amount of 5 mL (1 tsp.) per day.

  The goal of a federally appointed working group is to bring dietary sodium to healthy levels by 2020. The level of sodium in processed foods is of most concern and may mean that targeted legislation may be necessary (Kirkey, 2007). If children become more familiar with herbs and spices as interesting alternatives to processed foods and the salt shaker, their lifelong health will benefit.

The Foundation for Healthy Eating: *Eating Well with Canada's Food Guide*

Health Canada's ***Eating Well with Canada's Food Guide*** is based on two principles of healthy living: eating well and being active every day for everyone two years of age and older (Health Canada, 2007a). *Eating Well with Canada's Food Guide*'s recommendations for the amounts and types of food support meeting the daily requirements of vitamins, minerals, and other nutrients. Healthy eating contributes to your overall health and vitality and helps reduce your risk of medical conditions such as obesity, certain types of cancer, heart disease, type 2 diabetes, and osteoporosis (Health Canada, 2007a). The four **food groups** have a range of recommended daily servings based on the different ages and stages of individuals (see Table 5.3).

A young woman who is moderately active can eat five or six servings of grain products (e.g., 30 g [½ cup] of cereal, two slices of whole-grain bread, 120 g [2 cups] of noodles in a particular day), which is adequate for her needs. If she increases her daily physical activity or becomes pregnant, her daily need for grain products will increase to seven or eight servings.

TABLE 5.3	Recommended Daily Servings								
AGES IN YEARS	**2–3**	**4–8**	**9–13**	**14–18**		**19–50**		**51+**	
SEX	GIRLS AND BOYS			FEMALES	MALES	FEMALES	MALES	FEMALES	MALES
Vegetables and Fruit	4	5	6	7	8	7–8	8–10	7	7
Grain Products	3	4	6	6	7	6–7	8	6	7
Milk and Alternatives	2	2	3–4	3–4	3–4	2	2	3	3
Meat and Alternatives	1	1	1–2	2	3	2	3	2	3

Source: *Eating Well with Canada's Food Guide: A Resource for Educators and Communicators.* Health Canada, 2007. Reproduced with the permission of the Minister of Public Works and Government Services Canada, 2008.

Table 5.4 lists the **key nutrients** in each food group and highlights the importance of eating a variety of foods to obtain the daily recommended nutrients.

Eating Well with Canada's Food Guide recommends making food choices that are healthier and limiting foods and beverages that have few nutrients and are usually high in fat, salt, or sugar or a combination. Examples include cakes and pastries, chocolate and candies, cookies and granola bars, ice cream and frozen desserts, doughnuts and muffins, French fries, potato chips, nachos and other salty snacks, fruit-flavoured drinks, soft drinks, and sweetened hot or cold drinks. In early childhood programs, nutrition policies and practices that minimize the use of "less healthy foods" can contribute to children's interest in more nutritious foods.

Research on diet and disease has shown that most Canadians have a diet that is lower in fibre and higher in fat than is optimal for health and for lowering risk factors for chronic illnesses such as heart disease, some cancers, and obesity. Canadians are urged to continue to increase their intake of foods composed of complex carbohydrates (i.e., breads, cereals, vegetables, fruit) to replace the energy derived from the fat in meat and alternatives and particularly in high-fat, low-nutritive or junk foods such as potato chips, chocolate bars, and doughnuts. In response to this research, *Eating Well with Canada's Food Guide* emphasizes eating grain products, vegetables, and fruit (Health Canada, 2007a). For anyone ready to improve his or her eating habits, these two strategies are good places to start. However, Health Canada (2007a) reminds us that too much fibre can be a problem for growing children, whose small stomachs must be able to contain enough calories for growth. Serving raw vegetables with a dip made with a dairy product, for example, is a good way both to promote fibre and to provide enough food energy.

Four different types of fatty acids make up the fats in our foods: polyunsaturated, monounsaturated, saturated, and trans fatty acids (Health Canada, 2007b). Currently, most Canadians get more than they need of their daily

TABLE 5.4 Key Nutrients in *Eating Well with Canada's Food Guide*

SOME IMPORTANT NUTRIENTS IN THE FOOD GROUPS				
KEY NUTRIENT	VEGETABLES AND FRUIT	GRAIN PRODUCTS	MILK AND ALTERNATIVES	MEAT AND ALTERNATIVES
Protein			✓	✓
Fat			✓	✓
Carbohydrate	✓	✓	✓	
Fibre	✓	✓		
Thiamin		✓		✓
Riboflavin		✓	✓	✓
Niacin		✓		✓
Folate	✓	✓		
Vitamin B_6	✓			✓
Vitamin B_{12}			✓	✓
Vitamin C	✓			
Vitamin A	✓		✓	
Vitamin D			✓	
Calcium			✓	
Iron		✓		✓
Zinc		✓	✓	✓
Magnesium	✓	✓	✓	✓
Potassium	✓	✓	✓	✓

Source: *Eating Well With Canada's Food Guide: A Resource for Educators and Communicators,* Health Canada, 2007. Reproduced with the permission of the Minister of Public Works and Government Services Canada, 2008.

calories (or energy) from fats. Although fat is important for body functions such as providing essential fatty acids and carrying fat-soluble vitamins through the body, research into links between fat intake and disease has resulted in recommendations regarding the type and amount of fat we consume. The following summary outlines the general suggestions made by Health Canada (2007b), but keep in mind that ongoing research may result in future adjusted recommendations:

■ A diet low in saturated fat and trans fat reduces risk of cardiovascular disease. Saturated fats are found in meats, animal products (e.g., cheese, eggs), and tropical oils (e.g., palm kernel oil, coconut oil). Most trans fats are "artificial," created when liquid oils are manufactured to produce more solid fats, such as shortening and margarine. Health Canada's food label requirements include listing both saturated and trans fat percentages when applicable to help the consumer identify them (see Nutrition Labels, page 236, and Reduce Trans Fats and Promote Awareness of Saturated Fats, page 326).

- Unsaturated, monounsaturated, and polyunsaturated fats (e.g., olive, canola, soy, and sunflower oils, nonhydrogenated margarine and fats founds in nuts, seeds, and fatty fish) are thought to maintain or increase our high-density lipoprotein (HDL) ("good" cholesterol), helping to protect the heart and cardiovascular system. These fats are a healthier choice, eaten in moderation, than saturated and trans fats.

- The best polyunsaturated fats contain high amounts of essential fatty acids called omega-3 and omega-6 fats, which raise the HDL level. Omega-6 fatty acids are derived from corn, soy, safflower, and sunflower sources, and most Canadians consume enough of these foods to obtain the omega-6 fatty acids they need. However, fatty acids such as omega-3 docosahexaenoic acid (DHA), an essential component of all cells in the body, especially brain cells, tend to need more attention. Fish is high in omega-3, which is good for the heart and brain, making it an excellent choice for healthy eating two to five times a week. However, one caution is that some fish (higher up the food chain) contain methyl mercury. Mercury that is released into the environment may be deposited into water, where microorganisms can convert it to methyl mercury, a highly toxic form of mercury that can build up in living tissue (Health Canada, 2007c).

Health Canada's recommendation to limit certain fish is particularly important for pregnant and breast-feeding women, babies, and children. Mercury can damage a growing brain. Fish known to have higher mercury levels include marlin, orange roughy, shark, swordfish, and fresh or frozen tuna. Although canned white albacore tuna is a concern, canned light tuna (skipjack, yellowfin, tongol) is safe. Check the Health Canada website for current mercury advisories (see Resource Materials, page 283). Health Canada's standards for mercury in fish are some of the most stringent and protective in the world.

Fish may not be part of your diet if you dislike the taste of fish, have a fish allergy, or are a vegetarian. Other ways to get those important sources of omega-3 fatty acids may include fish-oil or vegan DHA capsules and plant-based omega-3 fatty acids, including crushed flax and walnut.

Although not all fats are equal when it comes to our health, the total amount of all fats is important to consider because all are equally high in calories. Do keep in mind that young children's needs for fat differ from those of older children and adults.

Relating *Eating Well with Canada's Food Guide* to Children

During the first two years of life, children undergo a period of rapid growth and development, including brain development. At no other time in your life does your body need a diet as high in fat—approximately 50% of the total daily calories—to provide you with adequate energy and fatty acids. This is the primary reason why children under two are not included in Canada's food guidelines. A second reason is that the gradual introduction of solid foods over the first two years does not relate to *Eating Well with Canada's Food Guide*. What about children over two years old? Health Canada's (2007a) recent changes to *Eating Well with Canada's Food Guide* include preschoolers.

Milk Products

In the second year of life, most infants make a transition from breast milk or **formula** to cow's milk. Between 12 and 24 months, children should drink homogenized milk. Children at that age need the fat from whole milk for brain development. Toddlers are not yet eating the variety and quantity of food to provide them with the daily dietary requirement for fat, so milk products remain the primary source of fat.

Some parents and even some doctors start the one-year-old on lower fat milk (skim, 1%, 2%) if they believe the baby is too chubby—although there is little or no correlation between body fat in infancy and later childhood. This example illustrates society's fear of fat. In fact, if the one- to two-year-old drinks lower fat milk, he or she may be hungry and tend to eat more food. Whole milk not only provides babies with essential fats but also contributes to their sense of fullness.

Partially skimmed milk (1% and 2%) can be offered to children between 2 and 5 years old, as they usually eat a number of foods that are higher in fat, supplying them with the essential fatty acids. By the time children are five years old, they can be offered skim milk. Although they still need the calcium and other nutrients that milk provides, they don't need the same percentage of dietary fat and are usually eating adult-sized servings (Canadian Paediatric Society, 2008).

Although cow's milk is commonly considered one of the staples of the Milk and Alternatives food group, it is important to acknowledge that other foods or beverages can provide the key nutrients supplied by cow's milk (see Table 5.4, page 228). A prime example of one of the key nutrients found in the Milk and Alternatives group is the mineral calcium. In childhood, calcium is necessary to build strong bones to support a growing body and help prevent osteoporosis later in life. The greater our peak bone mass when linear growth stops in our late teens, the less likely our bones are to become porous and fragile later in life (Osteoporosis Canada, 2003). The daily calcium recommendations for children 2 to 3 years old is 500 mg, for 4- to 8-year-olds is 800 mg, and for 9- to 18-year-olds is 1,300 mg (Health Canada, 2007d, p. 7). One of the concerns about children drinking carbonated and other low-nutritive drinks is that they then drink less of any calcium-rich beverages (see Reduce the Consumption of Carbonated and Other Low-Nutritive Beverages, page 329). However, there are several other reasons why children may not drink cow's or goat's milk, including cultural or religious reasons, allergies, or taste dislike. Lactose intolerance can usually be reconciled with several options, such as lactose-free products. For children who don't regularly consume cow's or goat's milk, Table 5.5 lists foods and beverages that contain calcium to compare with *Eating Well with Canada's Food Guide* recommendations.

TABLE 5.5 Amounts of Calcium in Foods and Beverages

FOOD OR BEVERAGE	CHILD SERVING SIZES	AMOUNT OF CALCIUM
Calcium-fortified orange juice	125 mL, 4 oz.	185 mg
Cheddar cheese	25 g, 3/4 oz.	180 mg
Firm tofu, set with calcium	87 mL, 3/8 cup, 3 oz.	174 mg
Cow's milk (chocolate, lactose free, or buttermilk)	125 mL, 4 oz.	173 mg
Fortified soy or rice beverage	125 mL, 4 oz.	160 mg
Goat's milk	125 mL, 4 oz.	150 mg
Sardines, Atlantic, with bones	3 fish, 38 g, 1¼ oz.	138 mg
Fruit yogurt, nonfat	87 mL, 3/8 cup, 3 oz.	133 mg
Canned salmon, with bones	38 g, 1/4 cup, 1¼ oz.	93 mg
Spinach, boiled	62 mL, 1/4 cup, 2 oz.	65 mg
Toasted almonds	30 mL, 1/8 cup, 1 oz.	50 mg
Bok choy, swiss chard, kale, okra, cooked	62 mL, 1/4 cup, 2 oz.	25–42 mg
Cooked beans (e.g., navy beans, kidney beans, chickpeas)	87 mL, 3/8 cup, 3 oz.	20–45 mg
Edamame	62 mL, 1/4 cup, 2 oz.	26 mg
Broccoli, cooked	62 mL, 1/4 cup, 2 oz.	17 mg
Dried figs	1 fig, 8 g	14 mg
Tahini	15 mL, 1 tbsp., 1/2 oz.	10 g

Source: Adapted with permission from Toronto Public Health, *Nutrition matters: Getting enough calcium without the cow.* PH0802SS038.

What Is a Child-Sized Serving?

To determine developmentally appropriate serving sizes, look at the recommendations in *Eating Well with Canada's Food Guide* and cut the quantity by approximately

- two-thirds to three-quarters for toddlers,
- one-quarter to half for preschoolers, and
- one-quarter or nil for school-agers.

See also Table 5.6. But remember that every child is an individual. His or her appetite can vary greatly with age, gender, activity level, and other factors. A child's appetite will also fluctuate based on growth spurts. When she or he is going through a growth spurt, the child is likely to be hungrier and to desire more food.

TABLE 5.6   Serving Sizes

What is a "preschooler-sized" serving?

A *Food Guide Serving* is used as a reference amount. In some cases, the serving size listed in the *Food Guide* will be close to what a two or three-year-old child would eat at a sitting (e.g., one slice of bread or 250 mL of milk), but in other cases it may not (e.g., 75 g of meat).

Preschoolers have small stomachs that fill up quickly and so they generally need to eat small amounts of food more often throughout the day.

One *Food Guide Serving* can be divided into smaller amounts served throughout the day. For example, the *Food Guide* recommends that a two or three-year-old child eat four *Food Guide Servings* of Vegetables and Fruit. This may translate into a meal schedule that looks like the following:

Breakfast: ½ banana (½ *Food Guide Serving*)
Morning snack: 125 mL vegetables with dip (1 *Food Guide Serving*)
Lunch: 60 mL cooked carrots (½ *Food Guide Serving*)
Afternoon snack: 125 mL (½ cup) 100% fruit juice (1 *Food Guide Serving*)

Dinner: 60 mL tomato-based spaghetti sauce (½ *Food Guide Serving*)
Evening snack: 125 mL applesauce (½ *Food Guide Serving*) For children who are having additional snacks, even smaller amounts (e.g., ¼ *Food Guide Serving*) can also add up to the recommended total.

What about mixed dishes?

- Mixed dishes contain ingredients from more than one food group, such as chicken spring rolls, vegetarian samosas or rice pudding.
- Count only the main ingredients toward the servings. For example, for rice pudding, count the milk and rice but not the few raisins. If the ingredient makes up only a small amount of the food (e.g., less than ¼ *Food Guide Serving*, don't use it as a serving measurement.
- Remember that the servings only tell us what we should offer preschoolers. Let them decide which foods and how much to eat.

Source: Developed by the team of Registered Dietitians at Dairy Farmers of Canada. www.goodbeginnings.ca

Multicultural Foods and *Eating Well with Canada's Food Guide*

Often educators caring for children from various ethnocultural backgrounds are unfamiliar with the foods that they commonly eat at home. They may wonder whether the foods fit into the four food groups. *Eating Well with Canada's Food Guide* is designed to be flexible enough to include most foods. Obviously, many foods are eaten by almost all cultures, where available. Often the style of cooking and the spices used differ between cultures. Chicken, for example, may be fried, baked, boiled, roasted, or cooked with different spices, batters, and sauces, depending on preferences and the availability of ingredients. A Mexican chicken dish that is prepared with chocolate tastes quite different from chicken Kiev, chicken parmesan, or stir-fried chicken with vegetables. Table 5.7 shows an assortment of foods that are commonly used in a variety of cultures, to help you identify the foods commonly associated with particular ethnocultural backgrounds. *Eating Well with Canada's Food Guide* is now available not only in English and French but 10 additional languages: Arabic, Chinese, Farsi (Persian), Korean, Punjabi, Russian, Spanish, Tagalog, Tamil, and Urdu. There is also a guide for

TABLE 5.7   Variety of Foods

FOOD GROUPS	FOOD IDEAS
grain products	pita, bagel, bannock, roti, tortilla, chapati, naan, baguette, pretzel, challah, pasta, couscous, bulgur (e.g., in tabouli salad), buckwheat, millet, quinoa, basmati rice, rice cake, dumpling wrapper, cassava bread
vegetables and fruit	okra, guava, mango, papaya, star fruit, breadfruit, soursop, plantain, coconut, wild berries such as huckleberries and thimbleberries, Asian pear, cassava (a root vegetable), akee, lychee, bok choy, mushroom, collard greens, dandelion and beet greens, water chestnut, fern root, vegetable marrow, mustard greens, bamboo shoots, soybean sprouts, summer squash, longan, cactus fruit, chayote, taro root (see also Table 6.4 Vegetables and Fruit Come in a Variety of Colours, page 327)
milk products or calcium-rich foods	Goat's milk, evaporated milk, feta cheese, tofu made with calcium, yogurt, fish or animal bones used in soups and stews, almonds (see also Table 5.5 Amounts of Calcium in Foods and Beverages, page 231)
meat and alternatives	moose; venison; beaver; wild game; chickpeas or garbanzo beans (e.g., in falafels, hummus); soybean (e.g., in soymilk, tofu); peas and rice; black-eyed peas; legumes (e.g., kidney beans, peas, navy beans, lentils, peanuts); organ meats such as kidney, heart, and liver; chorizo (a hot sausage); squid; shellfish; cockles; mussels

First Nations, Inuit, and Métis. All have culturally familiar foods and recommendations and are available on the Health Canada website to download, as pdf files, or to order copies.

Kidney and pinto beans are common in Latin American dishes; tofu is often used in Chinese dishes; roti, chapati, and naan are breads used in many Southeast Asian dishes; and wild berries are commonly used by nonurban Aboriginal Canadians.

Some cultural beliefs and religions restrict eating some meats or advocate vegetarianism. *For example, Hindus and Sikhs can eat goat, fish, and pork but not beef. Muslims can eat goat, beef, and chicken but not pork, and all meat must be prepared according to Muslim dietary law. Similarly, many Jews can eat fish, beef, chicken, and lamb but not shellfish or pork, and meat must be prepared according to Jewish dietary law.* Many cultures use meat sparingly, as a complement to the meal rather than the main focus. This may at times be due to the higher cost of meat, but it is becoming apparent that less rather than more meat is an effective way to reduce fat in the diet.

Religion is significant when it comes to food preparation and consumption. Islam, Judaism, Buddhism, Sikhism, Hinduism, and Christianity all have teachings regarding food, some on daily food preparation and consumption every day, and others relating to special times of religious observances such as Lent or Ramadan. As with all communication with families, it is important to avoid assumptions and obtain specific information from the families themselves. Table 5.8 outlines some basic differences between kosher (Jewish) and

TABLE 5.8   Kosher and Halal: An Introduction to Dietary Differences

	KOSHER	HALAL
Blessing of Animals	Blessing before entering slaughtering area, not on each animal	Blessing on each animal while slaughtering
Preparation of Meat	Soaked and salted to drain all blood. No special preparation.	Blood is drained during slaughtering
Gelatin		
• Dry bones	From kosher animals	From halal bones only
• Skin and bones	From kosher animals	From halal animals only
• Fish	From kosher fish only	From any fish
Fish and Other Seafood	Permitted except fish that do not have fins and scales (e.g., catfish, eels, rays, sharks, swordfish). Not permitted are shellfish (e.g., oyster, clam), crustaceans (e.g., crab, lobster), and mollusks (e.g., scallops).	Permitted
Combining Dairy and Meat Products	Not permitted	Permitted
Special Occasions	Additional restrictions during Passover	Same rules apply all the time

Source: Adapted with permission from Toronto Public Health. (2008). *Nutrition Matters: Frequently Asked Questions about Halal.* <http://www.toronto.ca/health/nm_faq_halal_foods.htm> (May 2008).

halal (Muslim) dietary rules. This table is not meant to be a complete list; as with all religions, ethnocultures, and lifestyles (e.g., vegetarians), there are degrees of beliefs, traditions, and adherence that fall on a continuum of practices. However, a beginning awareness is important for all and a reminder that when children in your care have specific dietary needs, it is the responsibility of the educators to learn more about the specifics and how best to respect and support the children and families' needs.

Vegetarianism

Vegetarianism means different things to different people. Generally, it means choosing a plant-based way of eating. It is hard to determine how many people in Canada are currently vegetarian, but at least reducing the percentage of animal foods we eat seems to be a practice growing in popularity and may reduce the risk of obesity and some chronic conditions such as diabetes and heart disease. Many vegetarians have based their decision on personal health reasons, religion or cultural tradition, animal rights, or cost. Others are concerned about world hunger and the environmental toll of a meat-based diet over a plant-based diet. Still others are not vegetarian but have decided to eliminate some meat, such as red meat, from their diet. The term "**flexitarians**" has been coined for this growing number of Canadians seeking to lower cholesterol or fat intake or reduce meat for any of the reasons listed above, sometimes as a transition to vegetarianism.

Vegetarians are classified according to the foods that they include in their diet:

- Lacto-ovo vegetarians, who comprise the vast majority of vegetarians in Canada, do not eat animal flesh but do eat animal products such as milk and eggs.
- Pesco vegetarians eat fish in addition to foods of plant origin.
- Lacto vegetarians eat milk and alternatives but not eggs.
- Ovo vegetarians eat eggs but not milk.
- Vegans eat only foods of plant origin.

It is important to remember that any family, vegetarian or not, can have adequate or poor nutrition. Vegetarians need to ensure that they find alternate ways to obtain adequate amounts of complete protein and minerals (e.g., iron, zinc) and vitamins (e.g., B_{12}) that are found in meat. The building blocks of protein are amino acids; we get eight essential amino acids from foods. Animal flesh and its products include all of these simultaneously, whereas most plant foods have fewer. Simply eating a lot of vegetables, grains, and fruit without complete protein is not healthy eating. Learning how to complement protein is easy. Some critics of vegetarianism believe that growing children cannot get the key nutrients they need, such as calcium, without eating meat. This concern is unfounded, particularly for lacto-ovo vegetarians, who consume milk products. As is true with any way of eating, vegetarians enjoy health benefits when their diet is balanced and varied and meets energy and nutrient needs. Parents who raise their children on a vegan diet must ensure that the children get enough of the nutrients they need to grow and develop. For all infants, exclusive breast-feeding is the best source of nutrition for at least the first six months of life.

Here are some examples, from Melina, Davis, and Harrison (1994, p. 56), of **complementary proteins**, along with the country or region known for them:

- Combining grains and legumes:
  - bread and split pea soup (Canada)
  - crackers and lentil soup (Middle East)
  - rice, kimchi, and tofu (Korea)
  - cornmeal tortillas and vegetarian chili (Mexico)
  - chapatis and dahl (India)
  - pita bread and falafel (Middle East)
  - pita bread and hummus (Greece)
  - sticky bun with black bean sauce (China)

- Combining grains and nuts:
  - granola or muesli with nuts (Switzerland)
  - pasta with pine nuts (Italy)
  - rice with cashew-vegetable stir-fry (China)

It is more challenging for vegans to get all the nutrients they need, but if they understand and practise good nutrition principles, they will ensure that their nutrient needs are met. In vegan families, it is important that pregnant women's and children's increased need for protein, fat, calcium, iron, vitamin B_{12}, and other nutrients be considered.

Macrobiotic diets, which are very restrictive vegan diets, are of particular concern for children. Milks made from grains, beans, and seeds, for example, are inadequate for infants and young children. The Canadian Paediatric Society (2007) suggests that vegan parents talk to a registered dietitian for advice on meal planning and preparation.

Educators who have concerns about a child's nutritional intake, regardless of the type of diet, should talk with the parents and recommend that they consult with the child's physician or a dietitian. If you still have questions or need clarification, you may wish to consult with a dietitian.

NUTRITION LABELS AND GROWING AND PROCESSING FOODS

Labels on food products can increase our understanding of healthy eating, enabling us to make informed decisions about choosing foods that are nutritious and fresh (check the expiry date on the label) and suit individual needs, such as allergy concerns or special dietary needs or restrictions.

A number of processes are included in the general definition of **food processing**, including curing meat (e.g., bacon, ham), increasing the length of time for storage or shelf life (e.g., canned fruit, vegetables), or combining a number of ingredients to make a food (e.g., hot dogs, bread). With few exceptions, the more processed the food, the more additives are used. Food biotechnology includes other processes, such as genetic modification and irradiation.

Nutrition Labels

We can learn a lot about foods and make informed choices by reading labels. In December 2007, Health Canada's New Nutrition Labeling Policy, which has standardized the **Nutrition Facts table** on all prepackaged foods, became mandatory. The Nutrition Facts table is easy to read, consistent in design, and includes information across almost all prepackaged products (see Figure 5.1). Exemptions include fresh fruit and vegetables; raw meat, poultry, and seafood; food products made and packaged on site; and products with little or no nutritive value (e.g., coffee beans, spices).

What information is included in a Nutrition Facts table? The table lists calories and 13 core nutrients for a specific amount of food (a serving). The nutrients are mostly given in weights such as grams or milligrams and then translated into a percentage of recommended daily value. Vitamins and minerals are given as percentages of daily value. Both saturated and trans fats are listed separately, and carbohydrates are divided into fibre and sugars. This consistent format helps the consumer learn to use it quickly and evaluate whether this food has enough of the nutrients he or she needs or wants.

In addition to the Nutrition Facts table, other nutrition information can be found as nutrition claims and the ingredient list are given from most to least weight. Nutrition claims are now regulated by Health Canada criteria, specifying

FIGURE 5.1 Nutrition Facts Table: A Sample

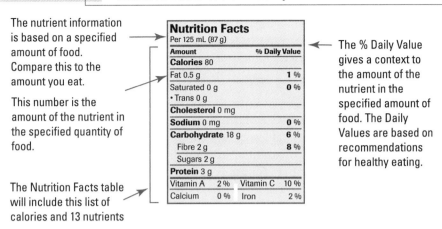

The nutrient information is based on a specified amount of food. Compare this to the amount you eat.

This number is the amount of the nutrient in the specified quantity of food.

The Nutrition Facts table will include this list of calories and 13 nutrients

The % Daily Value gives a context to the amount of the nutrient in the specified amount of food. The Daily Values are based on recommendations for healthy eating.

Nutrition Facts
Per 125 mL (87 g)

Amount	% Daily Value
Calories 80	
Fat 0.5 g	1 %
Saturated 0 g • Trans 0 g	0 %
Cholesterol 0 mg	
Sodium 0 mg	0 %
Carbohydrate 18 g	6 %
Fibre 2 g	8 %
Sugars 2 g	
Protein 3 g	

Vitamin A	2 %	Vitamin C	10 %
Calcium	0 %	Iron	2 %

Source: *Nutrition Facts Table,* Health Canada (2003). Reproduced with the permission of the Minister of Public Works and Government Services Canada, 2008.

the wording to be used to prevent misleading claims, which had been a problem in the past. Permitted nutrient content claims such as "low calorie" are defined and the exact conditions specified by Health Canada. These conditions are based on recognized health and scientific information.

To date, regulations only allow the following claims about diet and health relationships (Health Canada, 2008b, pp. 1–2):

- A healthy diet low in sodium and high in potassium—may reduce the risk of high blood pressure;

- A healthy diet adequate in calcium and vitamin D—may reduce the risk of osteoporosis;

- A healthy diet low in saturated fat and trans fat—may reduce the risk of heart disease;

- A healthy diet rich in vegetables and fruit—may reduce the risk of some types of cancer.

- As research findings continue, this list may change. Note that for foods intended solely for children under the age of two such as infant formulas and infant cereals, only the following five nutrient content claims can be used: "source of protein", "excellent source of protein", "more protein", "no added sodium" (or salt), and "no added sugars".

Source: *Health claims: Q&A #4,* Health Canada, 2008. Reproduced with the permission of the Minister of Public Works and Government Services Canada, 2008.

For individuals with food allergies (e.g., to peanuts, milk solids, soy, wheat, dehydrated eggs), the ingredient list on packaging is essential, since it names ingredients to be avoided. It is also useful for people on special diets (e.g., gluten-free, diabetic). Other information you may find on food labels includes statements related to allergens (e.g., "may contain traces of peanut"), food biotechnology information (e.g., regarding genetically modified organisms [GMOs]), organic certification, irradiation processes, and the "best before" date.

An expiry or "best before" date or code is stamped on the label or somewhere on the package (e.g., the bottom or top of the cereal box) to indicate when the contents may spoil or lose nutrients or taste. A date must appear on all foods that spoil within 90 days, except for meats, which show the date the food was packaged. Actual calendar dates are useful to both the consumer and the store manager.

Pesticides

Pesticides are commonly used in farming, except in organic farming, to kill organisms (or pests) on vegetables, fruit, and grains during the growing season. Pesticides are an example of unintentional additives, because some chemicals remain in or on the food after harvest. As a general rule, all of us should try to minimize our exposure to pesticides due to short- and long-term concerns about health (see Environmental Safety, page 422). Agriculture Canada approves all pesticides before use and has banned some that are still used in other countries (e.g., DDT). Relative to most countries, Canada uses fewer pesticides in agriculture. However, imported produce may have higher concentrations of pesticides, including those that are banned in Canada.

There are particular concerns about the potential effects of pesticides on children, often termed "neurotoxins" because they affect the developing nervous system. Children tend to eat a lot of fruit and drink fruit juice. What can we do to reduce the amount of pesticides we eat? Washing produce and peeling fruit and vegetables are two ways (see Safe Food Handling, page 276). Lobbying policy-makers to reduce both the commercial and residential use of pesticides is another way to promote everyone's health. Some municipalities have successfully done so, and others are in the process of reducing the use of pesticides.

Organic Foods

Organic foods are grown under strict farming requirements. Organic foods are grown without chemicals and are not genetically modified or irradiated. What do we know about organic foods? Organic farming is not 100% pesticide free; some pesticides are approved for both organic and conventional farming. Organic foods tend to be more expensive; perhaps this may change if buying locally becomes a more widespread practice and with additional government support for organic farming. However, buying organic foods is not currently recommended by Health Canada as a healthier way to eat. Instead, the recommendation by Health Canada, Dietitians of Canada, and many other national groups is the increased intake of vegetables and fruit along with milk and alternatives. Whether these food choices are organic remains a personal preference.

Food Additives

"A food additive is any chemical substance that is added to food during preparation or storage and either becomes a part of the food or affects its characteristics for the purpose of achieving a particular technical effect. Some nutrients may occasionally function as food additives. For example, ascorbic acid contributes vitamin C to foods and also acts as an antioxidant" (Health Canada, 2006). The legal definition of a food additive does not include common ingredients such as sugar and salt or vitamins. Monosodium glutamate (MSG) is commonly thought to be a food additive but is actually a flavour enhancer not included in the Canadian *Food Additive Dictionary* (Health Canada, 2006).

Generally, the functions of food additives are to

- maintain the nutritive components of the food (i.e., acidity-adjusting agents);
- enhance the shelf life of the food (i.e., preservatives);
- add to the appeal of the food (colours, flavours, texture agents); and
- help in the processing, packaging, or storage (processing agents, enzymes).

Source: *Food Additive Dictionary,* Health Canada, 2007. Reproduced with the permission of the Minister of Public Works and Government Services Canada, 2008.

Food additives are listed toward the end of a product's ingredient list as they are present in very low levels in foods. Research shows that most additives do not pose a threat to our short- or long-term health. However, some additives may be of concern when used regularly for long periods.

Many children favour meats that are highly processed, such as hot dogs, ham, bacon, bologna, salami, and other luncheon meats. They are easy to chew and taste salty, the result of food processing with numerous additives. If children eat these meats regularly, they often learn to choose processed meats over other meat and alternatives. This raises concerns because processed meats are usually high in saturated fat and salt and often contain the preservatives nitrates and nitrites. These preservatives are known carcinogens and have been of concern for many years.

On the other hand, it is now possible, by reading labels or asking at deli counters, to purchase nitrite- and nitrate-free processed meats. In addition, soy or other plant-based products, which resemble meat and provide protein, are also readily available. Many are easy to use in foods such as pasta, rice sauces, chili, and lasagna and are an inexpensive way to get protein without saturated fat or nitrates. We are exposed to hundreds of chemicals daily, many of them necessary and harmless. When we have a choice of ingesting some that may not be in our best interests, why not choose the healthier alternative?

Dietitians and other health professionals are also on the lookout for food reactions from some additives. Although studies are limited to date, some research shows that food additives may play a role in behavioural issues. In particular, chemical preservatives called "benzoates," which have been used for a hundred years as preservatives in foods and beverages, as well as specific artificial colours (tartrazine, sunset yellow, and ponceau), may trigger hyperactive behaviour. A British study of three-year-olds and eight- and nine-year-olds found that it wasn't just children with attention deficit hyperactivity disorder (ADHD) who were affected by the artificial food colours and additives; all the children had trouble with inattention, impulsivity, and overactivity (McCann et al., 2007).

Too much sugar in children's diets is often blamed for a range of behaviour. However, eating sugar actually makes someone feel sleepy, as it stimulates the production of serotonin, a sleep chemical in the brain. Foods that contain large amounts of sugar, such as soft drinks, candies, and other sweet foods, also contain artificial colours and preservatives, which, rather than the sugar, may be contributing to these behavioural changes seen in some children. The low-nutritive processed foods targeted at children often use colours for a bright colour effect, to look like popular cartoon characters. This is not to suggest that artificial food colours are the only contributing factor in behaviour changes. However, offering children foods that are high in key nutrients and do not contain additives such as benzoates and artificial colours is a healthier alternative.

We must also consider the concept of synergy. Synergism is the interaction of two or more agents or forces so that their combined effect is greater than the sum of their individual effects. All additives undergo rigorous testing and many are deemed safe, but the quantities and combinations may have unknown risks.

Food additives allow manufacturers to provide a wide variety of convenient and enjoyable foods. However, if you want to limit additives in your diet, follow these steps:

- Eat fresh foods.
  Generally speaking, eating fresh fruit and vegetables, eggs, and milk will reduce the amount of food additives you eat, as compared to eating processed foods.

- Learn more.
  Read the labels on food products and find out what is in the foods you buy. In Canada, most pre-packaged foods have to carry a list of ingredients, including food additives. In general, the list must show the ingredients in descending order of proportion by weight, so that the major ingredients are found at the beginning of the list. However, some ingredients, including food additives (which are often present in food in much smaller amounts), spices, flavours, vitamins, and minerals are allowed to appear at the end of the list in any order, regardless of their proportion.

- Make your views known.
  While the Food and Drug Regulations specify which food additives are allowed in Canada, it is up to food manufacturers to decide whether or not to use them. If you are concerned about what is in the foods you eat, contact the manufacturer or grocery retailer to let them know your views.

Source: *The Safety of Food Additives-It's Your Health*, Health Canada, 2007. Reproduced with the permission of the Minister of Public Works and Government Services Canada, 2008.

Fortified and Enriched Foods

Fortified or enriched food refers to the adding of nutrients to foods, such as milk fortified (or enriched) with vitamins A and D. Why are foods fortified in Canada? First, fortifying foods is a way to replace nutrients lost during the manufacturing process. Second, fortification can help prevent certain chronic diseases. Fortifying foods with calcium and vitamin D, for example, helps build strong bones and prevent osteoporosis. For those concerned about their intake of omega-3 fatty acids, omega-3-enriched eggs (produced by feeding the chickens flaxseed) are a popular choice. There is promising preliminary evidence that omega-3 fatty acids can help reduce the risk of coronary heart disease and possibly Alzheimer's disease.

Health Canada sets specific limits on what nutrients can be added to food, how much of an individual vitamin or mineral can be added, and which foods cannot be fortified at the discretion of manufacturers. The majority of foods are not fortified or enriched. *An example of the impact of fortified foods in Canada is the addition of folic acid in flour, which resulted in a significant reduction in neural tube defects, spina bifida, and other birth defects. Fortification of cereals and wheat flour with folic acid became mandatory in November 1998. A study in Ontario has shown that since the fortification, the incidence of open neural tube birth defects has been reduced by more than 50%, down from 1.13 to 0.58 per 1,000 pregnancies (Michaelides, 2007).*

For persons with a food allergy, intolerance, or a medical condition, fortified foods may be advantageous. Consider those who can't get their calcium from dairy due to lactose intolerance; they can find a helpful option in calcium-enriched orange juice.

Canadians should not base all their food choices on whether foods are fortified or enriched, just as children and adults cannot depend on a multivitamin as a substitute for healthy eating. The recommendation to eat a variety of foods from *Eating Well with Canada's Food Guide* continues to be very important.

Sweeteners

A number of sweeteners other than sugar (sucrose) are permitted for use in Canada. These include both nutritive sweeteners (other sugars and sugar alcohols) and non-nutritive or noncaloric sweeteners (e.g., aspartame, sucralose). Non-nutritive sweeteners are being added to many foods, beverages, and snack products. Definitions, permitted uses, and labelling requirements by Health Canada consider all available scientific information on the effectiveness and safety of sweeteners. Regulations are then developed to identify how they should be used and the allowable amounts. A recommended daily intake (RDI) based on body weight has been set by the Canadian government for most sweeteners. Current evidence suggests that with normal use, the concentrations of artificial sweeteners are not a health risk. There are many adults and children (e.g., diabetics) who may regularly use these sweeteners due to necessity. However, others choose to consume products with aspartame, such as gelatin desserts, yogurt, puddings, beverages, and gum. Some parents encourage their children to eat these products because they are concerned about children eating too much sugar.

Research has shown that sugar is not the evil that we once thought it was. It does not cause hyperactivity. Moreover, concern about high-sugar foods replacing more nutritious foods can also apply to foods containing aspartame. If children are filling up on high-sugar, low-nutritive foods, they should be encouraged to eat fewer sweet foods rather than substitute with sweet foods containing aspartame. The use of non-nutritive sweeteners does not prevent or combat obesity (see Reduce the Consumption of Carbonated and Other Low-Nutritive Beverages, page 329).

In early childhood programs, staff should provide foods that are as natural as possible and have been processed as little as possible. Non-nutritive sweeteners do not comply with this recommendation. Replacing high-sugar foods with foods containing sweeteners continues to promote a "sweet tooth," a habitual desire for sweets, rather than a focus on the natural sweetness of foods such as fruit and some vegetables.

Food Biotechnology

Genetically Modified Foods

The term "genetically modified" refers to altering genetic material; put simply, the genes of one organism have been "cut out" and then "pasted" into another organism.

For hundreds of years, farmers have performed genetic engineering on their plants and animals by breeding them selectively to possess superior qualities, such as corn that is much larger and sweeter than its original wild ancestor. This process took centuries, but today's biotechnology is able to speed up and make the process of genetic selection much more precise. One such example is that one bacterium was given the ability to make the enzyme rennin, needed to produce cheese. The gene for making rennin was snipped from a calf's DNA cell, transferred to a bacterial cell, which reproduced itself into mass production to be used in making cheese (Sizer & Whitney, 2000, p. 540).

Modern genetic engineering holds the power to change even the most basic patterns of life by manipulating DNA material. Genetic engineering is much more far-reaching than simple food technology, as demonstrated by the controversies in animal and human cloning. The potential for both positive and negative outcomes is awesome. This powerful science has and will have a definite impact on our food supply. Two food technologies that are receiving a lot of attention and consumer concern are genetically modified organisms (GMOs) and food irradiation (see page 243). Health Canada assesses the safety of all genetically modified and other novel foods proposed for sale in Canada. Companies are required to submit detailed scientific data for review and approval by Health Canada before such foods can be sold.

Canada's *Food and Drug Act* defines a **GMO** broadly as an organism exhibiting characteristics not previously observed in that organism, regardless of how the new characteristics were developed. This definition has contributed to much debate in Canada over the development of labelling for GMOs, mostly because the transfer of genetic material from one species to another concerns many consumers and environmental groups. Mandatory labelling based on a more specific definition is in place in the European Union and Japan. As with all foods in Canada, labelling of genetically modified foods is mandatory if there is a health or safety issue. When the nutritional value or composition of the food has been changed, or when an allergen is present in the food, that food must be labelled as such to alert consumers or susceptible groups in the population.

Many commonly used foods, such as soybeans, are genetically modified to be used for a variety of purposes in food production. The potential benefits of GMOs include the ability to feed many more people with increasing demands for foods and shrinking farmland and for affordable, easy-to-prepare foods that are nutritious and safe and taste good. However, the full extent of human health risks is not known, with the possibility of allergic reactions, nutritional changes, and the creation of toxins. This issue will continue to be debated over the next few years.

Food Irradiation

Another process that Health Canada (2008a, p. 1) uses to improve food safety is **irradiation**, exposing food to gamma rays for the following purposes:

- To prevent food poisoning: by reducing the level of harmful bacteria such as *E. coli* O157:H7, *Salmonella* and *Campylobacter*, and parasites which cause foodborne diseases.
- To prevent spoilage: by reducing the microbial load on foods, meaning it destroys bacteria, molds and yeast that cause food to spoil, and controls insect and parasite infestation.
- To increase shelf life: by slowing the ripening or sprouting in fresh fruits and vegetables, thereby allowing for longer shelf life.

Proponents of irradiation believe that this process helps protect the public through more thorough food safety procedures. They also claim it is safer than spraying food with chemical pest-control products to protect them from spoilage caused by bugs and moulds. Although most of the radiation passes through the food, a small amount is absorbed and remains in the food. Irradiation does not make food radioactive.

Critics point out that although the process eliminates the use of some chemicals, most pesticides are applied before harvest, while plants are still growing. Irradiation does not cut down on the use of chemical pesticides by farmers. There are concerns that irradiation kills bacteria, but not necessarily the toxins that the bacteria produced in the food before they were killed. Foods that look and smell fine may be contaminated with dangerous toxins that lead to food poisoning. Like labelling of GMOs, the issue of food irradiation will continue to be debated in Canada over the coming years.

Health Canada approved irradiation for potatoes, onions, wheat, and wheat flour in the mid-1960s and for spices in 1984. Spices are the most commonly irradiated food worldwide. Canadian law requires all food products intended for human use that have been irradiated to be labelled with this logo.

Note that spices sold in bulk or retail, as well as herbs or ingredients that have been irradiated, must be labelled with the Radura logo. "However, when these ingredients are added to mixtures, processed meats and finished products, and do not exceed 10% by weight or volume, the labelling requirement no longer applies" (Canadian Spice Association, 2003, p. 4).

Health Canada has proposed amendments to the *Food and Drug Act* to expand the types of foods allowed to undergo irradiation (e.g., meat, poultry, fish).

Being Informed Consumers

Nutrition labels help us select foods for healthy eating. If you're not in the habit of reading product labels, you will probably be overwhelmed by a list of unpronounceable and obscure ingredients. You may also find that it is a time-consuming process at first, especially if you are comparing your favourite brand with its competitors. No one expects you to remember the names of all the ingredients, what they are and do, and which should be avoided or at least limited in consumption. But by reading the labels of products used in the home or early childhood program, you will soon compile a list of acceptable and unacceptable products for the shopping list. This will drastically reduce the time that is needed to shop.

Whether you are at home or at work, when you are trying to reduce the amount of fat, sugar, salt, and additives, here are a few tips for reading labels to evaluate products for healthy eating:

Fat:

- Remember when buying foods for children that moderate fat, not "fat free," is important for healthy growth and development.
- Use equal serving sizes when comparing two products for fat content.
- Choose milk, yogurt, or cottage cheese with 2% fat rather than whole milk for children over two years of age. For school-age children and adults, the fat content can be reduced to 1% or skim if their needs for fat are being met with other healthy foods.
- Choose cheeses with 15% milk fat (m.f.) or less.
- Select meats that are lower in fat (e.g., poultry, fish), and when selecting red meats, choose leaner cuts (e.g., lean ground beef).
- Look for canned fish packed in water or vegetable broth.
- Read the product's label for the content of saturated and trans fats. Remember that daily values of these combined should not exceed 20 g.

Note: If you are wondering why adding the grams of saturated and trans fats on the Nutrition Facts table does not equal the Total Fats (e.g., Saturated = 1 g, Trans Fats = 0.5 g, Fat = 4 g), the reason is that the 2.5 g fat unaccounted for is either monounsaturated and/or polyunsaturated fats, which are the healthier fats.

Sugar:

Note that ingredients ending in "ose" are types of sugar—glucose, maltose, lactose, dextrose, fructose. You may be familiar with the obvious types of sugar, such as granulated and icing sugar, brown sugar, honey, corn syrup, and molasses. Compare the amount of sugar and fibre in the carbohydrate section of the Nutrition Facts table on the label. Remember to choose foods higher in fibre and lower in sugar. Be aware of the added sugar content in beverages (e.g., pop and drinks with fruit juice) and foods.

Salt:

The word "sodium" in the Nutrition Facts table alerts you to the presence of salt. If the word "salt" does not appear on the list of ingredients, salt may still be in the product. There may be a number of sodium additives, such as monosodium glutamate, sodium bicarbonate, sodium metabisulphite, and disodium guanylate. As stated earlier, the amount of salt Canadians, including children, consume is often more than recommended daily amounts, especially when eating a range of highly processed or fast foods.

HEALTHY EATING HABITS

OBJECTIVES

The foundation for supporting the development of healthy eating habits in the early childhood program starts with a philosophy of trust rather than control. In children's early childhood, they are developing eating habits that can last a lifetime. This fact can either work to their advantage or to their detriment. Educators have great opportunities to promote good eating habits. Positive nutrition policies and practices recognize and respect children's ability to respond to their own bodily needs and learn to eat for the right reasons.

To state the practices that create a positive eating environment and encourage children to try new foods.

To describe appropriate principles and practices in infant feeding.

To consider the unique aspects of the growth and development of toddlers that affect their nutrition and eating habits.

To identify developmental issues for preschoolers and school-agers that affect their eating behaviour.

Mealtime situations can affect children's relationships with educators and parents when tensions and frustrations run high. Insisting that a child finish eating what is on her plate after she has indicated that she is full can result in several scenarios that contribute to future eating issues:

- anxiety about mealtime,
- eating more than she needs, contributing to future overweight, or
- asserting herself and not eating.

As with all best practices in early childhood programs, children's trust in the adults who care for them and trust in the environment are key to optimal development and learning.

Ellyn Satter, a dietitian, family therapist, and author of *Child of Mine: Feeding with Love and Good Sense* (2000), is well known by educators and parents. Her philosophy on the **division of responsibility** on feeding (Satter, 1990) is a standard principle for successful feeding. Taken from Satter's child care feeding policy, available at http://www.EllynSatter.com, the parent or caregiver is responsible for *what* the child eats, and the infant is responsible for *how much* will be eaten (and everything else). The adult helps the infant be calm and organized and feed smoothly, paying attention to information coming from the infant about timing, tempo, frequency, and amounts (Satter, 2000).

- Adults are responsible for what, when, and where:
  - We follow Canada's food guidelines to plan meals and snacks.
  - We provide nutritious, regularly scheduled meals and snacks that are an important part of our program day.
  - We take time to help children relax and prepare to eat.
  - We sit down to eat with children and have enjoyable times where there is respect for ourselves and each other.

- Children are responsible for how much and whether they eat:
  - We trust children to manage their own eating.
  - Children pick and choose from the food we make available.
  - Children will eat, they will eat what they need, and they will learn to eat the new foods that we offer, without coercion or forcing.

– Children eat as little or as much of the food as they want. Some days children eat a lot, but other days, not as much. But they know how much they need.

Source: *Child of Mine: Feeding with Love and Good Sense*, 2000. Reprinted with permission of the author.

Children's growth and development, as well as their family's cultural eating patterns, play key roles in determining their readiness for food and their interests in food and socializing. By accommodating children's development, educators ensure that individual nutritional needs are met and that eating environments are designed to promote positive eating habits.

Table 5.9 lists the developmental characteristics related to eating. Learning to recognize these characteristics will help you make sure that children are receiving the food and nutrition they need.

TABLE 5.9   **Developmental Characteristics Related to Eating**

AGE	PHYSICAL	SOCIAL/PERSONAL
Birth to 4 months	■ turns mouth toward nipple that brushes cheek ■ sucks and swallows	■ recognizes the breast or bottle as the source of food by about 10 weeks ■ excited by sight of food (e.g., breast, bottle)
4 to 6 months	■ sucking strength increases ■ chewing motion begins ■ uses tongue to move food in mouth ■ begins to finger-feed	■ excited by sight of food
6 to 9 months	■ holds a bottle ■ drinks from a cup held by adult ■ rotary chewing begins ■ tongue movement has increased and allows for more manipulation of food	■ begins to show likes and dislikes for foods
9 to 12 months	■ tries to use spoon ■ chews up and down ■ finger-feeds with a refined grasp	■ conscious of what others do and imitates their examples
12 to 18 months	■ grasps and releases food with fingers ■ uses spoon awkwardly ■ turns spoon in mouth ■ uses cup, but release poor	■ wants food others are eating ■ loves performing
18 to 24 months	■ appetite decreases ■ likes eating with hands ■ likes experimenting with textures	■ ritual becomes important (e.g., has to have milk in red cup) ■ displays food preferences ■ distracts easily

(continued)

| TABLE 5.9 | Developmental Characteristics Related to Eating *(continued)* |

2 to 3 years	■ holds glass in hand ■ places spoon straight into mouth ■ spills a lot ■ chews more foods, but choking still a hazard	■ has definite likes and dislikes ■ insists on doing it "myself" ■ ritualistic ■ dawdles ■ has food jags (e.g., refuses to eat anything but peanut butter sandwiches) ■ demands foods in certain shapes or whole foods ■ likes to help in kitchen
3 to 4 years	■ holds handle on cup ■ pours from small pitcher ■ uses fork ■ chews most food	■ improved appetite and interest in food ■ favourite foods requested ■ likes shapes, colours, ABCs ■ able to choose between two alternate foods ■ influenced by TV commercials ■ likes to copy food preparer
4 to 5 years	■ uses knife and fork ■ good use of cup ■ good self-feeder	■ rather talk than eat ■ food jags continue ■ motivated to eat by incentives ■ likes to help ■ interested in nature of food and where it comes from ■ peer influence increasing
5 to 6 years	■ feeds self	■ conforming ■ less suspicious of mixtures but still prefers plain foods ■ social influence outside home increasing ■ food important part of special occasions
6 to 8 years	■ refined small motor skills and eye–hand coordination (e.g., able to use some simple kitchen equipment such as can opener, toaster) ■ slow growth ■ high energy level	■ shares and takes turns ■ table manners improving ■ eager to please ■ significant peer pressure (e.g., less willing to try new foods) ■ can follow steps for simple recipes almost independently ■ good sense of humour (e.g., creating funny names for recipes) ■ can delay gratification for a short time

(continued)

TABLE 5.9	Developmental Characteristics Related to Eating *(continued)*	
AGE	**PHYSICAL**	**SOCIAL/PERSONAL**
8 to 11 years	■ more coordinated (can usually use most kitchen equipment, e.g., knives, micro-waves; may need supervision with stove) ■ physical competence important for self-concept status with peers ■ responsible for most self-care	■ can set standards for own behaviour ■ often conforms to rules set by peers (e.g., high-status foods, trading lunch foods) ■ enjoys choosing and preparing foods, connecting nutrition with everyday life
11 to 13 years	■ dramatic physical changes associated with onset of puberty, approximately a year earlier for girls than boys ■ increased nutritional needs (e.g., calcium, iron)	■ may be moody with hormone changes ■ looking for self-identity, may resist adults' nutritional advice ■ may restrict food intake due to body image pressures, especially but not only girls

Source: *Promoting Nutritional Health During the Preschool Years: Canadian Guidelines,* Ottawa: Network of the Federal/Provincial/Territorial Group on Nutrition and National Institute of Nutrition, 23, Health Canada (1989). Reproduced with the permission of the Minister of Public Works and Government Services Canada, 2008.

Creating a Positive Eating Environment

A positive eating environment for children has a lot to do with the expectations of adults involved, in addition to the physical environment in which children eat. The environment can either promote or hinder healthy eating, and it can meet or inhibit children's social and emotional needs. Nutritious foods are of no value to children if they don't eat them. On the other hand, we know that any form of force-feeding or pressuring children does not work, especially for the long term. A positive environment is a much better option, regardless of the age group. When meals or snack times become negative experiences, with unhappy children or educators, review the checklist in Table 5.10 and identify which criteria have not been met.

Encourage children to try new foods. Here are a few suggestions:

■ Present one new food at a time.

■ Introduce the food when children are most hungry (e.g., at the beginning of a meal as an appetizer). You may be surprised at how excited preschoolers get when they hear you mention the word "appetizer" and how much they enjoy eating raw vegetables and dip or celery in a glass of tomato juice.

TABLE 5.10   **Positive Eating Environment: Checklist**

	YES	NO
The atmosphere is relaxed. For example, if children are expected to come in from outdoor play and immediately wash their hands to eat, their difficulty in relaxing at the meal is not surprising. Educators need to think about sequence and transition needs for children.		
Distractions are at a minimum, and children are encouraged to focus on what they eat. Balance this with a warm social environment in which children can talk calmly while sitting.		
Children's rights are respected (i.e., not forced to eat foods they don't like or teased for not being skilled with spoons or forks).		
Individual food likes and dislikes are acknowledged, promoting the child's sense of self.		
Children are guided (by adult modelling) to observe certain behaviour while eating, developing a sense of self-respect and respect for others. Educators eat meals with children and model positive eating attitudes and behaviour. Adult supervision is also necessary to prevent or respond to choking risks.		
Children are encouraged to develop their five senses in enjoying a variety of foods.		
Children are not forced to conform to rigid rules or expected to have perfect table manners. For example, positively reinforcing children's use of "please" and "thank you" is far more effective than demanding that every time a child wants or receives something at the table she must use these words (e.g., repeatedly asking children, "What's the magic word?"—which is not only patronizing but misleading since we don't always get what we want). Again, adult role modelling is important in fostering table manners.		
Food, beverages, and desserts are not used as bribes or punishments. Depriving children of food is never acceptable. When unacceptable behaviour does not relate to eating (e.g., arguments over toys at playtime), there is never any association made with food as a punishment or as a reward if he or she stops (e.g., "If you keep fighting, you won't have a snack" or "If you stop doing that, you can have dessert").		
Children are provided with developmentally appropriate opportunities to be involved in serving themselves. Children can start with giving themselves small servings and can have more if they would like, giving them control over the amount of food on their plate. Toddlers have some opportunity for independent serving; preschoolers and school-agers serve themselves as often as possible. ■ Snacks are set out where two or three children can serve themselves at a table. ■ Milk is served in small pitchers so children can pour their own. ■ Family-style serving dishes are used at the table.		
Individual children's rate of eating is considered. For example, a child who eats slowly is not rushed; the child is given enough notice if reasonable time has lapsed and the child needs to move to the next routine.		
A child who eats more quickly than peers, although encouraged to take time to eat, is not expected to stay at the table until everyone else has finished.		

(continued)

| TABLE 5.10 | Positive Eating Environment: Checklist *(continued)* |

	YES	NO
Adults recognize accidental spills as a natural part of mealtime and demonstrate patience. Children are encouraged to help clean up their spills (appropriate to their developmental skills) with a clean cloth available.		
There are well-maintained chairs, tables, plates, and utensils suited to the children's size and development.		
The table is made as attractive as possible (e.g., by laminating place mats that children make). Children are involved whenever possible in setting the table.		
Foods served for celebrations and holidays are nutritious and fun.		
Children are encouraged to share food experiences from their own ethnocultural or regional backgrounds and are introduced to foods from around the world as a part of the regular menu.		
Parents are encouraged to ■ comment on and ask nutritional questions about the program's and their child's nutrition, ■ contribute nutritional foods and snacks for special occasions and are invited to participate, and ■ provide favourite ethnocultural recipes.		

- Serve the new foods with familiar ones.
- Offer small amounts.
- Talk about the colour, texture, taste, shape, and smell of the food.
- Encourage the children to help you prepare the new food.
- Encourage but don't insist that children taste the new food. If they reject it or say "I don't like it," accept their comments and offer it again in a week or two. The more often they see the new food, the more familiar it becomes, and the more willing they will be to accept it.
- Ask children what they didn't like about the new food. Maybe you need only change the way the food is prepared. If this food is familiar to families in the program, ask the parents for ideas about preparing it for or with the children.
- Remember that if children see educators enjoying or at least trying the new food, they may be encouraged to try it too. However, you aren't expected to force yourself to eat something you dislike. Besides, if you have it in your mouth, but your body language says "It's disgusting" and your comments are negative, the children will understand your true feelings.

Infant Nutrition

At no other time in our lives is there as dramatic a rate in our growth and development as during the prenatal period and infancy. Infants double their birth weight by five months of age and triple it within the year. In the same year, they will be 1½ times as long as they were at birth (e.g., 51 cm, or 20 inches, at birth and 76 cm, or 30 inches, at 12 months). Infants' brains continue to grow, and they quickly develop motor skills. As well, infants move from being able only to suck and swallow to finger-feeding in 12 months (see Table 5.9, page 246). During the first year of life, one of infants' fundamental needs is to have their nutritional requirements met by their parents and caregivers. Without all the essential nutrients, infants' growth, development, learning, and play will be negatively affected. Parents and educators must communicate effectively—meaning daily written and verbal communication—so that consistency of care between home and the program can be provided.

Breast Milk and Infant Formula

The best nutritional choice for infants is breast milk, for a multitude of reasons. Here are some of them:

- Human milk is perfectly suited to infants. It is species specific.
- It contains the ideal quantities and quality of the three energy-producing nutrients (carbohydrate, fat, protein). The concentration of these nutrients adjusts to the needs of the baby, both daily and over time. For example, breast milk produced in the evening has a higher fat content, so the infant will stay full longer (Canadian Child Care Federation, 2001, p. 2).
- The essential fatty acids promote the best possible nerve and brain development.
- The large amount of lactose (sugar), compared with the milk of other species, helps in the development of the central nervous system.
- Breast milk contains the right balance of most essential vitamins and minerals. It does not contain vitamin D; the infant should be given 10 µg (400 IU) of vitamin D daily (Canadian Paediatric Society, 2008).
- The protein in breast milk is easily digested in comparison with proteins from other foods. Protein is the most difficult nutrient for us to digest. Cow's milk, peanuts, and eggs are some of the most highly allergenic foods because they are high in protein.
- Breast milk contains antibodies that provide infants with immunity against some infections during breast-feeding, whereas infant formula does not offer that benefit. Exclusively breast-fed infants are also less likely to be the victims of sudden infant death syndrome (SIDS) (Canadian Child Care Federation, 2001, p. 2).
- Breast-fed infants are less likely to develop allergies. Infants may react to certain foods that their mother has recently eaten (e.g., after she eats broccoli, the infant may experience flatulence).
- Breast-feeding is thought to be associated with increased cognitive outcomes (development), although the mechanism is not fully understood to date (Petryk, Harris, & Jongblood, 2007).

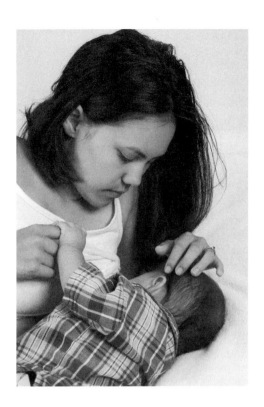

There are also benefits for the mother, "breastfeeding promotes mother-baby attachment, which increases baby's cognitive, social and emotional development" (Canadian Child Care Federation, 2001, p. 2). Many mothers who breast-feed need support in making the transition from home to work. Early childhood settings can play a vital role in supporting and facilitating parents in their decision to breast-feed successfully and for as long as possible. When babies are breast-fed exclusively (without added complementary foods) for the first six months of life, and longer with complementary foods, there are optimal benefits for the child and the mother.

Infants who are offered expressed breast milk or formula at the early childhood program will usually have been introduced to a bottle at home first. Infants who are used to receiving their nourishment from the breast may have a difficult time with this transition or they may accept the bottle readily.

A mother may want to continue nursing after her infant is enrolled in the early childhood program. Those women whose workplace is located close to the program may be able to come during the day to nurse their infant. Other mothers may bring in bottles of expressed breast milk and may breast-feed the infant at drop-off and pick-up. Find ways to be flexible so that the infant's needs are met and to encourage continued breast-feeding. Many mothers nurse at home and provide formula for the child during the day. There are also mothers who wean their infants before returning to work, so the child has infant formula exclusively. If the policies and educators have made the breast-feeding-friendly environment known, mothers may be encouraged to continue breast-feeding upon returning to work rather than weaning the infant.

Early childhood settings can be breast-feeding-friendly environments in a number of ways (Canadian Paediatric Society, 2008):

- Have a written policy on how breast-feeding is supported in your program and include it in the information package.
- Provide a comfortable place on site for mothers to breast-feed and express milk.
- Promote breast-feeding on site with wall posters and free brochures.
- Encourage staff members to discuss breast-feeding with current and prospective parents and to refer them to breast-feeding community supports and resources. Your local public health agency can also help, and for peer breast-feeding support, call La Leche League of Canada's referral service (See Resource Materials, page 283).
- Include fathers in breast-feeding discussions.

Source: Canadian Paediatric Society, *Well Beings: A Guide to Health in Child Care.* (Ottawa: Canadian Paediatric Society, 2008), 30. Reprinted with permission.

All of the baby bottles need to be labelled with the children's first name and possibly the surname's first letter when more than one child has the same name. Educators must ensure that the baby receives only his or her bottle. If a baby is fed a bottle of breast milk that is not his or her own, educators must call the local public health agency. Public health staff will then determine whether the baby has been exposed to human immunodeficiency virus (HIV) (*a very unlikely possibility*) and how to proceed. The director should also be instructed about notifying the baby's parents. Expressed breast milk does not present risks when it comes in contact with someone's skin (e.g., it has been spit up or during a test of the milk's temperature on the top of your hand). Discouraging mothers from providing expressed breast milk for their infants in programs is not an acceptable response to the issue of HIV. High-quality early childhood programs already implement the practices that prevent the spread of HIV in children. For information on storing and handling breast milk, refer to the Nutrition chapter in *Well Beings* (Canadian Paediatric Society, 2008).

For babies who are not breast-fed, commercial formula is essential for the first 9 to 12 months of life. Most formulas are made of either modified cow's milk or soy protein and include the infant's needs for water, fatty acids, carbohydrate (lactose), protein, and vitamins and minerals. Iron-fortified formulas are recommended for the first 9 to 12 months. It is important to prevent iron-deficiency anemia, rather than treat it, because anemia is a risk factor for possible irreversible developmental delays (Health Canada, 2005, p. 39). Commercial formulas are designed to be as similar to breast milk as possible. Even in breast-feeding-friendly early childhood programs, it is essential for educators to be supportive and positive to all families, whatever their choice.

Bottle-Feeding

Bottle-feeding time is an ideal time for educators to hold and cuddle infants. It is not a time to be rushed. The practice of bottle propping is absolutely unacceptable because of the risk of choking and dental caries (tooth decay). Feeding is one of the important daily care routines; it helps infants develop safe, secure, and trusting relationships with their educators. At this time in the child's life, the division of responsibility around feeding is very simple: the parent or caregiver is responsible for *what* the child eats, and the infant is responsible for *how much* will be eaten (and everything else). The adult helps the infant be calm and organized and feed smoothly, paying attention to information coming from the infant about timing, tempo, frequency, and amounts (Satter, 2000).

Older infants who can sit without support and, especially, toddlers may prefer to sit and drink their bottle independently. Educators should discourage toddlers from walking around with a bottle in their mouth. Obviously, the child must never be left unsupervised.

In many infant programs, parents bring in one bottle for each feeding during the day. Each bottle is filled with approximately the amount of expressed breast milk or formula that the infant drinks in one feeding. There could be four bottles, each with 90 mL (3 oz.) of milk. After the child has drunk from the bottle, do not give him or her leftovers at the next feeding. Milk is the perfect medium for the growth of germs, and during sucking, germs enter the bottle. Therefore, leftovers must be discarded (see Food Safety Practices, page 273).

Some early childhood programs are in the practice of having educators prepare the formula, when used, for each infant every day. The parents provide cans of their infant's specific brand. However, considering the amount of care and interaction that infants and toddlers need from their educators and that the educator–child ratio is already 1:3 or 1:4, a policy of parents bringing in the formula ready to serve in bottles is best, unless circumstances warrant preparation by the educators. As well, the logistics of clearly identifying all the individual bottles and nipples; sterilizing water, containers, measuring equipment, (unlined) bottles, and nipples; and ensuring the sterility of the formula add increased risk of foodborne illness. For information on safe handling, preparation, and storage of commercial formula, refer to the Nutrition chapter in *Well Beings* (Canadian Paediatric Society, 2008).

First Foods

Before six months of age, children's bodies are not fully ready for complementary food. Breast milk or formula provides all the essential nutrients. Early introduction of **semisolid foods** is not the best practice in promoting optimal nutrition. At around six months of age, most infants are ready to try chewing and swallowing some semisolid foods and require additional iron. At this time, offering iron-rich foods is a good way to start.

If a young infant is fed semisolid food, most of it will be found undigested in the stool. Infants' digestive and renal systems are too immature to cope with anything other than breast milk or formula. Infants don't produce enough saliva or digestive enzymes, and their kidneys cannot yet filter much protein. These infants are also more vulnerable to developing food allergies. Semisolid foods are less of an allergy risk to infants once they've reached the age of six months and their immune system has begun to mature.

Parents may believe that their infants need to eat solid foods as early as two or three months of age because the child seems more hungry or is waking up more often during the night. Many parents interpret this to mean that the breast milk or formula isn't filling up the child. In fact, infants simply go through growth spurts and need extra nutrients; all they need is extra breast milk or formula for a week or two to get through the spurt. It is a myth that very young babies sleep better at night when they are fed infant cereal. In reality, "prolonged sleep reflects the baby's total neurological development and has very little to do with the food she eats, colic being one exception" (Lambert-Lagacé, 2003, p. 126).

Understandably, parents want the best for their baby and are concerned about why she or he seems hungry. Relatives and friends may also have assumed

that adding solid foods early was good practice and may be encouraging (or pressuring) parents to do the same. They may suggest, for example, adding infant cereal to the formula in the bottle. There is no evidence to indicate that this practice helps infants sleep through the night, and it also can pose a choking risk (Health Canada, 2005).

Ideally, parents consult their infant's physician to determine on an individual basis when to introduce semisolid foods. This decision will be based somewhat on increased nutrient needs and on whether the infant has at least doubled his or her birth weight, although motor abilities and interest in other family members' foods or peers' food in the early childhood program can also influence the decision. In turn, parents and educators work together in the feeding process.

The introduction of semisolid foods should be a slow process and follow each infant's lead. This respects the infants' nutritional and emotional needs, so that eating food is a positive experience rather than a process that infants can fail at or experience negative feelings about because it happened too early or too quickly. Infants should have as much control as possible in the feeding process, including some self-feeding. Watch for the following signs of infants' readiness to start with semisolids:

- around six months of age
- better able to sit up
- move their head back to indicate fullness or disinterest
- move their head forward to indicate hunger or interest
- open mouth wide when offered food on a spoon
- close lips over the spoon; keep food in the mouth and swallow it instead of pushing it out
- can hold a spoon, although it will be months before they use it effectively
- have shown interest in putting food on their hands, and some food has eventually reached their mouth

Developmentally, infants need sensory experiences, including food experiences, to begin to understand their world. Some babies need and enjoy this type of sensory exploration more than others. Don't be surprised if some parents are concerned about seeing their infants with their hands in the food—perhaps feeling that educators are encouraging their infants to play with their food. Once again, effective communication between parents and educators is important in negotiating compromise. One obvious difference in feeding practices has to do with fundamental values in cultures.

Your program's goal is to encourage infant and toddler independence. You encourage the infant to use a spoon while you have a second spoon for feeding. However, the parents' philosophy may emphasize the importance of interdependence—connection with the family is a priority; the feeling of being connected is much more important than self-sufficiency. Feeding with interdependence in mind means that the adult feeds the infant, perhaps into the preschool years, as part of this value. This is not an issue of right or wrong but of two different views. With discussion, a compromise will be reached.

The Process of Introducing Semisolid Foods

Even though infants are now ready for semisolid foods, they are not ready to have the food replace the nutrients in the breast milk or formula. Remember that young infants' primary nutrition comes from the breast milk or formula until they are eating a variety of foods and in enough quantity to ensure they are getting the essential nutrients, usually around nine months of age.

Parents should introduce each food at home several times before it is offered in the early childhood program. Parents know their child best and will recognize any allergic reaction to the new food. Parents should wait three to five days before trying the next new food to observe any reaction the child may have, such as undigested food in the stool, gas, rashes, vomiting, breathing difficulties, or any other sign that the child may be sensitive or allergic to the food.(see Allergies, page 186). Parents often introduce cereals first, or possibly meat and alternatives. Both options are high in iron, which is important to supplement around six months to prevent anemia. If the physician is concerned about anemia, meat or alternatives will likely be suggested first, as iron from these sources is better absorbed.

Cereals

Iron-fortified rice cereals are least likely to cause allergies; they can be followed by other single-grain cereals such as barley, oats, and wheat before introducing mixed-grain cereals. Commercially prepared infant cereals are best suited to infants because they are a good source of iron in a form that can be absorbed. Their other nutrients, including protein, carbohydrates, and fats, are easily digested. The introduction of cereals takes three weeks to a month if these foods are introduced gradually. The dry cereal is mixed with breast milk or formula, with a thin consistency at first and less liquid for a thicker consistency as the infant is ready.

Meat and Alternatives

Meat and alternatives are high in protein, a number of minerals, and some fat. Iron from meat sources is better absorbed than iron from nonmeat sources. The foods in this group include meats, fish, poultry, cooked egg yolks, and alternatives such as tofu and well-cooked legumes. Infants in vegetarian families will receive plant proteins, such as legumes, tofu, and meat-like products made from vegetable protein. Lacto-ovo vegetarian families will also introduce cheeses and egg (yolks).

Suggestions from Best Start: Ontario's Maternal Newborn and Early Child Development Resource Centre and Nutrition Resource Centre (2007, p. 5) include the following:

- Keep meats and alternatives moist so they are easy to swallow. Add extra water or broth to meats and cooked beans. Use silken (soft) tofu.
- Do not give your baby deli meats such as ham, wieners, bologna, salami, or sausages. These are high in fat and salt.
- Give your baby fish such as white fish, salmon and light canned tuna. Swordfish, shark, fresh or frozen tuna steak, canned albacore tuna, marlin, orange roughy and escolar are often high in mercury. Do not give your baby these fish more than once a month.

Source: *Feeding Your Baby From Six Months to One Year.* (Toronto: Best Start: Ontario's Maternal, Newborn and Early Child Development Resource Centre, 2007), 5. Reprinted with permission.

Here a few more points to remember:

- Introduce cooked egg yolk without the egg white. Egg whites are more allergenic and often better tolerated after one year of age.

- White meats such as chicken, turkey, and fish tend to be easier to digest and therefore are often introduced before meats such as beef, veal, liver, or lamb.

- As with all new foods, introduce one new meat (or alternative) every three to five days.

- At first, serve only 5 mL (1 tsp.) alone, not mixed with vegetables, and offer this food group at the midday meal. Gradually increase this serving to a maximum of 90 mL (6 tbsp.) daily by the end of the first year. Added salt is unnecessary and may contribute to long-term concerns about overconsumption of salt.

Vegetables and Fruit

After the infant is regularly eating iron-rich foods such as infant cereals or meat and alternatives, introduce vegetables and fruit. Again, they should be introduced one at a time, with three to five days before starting another new food to ensure that there is no allergy to the food. Here are some points to keep in mind when feeding infants:

- It is never acceptable to pressure a child into eating.

- Foods that are helpful for teething infants include dry toast and soft pieces of fruit or vegetables (e.g., a ring of green pepper). Most store-bought teething biscuits contain sugar and are not recommended.

- All foods need to have a puréed texture when they are introduced and become less puréed and more lumpy as the infant is better able to chew and may have some teeth.

- Changing texture is important to support infants' abilities as they learn to chew. Generally, from 6 to 12 months, the texture offered to babies undergoes ongoing change from purée to choppy to regular table food, for the most part. Infants who eat puréed foods too long may be less willing to eat more textured foods. As infants develop a repertoire of foods and can chew more effectively, fewer table foods need to be restricted from them, except foods that are a concern for choking. By one year of age, the infant should be eating a variety of foods from each food group and drinking liquids from a cup.

- Carrots, squash, sweet potatoes, asparagus, green peas, cauliflower, and broccoli need to be cooked and puréed at first. Cooking continues to be required, but the texture will change with readiness (e.g., whole peas, small pieces of cooked carrot).

- Ripe fresh fruit such as bananas, mangoes, and papayas can be mashed. Apples, pears, peaches, and plums need to be peeled, cooked, and puréed at first and then mashed until the child is ready for choppier pieces.

- When fruit juice is offered, ensure that it is 100% fruit juice, pasteurized, and without added sugar. The consumption of a lot of juice can contribute to inadequate intake of other nutrients and energy, poor weight gain, and possibly diarrhea. Limit the daily intake of fruit juice to no more than 120 mL (4 oz.) (Canadian Paediatric Society, 2008). Although dilution of juice is a common practice, there is no clear rationale for this practice.

■ Children usually drink juice at home. Educators can minimize offering additional juice by

– serving fruit.

– providing water to drink.

– having a policy that states that juice will be served in cups only and that when bottles of juice are brought from home, it will be transferred to a cup. By the time a child is ready for juice, he or she is developmentally ready to drink from a cup. Juice in bottles encourages children to drink far more than the daily requirement of fruit and contributes to dental caries (see Dental Health Education, page 550).

For children from 9 to 12 months old, refer to Table 5.11 for tips on foods.

CRITICAL THINKING

The parents of an eight-month-old girl haven't yet introduced semisolid foods, not even infant cereal. Marie's source of nutrition is her mother's breast milk. Marie is interested in what the other children are eating. She is hungry half an hour after you feed her a bottle of expressed breast milk. However, when you mention this to her mother, she assures you that she will be starting Marie on infant cereal soon. That was three weeks ago, and Marie's mother hasn't followed through. What are the issues of concern for educators? How should you proceed?

Toddler Nutrition

Toddlers are at a stage when they are developing a sense of autonomy (a sense of independence) and balancing that need with the need to feel connected to their parents, families, and peers. As a result, parents and educators have the challenging role of respecting toddlers' need for autonomy but setting limits to promote trust and security (see Table 5.9, page 246).

Toddlers' growth slows to a rate of only half to one-third of what it was in the first 12 months, but exploration speeds up. Except during growth spurts, toddlers won't be as hungry as when they were younger and may eat less overall. Educators often find that this is less true in the early childhood program than at home, as many children eat more consistently when surrounded by peers. Their appetite can be inconsistent. Many toddlers can override any desire to eat when they are overexcited, overtired, or angry with their parents or educators. Some parents and educators become concerned about this natural change in eating habits and pressure toddlers to eat. This is not appropriate practice at any age but is a big mistake with toddlers, who will assert their independence. When an adult and a toddler get into a power struggle, nobody wins!

TABLE 5.11 **Tips for Feeding Children from Nine Months to One Year**

NINE MONTHS TO ONE YEAR	
FOOD GROUP	**TIPS**
Vegetables and fruits	Offer soft, cooked vegetables cut in bit-sized pieces.
	Give pieces of soft, ripe fruit like bananas, peaches, kiwi, and cantaloupe.
Grain products	Continue to give your baby infant cereal. It is a good source of iron. If your baby refuses to eat it, mix it with fruit or other healthy foods.
	Offer finger foods such as pieces of bagel, dry toast strips, rice, roti, noodles, cooked pasta, flat bread, and unsalted crackers.
Meat and alternatives	Give bite-size pieces of tender meat, fish, cooked beans, and tofu.
	If your baby refuses meat, try mixing fish, beans or tofu in sweet potatoes or squash to enhance flavour and texture. Be sure your baby has tried each new food on its own first.
	Give cooked egg yolk. Your baby can try cooked egg whites after one year of age.
Milk and milk products	Breast milk is still the most important food. Continue to breast-feed until your baby is two years old or more.
	In addition to breast milk, when your baby is eating a variety of foods everyday, you can offer your baby homogenized cow's milk (3.25% milk fat).
	Do not give skim, 1%, 2%, or low-fat milk products. Babies need the fat to grow.
	Do not give soy, rice or other vegetarian beverages. They do not have enough fat and may not have vitamin D added to them.
	Never give unpasteurized milk.
	Offer yogurt, cottage cheese, and small cubes of soft cheese or shredded cheese.
By one year old, your baby should be eating a variety of foods from each food group and drinking liquids from a cup. Babies can go directly from breastfeeding to drinking from a cup.	

Source: *Feeding Your Baby From Six Months to One Year.* (Toronto: Best Start: Ontario's Maternal, Newborn and Early Child Development Resource Centre, 2007), 7. Reprinted with permission.

Poor eating habits now can pave the way for eating problems that last a lifetime. Toddlers can become anxious about mealtimes, or refuse to eat, or have temper tantrums because of frustration. Parents and educators need to remember that most young children will eat when they are hungry and when they are offered a variety of nourishing foods. It is a toddler's job to assert his or her independence, and it is the trusted adult's job to confirm the toddler's security by providing firm but reasonable limits.

Here are some things to keep in mind when toddlers are eating:

- Remember the division of responsibility described on page 245:
  - Educators have indirect control of feeding (i.e., for *what*, *when*, and *where*):
    - selecting and presenting nutritious foods,
    - setting routine times for snacks and meals,
    - creating a pleasant atmosphere,
    - maintaining developmentally appropriate standards of behaviour at the table, and
    - helping the children attend to their eating.
  - Children have direct control of eating (i.e., how much and whether they eat).
- Some enjoy or need adult assistance with feeding.
- Many have a hard time sitting long enough to eat a whole meal if it is holding them back from doing other things.
- Toddlers typically dawdle over food. Rather than focus on the dawdling and the inconvenience this brings to the flow of the program, it is more effective to give reasonable but firm limits, such as "You have 10 more minutes for lunch," and, after the allotted time, calmly remove the child's plate without commenting on how much the child ate.
- Practical hints:
  - Use child-sized unbreakable plates, bowls, and utensils.
  - Toddlers often eat very small serving sizes (sometimes one-quarter of an adult's serving size). Avoid dishing out large amounts of food; they may seem overwhelming to a toddler. This may turn the child off his or her food.
  - Provide finger foods so that toddlers are not always expected to use utensils, which is an emerging skill and not always an easy one to master.
  - Serve soup thin enough to drink or thick enough to eat with a spoon.
  - Cut foods into bite-sized pieces.
  - Avoid serving very chewy foods.
  - Children need to sit down to eat.
  - Take special care to avoid foods that may cause choking (see Reducing the Risk of Choking, page 272).
- Toddlers are often afraid to try new things (neophobic) and so tend to be afraid of new foods. The more familiar toddlers are with foods, the more

they like them. Coaxing toddlers to try new foods tends to make them resist the idea more. But if they see a new food offered with no outside pressure several times, they will eventually try it, and the food becomes less and less an aversion. Expect toddlers to refuse a new food and avoid thinking, "Oh, they didn't like it, so we won't make it again!"

- Toddlers learn to like most foods that they originally rejected. However, in the process, they may do things such as spit out the food if its texture, flavour, temperature, or other aspect is unusual to them. This is a learning process that should not be discouraged because it usually leads to more openness toward food. If their behaviour (e.g., spitting out) is not tolerated, toddlers are less likely to risk trying new foods again. You may argue that permitting this behaviour wastes food or encourages poor table manners. Throwing away a piece of vegetable a few times is worth the long-term benefit when the children decide that they like that vegetable after all. In terms of manners, if you expect toddlers to demonstrate proper etiquette, you will be disappointed! Table manners are learned over time, and they should not be a priority for toddlers at mealtime.

- Toddlers have **food jags**, which means that they refuse all but one or two favourite foods for a period. This, too, is part of normal development and should be handled casually. Continue to offer a variety of foods at meals and snack times, and most children will eventually start accepting other foods again.

- Toddlers should be offered a frequent, nutritious variety of foods, including energy-dense foods from the different food groups, to meet nutrient and energy needs.

Preschool Nutrition

During the preschool years, children gain only about 2.5 to 2.75 kg (5 to 6 lbs) per year. However, between the ages of two and five, children's head and body shapes change dramatically—a five-year-old no longer looks like a baby. Most preschoolers come through the toddler stage feeling that they have some power and autonomy, and most have an awareness that others have rights, too. Preschoolers take increasing initiative as they become better at everything they do. With more language, they learn to express themselves in social ways and to work things out with other people. Food jags, dawdling, fear of new foods, and other toddler nutrition issues tend to diminish and are fairly uncommon by four years of age, especially if adults have not given these issues undue attention when they were toddlers. Children in this age group tend to be interested in their body and keen to learn about how foods affect their body, where foods come from, cooking, and advertising (see Table 5.9, page 246, and Nutrition Education, page 544).

Here are some things to keep in mind when preschoolers are eating:

- Children are individuals, and their appetites and interest in food fluctuate.
- Establish clear expectations for mealtime behaviour. Preschoolers are capable of understanding what is and isn't appropriate behaviour, as well as logical consequences (e.g., Carlos spills milk on the floor and understands that he will help clean it up, or Emily throws the second piece of her sandwich on the floor and understands from your earlier comments that now she is finished eating and needs to leave the table).
- Children have a genuine interest in learning about others, so this is an opportune time for them to begin to learn about other cultures, foods, and ways of cooking.
- When introducing a new food, do not pressure a child to try it. Always remember the division of responsibility around feeding.

School-Age Nutrition

This stage in a child's life brings many developmental changes, but in terms of actual physical change, most children do not go through dramatic growth

until early adolescence. School-agers vary in height and body shape and are aware of these differences. Concerns about dieting and the fear of fat may heighten in later school-age years, particularly in girls but also with boys. Children make the transition from a primary focus on their families to increasing influence from peers and other outside influences (e.g., media). Concerns about sedentary lifestyles can be an issue at any age, but there seem to be obvious differences in energy level during the school-age years. Supporting and promoting healthy active living both with families and in our programs will provide children with the tools they need to make healthy choices a natural part of their lives when it comes to nutrition, physical activity, and balancing screen time. An important component of Satter's philosophy (1990) is that fundamental to parents' and educators' roles is trusting children to decide *how much* and *whether* to eat. If parents do their jobs with *feeding*, children will do their jobs with *eating*.

Most school-age children who are involved in physical activity with friends have a high energy level. Others who spend long periods of time sitting in front of a television or computer screen will likely be lethargic and lack motivation to be active.

The power of peers is evident in how children react to food among themselves, but these reactions are influenced also by their preschool experiences with foods. Children who are already open to trying new foods may continue in this positive way by increasing their repertoire. Children who have not been introduced to a variety of foods may be more judgmental about peers' food choices that are different from their own.

A vegetarian child who brings a tofu burger for lunch may be asked to share it by one child who is open to new foods but teased by another child for eating something unfamiliar to him.

School-agers need to understand the reasons for what they are doing. They are concerned with mastery and accomplishment as part of their self-esteem. For this reason, preparing food is popular with this age group. If a program can provide opportunities for learning to make breakfast, the children may also be able to do so at home. Through learning processes such as this, we promote their need to experience success that is recognized by self and others. School-age nutrition education can include the relationships between food production and consumption, recycling and composting, food wastage and packaging, and the environment (see Table 5.9, page 246, and Cooking with Children, page 545).

Older school-agers may find it stigmatizing to be separated from other children (some of their friends) while eating lunch at school just because they participate in the program's lunch program. Children who bring lunches may do a lot of trading of foods among themselves, which may not be a problem unless some children bring in high-status, low-nutritive foods for snacks or desserts and encourage other children to bring candy or chips to trade (see Concern about Amounts of Food Eaten, page 332).

PROVIDING FOODS AND MENU PLANNING

OBJECTIVES

To outline ways in which foods can be provided in an early childhood program.

To explain rotation menus and list the steps in writing menus.

Food is provided in early childhood programs in a number of ways. The most common arrangements are

- having the food prepared somewhere else and brought to the program (e.g., by a caterer, restaurant, or community kitchen). Often programs choose this option when they do not have complete kitchens.

- preparing food in the program, with an on-site kitchen and cook.
- requiring the families to bring food for their children.
- combining two of the above (e.g., an infant and toddler program provides the snacks and the parents supply their child's lunch and formula or breast milk, or a preschool program prepares the snacks and meals are catered).
- having agency nutrition programs, often sponsored by government or foundations, conduct breakfast or lunch programs.

Understanding the basics of menu planning helps you not only as a student but also after you graduate. The menu is basically the culmination of the program's nutrition program put into practice.

Providing Food in the Early Childhood Program

Regardless of how the food is provided, educators are responsible for ensuring that children have access to adequate nutrition each day. This must be clearly stated in a nutrition policy, outlining the provincial or territorial legislative requirements as a minimum but reflecting best practices beyond those requirements. As with all policies relevant to children and families, it should be written in positive language and communicated to parents before enrollment and on an ongoing basis. The nutrition policy will include additional information, such as

- foods, if any, that can be brought in by families and visitors.
- where menus are posted and how often they are revised.

Early childhood programs that prepare food on the premises or bring in catered food usually offer one or two snacks and lunch, supper, or both, depending on the hours of operation and their early childhood regulations. As part of the conditions for a program's licence, public health inspectors usually review the food preparation, equipment, and storage and serving facilities annually.

Financial constraints or limited kitchen facilities are often the reason why parents bring in some or all of the food. Programs need a refrigerator to store food and a stove, hot plate, or microwave oven to warm food. In some cases, the program provides milk and juice.

This job is simpler when food is prepared in-house or is catered because staff develop the menus and establish the list of acceptable foods and beverages to be served to the children based on the program's nutrition policy. And, of course, enough food is available to provide children with second helpings. You may think that when families bring food for children, educators can relax and focus on other aspects of the program. However, since the educators are responsible for ensuring adequate nutrition for the children during the day, the nutrition policies in place cover

- the food and/or beverages that the program provides,
- the times for snacks and meals,
- the parents' responsibilities,

- a list of acceptable or unacceptable foods and beverages for parents to use as a guideline in providing the food, taking care to respect families' food preferences, and

- recommendations for environmentally friendly food containers and packaging.

Even in these programs, supplementary food will be on hand. There may be times when someone forgets a lunch at home or in the car, a child is still hungry after finishing her or his snack or lunch, a parent does not send or cannot afford to send enough food, or a parent consistently sends foods that are high in fat, sugar, or salt but low in other nutrients. So it can be more of a challenge for staff when the families provide food and/or beverages for the children.

Putting a basket of fruit or other nutritious finger foods out at lunch makes sense. Hungry children can help themselves. This reduces the stigma associated with the children having to ask educators for food.

Educators and families want children to have adequate nutrition and to become knowledgeable about food choices. Nutrition education is an ongoing part of the program and is based on developmental and cultural appropriateness. As with any issue that educators have about children, they need to be sensitive in their approach, handle the issue discreetly, and maintain confidentiality. Food and eating habits are personal aspects of someone's identity, upbringing, and ethnicity and can be closely connected to feelings of self-worth. Making disparaging comments about a child's lunch and, even worse, throwing part or all of the lunch away are unacceptable and disrespectful practices. These practices will not make families receptive to talking with educators.

Before approaching families, educators must ask themselves a number of questions:

- How frequent is the problem and how long has it been happening?

- Has the parent experienced a recent emotional or financial setback that may temporarily affect the family's everyday life?

- Are the food products familiar to the educators? If not, find out more about the food and its preparation. It may be nutritious after all, and it can be an opportunity for new foods to be integrated into the program.

Sonali is a vegetarian, and her lunches don't have milk or meat. Because you are unfamiliar with the principles of vegetarianism, you assume that she isn't getting the protein or calcium she needs. Some plant sources of calcium (e.g., almonds, figs) may be part of Sonali's daily mainstay. You want to educate yourself about vegetarianism; asking her parents to explain their family's diet helps you do this. As for the parents, you have demonstrated an interest in their child, and they are pleased that they have knowledge and skills to share with you. They may also have religious or cultural reasons for their dietary needs that will contribute to your responsiveness to Sonali.

Ways to Provide Enough Nutritious Food

Children and adults need to eat breakfast to obtain the food energy to work, learn, and play. Many young children go to bed between 7:30 and 9:30 p.m. With the exception of infants, who wake up for a bottle or nursing, children wake up in the morning having fasted for 10 to 12 hours. The demands that rapid growth, development, and everyday activities place on children make it important that they eat enough nutrients to fuel growth and activity for several hours.

Provincial regulations and occupational guidelines specify what food must be offered and how often, depending on a child's age and the number of hours spent in care. Here's a basic routine to follow regardless of the age of children in your care:

- For 2- to 4-hour sessions (either morning or afternoon), provide a snack 1½ to 2 hours before the next planned meal.
- For 4- to 6-hour sessions, provide one meal and one snack.
- For 7- to 8-hour sessions, provide one meal and two snacks.
- For 9- to 10-hour sessions, provide two meals and two snacks.

Source: Canadian Paediatric Society, *Well Beings: A Guide to Health in Child Care.* (Ottawa: Canadian Paediatric Society, 2008), 38. Reprinted with permission.

Try to offer a snack between 1½ and 2 hours before the next meal.

Morning Snacks

Many programs offer a flexible time for morning snack. They recognize that offering the snack at a designated time for all children cannot meet the individual nutritional needs of children.

Christopher gets out of bed as early as 6:00 a.m., eats breakfast, and leaves for the program. He is usually ready for his snack before 9:30 a.m.

Regular snacks provide a necessary and positive contribution to a child's food intake. Morning snacks that include foods from three of the four food groups provide the essential nutrients. They should be acceptable for dental health, too. The snack could be available for a set period—for example, from 7:30 to 9:30 a.m.—rather than offered as a group snack. Children then have control over when to eat and can respond to their body rather than to a time imposed by the program. Because they have a smaller stomach, growing children need the opportunity to refuel (if they choose to) every two to three hours. It is also helpful for relatively stable blood sugar levels rather than ones that drop low ("I'm starved") and then soar high ("I'm stuffed") due to ravenous eating.

Dietitians are sometimes concerned that if there aren't set times for eating, children will develop grazing habits—eating constantly with no awareness of body signals for hunger. Having a flexible morning snack enables children to eat when they are hungry (and not ravenous) and adequately addresses dietitians' concerns. Obviously, the snack would not be available between 9:30 and 11:30 a.m. or noon, when lunch is served.

Keeping in mind that children have individual body rhythms, just as adults do, there are those who do not eat breakfast, for a variety of reasons:

- Some children may not enjoy eating or drinking as soon as they get up in the morning.

- There may be no time to eat during the morning rush to get out of the house and drop everyone off. Time pressure on families is a significant reason for children being hungry in the morning.

- Children who have not had a good night's sleep may not have an appetite for several hours after they wake up.

- Some children will have eaten only part of their breakfast at home or on their way to the program. And they will need to finish it or have the morning snack to supplement it when they arrive at the program. Other children may have eaten a doughnut or danish on the way to the program, which provides some quick energy but none of the nutrients needed for a morning's activity.

- Some families just don't have the food available for breakfast every day. The problem may be more acute at the end of the month, when there is little or no money left in the budget.

- Some parents who don't eat breakfast themselves may not see the importance of providing breakfast for their children. Or because of the parents' modelling, the child refuses to eat breakfast.

Morning snacks can be simple yet nourishing. Children who eat a nourishing breakfast at home will probably want less of each food or fewer of the items.

Here are a few simple snack ideas that include three of the four food groups. These snacks are easy to prepare even in programs with limited kitchen facilities:

- cold or hot low-sugar cereal, milk, and fruit (fresh or canned in its own juice)

- pita bread with hummus and fruit or vegetable juice

- cottage cheese with fruit and whole-grain crackers

- melted cheese, tomato, and alfalfa sprouts on unbuttered whole-grain toast

- banana egg pancakes (blend one ripe banana with two eggs and grill the small pancakes on a nonstick griddle) and milk

- blender drinks (e.g., milk or yogurt and fruit or juice; eggs must not be used in blender drinks because of the risk of *Salmonella* food poisoning)

- scrambled tofu (soybean curd) on whole-grain toast with fruit

- almond butter on crackers with fruit
- yogurt with fruit and wheat germ

Child Nutrition Programs

It may be surprising to you that Canada is the only G8 country without a federal policy for a national child nutrition program. There is a piecemeal approach to child nutrition, with some local and provincial funding from a range of sources. On a positive note, many creative programs have emerged to respond to food insecurity of children, sponsored by government, nongovernmental agencies, nonprofit organizations (e.g., Breakfast for Learning, Canadian Living Foundation), and business. Many elementary schools have developed responsive programs because children were arriving at school hungry and unable to concentrate on their work, and have included early childhood programs in their mandate so that younger children benefit as well. Communities are recognizing the contribution of nourishing food to children's everyday well-being. Child nutrition programs are responsive to the communities served since they may be delivered in a variety of ways and may be part of an overall plan involving community kitchens or gardens, lunch salad bars, healthy snacks, or breakfasts, contributing to nutrition education that will benefit the child and family in the long term. *For example, the British Columbia Healthy Living Alliance (BCHLA), a provincial coalition of organizations, is piloting "Farm to School Salad Bar," improving access to locally grown, culturally appropriate foods in schools in the province's northern interior.*

FoodShare's Coalition for Student Nutrition, an Ontario-wide network of individuals and agencies committed to better nutrition for children, developed eight guiding principles for a child nutrition program. The following principles have now been mandated as policy for funding proposals:

- The program supplies nutritious and safe food, regardless of family income.
- The program is accessible and nonstigmatizing, so it is universal and flexible and does not replace welfare reform.
- The program is community based and administered in a way that respects the individuality of the community and addresses its unique needs.
- The program is culturally appropriate, so it is sensitive to and respects individual and community diversity.
- The program empowers children and families, so parents are not made to feel that their role in the raising of their child is being taken away from them.
- The program creates a nurturing, warm, caring environment in which children can participate freely.
- The program has enough financial stability to ensure continual funding.
- The program provides public education about creative ways to nourish children adequately and properly, both in school and at home.

Source: Adapted from Coalition for Student Nutrition, FoodShare, Toronto.

Menu Planning

Menus may be prepared in early childhood programs by

- the director,
- the educators,
- the cook, or
- the dietitian, who may be available for programs affiliated with a hospital, a community college, or a workplace with a cafeteria.

Each of these options brings strengths and challenges:

- The expertise of a dietitian is a definite asset. However, if the same menu is used in a number of programs, there is no opportunity to respond to individual aspects of the community in which each program is located.
- A knowledgeable cook can get immediate feedback from the children on how they feel about the food. A cook can be creative with the menu and see what works and what doesn't.
- When meals are catered, the menu plan is probably written by the caterers, but the program should make sure that the caterer accepts and responds to ongoing feedback.

Effective menus reflect a variety of foods that are developmentally appropriate, take into account ethnocultural dishes, have little repetition of recipes during the four- to eight-week rotation, and introduce new foods and recipes regularly, including foods that children are learning to prepare and eat. Educators' ability to read and develop menus is beneficial for a number of reasons:

- Educators identify the menus that are adequate in terms of nutrition, appeal, and variety.
- They know how menus can be corrected, improved, or made more creative, especially when younger children turn away from their food and older ones comment, "Not that again!"
- They suggest the appropriate substitutions for foods when a child is allergic. Serving foods as similar as possible to those that the other children eat is ideal to normalize children with allergies.
- They work within the nutrition budget and identify food wastage or unnecessary spending.

Advantages of Rotation Menus

Menus are planned on a rotational basis for periods of four, six, or eight weeks. Four weeks is a short period of time, which means that on every fifth Monday, the cycle starts again. Children are likely to become bored with the lack of variety in this case. Longer rotation cycles offer greater variety in foods, and no one has to eat the same recipe more than a few times every six or eight weeks. Not many of us could say that about our cooking at home!

Developing four six-week rotation menus, one for each season, has several advantages:

- You can take advantage of the fresh produce that is available in season at its lowest prices and, in the summer, food that is grown locally or regionally. Perhaps some vegetables can be grown by the children (depending on your geography and growing season).

- The six-week menu would be rotated only once, since each season lasts three months.

- You can serve foods that are more popular in certain seasons, such as soups in winter and cold plates in summer. Of course, favourite dishes (e.g., spaghetti) can be part of every rotating menu—once or twice in six weeks for the favourite foods is not too often!

- The six-week menu provides a vehicle for introducing new foods to children. It is in the children's best interests to plan a balance of familiar foods and new foods.

Getting Down to Writing Menus

The prospect of facing a page of blank squares and knowing that you must fill those and five more pages with exciting recipes can be somewhat daunting. Like other skills, planning menus takes experience to develop. A good place to start is by critiquing menus that you find in books or early childhood programs during your placements (see Appendixes 5.3 and 5.4, pages 293 and 294). As an educator, even if you are not responsible for menu planning, critiquing menus is an important skill as part of a team that consistently supports healthy and interesting food options for children. In menu planning, consider the following suggestions:

1. *Begin with a number of resources at your fingertips.* The most important one is *Eating Well with Canada's Food Guide*, followed by any guidelines for healthy snacks, simple recipes, and lists of different vegetables, fruit, juices, breads, and so on to which the program has access.

2. *Know the number of snacks and meals that are served each day.* Programs that are six hours per day or longer should offer foods that constitute at least 50% of *Eating Well with Canada's Food Guide* daily requirements. As a rule, the two snacks and one meal combined consist of three servings from grain products, three servings from the vegetables and fruit group, one to two servings from milk products, and one serving from meat and alternatives.

3. *A menu-planning format applies to children over 12 months of age.* As a student, you will gain a fundamental understanding of menu planning, which provides you with the basis for adapting menus to the age group with which you will be working.

There may be concerns about foods that can cause choking in younger children. Educators working with children under 12 months of age work directly with the parents to ensure that the nutritional needs of the infants are met, including the introduction of semisolid foods.

Steps to Follow for Each Week's Menu

■ Begin by choosing foods for the five lunches:

1. Select the meat and alternatives.

2. Select the grain products that would complement the meat and alternatives.

3. Select the vegetables and fruit.

4. Add the milk or alternative.

■ Next, choose foods for the morning snacks:

5. Select foods from three of the four food groups (see Morning Snacks, page 266).

■ Then choose foods for the afternoon snacks:

6. Select foods from two of the four food groups. (Children's nutritional requirements are usually lower in the afternoon than in the morning.)

■ Evaluate your week's menu with the menu-planning checklist (see Table 5.12).

TABLE 5.12	Menu Planning Checklist

Nutritional requirements:

■ vegetables and fruit—at least three servings

■ grain products—at least three servings

■ milk and alternatives—at least one serving

■ meat and alternatives—at least one serving

■ drinking water—availability at all times is encouraged

Menus are varied, interesting, and creative (e.g., variety of colours, shapes, textures, tastes). Natural colours of fruit and vegetables, especially when raw, are appealing; a single colour on a plate is not appetizing. Meals should have a variety of shapes and textures to appeal to children's sense of sight, taste, and hearing. Experimenting with new foods, ethnocultural recipes, and different herbs and spices encourages children to explore a variety of flavours. Be careful not to serve two strong-tasting foods together.

■ "At least half of the grain products served are whole-grain (barley, brown rice, oatmeal, quinoa, and wild rice; whole wheat versions of couscous, breads, pitas, tortillas, roti, crackers, and pasta)" (Harrison, 2008).

■ "Meat alternatives, such as fish, beans, chickpeas, soybeans, eggs, tofu, are served often" (Harrison, 2008).

■ "Milk, fortified soy beverages, and 100% fruit or lower-sodium vegetable juices are other good choices" (Harrison, 2008).

■ Real, unsweetened fruit juices are provided—not fruit drinks with added sugar or sweetener.

■ Desserts, if provided, are a nutritional part of the meal (e.g., fruit, yogurt, homemade puddings).

■ Snacks are low in sugar and are nutritionally acceptable.

■ Menus are planned and served with children in mind (e.g., some finger foods, child-sized servings, age-appropriate dishes and utensils). Preschoolers and school-agers have opportunities to serve themselves.

(continued)

TABLE 5.12   **Menu Planning Checklist** *(continued)*

- Foods that have been through a number of food processes or have several additives are not served (e.g., instant potatoes, pudding mixes, processed meats such as hot dogs, pepperoni sticks, bacon, corn dogs, sausages, luncheon meats, fish sticks, and chicken nuggets).

- Foods served for celebrations and holidays are nutritious and fun.

- All allergies have been considered while planning menus and at the time of serving meals and snacks.

- Menus are posted in an obvious place for parents to read.

- The posted menu corresponds with what is actually served.

  - Finally, because you are developing a rotational menu, the four, six, or eight weeks of menu plans should be checked for repetition of recipes, for the introduction of at least one new food or recipe a week, and against the food budget.

CRITICAL THINKING

When critiquing the month-long lunch menu in Appendix 5.3 (page 293), you note that a number of children in the lunch program do not drink milk for a range of reasons. Improve the calcium in the menu by making a substitution in one lunch every week (four in all) that improves the nondairy calcium content of that lunch (refer to Table 5.5, page 231).

OBJECTIVE

To outline ways to reduce the risk of choking, to prevent foodborne illnesses, and to use a microwave oven safely.

FOOD SAFETY

This section includes three safety issues relevant to food and children: choking, foodborne illnesses, and microwave ovens. Children are at risk of choking on food because pieces of food are too large or they are not concentrating on what they are doing (e.g., talking while they have food in their mouth, eating while running). The safety of Canada's food supply is a shared responsibility among all levels of government, industry, and consumers. We depend on government policies and regulations to set high standards to ensure a safe food supply and inspection at all levels to maintain it. In an early childhood program, providing nutritious food for children goes beyond purchasing it and menu planning. It is of the utmost importance that food is safely stored, handled, prepared, and served. Because the immune system of young children is not yet mature, they are even more vulnerable to foodborne illnesses than are adults. Microwave ovens are great timesavers in early childhood programs. Although using a microwave in an early childhood setting is basically the same as using one at home, extra care must be taken.

Reducing the Risk of Choking

As children grow and develop, they improve their ability to eat a variety of foods. They start with liquids and move to foods that are puréed and then to minced or chopped foods, and, finally, they are able to bite off and chew solid pieces of food. The risk of choking is high whenever children are given foods that are not developmentally appropriate. All children must be supervised when they are eating. Children can choke on food when they have food in the mouth while laughing or crying or when they put pieces in their mouth that are too big. Other behaviour that should be monitored while eating includes proper posture while seated, proper chewing, eating too quickly, or eating and drinking at the same time. Educators should be formally trained in handling emergencies, including choking.

Educators can follow simple guidelines in food preparation to reduce the risk to children significantly. Hard, small, and round foods, whether smooth or sticky, can block a young child's airway. Adults should avoid serving the following foods to children under four years of age:

- popcorn (lower risk grain products include pretzels or whole-grain dry cereals)
- hard candy or gum
- whole grapes or raisins
- foods with pits or seeds
- whole peanuts and other nuts
- foods on toothpicks or wooden sticks
- fish with bones

The Canadian Paediatric Society (2008, pp. 37–38) makes the following suggestions to make food safer:

- grating raw vegetables to aid chewing,
- slicing grapes into quarters or halves,
- removing pits or seeds,
- gently cooking or steaming hard vegetables to soften them,
- spreading sticky foods, like nut butters, thinly on pieces of cracker or toast, rather than on sliced bread,
- chopping or scraping stringy meat and adding broth to moisten it,
- de-boning fish, and
- cutting wieners lengthwise, in small pieces.

Source: Canadian Paediatric Society, *Well Beings: A Guide to Health in Child Care.* (Ottawa: Canadian Paediatric Society, 2008), 37–38. Reprinted with permission.

With regard to nut butters, never permit children to eat them straight from a spoon or finger. For many children under four, thin nut butter with juice or milk. Many programs are now "peanut-free" environments, due to life-threatening allergies, but they possibly allow other nut butters (e.g., cashew, almond, or nut-free, usually legume-based, butters that have the same consistency).

Food Safety Practices

Foodborne illnesses are usually caused by bacteria or by toxins produced by bacteria. Some types of foodborne illnesses are very serious (e.g., *Clostridium botulinum*, or botulism, which is rare but can be deadly), whereas others (e.g.,

Clostridium perfringens) produce symptoms such as mild abdominal pain, diarrhea, and nausea and usually last a day or less. What we may assume is a 24-hour "flu" may actually be food poisoning. Infants and young children are vulnerable to foodborne illness for many reasons, including body size and immature systems. Honey is a risk factor for infant botulism and should not be fed to infants under 12 months old. Staff have been directed to avoid raw eggs and foods containing them because of the risk of salmonellosis (caused by bacteria transmitted from hen to eggshell). Never serve unpasteurized milk or cheeses or any home-canned or preserved foods.

Health Canada and the Canadian Food Inspection Agency alert and protect the public in the case of outbreaks of food poisoning from bacteria or toxins in foods on the market. *For example, in 2006, Health Canada issued a policy on managing health risks associated with the consumption of sprouted seeds and beans. Alfalfa sprouts and mung beans, in particular, have been the cause of outbreaks of Salmonella and Escherichia coli illness. The risk of serious health effects is greater for young children, seniors, and people with weak immune systems. Health Canada recommends that these groups avoid eating raw sprouts (Health Canada, 2008b).*

Because the food we eat isn't sterile, some bacteria are always present. Food provides an ideal environment for bacteria to multiply or produce toxins. Bacteria thrive in warm and moist environments and need something to eat. Given time enough to multiply or produce toxins, bacteria occur in food in numbers large enough to cause food poisoning. Certain foods present a higher risk for foodborne illnesses:

- most of the high-protein foods such as meat, fish, and eggs
- custards and cream fillings, whipped cream, and other milk products
- salads with mayonnaise
- gravies and sauces

It is not surprising that summer picnics with sandwiches that have meat or egg fillings or devilled eggs, combined with poor refrigeration or cooling and the warm sun, can cause food poisoning. The bacteria are in their glory—absolutely perfect conditions for them to thrive!

Food becomes unsafe to eat when we do one or more of the following things:

- practise inadequate personal hygiene
- use dirty equipment or cooking surfaces (e.g., counters, playroom tables)
- handle and prepare food improperly
- serve food that has spoiled
- store food improperly
- do not control infestations of insects or rodents

The following is only a preliminary discussion of food safety, although it includes the essentials of what students and new graduates need to know when working in programs. However, educators who are responsible for cooking or persons who are hired as cooks should take a formal food-safety course. Information about these courses is available through any public health agency. In accordance with the public health inspectors' food protection guidelines, programs must develop and implement safe kitchen and food-handling practices.

Personal Hygiene

Effective hand washing is essential both before and after handling food in any way, as well as during food preparation when handling different types of food (e.g., after handling raw meat, wash your hands before you touch any other food). In addition, follow these hygiene practices:

- Keep your hair clean and, if it is long, tie it back.
- Avoid chewing gum because saliva easily falls on the food or cooking surfaces.
- Wear an apron to prevent bacteria from your clothes getting into food.
- Do not prepare or serve food to children when you know you have an infectious illness.
- If possible, avoid kitchen duties and feeding children if you are also responsible for changing diapers that day.

Cooking Equipment and Surfaces

Used bowls, utensils, cutting boards, and counters have bacteria on them. If they are not cleaned and sanitized properly, the bacteria remain on the surfaces and get into food. How can we prevent this cross-contamination?

- Post cleaning and sanitizing procedures. Daily and weekly schedules include all food contact surfaces, utensils, dishes, pots, and equipment (e.g., mixer, fridge, microwave oven).

Clean and sanitize cutting boards and knives that have been used for raw meat or poultry immediately after use. Assume that all raw meat and poultry have bacteria present (e.g., *Salmonella* in chicken and raw eggs), which will be killed with thorough cooking. Cleaning and sanitizing prevent the cross-contamination of food that comes in contact with the contaminated board or knife. What might happen is that the bacteria land in a food that doesn't need to be cooked, and the food is left at the danger-zone temperature range that allows the bacteria to multiply and cause food poisoning. Separate cutting boards should be used—one for raw meat, another for everything else—and thrown out when they appear rugged and after regular use for a few months.

- Clean and sanitize counters and food preparation areas before and after preparing food.
- Clean and sanitize tables that are used for playing and eating before and after eating.
- Follow the dishwashing routine to ensure clean dishes and utensils.

- Discard cracked dishes, cups, and glasses because cracks trap bacteria. If a utensil, plate, or cup drops to the floor, place it with the dirty dishes.

Safe Food Handling

The way we handle food affects its safety. One of the most important factors in handling food is its temperature. The general rule is "keep hot foods hot and cold foods cold." In other words, foods that are either piping hot (above 60°C, or 140°F) or refrigerator cold (below 4°C, or 39.2°F) are out of the danger zone. This zone is the temperature range in which bacteria thrive, and it includes our normal room temperature (20° to 22°C, or 68° to 71.6°F). High-risk foods should never be kept at room temperature for more than two hours (Health and Welfare Canada, 1993, p. 9).

It may seem like a waste to throw out food when you are unsure that it is still safe to eat, but the risk you take in serving it is too great. If children or adults eat contaminated food, they may experience discomfort, mild or serious illness, or even death. Clearly, summer outings and picnics must be well planned with food safety in mind.

Using an insulated container and ice packs to transport food and freezing the sandwiches so that they are thawed but not lukewarm by lunch time are safe strategies. Select foods that are low risk.

Thawing meat or poultry must be done carefully by ensuring that the food does not reach room temperature if possible. All frozen food should defrost in the refrigerator unless the microwave oven is used. Keep the thawed meat in the fridge until you are ready to cook it. This cold temperature prevents the bacteria from multiplying quickly.

Organize preparation times so that all the foods are ready at approximately the same time. This way, you avoid situations in which some foods are starting to cool, whereas others haven't finished heating. Because children don't like their foods really hot, programs often have all the food ready 10 to 15 minutes before serving the children. This period is long enough to let the food cool a bit but short enough to prevent bacteria from multiplying. For infants and toddlers, cool the food quickly by stirring. Other important suggestions follow:

- Use a meat thermometer when roasting poultry and meat to ensure that the internal temperature reaches the specified cooking temperature. When the outside of meat is cooked, the inside may still be harbouring live bacteria.

- Keep your fingers on the outside of clean cups and bowls and hold clean utensils by the handles.

- Rinse fruit and vegetables thoroughly under cold running water before using them. This should be done even if they are to be peeled (e.g., melon) to prevent cross-contamination from the outside of the food. If you suspect the use of pesticides or waxes, scrub under warm water (you may want to use a little dish soap with water or a diluted mixture of water and vinegar or lemon juice) or peel off the skin. Although you will lose some fibre and vitamins by peeling fruit and vegetables, you will reduce your exposure to pesticides (see Pesticides, page 238). Pay particular attention to leafy greens such as lettuce and spinach by discarding the outer leaves and washing them thoroughly, even those that say that they have been "prewashed" on the packaging.

- Wipe the tops of cans before you open them.
- Taste food with a spoon that you have not used for stirring and use a clean one if you taste again.
- Never transfer food from one child's plate to another's and ensure that children are eating from their own plate or bowl and are not sharing utensils.
- All food must be covered from the kitchen until ready to serve.
- Use serving utensils whenever possible, but don't go overboard by using tongs to pass out crackers and slices of bread.
- Discard food left on children's plates and liquid left in their cups as soon as possible.
- Separate large amounts of leftovers into small, shallow containers for quicker cooling in the refrigerator. Cover or wrap leftovers and transfer them to the refrigerator promptly. Serve leftovers the next day.
- If children bring their lunches, ensure that they are kept in the refrigerator.
- Baby bottles need only be warmed to room temperature. Placing the infant's bottle in a container of hot tap water or an electric bottle warmer is more than sufficient to do the job. Ensure that the bottle is warmed just before feeding as room temperature allows bacteria to multiply quickly. *Never use the microwave to warm milk bottles* (Canadian Paediatric Society, 2008).

Food Spoilage

We've all turned our nose away from a container that smells of sour milk. We can feel the green slime in the bottom of the bag of lettuce or see mould growing on food left at the back of a fridge. Yet we can't always tell when food has spoiled, and often food that causes food poisoning looks, tastes, and smells fresh. Beyond cooking and serving food safely, other preventive practices can be considered to ensure that no one eats spoiled food:

- Buy food from a reputable store or supplier.
- Don't buy or accept foods that are rotting or have passed the expiry date on the label. Avoid cans with large dents that could have broken the seal and cans that leak or have bulging ends.
- Never use home-canned foods in programs, even if you eat them at home. The biggest risk of botulism poisoning in this country involves home-canned (in Mason jars) vegetables or meat (Health and Welfare Canada, 1993, p. 13).
- Never use unpasteurized milk, even for cooking.
- Never give raw eggs in any form (e.g., eggnog, raw cookie dough, Caesar salad dressing) to children to eat because of the risk of *Salmonella*. Avoid cracked eggs.

- When in doubt, throw it out—whenever you are unsure about whether to use or serve a food.

Safe Food Storage

Safely storing uncooked foods and leftovers is one more way to prevent bacteria from multiplying quickly. Here are the basic guidelines for food storage:

- Regularly check the thermometer (which programs are required to have) in the fridge to ensure that it is set at the right temperature.
- Store meat and poultry in containers to prevent blood or juice from leaking onto other foods.
- Write the date on leftovers and use them within three days or discard.
- Store nonperishable foods in clean, airtight metal, glass, or hard plastic containers with a label and the date they were filled. Keep containers at least 15 cm (6 in.) off the floor and in a well-ventilated space that is cool, about 18°C (64°F), and dry.
- In the cupboards and the fridge, place newer containers of food behind the older ones, ensuring that you use older foods first.

CRITICAL THINKING

You notice a pot of spaghetti meat sauce sitting on the kitchen counter early one afternoon (spaghetti is on the menu for tomorrow). You ask the cook whether it should be in the fridge. She answers, "I'm letting the sauce cool down first because it has to be at room temperature before it goes into the fridge. Otherwise, it will go bad." Is it safe? Why? How would you handle the sauce to ensure its food safety?

Controlling Insect and Rodent Infestation

Insects (e.g., flies, cockroaches, ants) and rodents (e.g., mice, rats) carry germs and spread them wherever they go. An infestation of insects in food (e.g., ants in a container of flour) means the food is spoiled and must be discarded. Few early childhood programs have rodent problems, but those that do must consult with their local public health inspector and an exterminator to eliminate the problem immediately. Insects, however, are a constant concern. Flies and ants are widespread. In some areas, cockroaches commonly inhabit buildings. Controlling insects inside buildings presents a challenge because insecticides, although they get rid of insects, also have the potential to contaminate food, surfaces, toys, and so on. However, alternatives are available that are not as dangerous to humans. Public health inspectors advise staff on types of products and may suggest a "people-friendly" insecticide first.

Rather than having to deal with insect or rodent infestations once they are under way, staff can take the following preventive steps to make the building less attractive for pests in the first place:

■ Store food properly (i.e., in airtight containers, dry places).

■ Don't leave food on counters or tables.

■ Clean and sanitize cooking and eating surfaces so that crumbs and spills are removed.

■ Sweep the floor after children eat (cockroaches eat dust and food particles).

■ Avoid storing food under a sink.

■ Check boxes and other containers that are brought into the building— cockroaches like to travel!

■ Maintain screens and other barriers that insects might try to get through.

■ Close off spaces around pipes under sinks and close cracks and holes in doors and walls to the outside.

■ Act quickly when you notice the first few insects.

■ Rinse out recyclables before they are placed in the blue box.

■ Compost appropriate kitchen scraps outdoors, if possible.

■ Properly store and empty garbage both inside and outside the building. Keep the area around garbage cans free of litter and spills.

■ Line all garbage cans with plastic bags and use snug-fitting lids. Preferably, indoor containers should open with a foot pedal. Open wastebaskets should be kept out of children's reach. Containers should be emptied at least once a day— more often if there are problems with odours (e.g., in the diapering area).

Microwave Oven Safety

Microwave ovens are commonplace in homes, staff rooms in workplaces, cafeterias, and early childhood settings. Although they are convenient and easy to use, they can be hazardous if used improperly. To ensure the safe preparation of foods, the following guidelines are recommended:

■ Use only microwave-safe containers, preferably nonplastic containers. Plastic food wraps, which are made with nonylphenols, are of concern when heated. In addition, chemicals used to make plastics can be hazardous to long-term health. Remember that Health Canada responded quickly to ban bisphenol A from use in baby bottles in 2008, mostly due to the concern that when heated, the chemical leaches into the contents (e.g., baby formula) and is then ingested. Although now removed from baby bottles, this example highlights the need for caution with the use of plastic in microwaves.

■ All food should be covered while being heated.

■ Use a low or medium heat for short-time periods and test each food separately for even heating.

■ Stir and test all food coming out of the microwave oven to prevent scalds and burns. Food heats unevenly, resulting in hot spots in the food. As well, the food can be very hot, whereas the container remains cool.

- Keep the microwave clean of spills and splatters to prevent germs from contacting the food that is left inside.
- Ensure that school-agers who use the microwave oven to warm lunches and snacks do so safely.

REVISITING THE HEALTH PROMOTION ACTION PLAN

With reference to the Action Plan for Health Promotion introduced in Unit 1, the following are examples of possible actions relating to our food system. Keep in mind that because of the necessity of fresh, healthy food for optimal health, and its cultural and social importance, food is a powerful reason and tool for action.

Individual Problem Solving and Self-Reliance
- Learn how to read food labels. Use Health Canada's regulated Nutrition Facts table to make healthy choices when you're food shopping.
- Be aware of the fat (especially trans and saturated fats), sugar, and salt content of foods and keep *Eating Well with Canada's Food Guide* in mind when making food choices.
- Choose foods that are less processed.
- Buy produce and other foods grown in Canada and locally whenever possible (e.g., local farmers' market).
- Respect food and avoid food wastage.
- Handle and store food safely.
- Buy foods with a minimum of packaging.
- Routinely involve children in nutrition experiences.
- Incorporate active living to complement the benefits of good nutrition.

Collective Self-Help
- Get involved in a neighbourhood food cooperative.
- Participate in food share programs.
- Discuss nutrition and food distribution issues in the staff room to broaden everyone's awareness.
- Invite a local dietitian or public health nutritionist for parents and educators, with the goal of continued nutrition improvement for the children at home and in the program.

Community Action
- Join a community kitchen.
- Advocate for improvements at local supermarkets (e.g., to sell locally grown and sustainably sourced foods, a term defined as a way of raising food that is healthy for consumers and animals, does not harm the environment, provides a fair wage to farmers and supports, and enhances communities).

- Support community student nutrition programs. These programs are created and managed locally by parents, educators, public health departments, and local governments to meet the specific needs of local children and families. Many of the programs are based on a sustainable community-building principle, whereby the families who use the program are also meaningfully involved in it.

Societal Change

- Support a federal children's nutrition initiative. As stated earlier, Canada is one of the few developed countries without a nationally funded child nutrition program. This initiative would call for universal nutritious food programs to be available to any child in Canada in whatever venues the communities deem most appropriate, building on the existing knowledge base, programs, and infrastructure of local organizations and parent groups. The initiative would also fund programs in provinces and territories where they do not presently exist. The federal government would be required to develop national program standards for healthy foods, with an emphasis on nutrition education, cooking and growing skills, and inclusion of locally and sustainably sourced foods. Long-term monitoring and evaluation of standards and implementation will also be critical (Children's Health & Nutrition Initiative, 2007).

- Become an advocate for changes in federal law to protect children from marketing messages that encourage poor nutrition habits. This has already been done in Quebec. It is the only jurisdiction among developed countries with a legislated ban on all forms of commercial advertising to children. The province of Quebec's *Consumer Protection Act* (1980) states that "subject to what is provided in the regulations, no person may make use of commercial advertising directed at persons under thirteen years of age."

CONCLUSION

Although parents and educators cannot ensure that individual children develop good eating habits for a lifetime, they can provide children with

- an adequate variety of nutritious foods that are safe to eat,
- an environment that fosters or encourages healthy attitudes toward food and eating, and
- a model for healthy eating habits.

From infancy on, the right of children to decide how much to eat and what foods to eat in an emotionally respectful environment takes priority in early childhood programs. The five principles to healthy eating guide us to eat well and lead physically active lives. Children's minds and bodies, now and into their future, are very much influenced by healthy eating and physical activity. These themes are continued and expanded on in Unit 6.

ASSESS YOUR LEARNING

Define terms or describe concepts used in this unit.

- advantages of breast milk
- body image
- complementary protein
- disordered eating
- division of responsibility
- eating disorder
- *Eating Well with Canada's Food Guide*
- factors that shape eating habits
- flexitarians
- food groups
- food insecurity
- food irradiation
- food jags
- food processing
- food safety

- foodborne illnesses
- formula
- fortified or enriched
- genetically modified organisms (GMOs)
- key nutrients
- menu planning
- nutrients and functions
- nutrition
- Nutrition Facts table
- nutrition labels
- positive eating environments
- risks of choking
- semisolid foods
- vegetarianism

Evaluate your options in each situation.

1. The practice at your program placement is for the educators to serve food and to insist that the preschoolers eat everything. There have been a number of power struggles lately, and lunch time has become an unpleasant experience for everyone. The staff have asked you for suggestions.

2. Although the preschoolers eat in small groups at tables, there are a number of groups in the room. The noise level can get high, creating a less-than-calm eating environment, especially for children who are easily distracted.

3. An 18-month-old who has been in the program for 3 months will eat only jarred or puréed baby food that his parents provide. He refuses the more textured food that the program serves. Related to this, educators are concerned that his language development is being affected. The parents are worried that if they don't provide puréed food, their son will go hungry.

4. You are working in the school-age program at a local school and have decided to volunteer in the breakfast child nutrition program. You notice that most of the children in your after-school program who would benefit most from a nutritious breakfast do not get to school until the bell rings and therefore are not able to take advantage of this opportunity. One of the other volunteers has stated that they are not getting the number of children they expected in the program. The two of you have talked about proposing other options than breakfast to the coordinator.

5. You're planning a day-long summer trip to a park with all the infants, toddlers, and preschoolers. Your responsibility is to make arrangements for the food and beverages and write a list of important food safety considerations for handling the food.

TO RISE TO THE CHALLENGE OR NOT?

At a program, the parents provide lunches for their children and the staff warm foods in the microwave oven, as required. Educators have observed that one toddler's lunch routinely consists of highly processed foods. A typical lunch for Peter is a cut-up wiener or piece of salami, French fries, and a store-bought dessert (e.g., a cupcake with brightly coloured icing or a chocolate-covered granola bar). Vegetables or fresh fruit are rarely provided. The most natural and nutritious part of the meal is the milk provided by the program. When an educator speaks to the parents about the lunches and about providing more variety, Peter's mother says that those are the only foods that he will eat. The educator explains that Peter eats the variety of foods that the program provides for snacks each day. At a staff meeting, one of the other educators suggests that no further action be taken about Peter's lunches.

If you were working in the program, how would you feel about this situation? Has this situation been resolved to your satisfaction and in the best interests of the child and family? Support your position.

RESOURCE MATERIALS

Organizations

Allergy Asthma Information Association, National Office, 1-111 Zenway Boulevard, Vaughan, ON L4H 3H9. Tel: national toll-free 1-800-611-7011; fax: 905-850-2070 (or contact provincial/territorial office); http://aaia.ca

Canadian Paediatric Society, 2305 St. Laurent Blvd, Ottawa, ON K1G 4J8. Tel: 613-526-9397; fax: 613-526-3332; http://www.cps.ca

Canadian Restaurant and Food Services Association, Allergy Aware Program, 316 Bloor Street W., Toronto, ON M5S 1W5. Tel: 416-923-8416, national toll-free 1-800-387-5649; fax: 416-923-1450 (or contact regional office); http://www.crfa.ca

Center for Science in the Public Interest (Canada) (CSPI), Suite 4550, CTTC Bldg, 1125 Colonel By Drive, Ottawa, ON K1S 5R1. Tel: 613-244-7337; fax: 613-244-1559; http://www.cspinet.org/canada (promotes health through public education about nutrition and alcohol and advocacy)

Dietitians of Canada, 480 University Avenue, Suite 604, Toronto, ON M5G 1V2. Tel: 416-596-0857; fax: 416-596-0603; http://www.dietitians.ca/healthystart/index.asp

FoodShare, Education and Research Office, 90 Croatia St., Toronto, ON M6H 1K9. Tel: 416-363-6441 ext. 221; fax: 416-363-0474; http://www.foodshare.net (Available as a resource for any group in Canada interested in school nutrition programs, whether for breakfast, snack, or lunch.)

La Leche League of Canada, National Office, PO Box 700, Winchester, ON K0C 2K0. Tel: 613-774-4900; fax: 613-774-2798; http://www.lllc.ca/index.php (support groups in various cities across Canada)

National Anti-Poverty Association, 1 Nicholas Street, Suite 1210, Ottawa, ON K1N 7B7. Tel: 613-789-0096, national toll-free 1-800-810-1076; fax: 613-789-0141; http://www.napo-onap.ca

Other Websites of Interest

Canadian Association of Food Banks: http://www.cafb-acba.ca

Canadian Council of Food and Nutrition: http://www.ccfn.ca

Canadian Food Inspection Agency: http://www.inspection.gc.ca

Dairy Farmers of Canada:

- An easy-to-use module that compliments the early childhood program with interactive exercises, videos, and online quizzes. Developed for Ontario College Professors and their students: http://www.goodbeginnings.ca
- Resources and programs to help educators deliver fun and engaging nutrition lesson plans: http://www.teachnutrition.org
- Information and resources on a variety of nutrition topics for consumers, educators, and health professionals: http://www.dairygoodness.ca

Healthy Start for Life Resource Centre, Dietitians of Canada (free resources and online courses for parents and educators): http://www.dietitians.ca/healthystart/index.asp

Ellyn Satter's website (renowned dietitian): http://www.ellynsatter.com/

Health Canada: http://www.hc-sc.gc.ca

National Eating Disorder Information Centre: http://www.nedic.ca

Nutrition Labelling Education Centre, Canadian Diabetes Association: http://www.healthyeatingisinstore.ca

Vesanto Melina's website (Canadian writer on vegetarian education; site includes vegetarian and vegan Rainbow Food Guides): http://www.nutrispeak.com

Printed Matter

A New Food Guide for North American Vegetarians" (2003, Summer), by Virginia Messina, Melina Vessanto, and Ann Reed Mangels, *Canadian Journal of Dietetic Practice and Research, 64.* To download a copy, visit http://www.dietitians.ca/news/downloads/Vegetarian_Food_Guide_for_NA.pdf

Better Baby Food: Your Essential Guide to Nutrition, Feeding and Cooking for All Babies and Toddlers (2001), by J. Saab and D. Kalnins (Robert Rose Inc.).

How to Get Your Kids to Eat … But Not Too Much (1990), by E. Satter (Bull Publishing). See current resources and books on website: http://www.ellynsatter.com

Nutrition Action Health Letter. Including the May 2008 issue: "Chemical Cuisine: A guide to food additive" http://www.cspinet.org/nah/05_08/chem_cuisine_can.pdf. To view and subscribe, visit http://www.cspinet.org/nah/canada.htm(June 2008)

Nutrition for Healthy Term Infants (2005), by the Canadian Paediatric Society, Dietitians of Canada, and Health Canada. To download a copy, visit: http://www.hc-sc.gc.ca/fn-an/pubs/infant-nourrisson/nut_infant_nourrisson_term-eng.php

Raising Vegetarian Children (2003), by Joanne Stepaniak, M.S., Ed., and Melina Vesanto, M.S., R.D. (McGraw-Hill).

Real Food for a Change (1999), by W. Roberts, R. MacRae, and L. Stahlbrand (Random House Canada).

BIBLIOGRAPHY

Best Start: Ontario's Maternal Newborn and Early Child Development Resource Centre and Nutrition Resource Centre. (2007). *Feeding your baby from six months to one year.* Toronto: Ontario Prevention Clearinghouse. Retrieved May 2008 from http://www.beststart.org/resources/nutrition/pdf/feeding_baby.pdf

Canadian Child Care Federation. (2001, Spring). Supporting breastfeeding in child care (Resource Sheet #57). *Nourish and Nurture Neurodevelopment,* 1–2.

Canadian Paediatric Society. (2007). *Feeding your vegetarian child.* Retrieved May 2008 from http://www.caringforkids.cps.ca/eating/Vegetarian.htm

Canadian Paediatric Society. (2008). *Well beings: A guide to promote the physical health, safety and emotional well-being of children in child care centres and family day care homes*. Ottawa: Canadian Paediatric Society.

Canadian Spice Association. (2003, Spring). Taking a closer look at food irradiation. *CSA Tech Bulletin*. Retrieved June 2008 from http://www.canadianspiceassociation.com/csa_bulletins.asp

Carruth, B. R., et al. (2004). Prevalence of picky eaters among infants and toddlers and their caregivers' decisions about offering a new food. *Journal of the American Dietetic Association, 104*(1 Suppl.), S57–S64.

Che, J., & Chen, J. (2001). Food insecurity in Canadian households. *Health Reports, 12,* 11–22.

Children's Health & Nutrition Initiative. (2007). *A proposal to make safe and healthy food available to all of Canada's children*. Retrieved June 2008 from http://www.toronto.ca/legdocs/mmis/2007/cd/bgrd/backgroundfile-1579.pdf

Deverell, J. (1998, August 14). Are we buying better health with vitamins, herbals? *The Toronto Star,* pp. E1, E5.

Dietitians of Canada. (2008). *Should I be taking a vitamin & mineral supplement?* Retrieved May 2008 from http://www.dietitians.ca/resources/resourcesearch.asp?fn=view&contentid=1254

Escobar, A. (1999). Factors influencing children's dietary practices: A review. *USDA Government Documents ,12*(3&4), 44–55.

Forge, F. (2007). *Biofuels – an energy, environmental or agricultural policy? Library of Parliament, Ottawa Canada PRB06-37E*. Retrieved from http://dsp-psd.pwgsc.gc.ca/collection_2007/lop-bdp/prb/PRB0637-e.pdf

Gillis, D. (1989). *Promoting nutritional health during the preschool years: Canadian guidelines*. Ottawa: Network of the Federal/Provincial/Territorial Group on Nutrition and National Institute of Nutrition.

Harrison, C. (2008). *Teaming up for children's nutrition*. Toronto: EatRight Ontario. Retrieved from http://www.eatrightontario.ca/Doorway.aspx

Health and Welfare Canada. (1993). *Food safety: It's all in your hands*. Ottawa: Minister of Supply and Services.

Health Canada. (2003, July). *Nutrition Facts: To help you make informed food choices* (Catalogue No. H49-177/1-2003E-1). Retrieved July 2008 from http://www.hc-sc.gc.ca/fn-an/alt_formats/hpfb-dgpsa/pdf/label-etiquet/cr_tearsheet-cr_fiche-eng.pdf

Health Canada. (2005). *Nutrition for healthy term infants. Joint statement of the Joint Working Group: Canadian Paediatric Society, Dietitians of Canada and Health Canada* (Catalogue No. H44-76/2005E-PDF). Retrieved June 2008 from http://www.hc-sc.gc.ca/fn-an/pubs/infant-nourrisson/nut_infant_nourrisson_term-eng.php

Health Canada. (2006, April 21). *Food additive dictionary*. Retrieved June 2008 from http://www.hc-sc.gc.ca/fn-an/securit/addit/diction/index-eng.php

Health Canada. (2007a). *Eating well with Canada's Food Guide: A resource for educators and communicators* (Catalogue No. H164-38/2-2007E-PDF). Ottawa: Minister of Public Works and Government Services Canada. Retrieved June 2008 from http://www.hc-sc.gc.ca/fn-an/alt_formats/hpfb-dgpsa/pdf/pubs/res-educat-eng.pdf

Health Canada. (2007b). *General Q&As on trans fat*. Retrieved June 2008 from http://www.hc-sc.gc.ca/fn-an/nutrition/gras-trans-fats/tfa-age_question-eng.php. The material on pages 228 and 229 is used with the permission of Public Works and Government Services Canada.

Health Canada. (2007c). *Mercury: Your health and the environment*. Retrieved June 2008 from http://www.hc-sc.gc.ca/ewh-semt/pubs/contaminants/mercur/index-eng.php. The material on page 229 is used with the permission of Public Works and Government Services Canada.

Health Canada. (2007d, November 14). *Monograph – calcium*. Retrieved June 2008 from http://www.hc-sc.gc.ca/dhp-mps/prodnatur/applications/licen-prod/monograph/mono_calcium-eng.php

Health Canada. (2007e). *The safety of food additives: It's your health*. Retrieved June 2008 from http://www.hc-sc.gc.ca/hl-vs/alt_formats/pacrb-dgapcr/pdf/iyh-vsv/food-aliment/food-add-aliment-eng.pdf

Health Canada. (2008a). *Frequently asked questions regarding food irradiation*. Retrieved June 2008 from http://www.hc-sc.gc.ca/fn-an/securit/irridation/faq_food_irradiation_aliment01-eng.php

Health Canada. (2008b). *Health claims*: Q&A #4: What health claims are currently allowed in Canada? Retrieved June 2008 from http://www.hc-sc.gc.ca/fn-an/label-etiquet/claims-reclam/qa-qr_claims-allegations-eng.php

Heart and Stroke Foundation of Canada. (2008). "The shakedown on salt. *e-newsletter*. Retrieved June 2008 from http://ww2.heartandstroke.ca/Page.asp?PageID=33&ArticleID=4032

Infant & Toddler Forum. (2006, July). *Nutrients: Functions, sources & requirements: Toddler factsheet 1.1i* (ITF1 10). Retrieved June 2008 from http://www.infantandtoddlerforum.org/objects/pdf/fact_sheet3.pdf

Jones, J. M., et al. (2001). Disordered eating attitudes and behaviours in teenaged girls: A school-based study. *Canadian Medical Association Journal, 165*, 547–559.

Kirkey, S. (2007, October 26). Salt has invaded Canada's food supply. *The Gazette* (Montreal). Retrieved May 2008 from http://www.canada.com/montrealgazette/news/story.html?id=be71fc2d-0c7f-442b-b8c3-a0b8f54025d9&k=26898

Lambert-Lagacé, L. (2002). *Feeding your preschooler: Tasty nutrition for kids two to six.* Toronto: Fitzhenry &Whiteside

Lambert-Lagacé, L. (2003). *Feeding your baby the healthiest foods: From breast milk to table foods.* Toronto: Fitzhenry &Whiteside

Latner, J. D., Rosewall, J. K., & Simmonds, M. B. (2007). Childhood obesity stigma: Association with television, videogame, and magazine exposure. *Body Image, 4,* 147–155.

Latner, J. D., & Stunkard, A. J. (2003). Getting worse: The stigmatization of obese children. *Obesity Research, 11,* 452–456.

Magnan, M. (2008, May 5). How the global food crisis will hit home: Prices rising with diesel costs, droughts, biofuel. *Calgary Herald.* Retrieved May 2008 from http://www.canada.com/calgaryherald/news/city/story.html?id=2d5a00ed-6c36-4dc4-827a-2e3d894cc91e

McCann, D., et al. (2007). Food additives and hyperactive behaviour in 3-year-old and 8/9-year-old children in the community: A randomised, double-blinded, placebo-controlled trial. *The Lancet, 370,* 1560–1567.

McIntyre, L. (2002, November). *Food insecurity as a determinant of health.* Paper presented at The Social Determinants of Health Across the Life-Span Conference, Toronto.

Melina, V., Davis, B., & Harrison, V. (1994). *Becoming vegetarian: The complete guide to adopting a healthy vegetarian diet.* Toronto: Macmillan Canada.

Michaelides, J. (2007, June). Food additives, processing aids and fortification in Canada: An overview. *Guelph Food Technology Centre,* (Number 49). Retrieved June 2008 from http://www.gftc.ca/newslett/pdf/GFTC-Newsletter-reprint-2007-06-Additives.pdf

National Eating Disorder Information Centre. (2008). *Prevention and health promotion.* Retrieved June 2008 from http://www.nedic.ca/knowthefacts/preventionhealth.shtml

Osteoporosis Canada. (2003, July). *Education and support for the risk reduction of osteoporosis.* Retrieved May 24, 2008, from http://www.osteoporosis.ca/english/home/default.asp?s=1

Petryk, A., Harris, S. R., & Jongblood, L. (2007). Breastfeeding and neurodevelopment: A literature review. *Infants & Young Children, 20,* 120–134.

Ratey, J. J. (2008). *SPARK: The revolutionary new science of exercise and the brain.* New York: Little, Brown & Company.

Satter, E. (1990). *How to get your kid to eat . . . but not too much.* Palo Alto, CA: Bull Publishing.

Satter, E. (2000). *Child of mine; feeding with love and good sense.* Palo Alto, CA: *Bull Publishing.* Available at http://www.EllynSatter.com

Sizer, F., & Whitney, E. (2000). *Nutrition concepts and controversies* (8th ed.). Toronto: Wadsworth Thomson Learning.

Tarasuk, V. (2002, November). *Health consequences of food insecurity.* Paper presented at The Social Determinants of Health Across the Life-Span Conference, Toronto.

Toronto Public Health. (2008). *Nutrition matters: Frequently asked questions about halal.* Retrieved May 2008 from http://www.toronto.ca/health/nm_faq_halal_foods.htm

Toronto Public Health. (n.d.). *Nutrition matters: Getting enough calcium without the cow.* PH0802SS038. Retrieved from http://www.toronto.ca/health/pdf/nm_calcium.pdf

World Health Organization. (2003). *Diet, nutrition, and the prevention of chronic diseases: WHO Technical Report Series 916. Report of a Joint WHO/FAO Expert Consultation.* Geneva: World Health Organization.

Eating Well with Canada's Food Guide

Canada

Recommended Number of Food Guide Servings per Day

Age in Years	Children 2-3	4-8	9-13	Teens 14-18 Females	Males	Adults 19-50 Females	Males	51+ Females	Males
Sex	Girls and Boys								
Vegetables and Fruit	4	5	6	7	8	7-8	8-10	7	7
Grain Products	3	4	6	6	7	6-7	8	6	7
Milk and Alternatives	2	2	3-4	3-4	3-4	2	2	3	3
Meat and Alternatives	1	1	1-2	2	3	2	3	2	3

The chart above shows how many Food Guide Servings you need from each of the four food groups every day.

Having the amount and type of food recommended and following the tips in Canada's Food Guide will help:
- Meet your needs for vitamins, minerals and other nutrients.
- Reduce your risk of obesity, type 2 diabetes, heart disease, certain types of cancer and osteoporosis.
- Contribute to your overall health and vitality.

What is One Food Guide Serving?
Look at the examples below.

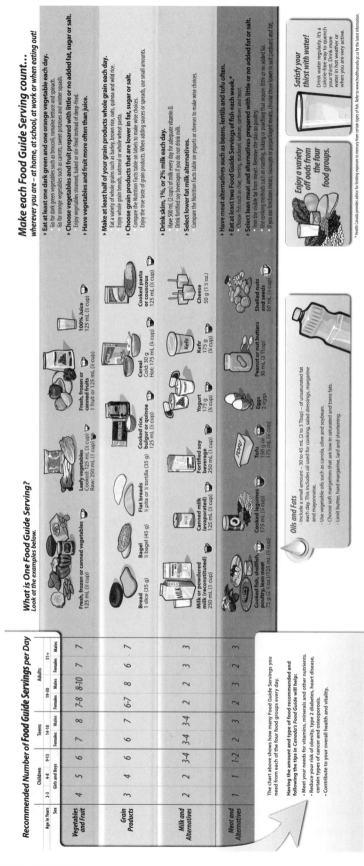

Vegetables and Fruit

Fresh, frozen or canned vegetables
125 mL (½ cup)

Leafy vegetables
Cooked 125 mL (½ cup)
Raw: 250 mL (1 cup)

Fresh, frozen or canned fruits
1 fruit or 125 mL (½ cup)

100% Juice
125 mL (½ cup)

Grain Products

Bread
1 slice (35 g)

Bagel
½ bagel (45 g)

Flat breads
½ pita or ½ tortilla (35 g)

Cooked rice, bulgur or quinoa
125 mL (½ cup)

Cereal
Cold: 30 g
Hot: 175 mL (¾ cup)

Cooked pasta or couscous
125 mL (½ cup)

Milk and Alternatives

Milk or powdered milk (reconstituted)
250 mL (1 cup)

Canned milk (evaporated)
125 mL (½ cup)

Fortified soy beverage
250 mL (1 cup)

Yogurt
175 g (¾ cup)

Kefir
175 g (¾ cup)

Cheese
50 g (1 ½ oz.)

Meat and Alternatives

Cooked fish, shellfish, poultry, lean meat
75 g (2 ½ oz.)/125 mL (½ cup)

Cooked legumes
175 mL (¾ cup)

Tofu
150 g or 175 mL (¾ cup)

Eggs
2 eggs

Peanut or nut butters
30 mL (2 Tbsp)

Shelled nuts and seeds
60 mL (¼ cup)

Oils and Fats

- Include a small amount — 30 to 45 mL (2 to 3 Tbsp) — of unsaturated fat each day. This includes oil used for cooking, salad dressings, margarine and mayonnaise.
- Use vegetable oils such as canola, olive and soybean.
- Choose soft margarines that are low in saturated and trans fats.
- Limit butter, hard margarine, lard and shortening.

Make each Food Guide Serving count...
wherever you are – at home, at school, at work or when eating out!

▸ **Eat at least one dark green and one orange vegetable each day.**
Go for dark green vegetables such as broccoli, romaine lettuce and spinach.
Go for orange vegetables such as carrots, sweet potatoes and winter squash.

▸ **Choose vegetables and fruit prepared with little or no added fat, sugar or salt.**
Enjoy vegetables steamed, baked or stir-fried instead of deep-fried.

▸ **Have vegetables and fruit more often than juice.**

▸ **Make at least half of your grain products whole grain each day.**
Eat a variety of whole grains such as barley, brown rice, oats, quinoa and wild rice.
Enjoy whole grain breads, oatmeal or whole wheat pasta.

▸ **Choose grain products that are lower in fat, sugar or salt.**
Compare the Nutrition Facts table on labels to make wise choices.
Enjoy the true taste of grain products. When adding sauces or spreads, use small amounts.

▸ **Drink skim, 1%, or 2% milk each day.**
Have 500 mL (2 cups) of milk every day for adequate vitamin D.
Drink fortified soy beverages if you do not drink milk.

▸ **Select lower fat milk alternatives.**
Compare the Nutrition Facts table on yogurts or cheeses to make wise choices.

▸ **Have meat alternatives such as beans, lentils and tofu often.**

▸ **Eat at least two Food Guide Servings of fish each week.***
Choose fish such as char, herring, mackerel, salmon, sardines and trout.

▸ **Select lean meat and alternatives prepared with little or no added fat or salt.**
Trim the visible fat from meat. Remove the skin on poultry.
Use cooking methods such as roasting, baking or poaching that require little or no added fat.
If you eat luncheon meats, sausages or prepackaged meats, choose those lower in salt (sodium) and fat.

Enjoy a variety of foods from the four food groups.

Satisfy your thirst with water!
Drink water regularly. It's a calorie-free way to quench your thirst. Drink more water in hot weather or when you are very active.

* Health Canada provides advice for limiting exposure to mercury from certain types of fish. Refer to www.healthcanada.gc.ca for the latest information.

Source: *Eating Well with Canada's Food Guide* (2007). http://www.hc-sc.gc.ca/fn-an/food-guide-aliment/index_e.html, Health Canada. Reproduced with the permission of the Minister of Public Works and Government Services Canada, 2008.

Nutrients: Their Functions and Food Sources

THE ENERGY PROVIDERS	ROLE	FOUND IN
Carbohydrates[1]	supply the body's main source of energy; assist in utilization of fats, spare protein so it can be used for tissue formation	breads, cereals, pasta, potatoes, rice, couscous, legumes and lentils, fruit and vegetables and their juices, milk and alternatives, sugar
Proteins[2]	build and repair body tissues, including muscles, bones, blood; manufacture antibodies necessary to fight infection; growth increases protein requirement for new muscles and other cells	meat, fish, poultry, milk and alternatives, eggs, legumes and lentils, tofu, nuts and seeds and their spreads (e.g., peanut butter), breads and cereals in combination with other protein sources (i.e., to include all 8 essential amino acids)
Fats[3]	provide the most concentrated source of energy, carry fat-soluble vitamins, provide essential fatty acids necessary for all cell membranes; the omega-3 and -6 fats are essential for brain and nerve function and healthy skin	foods high in saturated fats: animal products such as butter, cheese, and cream and coconut, palm, and palm kernel oils; foods high in monounsaturated fats: olive oil, avocado, nuts (macadamia, peanuts, almonds, pecans, pistachios); foods high in omega-3 docosahexaenoic acid): cold-water fish (salmon, herring, mackerel), sardines, flaxseed; foods high in omega-6: vegetable oils (corn, sunflower, sesame, soybean, safflower), margarine

(appendix continues on next page)

THE FAT-SOLUBLE VITAMINS	ROLE	FOUND IN
Vitamin A[4]	forms healthy skin and membranes, assists in bone growth and tooth development, promotes good night vision, repairs tissues	yellow or orange fruit and vegetables, such as carrots, red peppers, sweet potatoes; dark-green leafy vegetables such as spinach and broccoli; egg yolk, cheese, milk, butter, and margarine
Vitamin D	needed to absorb calcium and phosphorus and regulates the movement of both in and out of the skeleton and teeth to ensure strength	fortified fluid, evaporated or powdered milk, margarine, tuna, salmon, sardines. Vitamin D is the "sunshine vitamin" available through exposure to ultraviolet rays outside in the summer.
Vitamin E	prevents oxidation of fat in tissues, especially important in red blood cell membranes and lungs	vegetable oils, margarine, whole-grain cereals, wheat germ, bean sprouts, nuts and seeds and their spreads
Vitamin K	clots blood	mainly produced by bacteria in the large bowel; food sources are green leafy vegetables and broccoli

WATER-SOLUBLE VITAMINS	ROLE	FOUND IN
Vitamin B_1 (thiamin)	helps release energy from carbohydrates; enables growth and repair of tissues, especially nerve and muscle; aids in maintaining normal appetite	whole-grain or enriched breads, cereals, and pasta, milk and alternatives, pork, nuts and seeds and their spreads
Vitamin B_2 (riboflavin)	assists in release of energy, aids cell division and promotes growth and repair of tissues, maintains healthy skin and eyes	milk, yogurt, cottage cheese, whole-grain or enriched breads, meat and poultry
Vitamin B_3 (niacin)	helps release energy from carbohydrates, protein, and fats; assists in the synthesis of fat; maintains healthy skin, gut, and nervous system	whole-grain and enriched bread, cereals, and pasta, peanut butter, meat, fish, poultry, legumes, milk, cheese
Vitamin B_6 (pyridoxine)	assists in protein, carbohydrate, and fat metabolism; promotes normal functioning of central nervous system	chicken, fish, whole-grain breads and cereals, egg yolk, bananas, avocados
Folate (Folic Acid)	aids red blood cell formation and protein metabolism; all women of childbearing age need folic acid everyday to help prevent birth defects of the spine and brain	dark-green leafy vegetables, broccoli, Brussels sprouts, oranges and orange juice, bananas, milk and alternatives, wheat germ, cereals enriched with folate
Vitamin B_{12} (Cobalamin)	promotes normal blood formation, maintains healthy nervous tissue, aids in protein synthesis	meat, fish, poultry, milk and alternatives, eggs
Vitamin C (Ascorbic Acid)	antioxidant that strengthens connective tissue, bones, skin, muscles, teeth, blood vessels; promotes normal nerve function; helps absorption of iron from nonmeat sources (e.g., orange-spinach salad); strengthens immune function; aids in wound healing	citrus fruit, vitaminized apple juice, dark-green leafy vegetables, green and red pepper, tomatoes, broccoli, potatoes, strawberries, kiwi

(appendix continues on next page)

MACROMINERALS	ROLE	FOUND IN
Calcium	builds and maintains strong bones and teeth, promotes normal blood clotting and healthy nerve function	milk and alternatives, salmon and sardines with bones, calcium-fortified orange juice, fortified soy or rice beverages, tofu, dark-green leafy vegetables, broccoli, bok choy, edamame
Phosphorus	aids in formation and maintenance of strong bones and teeth, transportation of nutrients, and regulation of energy balance; helps maintain body's acid balance	meat, fish, poultry, eggs, milk and alternatives, soy milk, tofu, whole-grain breads and cereals; richest source is milk; present in most other foods
Magnesium	helps in formation and maintenance of strong bones and teeth, protein production, transmission of nerve impulses, and release of energy	dark-green leafy vegetables, legumes, seafood, milk and alternatives, whole-grain cereals; also in meat, eggs, dhal, lentils, hummus, potatoes, some vegetables
Potassium	important for fluid balance, muscle contraction, and nerve conduction	milk, vegetables, potatoes; bananas, dried apricots, prunes, dates, and kiwi are also good sources

THE MICROMINERALS	ROLE	FOUND IN
Iron	combines with protein to form hemoglobin, the part of red blood cells that transports oxygen and carbon dioxide, and also myoglobin, which provides oxygen to cells; involved in energy metabolism and the immune system	red meats, fish, and poultry (e.g., chicken legs and thighs), whole-grain or enriched breads, cereal, and pasta, iron-fortified infant cereal, dark-green leafy vegetables, dried fruits such as raisins, legumes such as lentils and chickpeas (e.g., hummus)
Fluoride	strengthens tooth enamel and helps prevent tooth decay	fluoride-containing water and foods prepared in it, toothpaste
Zinc	functions as part of several enzymes involved in many diverse metabolic roles necessary for growth, development, and energy release; structural role in growth hormone and insulin	meat, poultry, fish, shellfish, eggs, whole-grain breads and cereals, legumes, lentils, nuts and their spreads
Iodine	aids in production of thyroid hormones, which regulate energy metabolism and growth rate	iodized table salt, seafood, vegetables depending on regional iodine content of soil and water

DIETARY FIBRE[5]	ROLE	FOUND IN
	indigestible material, which promotes normal elimination of waste from the colon; normal functioning of intestines and bowel; may have other physiological effects	whole-grain breads and cereals, legumes, fruit, and vegetables

PHYTOCHEMICALS[6]	ROLE	FOUND IN
	important antioxidants; play a part in immune function; provide some protection against cancer and heart disease	all fruit and vegetables, especially brightly coloured (5 servings of fruit and vegetables per day will ensure adequate intake), cocoa and chocolate

(appendix continues on next page)

WATER	ROLE	FOUND IN
	the main constituent of the body; needed for transporting nutrients, promoting metabolic processes, regulating body temperature, eliminating body waste, maintaining blood pressure and fluid balance	tap water, beverages such as milk and juices, soups, and a wide variety of foods, especially fruit and vegetables

[1] May be "simple" sugars, such as sucrose and glucose, or "complex," such as starches and some fibre. Fructose is the sugar in fruit and honey. Lactose is the sugar in milk.

[2] Made of peptides and amino acids.

[3] Made up of fatty acids (saturated, monounsaturated, polyunsaturated fats, including omega-3 and omega-6 fatty acids, or complex fats [e.g., cholesterol]).

[4] Retinol and beta-carotene.

[5] Fibre includes nondigestible carbohydrates, mostly derived from plant material, that are fermented in the colon, and prebiotics, which are nondigestible food ingredients that benefit us by stimulating the growth or activity of a limited number of bacteria in the colon.

[6] Substances in plants. Also called flavonoids, flavanols, and soflavones (e.g., lycopene and lutein, which are carotenoids found in vegetables such as tomatoes and broccoli with strong antioxidant properties and great potential as battling agents of degenerative disease).

Sources: Adapted from D. Gillis (1989), *Promoting nutritional health during the preschool years: Canadian guidelines.* Ottawa: Network of the Federal/Provincial/Territorial Group on Nutrition and National Institute of Nutrition, 29–32. Infant & Toddler Forum. (2006, July). *Nutrients: Functions, sources & requirements: Toddler factsheet 1.1i* (ITF1 10) - July 2006. <http://www.infantandtoddlerforum.org/objects/pdf/fact_sheet3.pdf> (June 2008).

Lunch Program Menu

MONDAY	TUESDAY	WEDNESDAY	THURSDAY	FRIDAY
• tomato & rice soup • tuna sandwiches • cucumber rounds • oranges	• Jamaican beans & rice with roti • celery & carrot sticks • apples	• cheese & potato perogies • garlicky green beans • tomato wedges • apples	• pineapple meatballs • brown rice • peapod & carrot stir-fry • bananas	• lentil burger in pita pockets • salad • baked potato wedges • ice cream
• macaroni & cheese • spinach salad • watermelon	• beefy Spanish rice casserole • broccoli (raw & cooked) • cantaloupe	• spaghetti • Caesar salad (without egg in dressing) • pears	• chicken with teriyaki vegetables • brown rice • honeydew melon	• P.D. Day
• scrambled eggs in pita pockets • oven-baked potato wedges • green pepper sticks • oranges	• lasagna • garlic bread • garden salad • apples	• tacos (hard tortillas or pita with refried beans, cheese, lettuce, tomato, guacamole) • oranges	• three-cheese pasta • garden salad • strawberries	• chicken, rice, & bean soup • cheese sandwiches • apples
• Santa Fe beans • garden salad • apples	• tofu sausages • mashed potatoes with parsley • broccoli (raw & cooked) • strawberries	• cheesy-bean burritos • Caesar salad • cantaloupe	• chicken curry • brown rice • cauliflower & broccoli (raw with yogurt dip) • pears	• pizza • vegetable sticks • bananas
		• chicken cacciatore • garlic bread • salad • oranges	• fish sticks (homemade) • fries • zucchini & carrot bake • watermelon	

Note: Milk and water are provided at lunch.

Source: Adapted with permission from Ferncliff Day Care and Fern Avenue Public School, Toronto, ON.

Summer Menu

WEEK 2 SUMMER MENU

	Monday	Tuesday	Wednesday	Thursday	Friday
S **N** **A** **C** **K**	CHEESY MINI QUICHE CUCUMBER SLICES	BLUEBERRY WHEATGERM PANCAKES MANGO SLICES	MULTIGRAIN TOASTED BAGELS TUNA SALAD ORANGE WEDGES	APPLE-GINGER GRANOLA & YOGURT	WHOLE-WHEAT FRENCH TOAST ORANGE WEDGES
L **U** **N** **C** **H**	CHICKEN & VEGETABLE STIR-FRY (CARROT, CELERY, YAM, WAX BEANS, CORN, PEAS) BROWN RICE ORANGE WEDGES MILK	VEGETARIAN CHILI WIH KIDNEY BEANS, QUINOA BABY CARROTS YOGURT & STRAWBERRIES MILK	BUILD-YOUR-OWN TACOS (CORN TORTILLAS, REFRIED BEANS, CHEDDAR CHEESE, RED & GREEN PEPPER STRIPS, BLACK OLIVES, SALSA) CUCUMBER ROUNDS CANTALOUPE MILK	WHOLE-WHEAT VEGGIE PIZZA (2 CHEESES, RED PEPPER, ZUCCHINI, BROCCOLI) BABY CARROTS PEAR SLICES MILK	LENTIL AND VEGETABLE RICE SOUP HAVARTI CHEESE CUBES MULTIGRAIN CRACKERS GREEN & RED SEEDLESS GRAPES MILK
S **N** **A** **C** **K**	WHOLE-WHEAT CARROT CAKE WATERMELON CHUNKS	HUMMUS & PITA TRIANGLES BABY CARROTS	SNACK: LEMON SQUARES BANANAS	WHOLE-WHEAT BANANA BREAD CELERY STICKS	APPLE-OAT CAKE CUCUMBER ROUNDS

Note: Water is available at every meal and snack. Whole-grain bread or crackers are available at every lunch. Children are involved in preparation and in serving themselves whenever possible.

Source: Contributed by Robert Caspary, Chef at George Brown College, School of Early Childhood.

Healthy Active Living

HEALTHY ACTIVE LIVING

What does the term **"healthy active living"** refer to? Generally, that term brings healthy eating and physical activity to mind. There are many other aspects to a healthy lifestyle, but when the term *healthy living* is combined with the word *active*, the majority of the literature and the general public denote those two

components. Other healthy lifestyle components, such as rest, relaxation, dental hygiene, and stress management, are discussed in Unit 9.

In this unit, we explore the reasons behind the relatively recent panic about healthy active living in Canada, particularly how this relates to children. Are the concerns hype or reality? What are the implications for early learning and educators? Are we able to contribute to healthy active living that will be sustained for the long term in children's lives? And if so, how?

Concerns about Childhood Obesity

Over the past quarter-century, the prevalence of children and adults who are overweight or obese is an alarming trend. The World Health Organization (WHO) reports that obesity has reached epidemic proportions globally, with rates that have risen threefold or more since 1980 in many parts of the world. Obesity is a complex condition, with serious physical, mental, and social implications, affecting all ages and socioeconomic groups. Although this epidemic began with developed countries, it is now growing quickly in developing countries. *For example, in Thailand, the prevalence of obesity in 5- to 12-year-olds rose from 12.2% to 15.6% in just 2 years (World Health Organization, 2008).*

With so much concern about how to deal with this complex and rising global epidemic of obesity, there is a consistent message almost universally about the major reason for it: "profound changes in society and in behavioural patterns of communities over recent decades" (World Health Organization, 2008, p. 1). We know that genetics and other factors are significant with regard to individual tendencies to gain weight, but, ultimately, energy balance is largely determined by calories in and energy expenditure out. Worldwide transitions in nutrition patterns and a reduction in physical activity are having an overwhelming impact. The increasing use of automated transportation to distribute food globally has resulted in less reliance on local foods. For many, this has meant that diets that were rich in vegetables, fruit, and complex carbohydrates have been replaced with foods high in saturated and trans fats and sugar, often highly processed, with a long shelf life.

In Canada, many Aboriginal communities have abandoned or restricted their traditional primary sources of food due to changes in hunting, fishing, and harvesting practices. These dietary changes have contributed to high rates of obesity and type 2 diabetes. These changes have also had devastating effects on "community solidarity, social organization and culture that were strengthened by the necessity of food gathering" (Williamson & Roberts, 2004, p. 195).

With increased **urban sprawl** (automated transport-dependent communities built on the outskirts of an urban area), many residents in Canada walk or bike less due to poor layouts and distance to stores and other community destinations (Lopez, 2004). Less physically demanding work and more passive leisure, such as TV, computer, and video games, are examples of why there has been a substantial reduction in healthy active living.

The WHO is concerned about the major risks of early death, quality of life, and health care costs to society that come with the chronic diseases common in obese children and adults, including type 2 diabetes, cardiovascular disease, hypertension, stroke, and certain forms of cancer. *For example, type 2 diabetes was confined to older adults for most of the 20th century but is now affecting children who are obese even before puberty (World Health Organization, 2008).*

Is this of concern in Canada? The rates of childhood obesity in Canada tripled in less than 20 years, from 5% of 7- to 13-year-olds in 1981 to 17% of boys and 15% of girls in 1996 (Tremblay & Willms, 2000, p. 1429). A study in Quebec indicated that almost 25% of 9-year-olds and half of 16-year-olds in Quebec were at risk of developing heart disease later due to lifestyle factors such as obesity, physical activity, or smoking (Spurgeon, 2002, p. 1416). Not all heavy children have weight problems as adults. However, as children get older, their risk for remaining overweight does increase, especially if they have a parent who is overweight. A more recent national survey conducted in 2004, *Nutrition: Findings from the Canadian Community Health Survey,* found that 26% of Canadian children and adolescents aged 2 to 17 years old were overweight or obese (Shields, 2005). See Table 6.1.

TABLE 6.1	Overweight and Obesity Rates, by Age Group, Household Population Aged 2 to 17, Canada Excluding Territories, 1978–79 and 2004

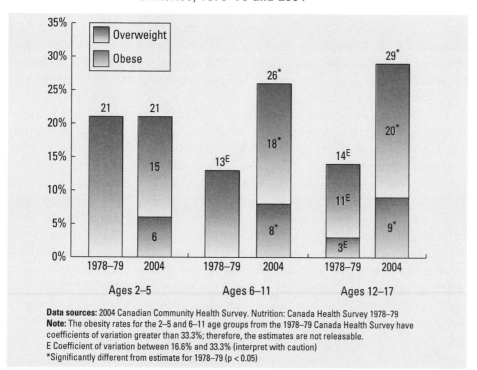

Data sources: 2004 Canadian Community Health Survey. Nutrition: Canada Health Survey 1978–79
Note: The obesity rates for the 2–5 and 6–11 age groups from the 1978–79 Canada Health Survey have coefficients of variation greater than 33.3%; therefore, the estimates are not releasable.
E Coefficient of variation between 16.6% and 33.3% (interpret with caution)
*Significantly different from estimate for 1978–79 (p < 0.05)

Source: Adapted from Statistics Canada, "Measured Obesity", *Nutrition: Findings from the Canadian Community Health Survey,* Catalogue #82-620-MEW, Issue #1. Released July 6, 2005, url: http://www .statcan.ca/english/research/82-620-MIE/2005001/pdf/cobesity.pdf chart 2.

Body mass index (BMI) is commonly used to assess the degree of overweight and obesity. The BMI calculates the weight (kg) divided by the height (metres squared). The BMI is more of a rough guide than an ideal measure. One example of the BMI's limitation is that it does not take into account an individual who is quite muscular. Although not typical during childhood, a child who has a larger muscle mass may have a high BMI and be classified as overweight using BMI as the measure. A BMI of over 25 kg/m^2 is defined as **overweight**, and a BMI of over 30 kg/m^2 is defined as obese. In countries undergoing nutrition transition, overnutrition often coexists with undernutrition. People with a BMI below 18.5 kg/m^2 tend to be **underweight**.

To date, there is no perfect determinant of overweight or obesity. The combined overweight/obesity rate for boys and girls from 2 to 17 years old was about 70% higher than it had been in 1978–79, and the obesity rate was 2.5 times higher. Although this survey did not find an obesity rate increase in the preschool age group, keep in mind that the prevalence of nutritional problems such as overweight and obesity in this age group is 21% in Canada (Shields, 2005). This in itself is of concern. In addition, with the overweight/obesity rate increases since 1978 beginning in the six-year-old and older age ranges, we must also ask ourselves what this means in the preschool years. In the preschool years, children are developing the lifestyle habits that pave the way for long-term health benefits or detriments. The preschooler who is introduced to a range of healthy foods, offered a minimum of low nutrition foods, and has a lot of opportunity for active play that includes adult role modelling is less likely to join the ranks of obesity later in childhood. It is not unreasonable to assume that very young children who routinely drink pop, are exposed to serving sizes in restaurants that are more than double the size of those listed in *Eating Well with Canada's Food Guide* (see Appendix 5.1, page 287) recommendations, and spend several hours daily watching TV are at risk of strengthening these habits in the long term. In addition, a systematic review of 36 studies on short sleep duration and weight gain suggests that insufficient sleep is strongly and consistently associated with existing and future obesity in children (Patel & Hu, 2008).

A child with a normal BMI can also be unhealthy when combined with significant inactivity, poor eating habits, or both. Obesity should not be the only marker of focus for child health. Healthy active living strategies that are targeted only at children who are overweight are wrought with traps and possible negative consequences for all children. We must also take care to avoid assumptions or judgments about the health of children who are not lean at any age. Remember that we come in all shapes and sizes. Our genetics, biology, ethnic origin, environment, lifestyle, and other factors, some of which we have little or no control over, come into play in the formation of body size. *For example, young people of Aboriginal origin, living off a reserve, have a combined overweight/obesity rate of 41% and youth of Southeast Asian or East Asian origin have a rate of 18% (Shields, 2005).* Lifestyle factors do not fully account for this wide discrepancy, and it must be acknowledged that factors contributing to obesity are more complex than a prescription of healthy eating and physical activity. One of the considerations as an underlying cause of obesity is the increased hormone cortisol produced by children who experience ongoing stressors. Cortisol helps the liver convert fat into bursts of energy needed to escape danger, but also signals the body to gather fat in the abdomen, building the health-hazardous apple shape (Evenson,

2003). According to Dr. Liz Goodman, who has conducted research on cortisol in children, children raised in poverty produce greater amounts of cortisol (Evenson, 2003). On the flip side, children in the healthy weight or BMI range are not necessarily fit or eating a diet that is optimal for health.

Nonetheless, it is very likely that positive lifestyle habits support physical, mental, and emotional health, as well as reduce obesity and risk factors. As a society, one of our most important tasks to this end is to reduce barriers to a healthy lifestyle.

As stated in Unit 1, Aboriginal people face disparities in housing, education, employment, and food security. Addressing these is a priority to eliminate barriers to a healthy active lifestyle, making healthy choices easier rather than almost impossible.

The approach to the epidemic of childhood obesity in Canada needs to be "integrated, multi-sectoral, [and] population based, which includes environmental support for healthy diets and regular physical activity" (World Health Organization, 2008). This can happen in multiple ways and with various strategies that fit into a health promotion approach, discussed later in this unit. The good news is that educators can make a positive contribution by integrating healthy opportunities daily in the lives of all the children and their families. They will have opportunities to

- promote and support healthy habits from an early age.
- participate in advocating for change in local, regional, national, and global agencies.

Concerns about Physical Activity Levels of Children

Canada's Report Card on Physical Activity for Children and Youth reports that one half of Canadian children are not active enough for optimal growth and development. The report also points out that children, particularly girls, tend to become less active as they get older. They published their fourth annual overview of physical activity levels of Canada's children and youth in May 2008, with very disappointing grades (Active Healthy Kids Canada, 2008, p. 66). Using data analysis from various sources across the country, the Research Work Group for the report card assigned grades to specific indicators. Selected examples of indicators with their grade include the following:

Physical activity levels	F
Screen time	F
Sport participation	C
Healthy body weight	F
Active transportation to and from schools (walking, bike riding)	D
Family perceptions and roles regarding physical activity	D
Use of parks and playgrounds	D
Progress of government strategies and investments	C+
2008 Overall Grade	D

(Active Healthy Kids Canada, 2007, pp. 6–15)

Source: *It's Time To Unplug Our Kids: Canada's Report Card on Physical Activity for Children & Youth—2008*. Reprinted with permission from Active Healthy Kids Canada.

With reference to physical activity for preschoolers, a previous assumption that young children are naturally active is becoming less obvious. Young children may need adult role modelling and guidance in addition to opportunity for movement outdoors and indoors. How active are preschoolers? It's a difficult question to answer, one that Timmons, Naylor, and Pfeiffer (2007) investigated by analyzing available studies. Pate, Pfeiffer, Trost, Ziegler, and Dowda (2004, p. 1261) reported that vigorous intensity of physical activity by preschoolers occurs in short spurts, approximately two minutes per hour, and moderate intensity for about five minutes per hour. Benham-Deal (2005) found that the majority of the children's physical activity was in bouts of 5 to 10 minutes. Clearly, young children prefer intermittent activity, but most studies also noted large individual differences. Some children are extremely active, whereas others have low interest in vigorous physical activity (Timmons et al., 2007, p. S125). One of the complexities is that no clear guidelines have been developed for preschool children's level of activity. ***Canada's Physical Activity Guide for Children*** (Health Canada, 2002) starts at age six and calls parents, educators, physicians, and community leaders to action to support children's daily active time (see Appendix 6.1, page 352).

How much physical activity time is needed for optimal growth and development of preschoolers? The easy answer is, we don't know. Evidence is accumulating that increasing physical activity in the early years contributes to better physical health status (Binkley & Specker, 2004, p. 1383), but it has been difficult to determine how much overall and of each type (**endurance**, **flexibility**, and **strength**) is optimal. There are many variables that make this hard to measure.

Boldemann et al. (2006, p. 301) found that children's physical activity was related to the quality of the preschool play environment, with an outdoor green environment being optimal. Overall, the authors' interpretation of the results was that physical activity is a multidimensional behaviour that depends on social and environmental factors in addition to time spent outside and prompts to be active.

Canada has made some progress, but we have far to go in turning around an appalling record that relates to concerns about the health of children now and into adulthood. One positive aspect is that awareness of the issue is on the upswing, translating into beginning support for change by parents, educators, communities, and legislators. However, change can be slow. *For example, parents may underestimate the weight and overestimate the physical activity of their own children. The point of reference has changed in recent years due partly to the normalcy of larger children (Butler, 2008).*

Reaching a broad preschool audience is also not a simple task. Universal accessibility to children age six and up in the public school system is not a reality for the five and under age group. Also, developmental milestones vary widely in age, with some two-year-olds ready to jump and hop and others just beginning to toddle without often losing their balance. This reality can make it difficult to get specific messages to parents and educators, although the general message is that daily opportunities for movement exploration with adult supervision and role modelling are essential for optimal healthy development. Your province or territory and city, town, or community are likely finding ways to support preschool physical activity. Find out about these campaigns or programs and how young children and families can benefit from each. It's worth keeping a list to share with colleagues and families.

SUPPORTING PHYSICAL ACTIVITY

Every child, taking into account development, individual differences, and physical challenges, can move in ways that fit his or her needs and interests. We know this to be true, but do we walk the talk in providing and promoting these opportunities? There are no hard data to answer this question, but it is doubtful that this question would be answered with a resounding "yes."

To identify physical activity guidelines embedded in a play-based program.

To discuss educator considerations in responding to and promoting physical activity in each age group.

To discuss curriculum guidelines for each age group.

To discuss the reasons why educators need to emphasize outdoor play and the elements of an outdoor play environment that supports physical activity.

To list and discuss benefits to greening the outdoor environment.

It is hoped that you can confidently answer yes to this question as you engage with children in your placements and in your career. In the study "Employer Partnerships and Role Modelling for Physical Activity Programs in Early Childhood Education," Crossley and Wright (2003, p. 69) list the three requirements adults need to become effective and valued role models for physical activity for children. Adults need to

- Understand the barriers they and children may be experiencing to both initial and ongoing involvement in physical activity
- Understand the developmental and health risks associated with inactive lifestyles
- Understand the need for and significance of outdoor programming for the development of children and their ensuing lifestyle choices.

Source: Employer Partnerships and Role Modelling For Physical Activity Programs in Early Childhood Education by B. Crossley and S. Wright from *Outdoor Play in Early Childhood Care and Education Programs*, 2003. Reprinted with permission of Canadian Childcare Federation.

It is essential to recognize the benefits of physical activity for all children in your program, regardless of body type, size, or physical agility. With the current focus on childhood obesity, the inactivity levels of lean children can sadly go unnoticed. Observation of each child's movement during the day may surprise educators who assume that lean children make active choices. Children with special needs must have equal consideration and individualized planning by educators to ensure that they also have ongoing opportunities to move.

Benefits of Physical Activity

Physical activity enables children and adults to release tension, have fun, learn social skills, and build self-esteem as they develop skills. A body that is physically fit works better. Physical activity should be part of everyday life for everyone. It is common knowledge that exercise builds a stronger heart and contributes to increased energy and better eating and sleeping habits. Better posture and balance; stronger bones, muscles, and joints; social interactions; and skill development are other benefits. On the other hand, physical inactivity increases the risk of at least 17 unhealthy conditions, almost all of which are chronic diseases or considered risk factors for chronic diseases and premature death (Booth, Gordon, Carlson, & Hamilton, 2000, p. 781).

In addition to the physical benefits of moving, there are physiological and psychosocial benefits, many of which are listed in this unit. The Canadian Paediatric Society (2008, p. 10) reminds us about additional reasons for ensuring that ongoing opportunities for active play are integrated into the young child's day:

Active children learn to run, jump and kick while playing. As they develop, basic skills helps to support a positive body image and facilitate recreational and sports activities later in life. Inactive children who don't develop these skills may lack confidence or feel awkward during physical activities as they get older. These feelings can contribute to a sedentary lifestyle as children mature and increase the risk of early obesity. Children with more opportunities to be physically active tend to make positive, healthy choices in other areas of life as they mature. Studies show they eat more nutritious foods and are less likely to smoke, use drugs or abuse alcohol. Physical activity is also associated with better mental health because it helps children express intense emotions in a constructive way. Exercise and having fun alleviate stress.

Source: Canadian Paediatric Society, *Well Beings: A Guide to Health in Child Care.* (Ottawa: Canadian Paediatric Society, 2008), 10. Reprinted with permission.

Supporting Activity in Early Childhood Programs

Educators should plan a program that integrates physical activity in ways that invite children to become involved. Pate et al. (2004, p. 1262) concluded from their studies on physical activity in preschool programs that policies and practices have a significant impact on how physically active children are. Most children want to be active, especially when offered a range of possibilities. Ideally, physical activity is embedded into the child's play during the day. To support this, options need to be of equivalent status.

The choice of outdoor play or a computer game may not hold equal appeal for many children. The high status of computers or other screen time gives that choice an unfair advantage. This can be compared to snack choices: for most children, being offered apple slices or a brownie will result in the brownie choice being made much more often, not supporting healthy eating choices. A healthier choice is apple slices or a banana. The child who is reluctant to join active games or activities may need more encouragement. However, children should never be singled out or embarrassed into physical activity. Instead, educators can use their observation skills to identify clues to explain the reluctance and then find ways to encourage that child's involvement.

Physical Activity Guidelines

By evaluating the variety of opportunities for physical activity embedded in a play-based program, educators can determine to what degree the children are able to be active for short time periods throughout the day, as well as the components of these activities. The following are implementation considerations for the educators providing a high-quality physical activity program.

Development

- Ensure that children's development is the basis for planning the curriculum. Refer to developmental milestones for all areas of development, with a focus on, but not limited to, large motor development. In addition to other physical skills, such as small motor, balance, and coordination, there are cognitive, emotional, and social developmental behaviour and skills occurring during physical activity.

- Children aren't expected to go beyond their skill or energy level. Each child has support and encouragement to build skills and energy level.

- At all ages, children learn to move and move to learn.

Infant: Problem solving—how to reach her favourite toy that is on the far side of the table.

Toddler: Problem solving—at the top of a snow bank, his boots are sinking into the soft snow.

Preschooler: Problem solving—how can you jump and land quietly, how small can you make your body, or how wide can you make your body? Predicting—how many giant steps will it take to get to the other side of the playground?

School-ager: Social problem solving—what is a rule of the game that would prevent players from bumping into each other?

- Although children follow the same developmental pattern, they will do so at widely varying times.

  It is important to follow a child's pace and not to make comparisons with others. It is also important to remember that activities that stimulate one child may not interest another. This is true at any age.

- Downplay competition.

  Focus instead on individual mastery and cooperating together with group activities.

Educator/Curriculum

- Model a physically active lifestyle that contributes to the children's interest in activity. When educators participate with children and observe them in active play, they use their observations to design the environment and to facilitate curriculum so that children can challenge themselves in play.

- Appreciate the educators' role in promoting both physical activity and physical education by supporting children's development of basic skills to ready their participation in a wide variety of physical activities.

- Ensure that the indoor and outdoor curriculum planning and implementation for physical activity are an integral part of the program.

- Emphasize fun, socialization, and active living all year round.

- Ensure that most physical activity opportunities are child directed and open ended.

- Incorporate music into activities when possible.

  Fit the tempo of the activity-promoting rhythm and cultural diversity. Ideally, music also reflects the families' cultures and interests.

- Provide children with the opportunity to make choices and actively explore their environment, while educators facilitate and prepare a stimulating environment and challenging activities.

  Movement exploration, guided discovery, and creative problem solving are the most common teaching strategies.

- Include a wide variety of physical activity opportunities in the curriculum, developing children's endurance, flexibility, and strength.
- Promote appropriate opportunities for all children.

  Respect individual skills and abilities, energy, and interest level and encourage and celebrate each child's attempts and successes.
- Use directional instructions often so children practise spatial and body awareness.

Can you walk backward from the playground door to the fence? Or scurry like a mouse to the front wall and back?

- Encourage the development of pro-social skills.

Children go through the obstacle course one by one, learning to respect that their turn follows the child who is in front of them.

- Use clear, simple, and minimal restrictions and directions to promote maximum child-directed involvement in the activity, encouraging children to challenge themselves.
- Recognize the importance of children valuing physical activity as a lifelong habit, but be careful not to plan activities designed to enhance their fitness levels (e.g., running laps).

Use a family-centred approach in your physical activity curriculum, as in all aspects of the program.

Perhaps a school-ager can teach his peers a skipping or ball game that he learned from his country of origin.

- Observe the children's skills and interests and support opportunities for physical activity through one-to-one support.

Safety/Environment
- Ensure that the environment reflects the developmental skill set of the children in the program and their problem-solving abilities.
- Maintain safety in all aspects of the physical activity program (i.e., equipment is well maintained, clutter hazards are removed, children's level of involvement fits the environment, adults actively supervise).
- Provide various types of equipment in quantities that do not overwhelm children with choices or result in children being left out or fighting over the few pieces of equipment.
- Include active indoor alternatives into the plan when the weather doesn't permit outdoor play.

Family/Community

- Invite parents, older siblings, and extended family members and encourage them to provide input and be involved whenever possible (e.g., share active games from their childhood).
- Provide music and activities that reflect a range in musical styles (e.g., jazz, rhythm and blues, folk, classical, reggae) and ethnocultural diversity, including family preferences whenever possible.
- Consider children's opportunity to move when planning for walks or field trips in the community.

Motor Skill Development

Children's development is integrated, involving more than one developmental domain at a time: physical, cognitive, social, and emotional areas of development occur simultaneously.

The patterning motion involved as an infant is learning to crawl is as much cognitive development as physical. Movement tends to invite sensory exploration and social interaction from infancy onward. However, if we "isolate" motor development, we find that it follows two fundamental principles:

- It proceeds from head to foot.
- It proceeds from the centre of the body outward.

This is evident as the infant must first get control over holding up his head and then sit up before learning to crawl. The small **motor skills** and dexterity develop later than the large motor skills.

Although we acknowledge that motor development is a continuous process of building, refining, and combining skills and abilities, there are four general phases:

- reflexive movement phase (beginning in utero)
- rudimentary (simple) movement phase (ending around two years old)
- fundamental movement phase (from approximately two to seven years old) (basic movement patterns include **locomotor skills**, stability and balance skills, and manipulative skills)
- specialized or sports-related movement phase (seven years old to adolescence)

Growing ability in cognitive and other areas of development (social, emotional, and language) interacts with motor and sensory skills to contribute to more mature levels of performance as the child becomes interested in sport or dance (Gallahue & Donnelly, 2007, pp. 62–63).

Locomotor skills involve moving the body from one place to another, such as walking, running, jumping, galloping, hopping, skipping, sliding, leaping, and climbing. **Nonlocomotor skills** involve moving the body in one place, such as bending, stretching, twisting, turning, swinging, rolling, stopping/landing, dodging, and balancing. **Manipulative skills** tend to involve objects such as balls and include throwing, catching, kicking, trapping, striking, volleying, dribbling, bouncing, rolling (object), and punting. Remember that children are also developing other motor skills, such as body and spatial awareness, and abilities such as balance and eye–hand and eye–foot coordination, which are essential aspects of the locomotor, nonlocomotor, and manipulative skills. Opportunities to practise a range of these (and other) motor skills help a child develop the skills and confidence to master more complex skills, opening up avenues for a lifelong active lifestyle. Refer to Table 6.2 for some activities at each age spectrum to support large motor development and practice.

TABLE 6.2	Some Activities for Large Motor Development
AGES	**SKILLS**
Up to 2 Years Old	kicking, rolling over, crawling, sitting independently, pulling to standing, cruising, down and up, standing alone, toddling, scooting, squatting, running, climbing, begin sitting on and moving on riding toys (often going backward first); rolling a large soft ball
2- and 3-Year-Olds	walking forward and backward, running, climbing, crawling through and around, jumping, running and jumping, hopping, galloping, balancing/rotating (e.g., walk along a low balance beam with or without help), bending, stretching, rolling and tossing balls or bean bags (often with both hands), kicking balls, hitting balls with a large object, sits with balance on a swing (swing with gentle pushing from adult), sits on and skillfully moves a riding toy with two feet
4- and 5-Year-Olds	walking, running, jumping, hopping, skipping, balancing/rotating/pivoting, climb large play structures to their own comfort level, bending, stretching, tumbling, rolling/throwing or kicking balls with more accuracy due to developing eye–hand and eye–foot coordination, catching balls, batting/dribbling balls, dribbling balls, hitting a ball with large bat, developing spatial awareness, concept of teamwork developing, but not yet most game skills, building stamina for longer duration of vigorous activity
6- and 7-Year-Olds	running/jumping, leaping, rotating/balancing/pivoting, skipping, tumbling, throwing/passing/catching balls, kicking balls, dribbling/shooting to hoop. Fine motor skills require the use of smaller muscles and involve more precise movements, such as using the fingers to draw.
8- and 9-Year-Olds	running/jumping, skipping, leaping, rotating/tumbling, balancing/pivoting, throwing/catching balls, batting balls, dribbling balls, dribbling/shooting to hoop, building endurance and strength, as well as sports and dance skills, as fundamental motor skills are developed (keeping in mind individual differences as always)

Active Infants and Toddlers

Infants' need for physical activity changes dramatically in the first year—from holding the head up, sitting, and rolling over, to pulling themselves up, to creeping, crawling, standing, and walking. Educators are continually responding to these needs by providing an environment that is developmentally appropriate, challenging, and safe.

Follow the child's lead while she shows interest in

■ reaching for her favourite toy over and over as you continue to place it just barely out of reach,

■ repeatedly crawling in and out of a box, and

■ pulling herself up to standing using a sturdy table and holding on while moving around it.

The integration of cognitive and physical skills in this exploration, as well as the developing strength and confidence in her abilities, forms a foundation for continued motivation to move and explore. Adequate floor time is essential for this process.

Educators set up the environment to enhance each child's physical development. Taking cues from the child, educators engage in one-to-one interaction when the child is alert and interested. This provides an opportunity to focus on the child's needs and interests (e.g., action songs such as *Row, Row, Row Your Boat* to practise rocking or surrounding the baby with soft pillows to topple on as he attempts to sit up independently).

When implementing physical activity with a young infant on a one-to-one basis:

■ Begin an activity only when the infant is alert and willing. When a child is hungry, tired, or unhappy, it is not an appropriate time to initiate the activity.

■ Be totally committed to the infant by avoiding distractions and try to reduce distractions for the child.

■ Adapt the timing of the activity to the tempo of the room and of the day.

■ Follow the infant's lead in your interactions.

■ Try an activity with the infant in a relaxed and reassuring way on a soft covered mat or carpet.

When the child responds by laughing or other signs of enjoyment, continue and possibly repeat the activity several times. However, if not, stop and try the activity again some other time.

■ Begin with relaxation exercises to establish trust and to set the tone. Then introduce some stretching and bending exercises to increase flexibility and range of motion. Follow with more vigorous activity to support strength, endurance, flexibility, and coordination.

The process should be enjoyable for the infant and adult.

Repeat the activities for several days, progressing only as quickly as the infant appears to want to. Follow the child's cues.

■ Use favourite toys whenever possible.

It can be part of the activity or help the infant to relax (familiarity/comfort), or it can help draw attention to a movement (e.g., favourite toy is peeking out of the tunnel, which may motivate the infant to creep or crawl toward it).

Remember not to

- force the infant or the infant's body in any way to tire the child.
- compare the infant's development or accomplishment with that of another child. Each infant is unique and progresses at a unique pace.

Most infants and toddlers go for daily walks in strollers or wagons, which provides them with fresh air and stimulation and sometimes rest. They also need plenty of opportunity to move around freely, out of strollers and wagons, with a minimum of restrictions.

Toddlers are at a stage of motor development when they often need to run more than walk. They need an adequate open space, small climbing equipment, and slides. Ramps and steps need to be the right size to encourage toddlers' exploration, not to frustrate them or make them prone to falls. Creative movement can be enhanced when the toddlers are in smaller groups. Provide opportunities to dance to music or move like an animal. Minimize the expectation for sit-down time and maximize opportunities to move in short spurts. Passive activities such as reading a book and singing quiet songs are more appropriate with one or two toddlers, who join and leave the activity as they wish. Of course, toddlers should always be permitted to come and go with group activities, unless supervision and safety are an issue (e.g., walking to the park).

A motor development explosion occurs because once children learn to walk, they quickly develop a vast repertoire of other motor skills, involving body and spatial awareness, locomotor and nonlocomotor skills, and manipulative skills.

When planning and implementing curriculum for more mobile infants and toddlers, keep the following recommendations in mind:

■ Physical activity opportunities and curriculum should be embedded into play whenever possible, not seen as a structured time of day. When educators have an active living way of life, they tend to optimize the natural opportunities for physical activity, recognizing and using possibilities. *For example, marching or tiptoeing down the hall, when coming inside or going outside, singing and moving to an active song when there is a short wait, and "shaking our sillies out" after sitting reading a book are all easy ways to contribute to short but numerous opportunities to move our bodies during the day.*

■ An environment and adult involvement that promote freedom of movement are essential for children to be able to assess their own motor capabilities and practise accordingly.

■ When the children's environment is modified to prevent injuries as much as possible, it is obviously safer and less restrictive.

As well, the educators are better able to ensure optimal supervision of busy, walking infants and toddlers.

Ensuring that the environment indoors and outdoors doesn't become too cluttered during the day with scattered toys also reduces frustration and makes it easier to practise emerging and acquired motor skills.

■ Incorporate the quantitative concepts that toddlers are busy discovering: some, more, big, and spatial relationships such as up, down, inside, outside, behind, and over and under.

■ As toddlers acquire more language and begin to develop the ability to pretend, the educator is able to plan for simple games such as *Ring Around the Rosey* and motor activities with suggested imagery (e.g., "Let's pretend we are fish swimming in the water.").

Remember

– to focus on the familiar for the child, ideally integrating ideas that come from the family (e.g., foods, pets, clothing, songs, stories).

– the importance of simplicity when stating instructions.

Active Preschoolers and School-Agers

Based on the best available evidence from the range of studies on physical activity for preschool children, Timmons et al. (2007, p. S131) made the following recommendations:

■ Promotion of physical activity for preschool children should consider their natural activity patterns, which are typically spontaneous and intermittent.

■ Physical activity for preschool children should focus on gross motor play and locomotor activities that children find fun.

- Physical experiences for preschool children will be enhanced by adult facilitation (including modeling) that provides mastery experiences and contingent feedback about those experiences.

- Whenever possible, preschool children should be given access to play spaces and equipment outdoors.

Source: Physical Activity For Preschool Children—How Much and How? by B.W. Timmons, P.J. Naylor and K.A. Pfeiffer, 2007 from *Applied Physiology, Nutrition, and Metabolism*, 32, s122–s134. Reprinted with permission from National Research Council Canada.

These recommendations hold clear messages for educators and parents who value preschoolers' active play: engage with children in physical activities that are spontaneous and enjoyable, fit their motor skills and interests, and are outdoors whenever possible. Young children tend to have bursts of energy, so several short periods of vigorous play throughout the day are best.

An early childhood program should include these **fitness components** into the activities: endurance, flexibility, and strength (Binkley & Specker, 2004).

For preschoolers:

- Endurance activities strengthen the heart and lungs.

  Running (e.g., games of tag or red light, green light), jumping in an obstacle course or in an active game, dancing to a quick tempo, and swimming (when your program has access to regular swimming lessons)

- Strength-focused activities build strong muscles and bones, supporting the child's body weight.

  Climbing stairs or swinging across the playground ladder or monkey bars. Many of these activities, including running, develop both endurance and strength.

- Flexibility refers to the ability of various joints to move their full range of motion. Flexibility is enhanced in activities that encourage children to bend, stretch, and reach, such as moving with scarves, simple yoga poses, and playing bowling games with different-sized balls and pins.

  It is important to stretch before and after vigorous activity to support flexible joints.

As children develop their skills and fitness levels into school age, they will branch out to other endurance activities, such as biking, walking to school, tobogganing, and sports such as soccer, hockey, ringette, lacrosse, or basketball in addition to swimming.

School-agers may build their flexibility and strength through hiking, martial arts, and yoga. These examples point to the importance of a range of activities to build all fitness components for lifelong wellness. In the preschool age group, organized sports tend

to be too complex with regard to many aspects of child development in addition to motor skills—cognitively, socially, and emotionally. As children show interest in and are ready for more organized games and sports, educators and parents can encourage those interests. Adults must also take care not to over-schedule children or to place a lot of pressure on sport performance, which can take the enjoyment out of the activities and add a lot of stress to children around competing. This can undermine the benefits of physical activity, reduce much-needed family time, and place financial burdens on families for sports that bring with them added expenses such as equipment or additional fees.

Curriculum Guidelines for Preschoolers and School-Agers

■ Although child-directed active play is predominant, adult-guided activities can also be part of the curriculum for preschoolers and school-agers, particularly when active play is not being observed.

Ask preschoolers to crawl with a bean bag balancing on one body part or move across the room with one body part leading the way. Children use their imagination, physical skills, interests, and problem-solving skills to rise to the challenge—resulting in all sorts of possibilities.

■ Provide instructions that have built-in flexibility so that children can start from their own skill set and point of reference.

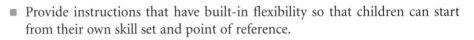

Even an instruction that may sound more directive, such as "hop like a frog," provides children with their own unique way of doing so.

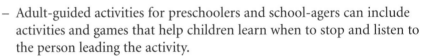

– Adult-guided activities for preschoolers and school-agers can include activities and games that help children learn when to stop and listen to the person leading the activity.

– When introducing new activities or games, educators do so with patience. Preschoolers and school-agers need time to practise and master new skills.

– Some children naturally have activity levels that require vigorous activity such as running and jumping as soon as they have the opportunity. Other children are attracted to moderate activity, such as marching and playing hide and seek (see Greening the Outdoor Environment, page 320). When these latter children are warmed up, they may be ready to try more vigorous activity. The hope is that they will, eventually, do some form of cardiovascular activity.

■ Plan **cooperative games** for preschooler and school-agers in which cooperation is incorporated into the rules and goals of the game while keeping competition to a minimum. Cooperative games do not eliminate children, thereby maintaining sustained activity for all children in the game. Children can also then join in and leave at any time.

Even traditional elimination games such as Hot Potato or Simon Says can be changed to avoid elimination, such as having two groups, with the child switching groups as he or she is left holding the hot potato, or doing the action when Simon didn't "say."

- Educators observe the children's skills and interests and support opportunities for physical activity through one-to-one support.

Eight-year-old Roberto, whose peers are more physically skilled and better coordinated than he is, is embarrassed to play ball games with the group. He always strikes out, highlighting his lack of batting skills, and his peers are impatient because he runs more slowly than they do. You can find a range of issues in this example:

- his lack of confidence
- his reluctance to join group games and sports
- his lack of interest in physical activity, which increases neither his skill nor his fitness level
- his peers' intolerance and focus on competition

The issue of competition is a difficult one to counterbalance when we consider the school-ager's developmental level and interest in rules and the constant messages about winning that bombard us in our society. Focusing on skill competence is developmentally important. Most children of this age have been playing cooperative games since their early preschool days. Educators can do their best to adapt competitive games to be more cooperative (i.e., by moving the emphasis away from winning and losing and toward participation, playing together, and having fun). Educators recognize in Roberto his need for long-term physical fitness and to be part of a social group. First, he is willing to practise ball skills with a trusted educator. As he progresses, one of his peers becomes interested in playing ball with him. Eventually, the group plays the ball game cooperatively (any game can be adjusted with minimal changes) part of the time so that all children can be involved.

Educators' sensitivity, creativity, and determination to support children's physical involvement encourage children like Roberto to build the interest, skill, and confidence they need to join in. This example is not meant to provide a recipe for success because, obviously, every child is unique and every group has its own social dynamics. However, educators can be confident that the effort they put into children's physical involvement is worth the long-term benefits.

The number of hours that most school-agers sit in class each day emphasizes the importance of providing physically active school-age programs. Some jurisdictions have mandated daily physical activity, but the short duration does not meet the needs for children from 6 to 9 years old, according to *Canada's Physical Activity Guide for Children* (Health Canada, 2002), which is 60 minutes of moderate and 30 minutes of vigorous physical activity. The guide calls for an increase in the time children currently spend on vigorous physical activity by a total of at least 30 minutes per day, while reducing nonactive time spent on TV, video, and computer games and surfing the Internet by at least 30 minutes less per day. This can be done in bouts as short as 5 or 10 minutes each to start.

Some school-agers desire sedentary after-school activities, including reading, playing cards or other games with peers, or doing homework. Perhaps those children can be encouraged by educators to move in 5- or 10-minute bouts to start, even between homework subjects, for example. With the support of the educators, the children can come up with movement ideas they would enjoy. There are also school-age children who are interested in more active options. Often school-agers plan their own active games or activities when encouraged by supportive adults. Problem-solving rules of the game, such as how to take turns, supports school-agers' social problem-solving skills. This age group is ready for these additional challenges.

Outdoor Play

The increase in sedentary indoor activities has in part been due to the decrease in opportunities for outdoor physical activity. Depending on life circumstances, children of all ages may have few opportunities to be physically active outdoors. Two main deterrents are involved: the dependence on motorized vehicles and the lack of outdoor play spaces deemed safe for children's play.

Countries and communities throughout the world that either lack the luxury of motorized vehicles upon which we have become so dependent or have planned the infrastructure to be community friendly for pedestrians and bicycles offer a vital ingredient for good health to their citizens: the importance of moving outdoors to get from place to place. This human-powered way of getting around is often called **active transportation.** In addition to walking and biking, rural and remote communities may have other forms of active transportation available to their residents, such as hiking, snowshoeing, and cross-country skiing.

In towns and cities in which the population is growing and people are moving to the suburbs to escape the "ills of the city," trees and grass are often replaced with malls and subdivisions. Although families who can afford it may have the benefit of a back yard for children to play in, there is also the likelihood that they are car dependent, even for a basic errand such as buying a loaf of bread. This urban sprawl typically results in a poorly planned infrastructure on the outskirts of an urban area, which often includes street patterns with a lot of loops, crescents, and circles; few sidewalks; and few bike paths or pedestrian crossings. In these communities, the infrastructure often separates residential areas from stores, offices, and services. In a number of European countries, such as Denmark and the Netherlands, 40% of trips are made without a motorized vehicle. In Canada, only 10% of trips are made by walking or cycling, and only 6% in the United States (Ontario College of Family Physicians, 2005, p. 3).

Research consistently shows that people who live in low-density towns and cities use cars more often and walk and cycle less than people living in more compact, dense communities (Ontario College of Family Physicians, 2005, p. 5). For every 30 minutes spent in a car each day, there is a percent greater chance of being obese. The same study found that people who live in neighbourhoods with a mix of shops and businesses within easy walking distance are 7% less likely to be obese, lowering their relative risk of obesity by 35% (Frank et al., 2003).

In most communities, especially in urban areas, parents are concerned about their children's safety outdoors when they are not actively supervised. Media coverage of rare incidents of kidnappings or perhaps less rare violent acts makes for hypervigilance on the part of parents, educators, and the general public. Children may live in urban dwellings (e.g., high-rise buildings) where there is no back yard or a perceived safe area in which to run and play. Parents may feel that they have neither the time nor the place available to take their children for regular physical activity. In addition, parents' lives may be so busy that preparing dinner, doing laundry, or finishing work from the office seems easier and less stressful if their child is safely indoors, watching TV, reading, or doing other passive activities. These issues are beyond the scope of the educator, but awareness of this reality for children and families reminds us of the importance to build physically active outdoor opportunities into the child's day and to promote ideas and initiatives that will have a positive effect on families' ability to be physically active with their children. It stands to reason that the more engaged children are outdoors in their younger years, the more likely it is that they will build their repertoire of interests and enjoyment outdoors, year round. In addressing several myths regarding outdoor play, the Canadian Child Care Federation (2003, pp. 2–6) states that myth #1 is as follows: "Outdoor play in [early childhood education (ECE)] programs is not really important because the children are there for such a short time. Truth: Movement is life and outdoor movement is child development at its very essence."

Included in Unit 7 is a range of considerations in ensuring that the outdoor play space of an early childhood setting is as safe as possible. However, not only is a risk-free environment impossible, it is also unlikely to offer the essential challenges for children at every stage of development to motivate their skill practice and mastery in all areas of development. The design and arrangement of the outdoor play environment can either limit or enable physical activity for all children.

Manufactured equipment, such as climbers, fire poles, slides, and teeter-totters, entice many, but not all, children to be active. Beyond the stationary equipment in the playground, which offers limited opportunity for movement and skill practice, children can be active on common movable equipment (e.g., asking a preschooler on a tricycle to ride in a zigzag pattern or setting up an obstacle course for a child to ride through).

Infants and toddlers need outdoor spaces that have safe areas for crawling and offer exploration of natural elements. *For example, a grass cover rather than a synthetic surface has so much more to offer in sensory stimulation and motor skills. Crawling on an uneven grass surface, with small mounds to crawl or walk up and down, develops the child's balance and spatial exploration to a much greater extent than the smooth, flat synthetic surface.*

Pardee, Gillman, and Larson. (2005, p. 13) suggest the following for infants and toddlers:

- a nonmetal slide with a gentle slope, with a low climbing ramp that has a few steps with a handrail
- sturdy ledges or low railings for infants to pull themselves to standing
- short tunnels and peek-a-boo places
- seating at various levels
- rocking toys that children can sit inside

- bucket swings at a safe distance from other play
- pushing or riding wheeled toys
- safe water and sand play with simple props

Source: *CICK Resource Guide–Volume 4: Creating Playgrounds for Early Childhood Facilities.* Published by Local Initiatives Support Corportation, 2005. Reprinted with permission.

In addition to sand and water play for a range of manipulative and imaginative play, preschoolers and school-agers need space in which to play and practise their locomotor skills. Although programs must meet the requirements for the amount of space in the early childhood provincial/territorial regulations, remember that those are minimum requirements. To optimize opportunities for children to move and explore outdoors often means creative thinking and planning on the part of program educators and directors, to use the space as efficiently as possible.

The outdoor curriculum should include materials and activities that are available indoors (e.g., easel painting, sand and water play, creative art). However, educators need to ensure that sedentary activities aren't so enticing to children, especially those who are less likely to choose active options, that they are drawn to these options to the exclusion of moderate or vigorous physical activity. The outdoor imaginative play of preschoolers and school-agers often involves moving moderately or vigorously, which is, of course, positive for all developmental areas. Pretending they are in medieval times with dragons and knights, modern super-heroes, firefighters, or fairies, or whatever other play themes they have, tends to involve running, jumping, flying, crouching down, and so on.

Children need a variety of play equipment, materials, and activities to develop the three components of physical fitness we have described (endurance, flexibility, and strength). It is quite possible to have a quality outdoor physical activity program without large, expensive equipment. Car tires, wide balance beams, scarves, ribbons, hoops, beanbags, balls, pylons, and other movable small equipment can be utilized for many spontaneous and adult-guided activities.

Table 6.3 outlines the benefits of physical activity for all areas of a child's development.

TABLE 6.3	**Benefits of Outdoor Play**
Physical	■ Increases energy and improves stamina ■ Encourages muscle growth and helps develop strong bones ■ Makes the heart and lungs stronger ■ Increases flexibility ■ Improves coordination ■ Helps improve sleeping habits ■ Helps improve eating habits ■ Helps maintain a healthy weight

Cognitive	■ Helps increase concentration, memory, creativity, and problem-solving skills/abilities and enhances learning
	■ Ratey (2008, p. 53) puts forward a compelling argument that exercise sparks new brain-cell growth. Aerobic exercise physically transforms our brains for peak performance. Exercise improves learning on three levels:
	  – It improves alertness, attention, and motivation.
	  – It prepares and encourages nerve cells to bind to one another.
	  – It then spurs the development of new nerve cells from stem cells in the hippocampus (part of the frontal temporal lobe, which plays a role in long-term memory and spatial navigation).

Emotional	■ Helps us feel good about ourselves ■ Presents opportunities to practise self-discipline ■ Develops positive lifelong attitudes toward physical activity ■ Reduces anxiety and depression and improves one's ability to deal with stress
Social	■ Provides opportunities to socialize and make friendships ■ Provides opportunities to cooperate with others and develop social problem-solving skills
Cultural	■ Encourages healthy family engagement ■ Provides opportunities to develop motor/sports skills and life skills ■ Provides opportunities to learn games and songs from various cultural backgrounds

Source: *Have a ball! A Toolkit for Physical Activity and the Early Years.* Published by Best Start Resource Center, © 2005. Reprinted with permission.

In addition to your outdoor play space, there may be regular opportunities to visit appropriate nearby facilities with the children, such as schools, recreation agencies with gyms, pools, skating rinks, and neighbourhood parks, when a facility isn't in use by others. Of course, these options must be evaluated for developmental appropriateness and safety before use.

Greening the Outdoor Environment

Greening the outdoor environment can offer more options to children of varying needs and abilities and provides green space that may be generally inaccessible to many children. Exploring nature is a joy that should be a right in childhood.

Greening the space brings in trees, shrubs, rocks, and logs to define a variety of places in which to run, climb, hide, and socialize. Natural movable materials such as sand, sticks, branches, leaves, and stones offer many opportunities for imaginative play and physical activity such as raking leaves or shovelling sand. Refer to Figure 6.1 for an example of a "green" outdoor playground design for preschoolers.

FIGURE 6.1	An Outdoor Design

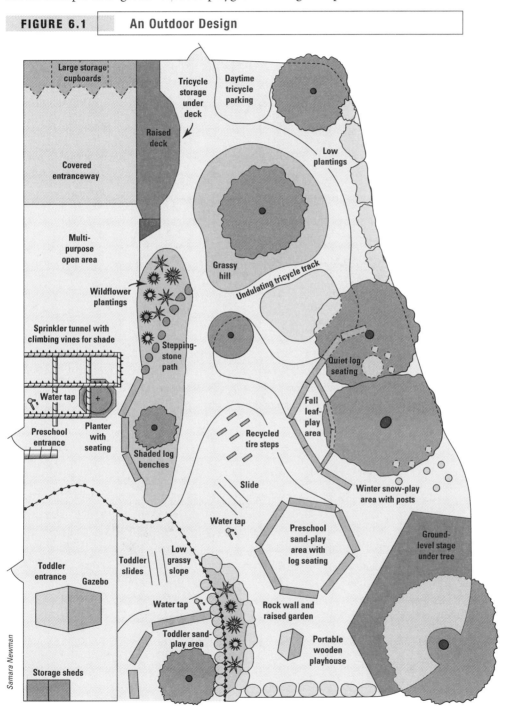

Illustration of the yard at Ryerson University Early Childhood Learning Centre by Samara Newman, based on an original Evergreen design by Adam Bienenstock and Heidi Campbell

A study for Evergreen Canada found that green school grounds can play a significant role in promoting physical activity, especially moderate and light levels of activity, by increasing the range of enjoyable, noncompetitive, open-ended forms of play. When asked to compare their school ground before and after greening, 71% of respondents (parents, teachers, principals) from 59 elementary schools in 5 provinces indicated that greening has resulted in more moderate and/or light physical activity:

> Through greening, school grounds diversify the play repertoire, creating opportunities for children of all ages, interests and abilities to jump, climb, dig, lift and generally get moving in ways that nurture all aspects of their health and development. These positive findings emerged consistently across the schools participating in the survey, despite the differences in size, student population and geographic location. (Bell & Dyment, 2006, p. 6)

This study found that children want outdoor spaces that are the following (Bell, 2007):

- places they can call their own (i.e., territoriality).
- well-defined places that include trees, rocks, walls, and nets.
- natural elements
- places to hide, slide, climb, and jump
- places that can be shaped (by body and mind)
- challenging
- places to socialize

These criteria can promote moderate activity, which also has health benefits and may appeal to children who are not drawn to vigorous activity. Evergreen has published *Small Wonders: Designing Vibrant Natural Landscapes for Early Childhood* to promote green spaces in early childhood program settings (see Resource Materials, page 348).

CRITICAL THINKING

In a suburban community, the green space is minimal, including none within the early childhood setting's playground. The playground is composed of manufactured surfaces throughout and stationary metal play equipment. The parents and educators are concerned about the time spent in cars or transit getting to the centre and that their children have little access to green space, both at the centre and in their home surroundings. What can be done to make this wish a reality? For each action, identify benefits, possible challenges or barriers, and possible solutions. Include one component of a green environment that you would like to add for each age group:

- infants and toddlers
- preschoolers
- school-agers

How does each component support moderate or vigorous physical activity? (see Evergreen in Resource Materials, page 348)

Supporting Physical Activity Nationally and Regionally

As we know, societal change contributes to health promotion for all. One example of federal government support to increase public awareness for parents is the reinstatement of funding to **ParticipACTION**, with an identified focus on children and youth. The original ParticipACTION was established in 1971, and for almost 30 years (until its closure in early 2001), it forged numerous successful campaigns to encourage active living for all Canadians. ParticipACTION was known in Canada and beyond for its effective utilization of media with clear, practical messages for everyone to be active. The inclusive nature of the messaging depicted young and old, ethnocultural diversity, large and thin, individuals and families, and persons with disabilities making physical activity part of their life. In late 2006, ParticipACTION received renewed commitment from the federal government's Sport Canada and Public Health Agency of Canada and was revitalized in February 2007. A benefit of ParticipACTION's current focus on parent awareness is the likelihood that today's parents grew up with ParticipACTION and are familiar with its messages.

The federal government introduced the Child Fitness Tax Credit starting in the 2007 tax year. In addition, the Canadian government allows a nonrefundable tax credit based on eligible fitness expenses paid by parents to register a child in an eligible program of physical activity. The Minister of National Revenue indicated that substantial additional support would be provided to children eligible for the disability tax credit to recognize the unique barriers they face in becoming more active. Another indication that our federal government is promoting physical activity is the reference to the need for increasing physical activity in the 2007 revised *Eating Well with Canada's Food Guide* (see Appendix 5.1, page 287).

Regional governments are trying to impact children's inactivity as well. Some jurisdictions have introduced mandatory daily physical activity in their elementary schools. Others, such as Newfoundland and Labrador, have made changes to secondary school requirements to ensure that all students take physical education courses. Much of the legislation around increasing physical activity and improving nutrition in the schools is being considered or will be in the near future. Where does your province or territory stand on this issue?

SUPPORTING HEALTHY EATING HABITS

OBJECTIVES

To identify the primary benefits of the NutriSTEP™ preschool nutrition screening tool.

As discussed in Unit 5, one of our priorities is to support children's nutritional needs and promote healthy eating both developmentally and culturally, with *Eating Well with Canada's Food Guide's* current recommendations at the forefront. It is also essential to ensure that each child has the autonomy to choose what and how much she or he eats among healthy options. Strict adult control over how much a child eats may be a factor in the development of weight issues in childhood or eating problems (Kerr, 2002). For this reason, among many others, the eating environment needs to be positive and noncoercive.

Unit 5 is devoted to children's nutrition needs, with information relevant to children's healthy growth and development. We focus our attention in this

To itemize the age-related daily recommendations for vegetables and fruit according to *Eating Well with Canada's Food Guide.*

To define trans fats, list examples, and describe Health Canada's position on reducing the availability of trans fats to Canadian consumers.

To explain the concerns about children's consumption of carbonated drinks (pop) and ways to promote healthier beverages.

To identify reasons why there may be concerns about children's under- or overeating and appropriate responses.

section to specific issues known to have a direct correlation with the prevention of childhood obesity or nutrition deficiencies.

"For preschoolers, nutrition risk runs the spectrum from under- to over-nutrition and occurs to those in poverty as well as those living in relative affluence. Systematic screening systems that identify these characteristics or risk factors before school entry may be an efficient means of identifying children who require services and preventive interventions" (Simpson, Keller, Rysdale, & Beyers, 2007, p. 2). NutriSTEP has recently been developed in Canada and was 10 years in the making, with the involvement of almost 2,000 preschoolers and their parents and more than 50 multisectoral partners.

NutriSTEP™, a community-based, parent-administered nutrition screening tool, includes 17 items, with most items focused on the aspects of nutrition risk for preschoolers: physical growth, food and fluid intake, physical activity, sedentary behaviour, and factors affecting food intake for the age group (food security, feeding environment). Responses range in score from 0 (no risk) to 4 (risk), and question responses are summed to provide an index whereby an increased score indicates increased nutrition risk. The tool, developed by two faculty members at the University of Guelph and a dietitian from the Sudbury and District Health Unit, has been gaining much recognition across Canada and beyond (Simpson et al., 2007, p. 3). *For example, it has the backing of the Ontario government and is being piloted in selected areas across Canada as part of immunization programs and preschool screening fairs.*

As the tool is self-administered by parents or caregivers and takes five minutes to complete, there is the potential for universal access. The authors of NutriSTEP™ are currently designing and evaluating models for its ethical implementation. It can potentially be used in doctor offices, public health clinics, child care centres, and schools to identify children who should be further assessed and treated by a dietitian before they have problems.

One of the NutriSTEP™ items was designed to determine parental control over feeding. Of the almost 300 parents who completed the questionnaire in their study, 37% reported that they often do not let their children decide how much to eat.

Also of great concern was the high proportion (33%) of preschool children whose sedentary activities, such as TV viewing, exceeded three hours a day. Excess sedentary activity, particularly in the form of TV viewing, presents the potential for nutritional risk, especially in young children (Veugelers & Fitzgerald, 2005). The prevalence of nutritional problems such as overweight and obesity in the 3- to 5-year-old age group is 21% in Canada (Shields, 2005).

One factor in the nutrition–obesity story may be the practice of exclusive breast-feeding in the first six months of life. A systematic review of 9 studies with over 69,000 participants concluded that breast-feeding has a small but consistent protective effect against childhood obesity (Arenz, Rückerl, Koletzo, & von Kries, 2004). This can be added to the many benefits of breast-feeding over formula feeding, as a reminder to educators to support and promote breast-feeding whenever and wherever appropriate.

As stated earlier, the WHO (2008) has cited worldwide transitions in nutrition patterns as a primary cause for the obesity epidemic. These relatively new patterns include such issues as increased food availability and variety through automated transportation, fast-food consumption, increased portion sizes, reduced frequency of family meals, increased consumption of pop and sports drinks, and restricted eating, resulting in meal skipping. This latter example speaks to the flip side of the obesity focus, the concern about an increase in healthy-weight children obsessing about weight and parents projecting fears about fat on their children (Kirkey, 2008). This is not an exhaustive list, but it speaks to the complex nature of food and eating patterns in the obesity epidemic. It is entirely possible for children to be taking in more calories than they need, especially when consuming a large volume of high-calorie, low-nutritive drinks, while being undernourished where essential nutrients are concerned.

Specific Nutrition Issues

The three nutrition issues we focus on here are the consumption of vegetables and fruit, reduction of trans fats and saturated fats, and concerns over carbonated beverages (pop) and other non- or low-nutritive drinks. Each of these issues has a direct correlation with concerns about childhood obesity and, more broadly, life-long health. *Eating Well with Canada's Food Guide* does not define foods as *good* or *bad*. Instead, the focus is on making wise and healthy food choices as much as possible. This theme is very important for educators to adopt in order to role model and support the positive aspects of healthy eating with the children and families with whom they come in contact.

Increase the Consumption of Vegetables and Fruit

The Canadian Community Health Survey (Shields, 2005) reported that children and adolescents who eat vegetables and fruit five or more times a day are substantially less likely to be overweight than are those whose vegetable and fruit consumption is less frequent.

One of the important aspects of the vegetable and fruit argument is that obesity has been linked repeatedly to consumption of low-cost foods. Refined grains and added sugars and fats tend to be less expensive, are good tasting to many children, and are convenient. The fact that low-nutritive foods tend to cost less than high-nutritive foods such as vegetables and fruit makes for a difficult ongoing scenario for families who are on a very limited budget (Drewnowski, 2007).

We all know that vegetables and fruit are rich in vitamins, minerals, and fibre, but they also offer **phytochemicals**, which are the compounds that give vegetables and fruit their colour. Scientists are still discovering specific phytochemicals and the roles they play, such as the antioxidant role that beta-carotene and flavonoids play in yellow and orange vegetables and some fruit, such as cantaloupe and mango (Dietitians of Canada, 2003). Phytochemicals help promote good health by working with the other nutrients occurring naturally in the fruit or vegetable. There are likely other aspects of plant foods that contribute to health. Ratey (2008, p. 239) states that small amounts of toxins in many vegetables and fruit that are meant to keep insects away also serve to trigger a beneficial stress response. Encourage eating a rainbow of colours daily for maximum benefits.

Eating Well with Canada's Food Guide recommends at least 4 vegetables and fruit a day for children from 2 to 3 years old, at least 5 for children 4 to 8 years old, and 6 for children 9 to 13 years old. The Vegetables and Fruit food group is the most prominent arc in the rainbow on *Eating Well with Canada's Food Guide*, emphasizing the important role these foods play in a healthy eating pattern (Health Canada, 2007a). Optimally, they are offered at all meals and snacks. This is a concern when we note that the NutriSTEP™ study found that more than half of the almost 300 preschoolers weren't getting enough grains and fruit and 45% weren't getting enough vegetables (Simpson et al., 2007). Advocating for a variety of daily vegetable and fruit servings in our early childhood program settings and finding ways to encourage child-friendly ways to offer these are important roles for educators and food service personnel involved in our programs. *Eating Well with Canada's Food Guide* recommends that people choose vegetables and fruit more often than juice to get more fibre. They can help people feel full and satisfied, which may help reduce the risk of obesity (Health Canada, 2007a). In the case of young children, of course, one caution is to balance their fibre needs with their need to take in enough calories. Young children need higher energy foods to sustain their energy levels, so a homemade cheese sauce with broccoli and a hummus dip with raw vegetables are ideal combinations.

Involve children as much as possible in the preparation of vegetables and fruit. Review Table 6.4 to answer this question: Are there vegetables and fruit that are not included in this table, especially ones that reflect the cultural food patterns of the families in your placement or early childhood setting? Try to find ways to incorporate new vegetables and fruit reflecting a range of colours. Find ways to promote vegetable and fruit eating at home.

Have a *Fave Family Vegetable* or *Fruit of the Week* (or month), with each family having a turn to share theirs. When children enjoy a variety of vegetables and fruit daily and learn more about their origin and different ways to serve them, this essential food group becomes integrated into their lifelong eating pattern, one important way to help prevent obesity.

Reduce Trans Fats and Promote Awareness of Saturated Fats

As discussed in Unit 5, it is common knowledge that the types and amount of fats we take in have a substantial impact on our long-term health. Health Canada's *It's Your Health: Trans Fat* (2007c) states that scientific evidence has shown that dietary trans fats and too much saturated fat can increase the risk of developing heart disease. In addition, there is concern, but no conclusive evidence to date, that trans fats are linked to some forms of cancer, among

		TABLE 6.4		Vegetables and Fruit Come in a Variety of Colours		

GREEN	RED	YELLOW/ORANGE	BLUE/PURPLE	WHITE/TAN/BROWN
avocados	cherries	apricots	blackberries	bananas
gooseberries	cranberries	cantaloupes	blackcurrants	pears
green apples	pink/red	lemons	blueberries	jicama
green grapes	grapefruit	mandarins	elderberries	white peaches
green pears	pomegranates	mangoes	figs	cauliflower
kiwis	raspberries	nectarines	plums	celeriac
limes	red apples	oranges	prunes	garlic
artichokes	red grapes	papayas	purple grapes	ginger
asparagus	watermelons	peaches	raisins	lychees
broccoli	beets	pineapples	eggplants	mushrooms
Brussels sprouts	radishes	carrots	purple	onions
celery	red cabbage	pumpkins	asparagus	parsnips
cucumbers	red onions	rutabagas	purple endive	plantain
green beans	red peppers	sweet potatoes	purple peppers	turnips
green cabbage	red tomatoes	yellow peppers	Saskatoon	white endive
green peppers	rhubarb	yellow squash	berries	
peas	strawberries	yellow tomatoes		
spinach				

other diseases. Health Canada recommends reducing these risks by choosing foods that contain little or no **trans fat** and by monitoring intake of **saturated fats**, which are found in coconut, palm, and palm kernel oils; animal fats; butter; cheese; and other full-fat dairy products. CAUTION: With regard to children, especially preschoolers, we must keep in mind that they need more fat and energy in their diet for brain development and rapid growth (Health Canada, 2007b). Foods such as eggs, lean meat, nut butters (if not allergic), milk, cheese, and other dairy or soy products that are not skim are beneficial for young children because they provide a concentrated source of calories. Children need to eat small amounts of food throughout the day, since their small stomachs tend to fill up quickly. Therefore, most young children do tend to take in more saturated fat until school age. Over time, the variations in the amount a child eats usually average out to provide the calories and nutrients needed. This is especially true if the child is encouraged to eat healthy foods when hungry and to stop eating when full (Health Canada, 2007b, p. 39).

Although of no concern and of potential benefit is the small amount of trans fats (conjugated linoleic acids) occurring naturally in some foods, such as dairy products, beef, and lamb, Canadians take in far greater amounts in processed foods made with partially hydrogenated oils, which produce trans fats. Trans fats form during a process called hydrogenation, when an oil is converted into a more stable liquid or semisolid form. These formulated trans fats raise our low-density lipoprotein (bad) cholesterol and reduce our high-density lipoprotein (good) cholesterol.

Trans fats benefit the food industry by producing the pleasing textures and flavours that make bakery products and other food products so tempting and add shelf life to food. With food being transported globally from large food-processing plants, a longer shelf life is a definite advantage, especially for foods such as bakery items. Many restaurants, including, but not exclusively, fast-food restaurants, use hydrogenated oils in their breaded seafood, chicken, and meats; French fries; and desserts. To date, up to 45% of the fat content in these foods may be trans fats (Health Canada, 2007c).

A Trans Fat Task Force, cochaired by Health Canada and the Heart & Stroke Foundation of Canada, was mandated in 2005 to provide guidance on how to reduce trans fat content in foods available in Canada. On June 20, 2007, Health Canada (2006),

- adopted the following recommendations of the Trans Fat Task Force with respect to the amount of trans fat in foods: limit the trans fat content of vegetable oils and soft, spreadable margarines to 2% of the total fat content and limit the trans fat content for all other foods to 5% of the total fat content, including ingredients sold to restaurants.

- called on the food industry to achieve these limits within two years, which is by June 2009.

- announced that if significant progress has not been made by this deadline, Health Canada will develop regulations to ensure that the recommended levels are met.

In doing so, companies and food manufacturers are encouraged to replace trans fats with healthier alternatives, such as monounsaturated and polyunsaturated fats, and not to replace trans fats with saturated fats. Now that food manufacturers and restaurants have become dependent on trans fats, it is challenging for them to find more healthy substitutes. Voluntary reduction or elimination of trans fats by the food industry has had some, but not total, success. To ensure that the industry is making progress in meeting the 2% and 5% limits of total fat, Health Canada closely monitors the actions of the industry via the Trans Fat Monitoring Program. By publishing the results, it will also inform Canadian consumers of the progress that is being made.

Canada was the first country to identify trans fats on nutrition labels of food products sold in Canada (discussed in Unit 5) and the first country to publish this type of monitoring data. Visit Health Canada's website (see Resource Materials, page 348). Rather than leaving all choices to the individual responsibility of Canadians, legislating standards to promote the health of all Canadians demonstrates a more socially responsible approach to trans fats. They are known to be unhealthy for all; ensuring that they are monitored is in everyone's best interest.

Reduce the Consumption of Carbonated and Other Low-Nutritive Beverages

The regular consumption of **carbonated drinks**, often called soft drinks or pop, is counterproductive to the nutrient needs of growing children. In addition to numerous health concerns in the early years, habitual consumption can have lifelong harmful effects (Jacobson, 2005). This reality underscores the importance of preventing children's daily intake of carbonated and other low-nutritive drinks at an early age; it is much more difficult to change unhealthy habits than to form healthy ones. This message is really the essence of healthy active living.

Do you know how much sugar is in the standard can of pop or the larger sized containers? Pop is the number one source of added sugar in the diet of many children and adults, and it is just empty calories. If you drank one can of nondiet pop a day for a year, you would consume almost 15 kg of added sugar. All of that would be empty calories, which in children replace the essential nutrients that they need for growth and development.

With regard to increased rates of childhood obesity, Plourde (2006, p. 323) states the following:

> Children began consuming more carbohydrates as a result of the recommendation to decrease dietary fat. Children increased their intake of simple sugars, mainly in the form of soft drinks, soda, and fruit drinks. Soft-drink consumption tripled between 1977–1978 and 1994 and now contributes to about 8% of adolescents' total energy intake.

One reason these beverages are so popular is that people like their taste. However, the power of advertising, universal availability, low price, and use of a mildly addictive ingredient (caffeine) have contributed to making pop a routine snack and part of meals instead of the occasional treat they were considered decades ago. Also, many of today's parents grew up drinking pop and may see it as normal to drink pop throughout the day (Jacobson, 2005, p. 35). Currently, there are a myriad of other beverages in addition to pop, such as sports drinks, energy drinks, and drinks touting a small percentage of real fruit juice. For a select few athletes or in specific circumstances, these products are warranted. For the vast majority of adults and children, they can be a negative factor to optimal health:

- Pop is a leading contributor to poor oral health. High acidity (phosphoric acid) causes tooth decay (even from sugar-free drinks), and drinks with sugar (high-fructose corn syrup) make the impact even more severe (Burry, 1999, p. 164). The acid in regular or diet pop starts to dissolve tooth enamel in only 20 minutes. For this and other reasons (e.g., new concerns about metabolic syndrome), diet pop is not a better alternative unless necessary, such as for individuals with diabetes.

- Much of the pop is high in caffeine, with a can of pop typically containing 40 to 45 mg of caffeine, leading to mild addictions over time. This often results in increased caffeine-containing beverage habits in the teen years, with further reduced milk intake. In other words, heavy consumption of pop and other nutrient-poor beverages pushes numerous minerals, vitamins, and dietary fibre out of the diet (Jacobson, 2005). In the example of reduced milk intake, calcium needs are very high in childhood and adolescence, building bone density before adulthood, when bone mass begins to deteriorate. Excessive intake of carbonated beverages can impact bone health. Children and youth often replace calcium-rich beverages such as milk with pop, affecting bone mass and increasing the risk of future osteoporosis (Minnesota Department of Health, 2005, p. 1). A Saskatchewan study of bone mass in adolescents (Whiting et al., 2004) found that replacing milk by pop appears to be detrimental to bone gain by girls but not boys. The gender difference may be due to the fact that girls are consuming less than their requirement for calcium, whereas boys are above their threshold, even with the pop intake. Specific dietary and nutrient recommendations for adolescents are needed to ensure optimal bone growth and consolidation during this important life stage to prevent bone fractures and early osteoporosis. Replacing milk with pop also means that children may be losing out on much-needed vitamins A and D and riboflavin.

You may wonder why this issue is discussed in this textbook when it is very unlikely that your placement or future workplace will be serving pop to the children. However, there are a number of possible ways this issue may be relevant to your work:

- when an early childhood setting does not provide food, then the children bring their lunches from home, which can include pop and other popular low-nutritive drinks that are packaged in convenient juice box containers

- nutrition policies that must include food brought into the setting for celebrations and fundraising

- your role modelling of beverage choices

- material posted on the bulletin boards and other venues for sharing information with families

- advocacy

In recent years, school boards and municipal and provincial governments in Canada have begun to put policies and recommendations in place to reduce or eliminate the availability of carbonated drinks and junk foods in elementary and some high schools. Some facts on the Ontario Ministry of Education (2004) include the following:

- Serving sizes of pop have increased by 300% since the 1950s.
- Approximately 27% of boys and 23% of girls in grades 6 to 8 consume candy and chocolate bars daily.
- Milk consumption is almost 30% lower in schools that also sell pop.
- By the time children reach the "tween" years (9 to 12), many have lifestyle habits that could put them in the fast lane for developing cardiovascular disease as early as their 30s.

The Dietitians of Canada has supported many jurisdictions in their transitions toward healthier policies and practices in schools across Canada. Several ministries of education made province-wide changes to policies, and other provinces made recommendations and guidelines for improved policy and practice in nutrition.

Healthy Child Manitoba's (2006) *Manitoba School Nutrition Handbook* offers suggestions for schools to develop polices and practices and on how to handle challenges that may arise. The premise is that healthy choices need to be available and promoted in the schools. Policy suggestions for schools in Manitoba include the following:

- There should be a focus on nutritional foods during classroom and school functions.
- Fundraising in the school is not to rely on the sale of non-nutritious foods.
- Milk, fruit juice, and water should be offered for sale to students and staff.
- Pop is not to be sold to students.
- School community members are encouraged to bring only food belonging to one or more of the four food groups of *Eating Well with Canada's Food Guide* for class parties, recess snacks, and lunches.

Source: *Manitoba School Nutrition Handbook: Getting Started with Guidelines and Policies.* Permission to reproduce is provided by the Queen's Printer for Manitoba. The Queen's Printer does not warrant the accuracy or currency of the reproduction information.

- School groups are encouraged to offer healthy lunch choices on special lunch days.
- Schools promote active living choices throughout the school year.

Healthy nutrition policies for early childhood program settings are discussed in Unit 5. These policies need to be the cornerstone for moving forward in developing best practices for children's healthy eating and drinking. Healthy drinks for children focus on milk products (whether cow based or soy), tap water, and the occasional 100% fruit juice. There is no place in a child's diet for routine consumption of pop or nutrition-void noncarbonated drinks, which, unfortunately, are so readily available in grocery stores, convenience stores, restaurants, and fast-food eateries. It is hoped that if consumers stop purchasing these beverages, their production and availability will be curtailed, benefiting us all.

CRITICAL THINKING

The children are used to drinking a lot of fruit juice both at home and in the early childhood program. As the director of a centre with preschoolers and school-agers who bring in their own foods and beverages from home, you are concerned about the high-sugar, low-nutritive beverages most children bring in, including fruit drinks, sports drinks, and pop. You want to promote more drinking of milk and water, as well as children eating more fruit rather than fruit drinks, which have added sugar and colours. What are some specific ways that you can support this vision with the children, parents, and staff? Consider challenges you may face with each of your suggestions and how you will meet each challenge.

Proof that consumer and government pressure can have an impact was evident when Refreshments Canada decided to pull all carbonated drinks out of vending machines (as of September 2004) in elementary and junior high schools. Several provinces and many school boards have gone beyond that beginning step to eliminate junk foods altogether from their schools. Where does your province or territory or local school board stand on this issue?

Concern about Amounts of Food Eaten

All children and adults fluctuate in the amount of food they eat, for any number of reasons: growth spurts, illness, fatigue, hot weather, time of day, or food preferences. Educators first determine whether the child's eating pattern is one that their program can easily accommodate or whether it is a legitimate reason for concern. To determine this, educators examine two issues:

- their own personal perceptions and preconceived definitions of how much a child of that age should eat and at what times of the day

- the child's body build—in other words, whether she or he is growing within the normal range of growth and development

Let's look at three reasons why children may be temporarily eating a lot of food. When the child is growing within the normal range, there isn't cause for alarm, for the following reasons:

1. Perhaps the child is going through a growth spurt.

   During a growth spurt, the child's body requires extra nutrients and calories (or energy) for a limited time (a few weeks or a month or two). Interestingly, growth spurts often occur in the spring and may also follow a period of illness (e.g., in a child with asthma who had a difficult time during the winter). Understanding growth and development and getting to know children assist educators in expecting growth spurts.

2. Perhaps the child enjoys eating more at a particular time of day.

   One child, like a lot of adults, is a slow starter in the morning and isn't ready to eat much of a breakfast before leaving home. By mid-morning, she is ready to eat more than one serving of the snack. Another child is too busy playing to leave the activity to eat a morning snack, but by lunch time, he is ravenous. Remember, *Eating Well with Canada's Food Guide* suggests that we avoid looking at food intake on a meal-by-meal basis and instead look at overall intake in a 24-hour period (Health Canada, 2007a). Early childhood programs that have incorporated some flexibility into the nutrition program can accommodate children's body rhythms. At the same time, we recognize that eating regularly during the day helps children maintain their energy level.

3. Perhaps the child does not have access to a lot of food at home.

   The family's budget does not stretch far enough to buy a consistent amount of food throughout the month. As a result, the child comes to the program hungry many days, or even every day. Programs need to have enough food available to provide extras and second helpings for hungry children. Educators' concern for the child and family does not end on Friday afternoon but extends to weekends and their access to enough nutritious food. Some programs work with food banks to supplement the food supply for families who live with food insecurity.

Therefore, daily observation of children and communication with parents are important in meeting children's nutritional needs and in determining their eating habits at home. *For example, parent tells you that the child eats a large breakfast at home, which explains why he usually does not eat a mid-morning snack or a full lunch. Although, because of their energy levels, most children are more interested in food in the morning or at lunch, every child's body rhythm and metabolism are unique.*

Early childhood programs with children who have recently arrived in Canada should ensure that the menus reflect the types of food eaten at home. The nutrition program should include some foods that are familiar to every child in the program. You can achieve this by asking parents for their favourite recipes. This is also one way that children learn about one another's ethnoculture. When you offer children familiar foods, they feel secure and relaxed and enjoy eating. New children are often shy and reserved around snack and mealtimes and need educators' extra support. *For example, three-year-old boy, who was new to the program and Canada, won't eat at all during the day. The parents and educators are concerned about his well-being. The mother explains to the educator that her son does not like to eat around people he doesn't know. They decide together that she will bring food from home and an educator with whom he is comfortable will sit with him at lunch separated from the rest of the group by a partition. They find that he is more relaxed and enjoys the one-to-one interaction and the familiar food. After a week of this arrangement, the educator and the boy move into the room with the rest of the group but sit at a separate table away from the rest of the children. The child observes the other children, who are more familiar to him now. They begin offering him food that is prepared at the program, which he begins to try. After this week of transition, the child feels much more relaxed, and by the third week, he joins his peers. He is soon eating only the program's food.*

Concern about Body Weight

We all have to be conscious of our society's notion of "ideal" body image and the role that we may play in perpetuating these stereotypes. Nevertheless, some children and adults are either below or above the average range of body mass by age, gender, and height. Physical or emotional concerns may be associated with being over- or underweight.

For children who eat large amounts of food, the best time to determine whether an imbalance exists between food energy and the body's demand for energy is when the child is gaining so much weight as to become overweight. If, however, the child is losing weight and is not growing in height, there may be concern about being underweight.

Because children grow at different rates at different times, it is not always easy to tell if a child is overweight. If parents think their child is overweight, encourage them to talk to their health care provider, who will measure the child's height and weight and let them know if he or she is in a healthy range. Children's growth patterns differ, and other factors may be involved, so it is best to get a health professional's assessment.

Educators' daily observations of children's eating patterns assist in identifying the contributing factors.

A CHILD WHO IS OVEREATING MAY	A CHILD WHO IS UNDEREATING MAY
■ eat more than the recommended daily servings of any of the four food groups, but in particular the milk products and meat and alternatives.	■ eat less than the recommended daily servings of any of the four food groups, but in particular the milk products and meat and alternatives, which results in an insufficient fat intake.
■ choose foods that are high in fat, sugar, or both (i.e., foods outside of the four groups) over nutritious foods.	■ choose not to eat enough food for fear of being overweight.

- not participate in physical activity.
- eat because of emotions (e.g., boredom).

- have a level of physical activity high enough that more food energy is used than is obtained by eating.
- not be active, but being more active will increase the child's appetite.
- not eat because of emotions (e.g., stress or sadness).

When educators determine that there is reason to be concerned, the next step is to meet with the child's parents. Obviously, consistency between home and the program is beneficial. Some parents may not share the educators' concern for the child; others may need nutrition education and information to enable them to support their child. Parents should be encouraged to consult with the child's health care provider, and perhaps the child and the parents would benefit from consulting with a dietitian. To ensure that the physician's or dietitian's recommendations are carried out consistently between home and the program, daily communication between parents and educators is essential.

EDUCATORS AND PARENTS CAN ADDRESS THE FOLLOWING REASONS WHY CHILDREN MIGHT BE	
OVEREATING	UNDEREATING
- poor eating habits (e.g., consistently choosing high-fat foods) - insufficient physical activity for the amount of food eaten - watching TV while eating (not being mindful of food ingested) - eating for the wrong reasons, such as emotional reasons - adults in their lives who model overeating - stress at home, the early childhood program, or school that may contribute to poor eating habits - a physiological or psychological reason for weight gain (a physician would need to diagnose such a medical or emotional condition)	- poor eating habits (e.g., drinking too much milk or juice, leaving no room for food) - fatigue - limited variety of foods they will eat - stress at home, the early childhood program, or school that may contribute to poor eating patterns - adults in their lives who model excessive dieting or negative stereotypes about larger body types - security felt only with family and the foods served at home - a physiological or psychological reason for the weight loss (a physician would need to diagnose such a medical or emotional condition—for example, anorexia)

The most important point to remember in approaching overeating and children is that dieting is never an option. Dieting (restricting food) produces a vicious circle of unhealthy eating patterns. It is dangerous enough when adults begin this dieting cycle, but much worse when children begin to diet. Considering children's great needs for growth, dieting robs them of their potential by

- not providing their body with the daily nutrient requirements;

- contributing to a lowered basal metabolic rate, and when the body is not getting the energy it needs, it slows to function on fewer calories than it needs; and

- making them feel deprived and singled out if the other children are not subject to dietary restrictions.

Depending on the circumstances, some programs that provide lunch may decide to limit the number of helpings to one or two (for example) from the meat and alternatives and/or milk and alternatives food groups. If they do so, it is important that children who are still hungry have access to further helpings from the vegetables and fruit and grain products food groups. When this limit applies to all the children, it is acceptable. However, care must be taken to ensure that individual children are not singled out by limiting their servings while other children are given extra helpings. Exceptions to this, of course, relate to allergies, food sensitivity, and religious or cultural dietary requirements. Having raw vegetable and dip appetizers may benefit all children by ensuring that when hungry, they are taking in at least one or two servings of vegetables, contributing to the recommended five servings a day.

Self-esteem is of great importance to children and adults, and dieting does not contribute to self-esteem, especially when more than 95% of individuals who diet and lose weight eventually regain the weight. In a word, dieting is inappropriate! Rather than consider weight loss, it is more effective to focus on decreasing the child's rate of weight gain. We help children develop a positive and balanced outlook toward healthy eating and physical activity through increased awareness of foods and nutrition, by focusing on enjoyable daily physical activity, and by modelling healthy behaviour, such as being active in the playground and eating well.

IMPACT OF SCREEN TIME ON HEALTHY ACTIVE LIVING

The majority of published materials related to healthy active living for children make reference to the significant negative impact of **screen time**: TV (and DVD/video), video games, and computers, including the Internet. Increasing children's physically active time and decreasing screen viewing from a young age may be advantageous ways to reduce the early onset of inactivity and obesity (Tucker et al., 2006).

Plourde (2006) reported a study of 700 children (aged 10 to 15 years) that followed their TV viewing habits for 4 years. The children who watched more than five hours a day of TV were five times as likely to be overweight as those watching less than two hours a day. Having a TV in the bedroom is a strong predictor of being overweight, even among preschool-age children (Dennisson, Erb, & Jenkins, 2002). A randomized controlled trial showed that reducing the screen time of school-age children, even without promoting more active behaviour, resulted in significantly lower increases in their BMI scores at the one-year follow up, compared with a control group (Robinson, 1999). Extended time at a TV can affect postural development and at a computer can contribute to wrist or carpal damage. Both of these can put a child at risk for early musculoskeletal problems.

One of the concerns about screen time is the almost inevitable increase in the duration of time children spend sitting at a screen as they get older. If a two-year-old is watching two or more hours of TV, you can probably predict that the daily screen time will increase substantially as the child starts to use the computer and play video games. A major marketing theme behind interactive video gaming is that children are moving, so it's an ideal way to pair physical activity with technology. Despite this claim, these products do not replace daily physical activity. Further

studies on these products are necessary to examine how they relate to physical activity. Of course, some movement during screen time is better than none, but there is a possibility that children will spend more of their time indoors in front of a screen rather than have access to the many additional benefits of playing outdoors, reconnecting with nature, or being part of a team sport.

As children get older, they are sitting at their computer, socially connecting with their peers through messaging networks. In addition to the concern about the duration of daily time spent on this activity, it has also been shown that, rather than connecting children and youth, these networks, in fact, contribute to isolation and can play a role in depression. Active Healthy Kids Canada reports

- that increased time spent on chatting, e-mailing, and surfing the Internet not only reduces physical activity levels but is also a significant risk factor for anxiety, depression, a low sense of belonging, and low self-esteem (2008 pp. 10–11) and
- similar risk factors for excessive TV viewing (2007, p. 10).

And, of course, the dangers of potential access to violent and pornographic material on both TV and the Internet, as well as the luring of children and youth by pedophiles or other dangerous online predators, adds another dimension of complexity (see Unit 8: Preventing Child Maltreatment).

The Canadian Paediatric Society's (2003) "Impact of Media Use on Children and Youth" position statement acknowledges the beneficial effects of media on children, particularly children's programs that have messages about positive values such as accepting diversity and cooperating with others. Visual tools on quality preschool programs support prereading and numeracy skills, and other developmentally appropriate programs bring children to destinations such as museums, zoos, and geographic locations around the world that may give them a taste of a world beyond their own. TV and computers are an essential component of the new literacy, and the role of parents and educators in supporting children to become fluent in this literacy cannot be understated. From an early age, and at developmentally appropriate levels, parents need to help children manoeuvre their way through the media. This requires active involvement on the part of adults in their screen time. Parents and educators who are not computer or Internet savvy are often amazed at how quickly some children go beyond their own computer skills. They need to continue to find ways to stay involved and connected to what the child or youth has access to. Simply activating the parental controls on computers and TVs does not replace watching TV with children and discussing it with them or finding out about the computer programs or video games they are playing (see Media Awareness Network in Resource Materials, page 348).

The Canadian Paediatric Society (2003, p. 302) notes concerns about media advertising:

> The developmental stage of a child plays a role in the effect of commercials. Young children do not understand the concept of a sales pitch. They tend to believe what they are told and may even assume that they are deprived if they do not have advertised products. Most preschool children do not understand the difference between a program designed to entertain and a commercial designed to sell. A number of studies have documented that children under the age of eight years are developmentally unable to understand the difference between advertising and regular programming.

Source: Canadian Paediatric Society, *Paediatrics & Child Health* 8(5). (Ottawa: Canadian Paediatric Society, 2003), 302. Reprinted with permission.

The Canadian Paediatric Society's (2003) position statement includes concerns about Canadian children having excessive screen time, including the following:

- the increased incidence of obesity, effects on postural development, undeveloped social skills, and a tendency toward a form of addictive behaviour.
- a substantial number of children are watching TV at an earlier age and in greater amounts than what experts recommend.

This reduces children's time for vital activities such as playing, reading, learning to talk, spending time with peers and family, storytelling, participating in regular exercise, and developing other necessary physical, mental, and social skills. The American Academy of Pediatrics (2001) recommends no TV viewing for children younger than two years. Instead, encourage these young children to engage in more interactive activities that will promote optimal brain development, such as talking, playing, singing, and reading. For preschool and school-age children, the following points should be considered:

- Because TV takes time away from play and exercise activities, children who watch a lot of TV are less physically fit and more likely to eat high-fat and high-energy snack foods. TV viewing makes a substantial contribution to obesity because prime-time commercials promote unhealthy dietary practices.

- Studies show that parents play an important role in their children's social learning, but if a parent's views are not discussed explicitly with children, the medium may teach and influence by default. Commercials tend to promote unhealthy dietary practices.

- Eating meals while watching TV may lead to less meaningful communication and poorer eating habits.

Source: Canadian Paediatric Society, *Paediatrics & Child Health* 8(5). (Ottawa: Canadian Paediatric Society, 2003). Reprinted with permission.

The highlights of the Canadian Paediatric Society's (2003, p. 305) recommendations to parents are as follows:

- Families should be encouraged to explore media together and discuss their educational value. Children should be encouraged to criticize and analyze what they see in the media. Parents can help children differentiate between fantasy and reality, particularly when it comes to sex, violence and advertising.

- No child should be allowed to have a television, computer or video game equipment in his or her bedroom. A central location is strongly advised.

- Watching should be limited to less than 1 to 2 hours per day. Families may want to consider more active and creative ways to spend time together.

- Older children should be offered an opportunity to make choices by planning the week's viewing schedule in advance. Ideally, parents should supervise these choices and be good role models by making their own wise choices.

- Families should limit the use of television, computers or video games as a diversion, substitute teacher or electronic nanny. Parents should also ask alternative caregivers to maintain the same rules for media use in their absence. The rules in divorced parents' households should be consistent.

The Role of Educators Regarding Screen Time

Early childhood programs need to bring awareness of this issue to their policies and practices to promote the optimal health and development of children. In day-to-day routines, computers and TVs should play a minor role in the curriculum, particularly for children under five years of age. Children under two should not be exposed to TV or computers in the program. The following are some suggestions to consider:

- When computer use is one of the activity options in the playroom, time should be limited, and, of course, adults should be involved when possible.

- Educators should observe which children consistently choose computer time and encourage more physically active activity at other times during the day. When a child continues to choose sedentary activities when opportunities for moving are available, educators should try to involve the child in adult-guided movement activities whenever possible (see Table 6.2, page 309).

- Avoid programming movies and TV watching into the weekly schedule. *For example, when there is a movie every Friday afternoon, the message educators are sending to parents is that sitting in front of a screen for an extended time must be good practice if the educators highlight it every week in their program. Couple this with the reality that many children, after having sat for an extended period, will then be in a car, bus, or stroller for the ride home, followed by more inactivity while the supper is being prepared. Some children even have access to DVD movies on the ride home, as they are now available for use in cars.*

- When your early childhood program includes a movie or TV program, which you feel is particularly appropriate and relevant to the children's current interests, avoid having the room in darkness as this gives the impression that it is the only option for children. Instead,

  - set the movie or TV program up in an area where children who are interested can watch, whereas others can come in and out as they desire.

  - other quiet activities should be available nearby that would not disrupt the movie watchers.

  - when it is a full-length movie, let children know at the beginning that you will be stopping it once or twice so they can stretch their bodies and move around. You could plan adult-guided stretching and other movements that fit into the theme of the movie (e.g., move like the animals in the movie).

- Find ways to support families in their endeavours to balance their busy lives with their children's reasonable use of TV, computers, and video games:

  - Refer parents (who read English or French) to the most recent *Canada's Report* Card on Physical Activity for Children and Youth or to the Canadian Paediatric Society's website to read their position statement on the effects of media on children (see Resource Materials, page 348).

  - A bulletin board or pamphlet sent home regarding the effects of media on children, including the early childhood setting's policy and practices, may be another good way to bring attention to this issue.

  - After awareness is established, provide an opportunity for discussion (in whatever format the program prefers) to hear parents' views. *For example, some parents may believe that a heavy dose of computers and TV gives their children a head start on computer literacy. If they are aware that physical activity contributes to brain development and learning, perhaps parents will recognize that children will learn the computer skills they need at a developmentally appropriate time (see Benefits of Physical Activity, page 304). Other parents would like their children to spend less time in front of a TV or computer but have not found other ways to get dinner made or their office work done without its use.*

- Be responsive to the needs of families by coming up with concrete strategies that they can try at home. Although outdoor activities are ideal, they may not suit their immediate situation. Find and share simple ideas that are more likely to fit their needs. For example, while making dinner, parents could put on a music CD that the toddler or preschooler can move to and have a box in the kitchen with scarves, hats, spoons, or other objects to make music or play with. Families can create a simple game with recycled paper crumpled into a ball with a wastepaper basket target, or "skate" with a piece of recycled paper under each shoe. Masking tape on the floor or carpet might encourage the child to pretend to walk on a circus tightrope or balance beam. Easy physical activity suggestions to send home to parents at different times of the year increase the likelihood that they'll try them out. Seasonal ideas encourage families to do things together outdoors. Perhaps an active game with a catchy song that the children enjoy in your program is a good one to send home in a newsletter.

- Invite parents to share their ideas with the educators and with other parents. Perhaps families may want to plan an informal kite-flying day or a hike on a weekend.

- Screen time is not taboo for children over two years old, and perhaps in encouraging parents to keep the one- to two-hour maximum recommendation daily in mind, they can come up with the most appropriate times of the day. Some children really do need downtime as soon as they get home, and if an hour or less of quality children's programming is available, this may be the best time of day to turn on the TV. The important component is balance rather than unlimited and unsupervised screen time.

CRITICAL THINKING

What are the positives and negatives of screen time in an early childhood program? Write a policy on and practices for the use of TV and computers in your preschool program with three- to five-year-olds. Who would you involve in this process and how?

REVISITING THE HEALTH PROMOTION ACTION PLAN

Recall the Health Promotion Action Plan introduced in Unit 1. The following two examples illustrate this plan in practice in terms of promoting healthy active lifestyles.

Example 1

Supporting children in Canada on the right track to healthy active living involves several recommendations for parents and educators. There are responsibilities at all levels of the health promotion plan to move this critical agenda ahead. Certainly, community action and societal change are instrumental in making healthy options an easier choice for children and families.

Individual Problem Solving and Self-Reliance

Supporting children on the right track to healthy active living involves several recommendations for parents and educators. There are responsibilities at all levels of the health promotion plan to move this critical agenda ahead. Let's begin with a summary of recommendations for young children that we can promote as individuals and collective self-help to promote children's healthy active lifestyles.

Physical Activity   Spend at least an hour a day being physically active. This can be in short bouts, especially with preschoolers. At least some of that time should be outdoors (year round) whenever possible. Six- to nine-year-olds should be moderately active for one hour and vigorously active for half an hour daily.

Eating Habits   Eat at least five fruit and vegetables a day (four for children two to three years old). Avoid pop as much as possible. Instead, drink or eat at least two dairy foods a day, as well as water throughout the day when thirsty, and limit fruit juice to one serving daily (have the fruit instead!). Try to keep fast-food and restaurant meals to "once-in-a-while" instead of regularly. Be aware of portion sizes according to *Eating Well with Canada's Food Guide*, as fast-food outlets and restaurants serve much larger portions than recommended. Avoid low-nutritive snack foods (e.g., chips, candy, most processed cookies and cakes) whenever possible. Many of these contain trans or saturated fats. Read the Nutrition Facts table on packaged foods and help children become aware of these in developmentally appropriate ways. Support children's healthy eating habits by respecting their decision when they state they are hungry or full at meals and snack times. Pressuring children about their eating does not contribute to long-term physical or mental health.

Screen Time   Curtail screen time, which includes TV, computers, and video games. Age-related suggestions include the following:

- no or very little screen time for children under two
- an hour or less of screen time (most days) for children 2 to 5 years
- less than 2 hours for children 6 to 10 years
- avoiding eating in front of the TV

Children may not notice they are full when watching TV. Keep in mind that food advertisements do not normally promote healthy foods.

Collective Self-Help

Collective self-help, supporting each other through policy, sharing ideas, and trying to be consistent with healthy active living messages and practices for the children makes for an even stronger likelihood that children will develop healthy habits. *For example, educators and the preschoolers' parents share physical activity ideas that are easy to incorporate, ways to introduce fruit and vegetables or healthy food experiences that the children enjoy, and any new information about changes in legislation that support health (e.g., regarding trans fats, label reading, marketing to children via TV). Another way to role model healthy active living as parents and educators could be to ensure that all of the program's fundraisers walk the talk. A weekend hike, bowl-a-thon, or other enjoyable activity could be turned into a fundraiser by having sponsors donate to your cause. Selling fruit, herbs, or other healthy fare rather than chocolate bars is another possible fundraiser that gives a consistent message. This is not to take away from the reality that the occasional sweet treat is a normal part of life, but to make a concerted effort to promote healthy options as positive role models.*

Another impetus for collective self-help in supporting healthy active living is the "walking school bus." This idea involves creating a support system whereby families who live near each other can arrange to have one or two adults walk the children to and from the early childhood setting if it is within walking distance. Of course, infants and toddlers would be in strollers, and preschoolers would only be able to walk a short distance, but they are developing this important habit.

Community Action

Community is a network of support systems. Building healthy communities lowers costs to government through reducing the need for health and social services. To this end, making physical activity and healthy eating easier options in our communities is a worthwhile endeavour that requires input from community members and decision makers. *For example, when concerned groups in a community approach municipal governments to support change, a new direction in policy and practices is possible. Vancouver's city council approved the Vancouver EcoDensity Initiative in 2006, which supports the greening of Vancouver's communities in multidimensional ways. EcoDensity involves finding ways to help people locate near work and, if that's not possible, putting housing near public transit (see Resource Materials, page 348). The urban landscape is changing thanks to the impetus of concerned citizens and policymakers. Active transportation is one of the important aspects of this initiative. Vancouver is creating density in the city to generate more opportunities for walking and cycling. Widened sidewalks, street trees, places to sit, and awnings on city buildings are making walking more attractive than driving. Also, the fastest growing mode of transportation in Vancouver is bicycling, thanks to continued exploration to make the city bicycle friendly. People who live in suburbs where urban sprawl has created car-dependent communities can work together to effect change. Urban planners are instrumental in creating or changing communities to be more conducive to safe and enjoyable walking and bicycling. Where it is possible to walk to their child care centre, school, work, stores, parks, and restaurants, the need to drive is significantly decreased. This has benefits for individual and environmental health.*

An aspect of an ecodensity strategy that supports healthy eating is the opportunity to buy fresh produce from local farmers' markets, such as the 100-Mile Diet, an idea that started in Vancouver, British Columbia, in 2005 and has set off a worldwide movement. The premise is to only eat foods that have been grown within 100 miles from home. The notion of buying locally is a strategy to reduce the use of motorized transportation in food production, as well as to have fresher produce in season for community members. These are just a few of the changes that can have a positive effect on healthy active living for families in communities.

Parents are concerned about advertising targeted to children and have noted that products deliberately marketed to children are low-nutritive, high-fat and -sugar foods and beverages and games and toys that increase sedentary activity. The directors and staff in the early childhood community can

- plan a "Buy Nothing Day" or" Logo-Free Day" (see Media Awareness Network in Resource Materials, page 348) and
- contact their local media and ask them to cover the day's event to promote awareness of this issue.

This example illustrates community action to reduce commercialization in the centre and the community.

Societal Change

Is societal change possible to improve healthy active living? Public policy has certainly made an impact on creating smoke-free environments; beyond public places, some jurisdictions are even passing laws to protect children's rights to a smoke-free environment by prohibiting smoking in cars when children are passengers. Recycling is another example of societal change; in this endeavour, children led the way. As with these and the many other examples of societal change, public policy is required across a range of sectors to adequately address the problems of inactivity and poor eating habits. Legislation at the federal and provincial and territorial levels is needed to ensure that changes at the local level are supported and maintained. *For example, the relatively recent push by a number of provincial governments to ban junk foods in schools and require daily physical activity is a clear message that the provinces recognize that change is necessary to support children's health. The federal government's legislation to reduce the use of trans fats in the food industry also has an impact that contributes to healthier eating for all Canadians.*

A more comprehensive approach is the **Integrated Pan-Canadian Healthy Living Strategy** (Secretariat for the Intersectoral Healthy Living Network et al., 2005), which was approved by the federal, provincial, and territorial ministers of health in 2005. The strategy provides a national framework, calling for a coordinated effort of parents, families, professionals, governments, nongovernmental organizations, and the private sector to address the overweight/obesity crisis. "The goals of the Strategy are to improve overall health outcomes and to reduce health disparities. Grounded in a population health approach, the initial emphasis is on healthy eating, physical activity, and their relationship to healthy weights" (Secretariat for the Intersectoral Healthy Living Network et al., 2005) (see Public Health Agency of Canada in Resource Materials, page 348).

Example 2

The children and their families who attend a community centre after-school program are frustrated because safety issues in their playground meant their equipment was removed. To top it off, the municipally funded recreation programs, such as tai chi, basketball, and swimming, that the educators took the children to each week instituted user fees as a cost-cutting strategy. At the same time, the municipal medical officer of health was dismayed to learn from a recent Health Canada survey that the citizens in her city were found to be the least physically active in the province. This prompted her to declare physical activity a priority public health issue for the city, with a strategic plan to improve population fitness levels.

The children, parents, and staff talked about their frustration at the mixed messages and barriers in their way but decided to make their own call to action. Following two group discussions in which the school-agers participated actively and competently, their action plan was outlined as follows.

Individual Problem Solving and Self-Reliance

The children identified after-school computer use as one of their most powerful distractions from active play and agreed as a group on a system to limit each child's weekly computer use to no more than two hours.

Educators evaluated how they are incorporating the three types of physical activity (i.e., endurance, flexibility, and strength) into the daily program. Weaker areas of programming (e.g., flexibility) are now receiving attention (e.g., a grandparent is running tai chi classes for interested children and adults). Educators ensure, with the children's input, that every program includes play, creative expression, and skills.

Collective Self-Help

In the spirit of *Canada's Physical Activity Guide for Children*, over the next 6 months, the children are helping each other add an additional 10 minutes to their daily physical activity, 1 month at a time, to incorporate daily active time as part of a healthy lifestyle. They are helping each other by

- suggesting games and encouraging peers to join them;
- helping educators keep large bags of small equipment appealing for the children, sorting out unused or broken equipment on a regular basis, and suggesting new and low-cost equipment; and
- encouraging peers to reduce their allotted computer time further or deciding as a group to reduce it in increments.

Educators have approached the local high-school physical education department with an idea that is a mutually beneficial activity. High-school students under the direction of their teacher are teaching the school-agers team skills in basketball, soccer, and other sports. Students use this experience as coop placement hours or volunteer hours while developing employability and life skills.

Community Action

A subcommittee of educators, parents, and children was formed to represent the community centre's interests at community meetings that were held to discuss needs and suggestions. The three goals in the strategic plan are

- child and youth development,
- lifelong health and wellness for all, and
- environmental stewardship.

The subcommittee put together a successful grant proposal for funding to build a "green learning ground," including an adventure playground, under the direction of a university urban planning committee with an environmentally sound focus. Although safety is a cornerstone of the project, meaningful ways to involve children and families are incorporated. The green learning ground integrates a range of options for children's play and youth sports interests and includes a vegetable garden to be maintained by the school-agers and educators. This responsibility offers children moderate physical activity, with a flexibility and strength focus.

Societal Change

The school-agers, parents, and educators are involved in a campaign to write letters to their city counsellors, highlighting the following important directions that the policymakers and funders need to take (Toronto Parks and Recreation Department, 2003):

- Restore (or continue) public availability of swimming pools, ice arenas, soccer fields, baseball diamonds, cricket fields, tennis courts, etc.
- Develop standards for providing no-charge recreation programs.
- Reduce barriers to participation by addressing support needs, including transportation, child care, program supplies, and equipment.
- Strive to make all parks and recreation facilities barrier free.
- Increase the number of youth leadership development programs.
- Target high-needs communities when setting geographic priorities for program and service development.
- Create community capacity by working with community organizations to deliver a wide range of programs reflecting the diverse nature of each community.
- Move beyond indoor facilities to increase the range and number of recreational opportunities in parks and natural areas.
- Help maintain continuous enjoyment of activity throughout life.

CONCLUSION

Healthy active living is important to the health of all Canadians. As educators, we have daily opportunities to support a lifestyle for young children that will help pave the way to lifelong healthy habits. We can do this in many ways:

- Ensure that the program is an environment that provides ongoing opportunities for activity and healthy eating through policies that are put into practice.
- Be positive role models in this regard.
- Communicate with and support each parent's endeavours in creating and maintaining their family's healthy active living.
- Become involved in community action and societal change that affect the healthy active living goals of all children and families in communities and in Canada.

"We have changed our environment more quickly than we know how to change ourselves" (Lippmann, 1914).

What's Your Opinion?

TO COMPUTE OR NOT TO COMPUTE?

Parents, educators, and health professionals have differing opinions regarding the advantages and concerns of computer access for kindergarten and school-age children during after-school programs. This has been of particular focus, as *Canada's Report Card on Physical Activity for Children and Youth* has been so dismal in recent years. Debate this issue, ensuring that each advantage is clear and measurable and that each concern includes criteria for minimizing the potential negative impact of daily computer time.

ASSESS YOUR LEARNING

Define terms or describe concepts used in this unit:
- active transportation
- *Canada's Physical Activity Guide for Children*
- carbonated drinks
- endurances
- flexibility
- healthy active living
- manipulative skills
- nonlocomotor skills
- reasons for overeating
- overweight
- phytochemicals
- screen time
- trans fats
- urban sprawl
- body mass index (BMI)
- cooperative games
- fitness component
- greening the outdoor environment
- locomotor skills
- motor skills
- NutriSTEP™
- reasons for undereating
- ParticipACTION
- saturated fats
- strength
- underweight

Evaluate your options in each situation:

1. A few preschoolers have recently moved to Canada from countries that are much warmer year round. They are having a difficult time adjusting to

winter. The parents have asked you to let them stay inside with another group of children rather than take them outside to play.

2. You are chairing early childhood centre fundraising committee and are planning a family walkathon event to raise the funds needed for greening your outdoor environment. A company that produces carbonated drinks and high-fat and -sugar snack foods has offered to provide free refreshments for everyone attending the walkathon.

3. The parents of an active, healthy eight-year-old tell you that they are concerned about their son's weight and insist that he be given only one serving of each food at mealtimes and only fruit or vegetables as snacks. No other children in the room have this restriction.

4. You are an educator in a program for four- and five-year-olds. Your colleague's boyfriend works at a video store and has access to all the newest DVDs and TV program series that have been put on DVD. Your early childhood centre does not have a policy regarding screen time, and your room partner brings in new DVDs weekly that she puts on for children to watch "to calm them down" or whenever it's a rainy day. The children ask for the newest DVDs and often ask to watch the same program over and over again.

5. One of the school-agers in your after-school program uses a wheelchair. On the playground, she watches as the other children play active games freely, and you notice that she often practises taking shots at the basketball hoop when no other children are using it. When the ball falls to the ground, however, she rarely retrieves it unless an adult is nearby to throw it back to her.

RESOURCE MATERIALS

Organizations
Canadian Paediatric Society, 2305 St. Laurent Blvd, Ottawa, ON K1G 4J8. Tel: 613-526-9397; fax: 613-526-3332; http://www.cps.ca

Dietitians of Canada, 480 University Avenue, Suite 604, Toronto, ON M5G 1V2. Tel: 416-596-0857; fax: 416-596-0603; http://www.dietitians.ca/healthystart/index.asp

Media Awareness Network, 1500 Merivale Road, 3rd Floor, Ottawa, ON K2E 6Z5. Tel: 613-224-7721; toll free in Canada: 1-800-896-3342; fax: 613-224-1958; http://www.media-awareness.ca/english/index.cfm

Other Websites of Interest
Active Healthy Kids Canada: http://www.activehealthykids.ca

Evergreen: http://www.evergreen.ca/en/index.html

Physical and Health Education Canada (PHE Canada): http://www.cahperd.ca

Heart & Stroke Foundation: http://www.heartandstroke.com

Healthy Canadians (Government of Canada): http://www.healthycanadians.ca

Public Health Agency of Canada:

- Healthy Living: http://www.phac-aspc.gc.ca/hl-vs-strat/index.html
- Healthy Living Unit: http://www.phac-aspc.gc.ca/pau-uap/fitness/about.html

Vancouver EcoDensity Initiative: http://www.vancouver-ecodensity.ca

Printed Matter

Active Minds, Active Bodies: Inspiring Children and Youth to Read and Move (2005), by Halton Active Living Network. To download a copy, visit http://adp.lin.ca/resource// html/activeminds.pdf

Active Minds Active Bodies Booklist: Recommended Reading List New Titles for 2007 (2007), by Halton Active Living Network. To download a copy, visit http://www .choices4health.org/downloads/New_book_titles__2007_Update_(04).pdf

Have a Ball! A Toolkit for Physical Activity and the Early Years (2005), by Best Start Resource Centre, Physical Activity Resource Centre, and the Nutrition Resource Centre. To order a copy, visit http://www.beststart.org/resources/hlthy_chld_dev/ index.html

Healthy Start for Life. Keeping Active Together Planner (2007), by Dietitians of Canada. To download a copy, visit http://www.dietitians.ca/healthystart/Active_Living_ Planner.pdf

Moving and Growing (2004), by Canadian Child Care Federation. To order a copy of the series, visit http://www.cccf-fcsge.ca/publications/publications_en.html

Quality Environments and Best Practices to Support Physical Activity in the Early Years (2007), by Canadian Child Care Federation. To order a copy, visit http://www.cccf-fcsge.ca/publications/publications_en.html

Small Wonders: Designing Vibrant Natural Landscapes for Early Childhood (2004), by Evergreen. To download a copy, visit http://www.evergreen.ca/en/lg/small-wonders.pdf

Their Future Is Now: Healthy Choices for Canada's Children and Youth June 2006, by Health Council of Canada. To download a copy, visit http://www.healthcouncilca-nada.ca/docs/rpts/2006/HCC_ChildHealth_EN.pdf

BIBLIOGRAPHY

Active Healthy Kids Canada. (2008). *It's time to unplug our kids: Canada's Report Card on Physical Activity for Children & Youth – 2008.* Toronto: Author.

American Academy of Pediatrics. (2001, February). Children, adolescents, and television policy statement. *Pediatrics, 107,* 423–426.

Arenz, S., Rückerl, R., Koletzko, B., & von Kries, R. (2004). Breast-feeding and childhood obesity—a systematic review. *International Journal of Obesity, 28,* 1247–1256.

Bell, A. C. (2007, October 3). *The contribution of green school ground design to moderate activity levels.* Presented at the Evergreen Community Urban Health Initiative Presentation, University of Toronto.

Bell, A. C., & Dyment, D. E. (2006). *Grounds for action: Promoting physical activity through school ground greening in Canada.* Toronto: Evergreen.

Benham-Deal, T. (2005, April). Preschool children's accumulated and sustained physical activity. *Perceptual and Motor Skills, 100,* 443–450.

Best Start Resource Centre. (2005). *Have a ball! A toolkit for physical activity and the early years.* Toronto: Author.

Binkley, T., & Specker, B. (2004). Increased periosteal circumference remains present 12 months after an exercise intervention in preschool children. *Bone, 35,* 1383–1388.

Boldemann, C., et al. (2006). Impact of preschool environment upon children's physical activity and sun exposure. *Preventive Medicine, 42,* 301–308.

Booth, F. W., Gordon, S. E., Carlson, C. J., & Hamilton, M. T. (2000). Waging war on modern chronic diseases: primary prevention through exercise biology. *Journal of Applied Physiology, 88,* 774–787.

Burry, A. B. (1999). Public health dentistry: 2000 to 2020. *Journal of the Canadian Dental Association, 65,* 163–166.

Butler, D. (2008, February 8). Area parents turn blind eye to obesity. *The Ottawa Citizen*. Retrieved March 2008 from <http://www.canada.com/ottawacitizen/news/story.html?k=17974&id=fcf3724a-9dbb-45f7-93fa-f2544edef301

Canadian Child Care Federation. (2003). *Outdoor play in early childhood care and education programs*. Ottawa: Author.

Canadian Paediatric Society. (2003). Impact of media use on children and youth. *Paediatrics & Child Health, 8*, 301–306. Retrieved March 2008 from http://www.cps.ca/english/statements/PP/pp03-01.pdf

Canadian Paediatric Society. (2008). *Well beings: A guide to health, in child care* (3rd ed.). Ottawa: Author.

Crossley, B., & Wright, S. (2003). Employer partnerships and role modelling for physical activity programs in early childhood education. In *Outdoor play in early childhood care and education programs*. Ottawa: Canadian Child Care Federation.

Dennisson, B. A., Erb, T. A., & Jenkins, P. L. (2002). Television viewing and television in bedroom associated with overweight risk among low-income preschool children. *Pediatrics, 109*, 1028–1035.

Dietitians of Canada. (2003). *Balancing the issues in agriculture – healthy vegetarian diets*. Retrieved August 2008 from http://www.dietitians.ca/public/content/eat_well_live_well/english/faqs_tips_facts/fact_sheets/index.asp?fn=view&id=2540&idstring=2540

Drewnowski, A. (2007). The real contribution of added sugars and fats to obesity. *Epidemiologic Reviews, 29*, 160–171.

Evenson, B. (2003, September 12). When rich and poor kids eat the same diet, poor ones get fatter. *The National Post*, p. A3.

Frank, L., et al. (2003). Obesity relationships with community design, physical activity, and time spent in cars. *American Journal of Preventive Medicine, 27*, 87–96.

Gallahue, D. L., & Donnelly, F. C. (2007). *Developmental physical education for all children* (4th ed.). Champaign, IL: Human Kinetics.

Health Canada. (2002). *Canada's physical activity guide for children* (Catalogue No. H39-611/2002-2E). Ottawa: Public Works and Government Services Canada.

Health Canada. (2006, June). *TRANSforming the food supply: Report of the Transfat Task Force submitted to the Minister of Health, Ottawa*. Retrieved August 2008 from http://www.healthcanada.gc.ca/transfat

Health Canada. (2007a). *Eating well with Canada's food guide*. Ottawa: Minister of Public Works and Government Services Canada.

Health Canada. (2007b). *Eating well with Canada's food guide: A resource for educators and communicators*. Retrieved March 2008 from http://www.hc-sc.gc.ca/fn-an/alt_formats/hpfb-dgpsa/pdf/pubs/res-educat_e.pdf

Health Canada. (2007c). *It's your health: Trans fat*. Retrieved March 2008 from http://www.hc-sc.gc.ca/iyh-vsv/alt_formats/cmcd-dcmc/pdf/Trans_e.pdf

Healthy Child Manitoba. (2006). *Manitoba school nutrition handbook: Getting started with guidelines and policies*. Winnipeg: Government of Manitoba. Retrieved March 2008 from http://www.gov.mb.ca/healthyschools/foodinschools/documents/handbook.pdf

Jacobson, M. F. (2005). *Liquid candy: How soft drinks are harming America's health*. Washington, DC: Center for Science in the Public Interest. Retrieved March 2008 from http://www.cspinet.org/new/pdf/liquid_candy_final_w_new_supplement.pdf

Kerr, S. (2002). Fundamentals of feeding children. *National Eating Disorder Information Centre Bulletin, 17*(4), 1–4.

Kirkey, S. (2008, January 19). Healthy kids hurting due to fear of fat. *Leader-Post*. Retrieved March 2008 from http://www.canada.com/reginaleaderpost/news/story.html?id=7f0ade1c-a22c-4812-a1d9-95918017775d

Lippmann, W. (1914). *Drift and mastery*. Madison, WI: The University of Wisconsin Press.

Lopez, R. (2004). Urban sprawl and risk for being overweight or obese. *American Journal of Public Health, 94*, 1574–1579.

Minnesota Department of Health. (2005). *Minnesota Department of Health fact sheet: Soft drinks*. St. Paul, MN: Center for Health Promotion. Retrieved March 2008 from http://www.health.state.mn.us/divs/hpcd/chp/5aday/2005pdfs/2005softdrinks.pdf

Ontario College of Family Physicians. (2005). *The health impacts of urban sprawl: Information Series, Volume 3: Obesity*. Toronto: Author.

Ontario Ministry of Education. (2004). *Making Ontario schools healthier places to learn: Backgrounder*. Toronto: Government of Ontario. Retrieved March 2008 from http://www.edu.gov.on.ca/eng/document/nr/04.10/bg1020.html

Pardee, M., Gillman, A., & Larson, C. (2005). *Community investment collaborative for kids, resource guide 4: Creating playgrounds for early childhood facilities*. New York: Local Initiatives Support Corporation.

Pate, R. R., Pfeiffer, K. A., Trost, S. G., Ziegler, P., & Dowda, M. (2004). Physical activity among children attending preschools. *Pediatrics, 114*, 1258–1263.

Patel, S. R., & Hu, F. B. (2008, March). Short sleep duration and weight gain: A systematic review. *Obesity (Silver Spring), 16*, 643–653. Epub 2008 Jan 17.

Plourde, G. (2006, March). Preventing and managing pediatric obesity: Recommendations for family physicians. *Canadian Family Physician, 52*, 322–328.

Ratey, J. J. (2008). *SPARK: The revolutionary new science of exercise and the brain*. New York: Little, Brown & Company.

Robinson, T. (1999). Reducing children's television viewing to prevent obesity: A randomised controlled trial." *JAMA, 282*, 1561–1567.

Secretariat for the Intersectoral Healthy Living Network, in partnership with the F/P/T Healthy Living Task Group and the F/P/T Advisory Committee on Population Health and Health Security. (2005). *The Integrated Pan-Canadian Healthy Living Strategy*. Ottawa: Ministry of Health (Canada). Retrieved March 2008 from http://www.phac-aspc.gc.ca/hl-vs-strat/pdf/hls_e.pdf

Shields, M. (2005). *Nutrition: Findings from the Canadian Community Health Survey Issue no. 1: Measured obesity: Overweight Canadian children and adolescents*. Ottawa: Statistics Canada. Retrieved March 2008 from http://www.statcan.ca/english/research/82-620-MIE/2005001/pdf/cobesity.pdf

Simpson, J. A. R., Keller, H. H., Rysdale, L. A., & Beyers, J. E. (2007). Nutrition Screening Tool for Every Preschooler (NutriSTEP™): validation and test-retest reliability of a parent-administered questionnaire assessing nutrition risk of preschoolers. *European Journal of Clinical Nutrition, 62*, 770–780.

Spurgeon, D. (2002). Childhood obesity in Canada has tripled in past 20 years. *British Medical Journal, 324*, 1416.

Timmons, B. W., Naylor, P. J., & Pfeiffer, K. A. (2007). Physical activity for preschool children – how much and how? *Applied Physiology, Nutrition, and Metabolism, 32*, s122–s134.

Toronto Parks and Recreation Department. (2003). *Toward a healthy, active future: Toronto Parks and Recreation in 2010—a strategic plan*. Toronto: City of Toronto.

Tremblay, M. S., & Willms, J. D. (2000). Secular trends in the body mass index of Canadian children. *Canadian Medical Association Journal, 163*, 1429–1431.

Tucker, P., et al. (2006, August). Preventing paediatric obesity: recommendations from a community-based qualitative investigation. *Obesity Reviews, 7*, 251–260.

Veugelers, P. J., & Fitzgerald, A. L. (2005). Prevalence of and risk factors for childhood overweight and obesity. *Canadian Medical Association Journal, 173*, 607–13.

Whiting, S., et al. (2004). Factors that affect bone mineral accrual in the adolescent growth spurt. *The American Society for Nutritional Sciences Journal of Nutrition, 134*, 696S–700S.

Williamson, P., & Roberts, J. (2004). *First Nations peoples: Second edition*. Toronto: Emond Montgomery Publications Limited.

World Health Organization. (2008). Obesity and overweight. In *Global strategy on diet, physical activity and health*. Retrieved March 2008 from http://www.who.int/dietphysicalactivity/publications/facts/obesity/en/

Canada's Physical Activity Guide for Children

(appendix continues on next page)

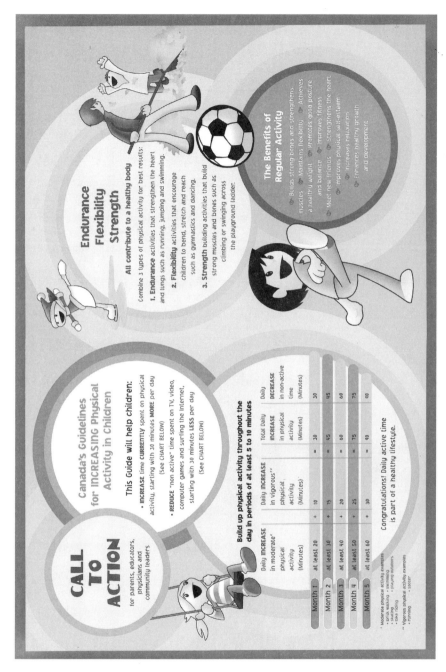

Source: *Canada's Physical Activity Guide for Children,* Public Health Agency of Canada, (2002). Reproduced with the permission of the Minister of Public Works and Government Services Canada, 2008.

Safety Promotion

CONTENTS

An integral part of growing up is trying new things to become competent. Whether it is learning to walk, ride a bike, cut with a knife, or draw with a crayon, acquiring a new skill is a learning process. As such, it may take a child a number of attempts before he or she masters the skill. Do you remember learning to ride a bike? You probably fell off more than once! Minor scrapes, bumps, and bruises are a normal part of childhood, and exploring challenges is an essential part of development.

It is a tremendous responsibility to ensure children's safety in early childhood programs, but it is not an insurmountable one. We don't want to design a risk-free environment. The goal of safety promotion in programs is to find a workable balance between a safe and a challenging program. Children who are not physically challenged are understimulated. This understimulation can have the following consequences:

- The children stop seeking challenges, which affects their development and self-esteem.

- They turn to their peers for stimulation, or they turn against them, which, either way, often results in antisocial and hurtful behaviour.

- They direct their natural desire for trial-and-error learning to times and places in which the risks may be much greater (e.g., toddlers climbing up on bookshelves or from chairs onto counters rather than using developmentally

appropriate climbing equipment or natural opportunities such as inclines [little hills] in green spaces under adult supervision).

- They spend progressively more time at "safe" activities such as sitting in front of a screen; this time is far from safe, as it contributes to a host of chronic conditions and, in essence, is not physically, emotionally, or socially beneficial after all (see Concerns about Physical Activity Levels of Children, page 302).

Quality early childhood programs offer children the physical and human resources to experience challenges safely and learn from them. Educators pay attention to the four components of safety promotion: training, physical environment, supervision of children, and safety rules. Before discussing how to promote safety, we'll look at childhood injuries from the perspective of the five W's: the who, why, where, when, and what of safety.

OBJECTIVE

To describe the nature of childhood injuries and factors that increase risk.

THE FIVE W'S OF SAFETY

An important role for educators is to design and implement **injury prevention strategies** in early childhood programs. To develop policies and strategies that are relevant, practical, and effective, educators first understand the nature of childhood injuries and factors that increase risk. Educators also draw on their knowledge of children's development and how that affects the types of injuries experienced at different ages.

Who

Safety is an important consideration in everyone's life. An average day for an adult includes several activities with an element of risk: showering, shaving, eating peanut butter on toast for breakfast, navigating the ice-covered front steps of the house, crossing the street, and driving or biking to work. Children face potential risks in their daily lives, too. Some children's injuries are the same as adults'. Others are directly related to children's growth and development and becoming competent at small and large motor skills. Learning to crawl, walk, climb, ride a bike, or use scissors involves risks, and children sometimes fall or cut themselves while developing these skills. We can't prevent injuries by stopping children's growth or development any more than our parents could prevent ours. However, it is also true that many injuries are preventable; the word "accident" implies bad luck or fate, so in this unit, as in current safety publications, the word "accident" is not used.

Safe Kids Canada (2007) published a national review of 10 years of unintentional injuries for children and youth in Canada. Injuries that children sustain due to physical abuse, violence, and attempted suicides are called intentional and are excluded from these statistics. Refer to Figure 7.1 for the causes of deaths and

Major causes of unintentional injury deaths among Canadian children aged 0–14 years, 1994–2003
Source: Statistics Canada [Deaths for 2003 were estimated from trends for the years 1994–2002]

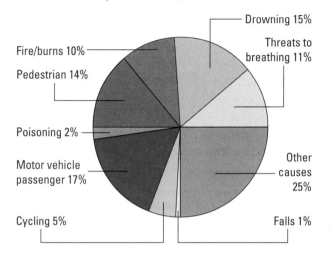

Major causes of unintentional injury hospitalizations among Canadian children age 0–14, 1994–2003
Source: Canadian Institute for Health Information

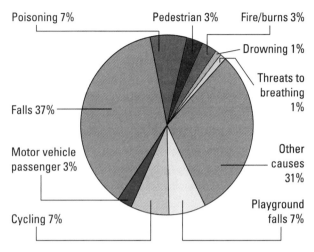

One cause of hospitalization clearly stands out from the others. Falls account for nearly half (44%) of all hospitalizations. Approximately 7% of falls take place at the playground; another 37% happen in other locations such as homes and schools.

Note: "Other causes" refers to types of childhood injury deaths that have not been covered in this report such as sports-related deaths, firearms, or machinery. The data is gathered in such a way that it often captures whether a child was struck by and/or struck against something rather than the activity that the child was involved in at the time of injury.

Source: *Child and Youth Unintentional Injury: 1994–2003 Ten Years In Review.* Copyright © The Hospital for Sick Children, 2007.

hospitalizations as a result of unintentional injuries over 10 years. The key findings include the following:

■ In 2003, 300 children from birth to age 14 died and 20,500 were hospitalized for unintentional serious injuries. Although one child's death from injury is too many, the promising news is that the overall child injury death rate declined by 37% and the injury hospitalization rate declined by 34% between 1994 and 2003 (p. 4).

■ "Over the 10-year period, an estimated average of 25,500 children age 14 and under were hospitalized each year for serious injuries such as traumatic brain injuries, internal injuries, and complex fractures. When evaluated against the population data, this means that 1 in every 230 Canadian children age 14 and under is hospitalized for a serious injury in any given year" (p. 4).

■ "The three leading causes of injury-related death in children are motor vehicle collisions (17%), drowning (15%), and pedestrian (14%)" (p. 4).

■ "The major cause of injury-related hospitalization is falls, accounting for nearly half (44%) of all admissions" (p. 4).

Source: *Child and Youth Unintentional Injury: 1994–2003 Ten Years In Review,* p. 4. Copyright © The Hospital for Sick Children, 2007.

Why

Individual differences in temperament may explain why one child is more of a risk taker, less fearful, more adventurous, or more inquisitive than another. Risk takers are more likely to be in situations that put them at risk of injury. Gender differences play a role in injuries because boys are often involved in more physically challenging activities. Gender differences in this respect are not yet fully understood. Possible factors include risk perception, peer influence on risk taking, and parental responses to children engaging in risky behaviour. Regardless of individual, gender, or family response differences, educators must evaluate the safety of the equipment being used and maintain levels of supervision appropriate for the activity and the age of the children. However, educators' supervision cannot focus only on the adventurous children, or boys in general, since all children are susceptible to injuries.

Children learn through exploration. Together with maturation, children reach developmental milestones. Understanding children's growth and development is essential in anticipating injuries and thus preventing or reducing their severity. The physical and cognitive developmental immaturity of young children increases their risk of injury compared with that of older children and adults. Here are some of the reasons why:

- Children go through such rapid growth spurts that sometimes their sensory perception doesn't keep up (e.g., a child gets taller, but she senses that she is shorter, misjudges her height with the monkey bar, and bangs her head).

- Children have yet to learn how to control impulses. They are unaware of the potential harm to themselves when they do whatever comes to mind (e.g., running into the street to retrieve a ball, leaning over into a pail of water, following peers to the highest level of the climber where they aren't physically able to handle the challenge to climb back down).

- Children learn through trial and error. When children's environments are not developmentally appropriate and challenging, their experiments involve activities that can be dangerous (e.g., a toddler trying to walk up the chute of a slide because no climber is available).

- Children under three years of age are usually not aware of others' safety and may contribute to the harm of others.

Let's consider the risk of drowning as a hazard based on a child's growth and development. Children under 5 years old account for nearly two-thirds (62%) of drowning incidents (Safe Kids Canada, 2007, p. 12). Most children under age five are attracted to the sensory opportunities of water but lack a sense of potential danger. This puts them at risk of drowning if not carefully supervised. Also, their heads are relatively much larger and heavier than the head of an older child or adult, making them more vulnerable to fall in head first, quickly filling their small lungs with water. You have likely heard that young children can drown in very shallow water (as little as 5 cm/2 in.).

Starting with infants and toddlers, we'll examine aspects of children's growth and development as they relate to safety.

Infants

- are learning to roll over from front to back, which puts them at risk of falling from heights (e.g., change tables, counters, furniture) or suffocating if placed on a soft or buoyant surface. They may roll onto their tummy but then, unable to roll back, smother themselves when their face is buried in a pillow or adult water bed.

Infants and toddlers

- are developing stronger grasps, and those who can stand, crawl, or walk put themselves at risk of
  - falling down stairs,
  - pulling on an appliance cord hanging down the front of a counter,
  - grabbing a cup of hot coffee or tea from a table,
  - becoming tangled in drapery cords and strangling, or
  - pulling off small parts from a toy and choking.
- have not yet developed an awareness of potential harm. Toddlers will run in front of a moving swing. At this age, most children love playing in water and are not able to discern the difference between supervised water play and playing in the toilet water alone.
- have a tendency to put everything in their mouth (sensorimotor learning), which puts them at risk of poisoning and choking.
- are active explorers and thus are prone to bumps, bruises, and scrapes from losing their balance and attempting new tasks.
- are often like little whirlwinds because their quest for learning about their world leaves little time for caution.

Preschoolers

- are adept at running, climbing, and pedalling a tricycle by the time they are four. They are becoming more competent and confident on playground equipment and are looking for new and advanced challenges (e.g., climbing even higher up the climber, jumping off the swing while it is still moving).
- are in the preoperational stage of cognitive development. As a result, they are unable to judge the speed of a car, the height of the climber's fire pole, or the danger of deep water or matches. They also are unable to distinguish clearly between reality and fantasy. Many children watch television, especially cartoons, which focus on invincible superheroes. These shows

may lead some preschoolers to believe that they, too, can leap from high places or fly.

- want and need to have increasing levels of independence, but with this comes risk (e.g., a child can't learn to cut with a knife without using one, so she may cut herself even when using a dull one)

School-agers

- are developing competencies in many areas and need to be given more independence and responsibility. Issues concerning children's personal safety arise both at home and in the school-age program. In school-age programs, there are fewer educators per child (a higher staff–child ratio), resulting in less direct supervision. Children are required to use their own decision-making skills and judgments in various situations—leaving the playground to go into the school to use the bathroom, riding a bike to school, using a neighbourhood playground in the evening without a parent. Before delegating new responsibilities to a child, adults must consider the child's age, level of maturity, track record, and reliability, as well as the inherent safety risks within the school, program, or neighbourhood.

Jessica took off her bike helmet after rounding the corner and didn't stop at stop signs. She is not permitted to bicycle to school until she demonstrates that she can follow safe cycling practices consistently.

- are paying more attention to interacting with their peers than to what they are actually doing (e.g., a child who is busy talking to friends on the ground may not notice that he or she has moved to the edge of the climber), so physical injuries often result. On the other hand, children can get so involved in an activity that they are oblivious to everything around them (e.g., during a game of tag, a child determined not to be tagged runs into someone else while running away).

Aside from injuries attributable to these growth and development factors, children are injured from both the use of developmentally inappropriate or poorly maintained equipment and the lack of adequate supervision or rules.

Where

Houses and apartments are designed for adults. Most children spend more time at home than they do in early childhood programs, so it is not surprising that children are more often injured at home:

- 81% of children under 1 year old
- 73% of children aged 1 to 4 years old
- 54% of children aged 5 to 9 years old

However, for children aged 10 to 14 years, the rate shifts from 23% of their injuries occurring at home to 29% occurring in educational settings (Canadian Institute of Child Health, 2000, pp. 46, 68, 98, 99).

Compared with other environments, early childhood programs are less dangerous places for children. Yet these facts do not mean that we can be complacent about safety in early childhood programs, because injuries happen there too. Children can slip in spills from a water table, pinch their fingers in a door, and run into each other. The playground is the site of the highest number of injuries at centres, mostly due to falls onto inadequate impact-absorbing surfaces under and around playground equipment. Injuries have decreased over recent years due in part to strict adherence in some provinces and territories to **Canadian Standards Association (CSA)** requirements. A research study into school playgrounds that had upgraded to the new standards concluded that approximately 520 injuries had been prevented over the four years of the study (Safe Kids Canada, 2007, p. 4). School-age children in particular are at risk of falling on stairs because of frequent use in many school buildings and the likelihood of going up and down unsafely (e.g., taking two stairs at a time, jumping down, not using the handrail).

When

Injuries can happen at any time. But there are particular situations or conditions in which the likelihood of injury increases. *For example, "Playground injuries most often occur in summer (43%), followed by fall (27%), spring (24%), and winter (6%)"* *(Safe Kids Canada, 2007, p. 26)*. Childhood injuries in programs often happen

- when children are tired or hungry;
- when children new to the program are not fully aware of the environment or don't know how to use play equipment safely;
- when educators relax their level of supervision (e.g., while talking among themselves in the playground), overestimate a child's abilities, or do not anticipate potential consequences of an activity or a child's behaviour;
- when educator–child ratios are not adequate for the activity, whether it is cooking with children or going for a walk;
- when the daily routine is disrupted (e.g., a familiar educator is absent and the care routine and level of supervision are affected);
- when a new piece of play equipment arrives and the children become too excited and preoccupied to follow safety rules; or
- when field trips introduce children to unfamiliar situations and unexpected hazards.

What

Every year children in Canada are killed or permanently disabled by six types of injuries: motor vehicle collisions, drowning, burns, threats to breathing (i.e., choking, suffocating, entrapment, and strangling), poisoning, and falls. From the educators' perspective, some of these injuries are more relevant to their day-to-day work than others.

In programs, threats to breathing and falls are, of course, much more likely than motor vehicle collisions. Educators must be aware of choking during snacks and meals. They must be prepared for falls all the time. And even though educators will not be thinking of car mishaps during the day, they can help children learn

traffic rules when they are riding tricycles (e.g., by staying on the right side of the path and putting up a stop sign at path intersections) or when they are out for walks.

Increasing our awareness of the major causes of childhood injuries and death can have a significant and positive impact on safety promotion at home and at work. The next section provides an overview of the six types of childhood injuries.

Motor Vehicle Collisions and Bicycle-Related Injuries

Motor vehicle collisions are the leading cause of injury-related death of children in Canada. "An estimated 68 children age 14 and under are killed every year in motor vehicle crashes, and another 880 are seriously injured" (Safe Kids Canada, 2007, p. 10). Somewhat related, a small but significant number of children are killed or injured as pedestrians. "An estimated 56 child pedestrians age 14 and under die every year in Canada, and 780 are hospitalized with serious injuries" (Safe Kids Canada, 2007, p. 20). "An estimated 20 children age 14 and under die every year in Canada because of a bicycle-related injury, and 1,800 are hospitalized for serious injuries" (Safe Kids Canada, 2007, p. 18). "Most serious injuries and deaths to child cyclists involve collisions with a motor vehicle" (Safe Kids Canada, 2007, p. 18).

Traffic-related injury, including injuries to passengers in vehicles, pedestrians, and cyclists, is a significant safety issue for all children. Many pedestrian and cyclist injuries have resulted from individuals not obeying traffic rules (e.g., jaywalking or crossing against a traffic light).

It is important to recognize that the majority of motor vehicle–related deaths and serious injuries are a result of a lack of or improperly fitted restraints. Safe Kids Canada (2007, p. 10) reports that "when used correctly, car seats reduce the risk of death by 71% for infants under age 1 and 54% for children by ages 1 to 4. Car seats also reduce the risk of hospitalization by 67% for children age 4 and under. Booster seats provide 59% more protection than seat belts alone." Refer to Chapter 6 of *Well Beings* (Canadian Paediatric Society, 2008) for detailed information on optimal restraints for all ages.

"Approximately 70% of deaths and 50% of serious injuries to child pedestrians happen where there is no form of traffic control. This means the child may have been trying to cross the street in the middle of the block, walking out from between parked cars, or crossing at an intersection without a stop light" (Safe Kids Canada, 2007, p. 20). Traffic-calming strategies reduce the speed of vehicles and lessen the impact. "At speeds less than 30 km/h, vehicles and pedestrians are able to co-exist with relative safety" (Safe Kids Canada, 2007, p. 10). Community pedestrian safety is an ongoing goal, with many agencies at all government levels working for improvements.

"Approximately 3 Canadian children are killed and 31 are injured in Canada each year as pedestrians hit by a school bus. The greatest risk of death related to school buses is when children are outside, not inside, the bus" (Safe Kids Canada, 2007, p. 28). This happens when the child disappears from sight in front of the bus and the bus pulls away. Some children are hit by another vehicle passing the bus as they cross the road. Programs that transport children on buses must supervise the children directly.

Cyclists' injuries tend to be more serious when safety equipment (e.g., helmet) is not worn (see Table 7.1). A head injury can traumatically change a child's life forever. The skull can be fractured or broken by the impact of a speed as low as 7 to 10 kilometres an hour. "A properly fitted helmet helps protect the head by absorbing the force from a crash or a fall, decreasing the risk of serious head injury by as much as 85% and brain injury by 88%" (Safe Kids Canada, 2007, p. 18). The majority of deaths of child cyclists are from being struck by a motor vehicle. Injuries are common from falls off the bike. "Falls may result from human factors, such as taking an action that surpasses their physical ability, or from external factors such as swerving to avoid hitting an object like a car or tree" (Safe Kids Canada, 2007, p. 18).

Children most frequently receive injuries to the head and neck (e.g., cuts, scrapes, dental damage, concussions, fractures), as well as cuts, bruises, abrasions, dislocations, sprains, and fractures of the legs and arms. How can educators reduce the number of cycling injuries in programs and help children learn life-long safety habits? Educators are encouraged to consider including the following practices in their policy:

- Have children wear bike helmets on riding toys and tricycles so they see them as a natural part of riding.
- Ensure that riding paths are designed so that children can't crash into objects.
- Ensure that children are actively supervised.
- In school-age programs, staff should develop a policy for bikes, in-line skates, and skateboards that stipulates that children travelling to their programs wear helmets and other safety equipment recommended for each activity. Parents may not support your position, but while the children are under your supervision, you can either have them wear the safety equipment or prohibit the activity. When helmets become required by law in your province or territory, you can enforce the law.

Currently, it is unlikely that you will find many programs with toddlers and preschoolers wearing helmets on the riding toys and tricycles. Some families find the cost of new or used safety equipment prohibitive. Perhaps programs could canvass families or the neighbourhood for equipment no longer in use. This equipment could be swapped or given to individual families. In the area of bike safety, national organizations provide support and education (see Resource Materials, page 439).

TABLE 7.1 Implementing Prevention Strategies

FALLS

INFANTS AND TODDLERS				PRESCHOOLERS			SCHOOL-AGERS						
Birth	12 mths	18 mths	24 mths	3 yrs	4	5	6	7	8	9	10	11	12

- off furniture, change tables, counters (1)
- out of high chairs, cribs, strollers (1, 7)
- out of windows (2)
- down stairs (3, 8)
- riding toys, tricycles, bicycles, and in-line skates (4)
- playground equipment (5)
- slip or trip on water, ice, sand, toys, carpeting, extension cords (6)

THREATS TO BREATHING

INFANTS AND TODDLERS				PRESCHOOLERS			SCHOOL-AGERS						
Birth	12 mths	18 mths	24 mths	3 yrs	4	5	6	7	8	9	10	11	12

- suffocate on pillows, matresses, and adult waterbeds (1)
- strangle in dangling blind and drapery cords, pull toys, soother strings (2, 10)
- choke on small toys (<4 cm or 1.5 in. in diameter), toy parts that can be pulled off (e.g., buttons, clothing) (3, 10)
- choke on latex balloons, suffocate from plastic bags (e.g., dry-cleaning bags) (4)
- choke on foods (5)
- suffocate when loose scarves and hoods get caught on playground equipment (e.g., slides) (6, 7)
- choke when eating too quickly or talking, laughing, or running while eating or eating large pieces of food (8)
- become entrapped under furniture or in play structures (9)

DROWNING

INFANTS AND TODDLERS | PRESCHOOLERS | SCHOOL-AGERS

Birth — 12 mths — 18 mths — 24 mths — 3 yrs — 4 — 5 — 6 — 7 — 8 — 9 — 10 — 11 — 12

- wading pools and swimming pools (1)
- puddles, pails, or large containers of water (2)
- creeks, rivers, lakes, oceans (3)

MOTOR VEHICLES AND BICYCLES

INFANTS AND TODDLERS | PRESCHOOLERS | SCHOOL-AGERS

Birth — 12 mths — 18 mths — 24 mths — 3 yrs — 4 — 5 — 6 — 7 — 8 — 9 — 10 — 11 — 12

- not in proper child-restraint seats (1)
- running or playing on the street (3)
- lack or improper use of seat belts (2)
- riding bicycles on the street (4)

POISONING

INFANTS AND TODDLERS | PRESCHOOLERS | SCHOOL-AGERS

Birth — 12 mths — 18 mths — 24 mths — 3 yrs — 4 — 5 — 6 — 7 — 8 — 9 — 10 — 11 — 12

- consumes potentially hazardous substances such as cleaning products; alcohol; medications (e.g., vitamins); certain flowers, plants, and berries; perfume, nail polish, and remover (1)
- eats cigarettes and butts (2)
- takes dare to seek approval from peers, drinks or eats unknown fluid or substance that is hazardous (3)

BURNS

INFANTS AND TODDLERS — Birth, 12 mths, 18 mths, 24 mths
PRESCHOOLERS — 3 yrs, 4, 5
SCHOOL-AGERS — 6, 7, 8, 9, 10, 11, 12

- scalds from hot tap water, beverages, soups (1)
- burns from stoves and ovens, heat radiators, fireplaces, wood stoves (2)
- sticking objects in electrical outlets, chewing on electrical cords (3)
- metal buckles and vinyl-covered car seats exposed to the sun (4)
- metal slides exposed to the sun (5)
- playing with matches or lighters (6)
- using the stove or electrical appliances while cooking (7)

The following suggestions appear in the order in which the risk factors are listed in each category.

FALLS

1. Always keep one hand on the child during diaper changes. Never put children on counters or tables even when they are in a baby chair or seat. Until children are able to climb on and off chairs, sofas, etc., never leave them there unattended.

2. Keep furniture away from the windows. Windows should be secured with screens or stops or grills to prevent opening more than 10 cm (4 in.).

3. Secure safety gates on all stairwells (top and bottom) so that infants and toddlers cannot access stairs without an adult. Safety gates must be screwed securely into the wall (do not use pressure-type gates). Install handrails at children's height. Make sure there is good lighting. Keep stairs clear of toys, shoes, clothing, etc. Model safe behaviour on the stairs. Supervise young children using stairs.

4. Actively supervise children. Establish developmentally appropriate rules for riding toys. Create safe riding paths. Begin using bike helmets for children on riding toys and tricycles. Encourage parents to enroll school-age children in bicycle safety courses. Establish a program policy covering school-age children riding bicycles and using in-line skates while in the early childhood program, including parental permission and the use of recommended safety equipment.

5. Actively supervise children. Help children learn the appropriate use of and safety rules for play equipment. Check and maintain play equipment and protective surfaces regularly. Ensure natural surfaces are topped up seasonally and as needed. Document the regular maintenance checks.

6. Immediately wipe up spills of water (e.g., water table). Keep sidewalks and stairs clear of ice and snow. Sweep up sand on floor under sand table. Keep toys off walkways in the rooms. Do not use scatter rugs. Do not run extension cords across floors where people walk or under carpeting (fire hazard).

7. Never place infant seats, bouncy chairs, and car seats on elevated surfaces.

8. Never use baby walkers with wheels in any early childhood setting, including family home child care.

THREATS TO BREATHING

1. Do not provide pillows in cribs for infants under 1 year old. Do not use bumper pads in the cribs. Remove plastic wrapping from crib mattresses. Never use garbage bags as mattress covers. Do not hang mobiles over the cribs. Keep plastic bags out of children's reach.

2. Strings on soothers and pull toys must not be longer than 15 cm (6 in.).

3. Avoid giving children under 4 years objects smaller than 4 cm (1.5 in.). If the object can fit into a toilet paper tube, it is a choking hazard for this age group. Check their toys for small parts that can be easily removed.

4. Ban the use of latex balloons in programs. Safely discard deflated foil balloons, because they can suffocate young children.

5. Know which foods can cause choking in children (see Reducing the Risk of Choking, page 272).

6. Encourage parents to use neck warmers in place of winter scarves. If scarves are worn, tie and tuck scarves into coats. Ensure that hoods are fastened snugly. Clothing manufacturers are redesigning hoods that fasten with Velcro rather than drawstrings. Have a policy prohibiting drawstrings on clothes. Do not permit children to wear dramatic play clothes on play equipment.

7. Prohibit the attachment of ropes, strings, cords, skipping ropes, etc., to play structures. Use only climbing ropes that are designed and manufactured for play structures.

8. Encourage children to eat slowly and chew properly. Model safe eating habits.

9. Ensure that all shelving and storage units are securely fastened to the walls or flooring. In family home child care, pay particular attention to bedroom furniture such as high-/tallboy dressers where children can climb to the top by pulling the drawers out and making the dresser unstable. Inspect the indoor and outdoor play structures for possible opening where a child's head or neck can become entrapped. Ensure that such equipment meets the CSA standards.

10. Regularly visit Health Canada's Consumer Product Safety website to remain up-to-date on product recalls related to toys and child-related products (see Resource Materials, page 439).

DROWNING

1. Never leave children unsupervised in the pool, regardless of their age. Empty portable wading pools immediately after use and store upside down. Teach children water safety.

2. Actively supervise infants, toddlers, and preschoolers in the washroom. Check playground for stagnant puddles of water. Keep diaper pails out of children's reach. Never keep pails or basins filled with water or cleaning solutions near children.

3. Teach children to respect water, not to play near creeks and rivers, and not to go on ice in the spring. Canals, rivers, and lakes used for ice skating must be safe to use. Boats used to transport children must have an appropriately sized approved flotation device for each child and adult.

MOTOR VEHICLES AND BICYCLES

1 & 2. When programs provide transportation for children, appropriate child restraints or seat belts must be used. Consult with the local fire department when unsure of how the car seats should be installed or if they have been installed properly. If educators are aware of parents not using proper restraints for their children, be advocates for children (e.g., encourage or assist parents in obtaining and using the restraints). Make sure safety education with preschool and school-age children includes the buckle-up message.

3. Actively supervise children. Ensure that gates and fences around the playground are maintained. Reinforce the message that very young children are never to run onto the street or cross it without holding an adult's hand. Help preschoolers and school-agers learn traffic safety and laws.

4. Help children learn bicycle safety rules and ensure that children wear CSA-approved and properly fitted bicycle helmets. Model safe bike riding.

POISONING

1. Regularly identify and remove potentially hazardous products in the interior space and playground. Keep all medication locked and out of reach of children. Keep first-aid kits out of reach. Staff and parents must keep purses, knapsacks, and diaper bags off the floor and out of children's reach. Post the poison control centre's phone number by every phone. Teach children not to eat plants or berries without checking with an adult first.

2. Enforce the no-smoking policy in programs. Educators who smoke outside must not leave cigarette butts on the ground where young children can pick them up. Ashtrays must be carefully emptied and kept out of reach.

3 & 4. Provide education opportunities on drug and alcohol abuse for school-age children and parents (e.g., invite a guest speaker).

BURNS

1. Younger children must be supervised around water at all times. Ensure that the temperature of the hot water from faucets does not exceed 43°C (110°F). Hot beverages or fluids are not permitted in the play area, nor may staff drink them while holding children.

2. Kitchens must be inaccessible to unsupervised children. Children must be supervised during all cooking activities. All sources of heat (e.g., radiators, hot-water pipes, registers) accessible to children must not exceed 43°C (110°F). Install physical barriers around fireplaces, wood stoves, furnaces, and hot-water heaters if children have access to them.

3. Cover all unused electrical outlets with plastic outlet covers. Electrical cords should be out of children's reach.

4. Cover car seats, child restraints, and strollers with a blanket or towel to shade them from the sun. Older children and educators should be in the habit of checking vinyl seats and belt buckles before getting in the vehicle.

5. Place metal slides in shaded areas or plant trees or erect a structure that provides shade. Use metal slides in the morning before it gets too hot. If possible, pour cold water to cool the metal; there may be days when the slide is closed.

6. Matches and lighters must never be within children's reach. Keep purses, diaper bags, knapsacks, etc., off the floor and out of reach. Children can learn the fire message "Stop, drop, and roll."

7. See Cooking with Children, page 545.

Educators who travel to work on bikes are encouraged to wear a properly fitted helmet, not only for their own safety but also to model safe behaviour to children. Legislation requiring bike helmets is mandatory for children under 16 years old in several provinces and under consideration in other provinces and territories.

Drowning

Safe Kids Canada (2007, pp. 12–13) reports the following:

- An estimated 58 children age 14 and under drown every year in Canada, while another 140 are hospitalized for near-drowning.

- For children ages 1 to 4, drowning is the second-highest cause of injury-related death (15%), closely following motor vehicle crashes (17%).

- Lack of supervision is a critical factor in drowning for children of all ages. In a 10-year review of drowning incidents, the Canadian Red Cross found that 42% of drowning victims ages 5 to 14 did not have adult supervision at the time. Another Canadian study showed that all children under age 2 who drowned in bathtubs had been left unsupervised for a period of time.

Source: *Child and Youth Unintentional Injury: 1994–2003 Ten Years In Review,* pp. 12–13. Copyright © The Hospital for Sick Children, 2007.

Few drownings or near-drownings occur in programs. Still, young children can drown in as little as 5 cm (2 in.) of water, which means that educators must supervise young children around all water and help them develop a respect for it. Remember that even in winter, outdoor drowning is possible if a child falls through thin or melting ice on a body of water. Another possible hazard is an open door that leads from the playroom to the washroom. Educators should remember that children under three years (and some older children) need adult supervision in the washroom to assist with hygiene and ensure safety around toilets, in particular to prevent drowning (see Table 7.1, page 364).

Burns

"A child's skin, thinner than an adult's skin, burns 4 times more quickly and deeply than an adult's at the same temperature" (Safe Kids Canada, 2008, p. 16). "An estimated 40 children age 14 and under die from fires and other burns each year, while another 770 are hospitalized for serious injuries. The majority of deaths (75%) are due to smoke inhalation" (Safe Kids Canada, 2007, p. 16). There are four types of burns: contact burns, scalds, electrical burns, and chemical burns. In early childhood settings, children's burns usually result from scalding by hot tap water, soups, or beverages (including burn injuries to the mouth from micro-waved bottles) and contact burns from hot metal, such as slides (see Table 7.1, page 364). Safe Kids Canada (2007, p. 16) also reports the following:

- More than half (56%) of hospitalizations are caused by scald burns. Young children under the age of 5 suffer 83% of all scald injuries requiring hospital admission.

- Tap water causes 29% of scald burns requiring hospitalization.

- Other causes of hospitalization include fire and flame (34%) and contact burns from appliances such as fireplaces and woodstoves (7.5%).

- Children under age 5 have the highest risk for all types of burns. Nearly three quarters (73%) of hospitalizations in this age range are for scald burns.

Young children cannot understand the dangers of hot liquids and other burn hazards, and have slower reaction times than older children. Among older children, the leading causes of burn-related injuries are also scald burns for ages 5 to 9, and flame-related burns for ages 10 to 14.

Source: *Child and Youth Unintentional Injury: 1994–2003 Ten Years In Review*, pp. 12–13. Copyright © The Hospital for Sick Children, 2007.

Threats to Breathing

Choking results from inhaling or ingesting food or objects that obstruct the person's airway. Suffocation or strangulation occurs when external forces (such as a pillow over the face or a dangling scarf wound tightly around the neck) prevent air from entering the lungs. Entrapment occurs when a person's body part is caught within or under something that prevents the person from being able to take breaths (e.g., the head is caught in an opening of substandard playground equipment). If a person is deprived of oxygen for four minutes, brain damage can occur.

Educators must focus on

■ food, unsafe eating behaviour, and toys that can cause choking.

Latex balloons (often used in celebrations) should be banned from programs, as they are a major choking risk. They have been banned from all children's hospitals in Canada. The use of Mylar balloons is safer; however, once deflated, Mylar balloons must be discarded safely, just like plastic bags.

■ clothing that can cause strangulation.

Strangulation can result when clothing becomes caught on slides and climbers, and the child's head or clothing gets trapped in play equipment.

■ furniture and equipment that can entrap a child.

Entrapment can result when a child attempts to climb up a shelving unit that is not securely attached to the wall and the child's weight pulls the unit and its contents onto the child, or a child's head becomes trapped in the opening in a play structure.

Refer to Table 7.1 (page 364) for prevention strategies in early childhood settings. Safe Kids Canada (2007, p. 14) reports that

■ An estimated 44 children age 14 and under die every year in Canada from threats to breathing, while another 380 are hospitalized for serious injuries.

■ 80% of children who are treated for threats to breathing are under age 5.

■ Nearly all (94%) hospitalizations due to threats to breathing are from choking on food or other objects, while the remaining 6% are related to a mechanical cause (for example, strangulation by blind cords).

Source: *Child and Youth Unintentional Injury: 1994–2003 Ten Years In Review*, pp. 14. Copyright © The Hospital for Sick Children, 2007.

A piece of latex balloon is particularly difficult to dislodge from the airway, making it a common cause of choking death. Young children are at particular risk of choking on food because they are not yet able to grind their food to a safe size and may choke while running, laughing, talking, or crying with food in the mouth. Foods of particular concern for choking are raw carrots, nuts, popcorn kernels, hot dogs, and grapes. Older children are at risk of strangulation if props such as ropes around the neck (pretending to be a dog) are used for dramatic play. Blind or curtain cords and chains are also a strangulation hazard. Safe Kids Canada (2007, p. 15) also notes that common mechanical causes of choking "include coins, batteries, small toys, and toy parts. Objects that can fit into a cardboard toilet paper roll are a choking hazard." This is especially relevant for children under four. Sleeping environments should be free of soft bedding that could suffocate a child, such as comforters, pillows, crib bumpers, and stuffed animals.

> Safe Kids Canada calls for enhancements to product-related injury surveillance, reporting, enforcement and consumer education along with a renewal of product safety laws. Safe Kids Canada recommends the renewal of federal product legislation to include a 'precautionary principle' and 'general safety requirement' for all products. This would bring the product legislation framework in line with consumer expectations for safe products on the market. (Safe Kids Canada, 2007, p. 15)

Source: *Child and Youth Unintentional Injury: 1994–2003 Ten Years In Review*, pp. 15. Copyright © The Hospital for Sick Children, 2007.

Falls

Falls account for the primary reason for children's hospitalization in Canada:

> Approximately 37% of childhood injury hospital admissions are attributed to falls.... Falls from chairs and beds or down stairs and steps cause nearly one-quarter (23%) of all (non-playground) fall-related hospital admissions to children age 14 and under. Almost half (45%) of these falls involve serious injuries to the head and neck. Head injuries can leave a child with permanent brain damage. This can take many forms, from speech problems and learning difficulties to memory loss and mood swings. Many of these effects can last a lifetime.
>
> Although falls from windows are rare and not captured in the data, they can cause devastating injuries and death. These incidents usually happen when a child reaches an open window by climbing onto furniture. Children under age 5 are particularly vulnerable to these falls because they like to climb and explore, but do not have a sense of danger. (Safe Kids Canada, 2007, p. 24)

Falls are by far the most common cause of injury in early childhood environments—not surprisingly, because they can happen anywhere at any time! These falls can happen both indoors and outdoors. Like adults, children trip on stairs, mats, loose carpets, toys, and other objects and slip in spills of water or sand. Although most falls result in minor injuries such as cuts, scrapes, or sprains, others can be serious or even life threatening, causing broken bones, head injuries, or internal or external bleeding. A fall down the stairs in a baby walker is twice as likely to cause a serious head injury. "One study found that more than two-thirds of babies in walkers were being supervised at the time of the injury" Safe Kids Canada, 2007, p. 35). Baby walkers with wheels have been banned in Canada.

Playground falls are common and can be serious, especially if the child falls onto an inadequate protective surface (see Table 7.1, page 364). With regard to all playground injuries, Safe Kids Canada (2007, p. 26) reports the following:

- Each year, Canadian children have an approximate 1 in 2,300 risk of being seriously injured on the playground from a fall.

- Approximately 14% of children are hospitalized for head injuries; 81% for broken bones in other parts of the body; and the remainder (5%) for injuries such as dislocations and open wounds.

- Falls from heights greater than 5 feet (1.5 m) double the risk of severe injury for children of all ages.

- Young children under age 5 are often injured because they are still developing their balancing and climbing skills, putting them at increased risk for falls.

- Older children ages 5 to 9 may be injured because they like to challenge themselves on equipment, such as jumping off the top of slides or using equipment in other ways for which it was not designed. Injuries are much less common in older children, since they use playgrounds infrequently.

Source: *Child and Youth Unintentional Injury: 1994–2003 Ten Years In Review*, p. 26. Copyright © The Hospital for Sick Children, 2007.

Poisoning

Poisoning is rarely fatal but can result in serious illness. "An estimated 7 children age 14 and under die every year in Canada from poisoning, and another 1,700 are hospitalized for serious injuries" (Safe Kids Canada, 2007, p. 22). It is a common pediatric emergency that can be a traumatic experience. In fact, poisoning is the fourth cause of injury hospitalization for preschoolers (Canadian Institute of Child Health, 2000, p. 73). "Poison proofing" is the term commonly used to describe the process of identifying and keeping potentially hazardous products out of children's reach. However, it's important to recognize that poison proofing is an ongoing process, not a one-time thing (e.g., in an early childhood setting, you have products locked away, but parents put purses and diaper bags on the floor that may contain products that children can get into). It's logical that poisonings happen much more often in children's homes. Early childhood settings usually don't have many hazardous products (pesticides, paints, gasoline, medications, nail polish and remover, ashtrays and cigarettes, alcohol, etc.), and the ones they have are locked out of the children's reach (as part of the poison proofing at the program). Almost any substance taken in sufficient quantities can be a poison (see Table 7.1, page 364). Poisoning can occur when someone

- Eats or drinks a hazardous product,

- Touches or spills a product on the skin and the chemical is absorbed through the skin, or

- Breathes in fumes of liquids.

Safe Kids Canada (2007, p. 22) also reports that

- Medication is involved in 67% of all unintentional poisoning of children age 14 and under. Other causes include a wide range of products such as household cleaners, alcohol, plants, fertilizers, pesticides, paint thinner, and antifreeze.

- Among medications, iron pills are a leading cause of death for children. Iron supplements are commonly taken by women of childbearing age; parents need to take extra care to make sure these pills are stored out of reach.

- Carbon monoxide poisoning, although rare, can cause coma or death.

- Nearly two-thirds (64%) of poisoning incidents occur in children age 1 to 4. This age group is at risk for poisoning in part because they are at a developmental stage of putting items in their mouths and exploring their environments.

Source: *Child and Youth Unintentional Injury: 1994–2003 Ten Years In Review,* pp. 22. Copyright © The Hospital for Sick Children, 2007.

HOW CAN WE PROMOTE CHILDREN'S SAFETY?

The challenge for educators is to provide an environment that is not only developmentally challenging but is also as safe as possible so that children can be physically active and gain new skills. Educators and parents recognize that bumps, scrapes, and bruises are a normal part of growing up. Children are inevitably injured when using play equipment. However, the likelihood of broken bones and head or internal injuries is minimized if the equipment is developmentally appropriate, the protective surfaces are adequately maintained, the children use the equipment properly, and the educators actively supervise their activities. By modelling safe but not overly anxious behaviour, adults help children develop an awareness of safety. The adage "Do as I say, not as I do" does not apply to safety, or to anything else, for that matter. Children will adopt adults' behaviour, whether it is appropriate or not.

. . . .

It is much more likely that children will learn safe pedestrian behaviour when they see adults using crosswalks (pushing the crosswalk's flashing light and pointing), waiting for walk signs, stopping to look both ways before crossing the street, and not walking between parked cars. The opposite can also be true. If children see adults breaking safety rules that they have been told to follow, they will not see how these rules apply to their own safety.

. . . .

Educators' observation skills are continually tested in terms of identifying the following elements to ensure children's safety:

- changes in children's physical and cognitive abilities

- the need for changes in the play area's design or layout

- hazardous equipment and playing surfaces

- inappropriate use of equipment

- tired or hungry children

- questionable use of safety rules or levels of supervision for specific activities

We use scenarios throughout this section to illustrate how educators can anticipate and prevent serious childhood injuries. Educators' understanding of children's development is an integral component in injury prevention.

OBJECTIVES

To identify the role of public policy in safety promotion.

To describe the importance of training, including emergency training, in safety promotion.

To identify strategies in an ongoing evaluation of the indoor and outdoor environment.

To view active supervision as an essential component of injury prevention and to identify the various factors that affect the level of supervision.

To understand the limited role that safety rules play in injury prevention and describe the essential considerations in developing and adapting rules for each age group.

You would not permit a toddler to use the school-ager's slide any more than you would permit a 10-year-old to drive. Although the toddler might manage to climb the steps and sit down before sliding, he or she could fall at any time. Moreover, the slide itself is designed for children much larger than a toddler and has spaces between the steps and at the top that toddlers could fall through. Similarly, although the 10-year-old could reach the gas pedal and drive a car in a straight line, that child is incapable of handling potential road hazards. In both of these examples, the children are neither physically nor cognitively ready to accomplish these tasks.

Role of Public Policy in Promoting Safety

As stated earlier in this unit, the overall child injury death rate declined by 37% and the injury hospitalization rate declined by 34% in Canada between 1994 and 2003 (Safe Kids Canada, 2007, p. 2). The most compelling reason for this reduction and positive direction is successful public policy changes that make children's environments safer. "The overall reduction in injury rates can be attributed in part to the combined efforts of legislators and public policy makers, medical and public health professionals, safety organizations, community partners that run local programs, and corporate sponsors" (Safe Kids Canada, 2007, p. 3).

Safer environments, such as municipalities and businesses installing speed bumps, provincial and territorial governments passing legislation on car seats and booster seats, and some provincial and territorial governments having legislation for bike helmets, and the establishment of national standards and guidelines on children's playspaces and equipment (CSA, 2007) are all examples of strategies that promote safety and reduce injuries for all children. Canada needs further public policy changes, ongoing enforcement of laws or standards, and data on the most effective strategies to continue to improve our track record on childhood injuries and injury-related deaths and hospitalizations. *Reaching for the Top: Report by the Advisor on Healthy Children and Youth* notes that Canada has a shameful standing of 22nd among 29 OECD (Organization for Economic Cooperation and Development) countries when it comes to preventable childhood injuries and deaths (Leitch, 2007, p. 3). At the top of Leitch's five key recommendations is "developing a national injury prevention strategy" (2007, p. 3). Priority strategies in this recommendation include the following:

- Creating a Strategic Plan for Injury Prevention for Children and Youth. The Government of Canada should take the lead role in the development and implementation of this five-year national strategic plan to be established in the next twelve months.

- Supporting Helmet Use.

  Extending the Children's Fitness Tax Credit to include the purchase of protective helmets used in physical activities that qualify within the guidelines of the Children's Fitness Tax Credit.

- Eliminating Toxic Toys.

  The Government of Canada should enact legislation that includes restrictions on hazardous substances in products designed for children and youth, such as lead and mercury.

■ Promoting Booster Seats and Protective Equipment.

Encourage provinces to show leadership and make mandatory the requirement for booster seats for children aged 4–8 until they weigh 36–45 kg (80–100 lbs.) or until they are 132–145 cm (52–57 inches) in height. (Leitch, 2007, p. 4)

Source: *Child and Youth Unintentional Injury: 1994–2003 Ten Years In Review,* pp. 3. Copyright © The Hospital for Sick Children, 2007.

At the centre of prevention is what is known as the precautionary approach, also referred to as the precautionary principle. The Canadian government began to adopt this approach in 2000, and its application is continuing to emerge in science-based regulatory programs. The impetus for this approach is to strengthen risk management practices across the federal public service.

Precautionary Approach

The absence of full scientific certainty (often called "burden of proof") is not a reason to postpone decisions that may result in serious or irreversible harm (Environment Canada, 2001, p. 1). This is known as the **precautionary approach** or precautionary principle within science-based risk management. In other words, although scientific research is essential in all matters of public health and safety, there are times when absolute proof of harm or death would likely mean unnecessary injury, disease, or death. If there is sufficient evidence determined by experts to call the product or practice into question, the ethical decisions would follow the precautionary approach. This precautionary approach primarily affects the development of options and the decision phases and is ultimately guided by judgment, based on values and priorities.

With regard to the chemical bisphenol A (BPA) used in the production of plastics (see Plastics, page 428), the Government of Canada banned its use in the production of baby bottles in April 2008. "In their assessment published in April 2008, Health Canada scientists adopted a precautionary approach in identifying that newborns and young infants may be more sensitive to BPA. Therefore, measures were recommended to ensure that they are exposed to the lowest levels of BPA possible" (Health Canada, 2008, p. 1).

This example illustrates the advancement of children's safety in Canada resulting from public policy changes and enforcement, as well as the use, when warranted, of the precautionary approach. However, in no way is this meant to undervalue the essential practices in day-to-day prevention strategies. Early childhood educators have an important responsibility in following policies and practices to ensure optimal safety for children in their care. The next section in this unit and Table 7.1 (page 364) outline how this is done.

Implementing Prevention Strategies

The following four components are interconnected, and one or more can either cause or prevent injuries:

■ training
■ physical environment

- supervision of children
- safety rules

> The climber is developmentally appropriate, but the protective surface is not maintained. The children understand the safety rules for using the climber, and an educator is assigned to supervise the children. Kamal loses his balance on the ladder and falls to the ground. He suffers a mild concussion because the protective surface was not up to standard.

Training

Once you complete your early childhood education (ECE) training, you will be equipped with entry-level skills and knowledge. No one should expect you to be ready or willing to accept a supervisor's role. However, you will be able to take an active role in safety promotion because you will know the fundamental principles of child development and how to integrate them with your observation skills. Your knowledge and abilities in injury prevention will be enhanced as you improve your observation skills through work experience. Promoting safety in the early childhood program involves positive attitudes, knowledge, and behaviour. Your commitment to seeking up-to-date information about safety, putting this information into practice, and modelling safe behaviour yourself are all part of your responsibility. Training opportunities may be on the job or through courses, conferences, and possibly ongoing committee work or networking.

One possible consequence of injuries is the need for educators to administer first aid to children. Although regulations vary across Canada, all early childhood regulations stipulate that a specified number of educators in a program must have current first-aid certificates. First-aid techniques cannot be learned solely from a book. Try putting on a sling properly from looking at a picture! It's not as simple as it may appear. Educators must know how to manage choking in children and adults and how to apply first aid. Ideally, ECE training programs ensure that their students take a standard first-aid course applicable to children and receive a certificate from a first-aid training program recognized by their early childhood office. Every student is strongly encouraged or required to obtain certification in cardiopulmonary resuscitation (CPR), including infant/child CPR. Certification in first aid and CPR not only demonstrates your professional commitment to safety but also is an important and relevant skill on a résumé. A second consequence of injuries is that educators must document all injuries that occur while children are under your care, even when first aid was not administered (see Injury Reports, page 431).

Serious Occurrences

Training can also arise from analyzing serious occurrence reports. Every province and territory child care office defines what is reportable as a serious occurrence and outlines the procedure and forms to be completed. The category of **serious occurrences** covers more than the obvious injuries that happen to children and adults, or even death, and also includes other incidents, such as

- a child being missing, even for a short period of time;
- a disaster on the premises, such as a fire;
- a threat of disaster, such as a bomb scare;

- any allegations of abuse or mistreatment of a child against staff, ECE students, volunteers, or other adults; and

- any serious complaint made by or about a child, a parent, or staff. Serious occurrence reporting is an ongoing process with annual summary and analysis reports. These reports provide the opportunity for the child care office to review and reflect on possible patterns of occurrences. Patterns of serious occurrences suggest a need for changes, such as training, support, or internal policy amendments, as well as steps to address any of these needs. Upon reviewing the report, ministry personnel may also identify other issues or additional action. For optimal safety promotion, it is essential that educators recognize the importance of reporting serious occurrences consistently and view the annual review process as a training opportunity to continue learning about high-quality early childhood environments. Reflecting and acting on program changes mean that everyone benefits. The provincial or territorial child care office goes beyond requiring accountability. It also play a critical role in advising and training to improve the quality of early childhood programs.

Physical Environment

Children's safety is one of the main priorities when designing and furnishing the physical setting. When prioritizing steps in promoting children's safety, the physical environment tops the list (ahead of supervision and safety rules). Regardless of the level of adult supervision or children's own awareness, children are at undue risk when the environment itself is inherently dangerous. Safety features should include the safe placement of electrical outlets and heating radiators and vents or electric baseboard heaters, safety glass in doors and the windows that separate rooms, doors that won't crush fingers, handrails on stairs for children, and hot-water temperatures that won't scald. These and other safety features, such as smoke alarms and carbon monoxide detectors, are the concern of the early childhood office, director, and board of directors.

Indoor Environments

Infants and toddlers are rapidly changing and learning new skills. Educators draw on their knowledge of growth and development and their observation skills to identify changes in each child and in the social relations among the children as a group. In response, educators may have to adjust the overall layout of the play area and frequently remove or add new and more challenging play material and equipment to meet individual children's next stage of development. Toddler programs that are sterile environments devoid of large motor challenges can result in children withdrawing, becoming aggressive (e.g., biting), or physically challenging themselves in inappropriate ways.

CRITICAL THINKING

Ten-month-old Jared is learning to climb. He is particularly fond of climbing on the box that covers the heat radiator in the playroom. On one attempt, he falls backward onto his bottom and bangs his head on the floor. How could you have prevented this injury?

Organizing the indoor space provides opportunities for educators to prevent injuries for all age groups:

- In planning the room arrangement, consider the traffic areas so that paths lead children between activity centres rather than through them, without creating congestion.
- Provide areas with enough space for children to explore material and so that other children don't have to walk through that area.
- Establish boundaries by using shelves or dividers and carpeting to your advantage, to break up open spaces that children would run in.
- When considering where to place the table and chairs in the playroom, allow enough space for the chairs to be pulled out while the children stand and sit during an activity and for a clear walkway behind the chair. (The walkway will reduce the likelihood of children tripping on chair legs.) This rule also applies to easels.
- Provide storage units and organize the space so that children can return materials and supplies. Add pictorial labels to shelves, boxes, and so on to guide children in putting toys and material away during cleanup.
- Secure all shelving so that it cannot be tipped over. Limit the height so that educators can view the room.
- Ensure that the block area is away from the traffic area.
- Choose round or curved tables rather than straight-edged tables.
- For the water and sand tables:
  - Place them on tile floor for easy cleanup (because children and staff can slip in spilled water and sand).
  - Keep cleanup tools handy at children's level (e.g., dustpan, broom, mop).
  - Sand on the floor should either be discarded or put into the outdoor sandbox.

Furniture

Furniture should meet the needs of both the children and the adults. Tables, chairs, cots, activity centres, bookshelves, and so on must be durable and of a size that suits the children who use them. However, early childhood facilities are also workplaces, so they must also meet the physical needs of the adults who work in them. Adult chairs should be available in the eating area and comfortable chairs or sofas in the play area for educators to read books, cuddle children, and feed infants. But don't forget that the adult-sized furniture must also be child-safe.

- A 15-month-old boy is crawling around a rocking chair at the same time that an educator is giving an infant her bottle. The boy's fingers become caught under a runner.
- A preschooler uses the levered handle for a recliner's footrest and her hand gets caught in the metal mechanism when she closes it.

From the standpoint of safety, much of the furniture manufactured for infants must meet the safety criteria established by Health Canada's Consumer Product Safety division. Their publication *Is Your Child Safe?* (see Resource Materials, page 439) assists educators and parents in purchasing used furniture that meets safety standards. With the cribs, highchairs, strollers, and possibly playpens in place in programs, what practices are needed to ensure children's safety on a daily basis? (See Table 7.2.)

As of 2004, Health Canada banned the sale, import, and advertisement of baby walkers. These walkers are dangerous equipment, and Canada's ban is the first in the world. "It is a criminal offence to sell, advertise, or import new or used baby walkers, even for your own use. It is also a criminal offence to give them away" (Safe Kids Canada, 2007, p. 3). Walkers give infants a vehicle that can propel them at speeds that they are unable to handle. An infant walker has a rigid frame with a fabric seat and leg openings attached to a wheeled base. Adults are surprised at how quickly a baby can pick up speed in a walker, which often makes it impossible for an adult to stop the child before she or he tips over or crashes down the stairs. Since the infant is off the floor, he or she can reach cords and objects off low tables, which can lead to burns, poisonings, and other injuries. Since 1989, 15 years before the ban, manufacturers had voluntarily ceased the production and sale of walkers in Canada. Yet parents continued to buy them from street vendors and garage sales, borrow and lend them, or buy them outside of Canada. A 2003 survey by Safe Kids Canada showed that nearly one-third (32%) of parents were using or had recently used baby walkers with wheels for their young children (Safe Kids Canada, 2007, p. 25).

In addition to the safety hazards, walkers put infants in an upright position, although many of them may not be able to sit unsupported. Infants' physical development evolves through a series of stages, each of which prepares them for the next. Walkers not only confine children but also prevent them from moving naturally and using their developing skills and abilities. The lesson learned from the deaths and injuries over the years from baby walkers is that new ideas and designs in furniture and play equipment must be evaluated for safety on an ongoing basis.

Indoor Play Equipment

Programs provide children with play materials, equipment, and toys manufactured for children. Play materials can also be inexpensive objects found around the house—empty containers, wooden spoons, measuring cups, blankets, scarves and hats, used clothes, pillows, cardboard boxes, pieces of wood, sand, and water. Toys and materials must be developmentally appropriate to ensure the safety of the particular age group using them. For children under three years old, toys or toy pieces must be too large to fit into a toilet roll tube to be deemed safe. Toys for school-age children, for example, often have small pieces and removable parts, such as doll clothes and accessories or limbs, which can be pulled off and might choke younger children. Paints, glues, and coloured paper must be nontoxic to protect children who put them in their mouth. Battery-operated toys should be avoided for young children: batteries are toxic (see Environmental Contaminants, page 421) and may wind up in the mouth or, worse, swallowed, in addition to the likelihood that there is little play value in battery-operated toys. Health Canada provides specific updated warnings and advisories on its website (see Resource Materials, page 439).

TABLE 7.2	Using Infant and Toddler Equipment Safely

EQUIPMENT	SAFETY PRACTICES
Cribs	■ The railing must be up and secure after putting the child in to sleep. ■ Bumper pads and large stuffed toys should not be in the crib once the child can stand up inside so that neither can be used by the child to climb over the side. ■ Never provide an infant with a pillow because of the risk that an infant who has rolled face down will be unable to roll over and avoid suffocation. ■ To prevent strangling, blind and drapery cords must be secured away from cribs. Strings attached to mobiles and crib gyms must not be within children's reach (lying or standing).
Highchairs	■ Never leave children unsupervised. ■ Always use the safety belts, but don't assume that children can't wiggle out of or unfasten them. ■ Ensure that the child's fingers, hands, and head can't be trapped when putting on or taking off the tray. ■ Help children learn that they must always sit down in the chair and that standing is not permitted. ■ Don't place chairs near doorways, stoves, fridges, or walls where children could tip the chair over by pushing against it with their feet. ■ When chairs are not in use, keep them out of reach of children to prevent toddlers from trying to climb on them.
Strollers	■ Never leave children unsupervised. ■ Check that all locking mechanisms are secure, ensuring that the stroller doesn't collapse. ■ Check all the brakes. ■ Use brakes when children are getting in and out or when parked with children inside. ■ Watch that hands and fingers are clear before reversing the handle. ■ Always use the safety belts, but don't assume that children can't wiggle out of or unfasten the belt. ■ Don't overload the handles with knapsacks, bags, etc., that can cause the stroller to tip. ■ Help children learn that they must always sit down.
Playpens*	■ Ensure that the sides are up and secure. ■ Avoid large stuffed toys and boxes, etc., that children can use as steps to climb over the side. ■ To prevent strangling, blind and drapery cords must be secured away from playpens; mobiles and crib gyms with strings must not be within children's reach (lying or standing). ■ Keep playpens out of direct sunlight as hot vinyl might burn the child's skin. ■ Keep playpens out of direct sunlight as hot vinyl might burn the child's skin. ■ Check the vinyl mattress or railings for tears that children could bite off and choke on. ■ Do not use for children who either are tall enough or weigh enough to crawl over or tip over the playpen.

*When not sleeping, infants and toddlers must have the freedom to explore, play, and socialize in environments that are safe and secure. The routine use of playpens is discouraged for children of any age. Some programs use them for young infants outside or as a temporary safe place before returning children to the play area after diapering.

Each day, educators inspect toys for the following:

- broken parts or pieces; when found, they are repaired or put safely in the garbage
- torn seams on stuffed toys and dolls that could permit stuffing to come out
- chipped paint, rusting metal, etc.
- sharp or splintered edges
- exposed hinges or pinch points between moving parts
- frayed rope

Outdoor Play Equipment

The outdoor environment in the early childhood program is filled with joy and learning, especially when it is designed to meet the needs and interests of the children and when educators give the outdoor curriculum the ongoing attention it deserves. The play-based nature of the outdoor environment provides an opportunity to enhance all areas of the child's development, such as physical development (see Unit 6, page 310), problem solving, language, social development, creative expression, and, of course, self-confidence. Outdoor play can enhance physical agility and fitness, reduce stress through games, provide contact with nature, fuel the imagination, and bestow freedom of movement—the list is almost endless. Many resources are available to support educators' awareness and planning of the outdoor curriculum, which is essential to a high-quality ECE and care program (see Resource Materials, page 439).

Most serious injuries in early childhood programs occur on the playground. The CSA standards are intended to promote and encourage the provision and use of outdoor play spaces that are well designed, well maintained, innovative, and challenging to support children's healthy development (CSA, 2007). If operators do so, the contribution to children's health is substantial. At present, the challenge with stringent standards is achieving optimal safety, but not to the extreme, which can eliminate the integrity of developmentally appropriate risk. Wherever possible, the standards indicate modifications to the development of play spaces and equipment to make them accessible to children with a range of special needs.

The CSA suggests a range of environments and equipment for play activities, dividing the age groups into preschool (18 months to 5 years old) and school age (5 to 12 years old), recognizing 5 as a transition age for physical growth and development and acknowledging the fact that as children get older, their abilities, interests, and needs change. Educators are responsible for ensuring that children safely use equipment designed for appropriate age and ability levels (see Table 7.2, page 380, and Table 7.3).

In the vast majority of playground injuries, two characteristics of the environment have a major influence on the severity: the quality of the cushioning material and the height from which the child falls. The ground space under and around each piece of equipment, called the **encroachment area**, must have a surface that cushions a child's fall as much as possible. The encroachment areas help protect not only the children using the equipment but also those walking by. Whenever possible, the areas should be clearly marked off to create pathways

TABLE 7.3   Suggested Facilities and Equipment for Play Activities

F.3.1   Preschool and kindergarten children (toddlers)

Suggested facilities and equipment for preschool and kindergarten children are shown in the following table:

Activity	Suggested facilities and equipment*
Physical play	– a hard-surface routes, preferably a large or circular one for wheeled toys – facilities and space for large-muscle activities such as climbing equipment or swings – soft open space for running or ball games; the space for physical play should approximate 40% of the space in a playground
Social play (playing in small groups)	– playhouse and other structures to encourage imaginative play – landscaped enclosure – table and benches or chairs
Manipulative cognitive play (to create or manipulate)	– sandbox – natural areas, pots and pans, outdoor blocks, boards, outdoor drawing boards, and water play such as spray pads
Quiet retreat play (to rest, imagine, or watch)	– enclosures, landscaped or fenced – table with seating – perch or hideaway

Facilities should be used only under supervision.

F.3.2   School-aged children

Suggested facilities and equipment for school-aged children are shown in the following table:

Activity	Suggested facilities and equipment
Physical play	
– Games with balls or aerial objects (such as Frisbee, ball hockey, or kite flying)	– open and level expanse of grass or hard surface, uninterrupted by trees or electric wires – enclosure — fence or berm – seating at periphery
– Ground-related games using the whole body (such as tag or roller skating)	– open, level, hard-surface area or grassy area, not necessarily flat – enclosure — fence or berm – seating at periphery
– Strategy games requiring smaller spaces (such as marbles, hopscotch, or tether ball)	– protected small areas, 1 to 3 m^2 (39.37 to 118, 11 in^2) – smaller hard-surface or grass areas
– Activities that challenge dexterity and muscular control	– climbing structures, balance bars, or swings
– Specific skills (such as skateboarding)	– see Clause F.3.4
Manipulative cognitive play	– loose materials, such as blocks, boards, ropes, sand, water sprays, natural areas (some of these activities require supervision; see Annex A)
Social play	– tables and seating, table games such as chess, sheltered space, natural area

F.3.3 Sand play areas

F.3.3.1 Size

The sand area should be large enough to encompass the activities of several groups of children without interference. The total sand play area should be in proportion to the size of the overall play area. Where there are likely to be large numbers of children of varying ages, the total area for sand play may be divided into several smaller sand play areas. A 2×2 m (78.74 × 78.74 in) sand area can be a comfortable cognitive sand play area for a group of up to ten children. A minimum total sand play area of 6 × 7 m (236.22 × 275.59 in) is desirable in public parks and other public play areas. (This total should not include impact sand in the equipment area.) Sand play is a popular play experience for children of all ages, and the play area design should maximize the total amount of space for sand play.

F.3.3.2 Types of sand

The sand for creative play should pack together for moulding. Thoroughly washed brick sand or an equivalent such as seaside sand should be used. Blow sand should not be used.

The sand should be free of organic material, dirt, clay, silt, iron, asbestos, and other contaminants.

F.3.3.3 Depth of sand for play

The sand depth should allow for major excavations by the child without disturbing the foundations and drainage. A minimum sand depth of 200 mm (7.87 in) is recommended. The preferred depth of sand is 450 mm (17.72 in), See Figure F3.

F.3.3.4 Location

The sand play area should be exposed to the purifying effects of sun and rain, but some natural shade and shelter (from wind and sun) should be provided.

F.3.3.5 Drainage

The sand play area, regardless of soil conditions, should be designed to drain well. Means of drainage should be prevented from clogging. For day or poorly draining soils, drainage tiles to an outlet are recommended.

F.3.3.6 Protection

The design, the location, and the maintenance schedule should discourage pets from soiling the sand. Sandbox covers, where used, should be designed to be safely secured both in the open and closed positions.

F.3.3.7 Design recommendations

The design recommendations for a sand play area are as follows:
(a) The sand play area should be located so that children are discouraged from using it for active play. It should not be located in the physical play zone.
(b) Where it is undesirable to have sand tracked onto other nearby surfaces, a paved strip or a strip of pea gravel can be provided. A sand grate at a building entry also reduces the problem of tracking sand.
(c) The sand container should provide flat ledges or tables for children to use. If the container edge is provided as a ledge, it should be a minimum of 85 mm (3.34 in). A curb at the periphery of the ledge to prevent sand from falling over the edge is desirable (see Figure F.3)
(d) The sand play area may have access to water for moistening the sand.

P.16

JUL–30–2008

© Canadian Standards Association

Children's playspaces and equipment

(continued)

F.3.3.7   Design recommendations

(e) A seating area for adults should be located near the sand play area.

(f) Young children show a preference to locate their play in corners and edges of sand play areas. A design that maximizes edges and corners is preferable.

(g) Where possible, natural elements (e.g., trees, boulders) should be included in the sand play area.

E.3.4   Skateboard hills

Skateboard hills, when provided, should be designed with the awareness that they will also be used by unauthorized users such as cyclists and roller skaters. A skateboard facility should have a detailed plan to minimize collisions between users. Appropriate fencing or other barriers should be provided at the top of the slope (see Figure F.4).

Source: Reproduced with the permission of Canadian Standards Association from "CAN/CAS-Z614/07-Children's Playspaces and Equipment" which is copyrighted by Canadian Standards Association, 5060 Spectrum Way, Suite 100 Mississauga, ON L4W 5N6. While use of this material has been authorized, CSA shall not be responsible for the manner in which the information is presented, nor for any interpretations thereof.

that can be followed by children and staff. This should prevent anyone from getting hit by a swing, by a child jumping off the climber, or by someone coming off the end of a slide.

Pressure-treated wood is permeated with a chemical called copper-chromium-arsenate (CCA), which is a mixture of salts of copper, chromium, and arsenic that protects the wood from damage by insects, mould, sun, and water. These chemicals potentially have an impact upon the health of a child, although the full effect may not be seen for many years. Arsenic, for example, is a known human poison and a carcinogen (i.e., it causes cancer) and is used to kill rats. Pressure-treated wood has been used in the construction of decks, fences, retaining walls, picnic tables, play structures, and borders to contain the cushioning material that covers the encroachment areas. Over time, chromium, copper, and arsenic can leach out of the wood onto its surface and into the ground surrounding the structure.

Because children often come into close contact with such structures built with pressure-treated wood, there is a serious concern for children. Although small amounts of arsenic are not thought to be harmful, it is always best to avoid unnecessary exposure. Children may be particularly vulnerable to long-term effects (see Environmental Contaminants, page 421). Children playing on such a structure can have substantial exposure because they often play for long periods of time and frequently put their hands into their mouth.

This issue came to the attention of the Canadian public in 2002, and most jurisdictions in Canada have made necessary changes to minimize children's exposure, such as using a penetrating oil-based wood-finishing sealant on the structure. Reapplying the sealant every 1 or 2 years can help reduce the amount of arsenic released by as much as 90% (Toronto Public Health, 2003). "As of December 31, 2003, the wood treatment industry in Canada stopped treating wood with CCA for use in residential and recreational settings" (Canadian Cancer Society, 2008, p. 1). Since 2003, when building structures or marking off encroachment areas, cedar, redwood, metal, and plastic are used. The CSA guidelines for wood intended for playground equipment state that "creosote, penta-chlorophenol, tributyl tin oxide, and surface coatings that contain pesticides shall not be used" (2007, p. 7). For facilities with existing pressure-treated wood, the safety of these structures should be evaluated by licensing bodies, which will make requirements or suggestions on minimizing exposure.

The layout of the equipment is another factor in the design of a safe playground. The CSA (2007, pp. 28–32) requires an obstacle-free protective surfacing zone, depending on the type of play equipment. According to the CSA's publication *Children's Playspaces and Equipment* (2007), play spaces are defined as areas that contain public-use playground equipment designed for children from 18 months to 5 years of age while being supervised by adults. In addition, this entire space is completely surrounded by at least a 1.2 m (4 ft.) high fence with a lockable entrance gate. Variations are around encroachment zones in this type of play space.

A child can receive a fatal head injury from falling just 30 cm (12 in.) onto protective surfacing or concrete. CSA standards specify the types of materials that can be used for each piece of equipment and how deep these materials must be. Sand, pea gravel, or wood bark chips are used. Some programs use synthetic (manufactured) materials as the cushion material in playgrounds. This material, made from recycled tires, comes in sheets of various thicknesses and allows for water drainage. The best-suited material depends on the specific piece of equipment, the age of the children using it, weather conditions, availability, and cost (e.g., sand that is constantly soaked by rain loses some of its impact-absorbing quality, so pea gravel that allows water drainage may be a better choice). Tables 7.4 and 7.5 elaborate on the various materials used as **protective surfaces**. These are materials used to cushion a fall, under and around playground equipment, with any defined fall height. The material most suitable may also depend on the focus of the play space. *For example, if a program has a vision to develop an outdoor space that is as natural an environment as possible, sand or wood chips are obviously more compatible with this vision.*

Cushioning materials are critical safety features, but falls from heights greater than 1.5 m (5 ft.) double the risk of severe injury for children of all ages (Safe Kids Canada, 2007, p. 26). This is true even with 22 cm (9 in.) of pea gravel covering the encroachment area. Challenging, enjoyable playgrounds offer a wide range of experiences; they do not place the emphasis on the limited challenges that the height of the equipment offers to children.

Over time, equipment shows the effects of daily use and weathering. Walking and running pack down some protective surfaces, such as sand. Whatever material is used must be maintained to ensure that it is fulfilling its purpose. For these reasons, educators are responsible for regularly checking the surfaces and maintaining the equipment. Programs that use public or school playgrounds cannot assume that the equipment is inspected regularly. Educators should check the

TABLE 7.4   Comparison of Protective Surfacing Materials

Table D. 1
Comparison of protective surfacing materials chart
(See Clauses 10,3.3, D.1, and D.2)

Material type	Characteristics	Advantages	Disadvantages	Maintenance
Loose fill materials				
Sand	A natural, clean, and non-packing material. Size, texture, and composition of particles can vary. Some sand types are not appropriate for playground use because of a tendency to compact. With 300 mm (11.81 in) depth of material, an impact attenuation of more than 2.5 m (98.43 in) critical height, depending on the type of sand, can be achieved.	– Low to medium cost – Easy to obtain – Easy to install – Durable – Non-flammable – Some types provide excellent impact absorption qualities – Does not support microbial growth	– Can be hard to walk on – Cannot be used with wheelchairs or other mobility aides – Can be swallowed or get into user's eyes, hair, clothes, and shoes – Can hide insects, animal excrement, and sharp objects – Can be thrown, scattered, or tracked onto other surfaces – Moisture, high humidity, and freezing temperatures can reduce its effectiveness	– Can have higher ongoing maintenance costs (due to kick-out, redistribution, topping-up, etc.) – Requires regular inspection, periodic raking, levelling and sifting of compacted sand, removal of foreign matter. – Requires periodic addition of sand to top it up, typically every 1 to 3 y – Subsurface preparation is essential; it should not be installed over asphalt or concrete.
Pea gravel	Pea gravel consists of small, clean, and rounded particles. Crushed, broken, or irregular particle sizes should be avoided. With a 300 mm (11.81 in) depth of clean material, impact attenuation up to 2.5 m (98.43 in) critical height can be achieved.	– Low cost – Easy to obtain – Easy to install – Less attractive than sand to animals – Non-flammable – Does not support microbial growth – Can provide good drainage with proper base	– Can be hard to walk on and cannot be used with wheelchairs or other mobility aides – Can conceal insects, animal excrement, and sharp objects – Can be swallowed and put in ears or nose – Potential of formation of "hard pan" under surface – Can be thrown, scattered, and tracked onto other surfaces. On hard surfaces, it can contribute to slip-fall injuries – Moisture, high humidity, and freezing temperatures can reduce its effectiveness	– Can have higher ongoing maintenance costs (due to kick-out, redistribution, topping-up, etc.) – Requires regular inspection, periodic raking, and removal of foreign matter – Requires periodic addition of gravel to top it up, typically every 1 to 2 y – Clean-up of adjacent lawns and sidewalks is necessary – Subsurface preparation is essential; it should not be installed over asphalt or concrete.

| TABLE 7.4 | Comparison of Protective Surfacing Materials (*continued*) |

Material type	Characteristics	Advantages	Disadvantages	Maintenance
Loose fill materials				
Wood/bark mulch	Bark mulch comes from trees used in urban tree management and landscaping programs. Bark mulch can contain twigs and leaves. Wood chips generally do not contain twigs or leaves. Wood sources should be checked prior to chipping for toxins or allergens. With a 300 mm (11.81 in) depth of material, critical height of up to 3 m (118.11 in) can be obtained.	– Low cost – Easy to obtain – Attractive natural appearance – Retards insect infestation and fungal growth with its mildly acidic composition	– Can be swallowed or get into user's eyes – Can be thrown or scattered – Decomposes and compacts over time – Can conceal animal excrement and sharp objects – Supports microbial growth when wet – Moisture, high humidity, and freezing temperatures can reduce its effectiveness	– Can have higher on-going maintenance costs (due to kick-out, redistribution, topping-up, etc.) – Requires regular inspection, periodic raking, and removal of foreign matter – Requires periodic addition and replacement of bark mulch or wood chips, typically every 1 to 3 y – Should not be installed over asphalt or concrete
Engineered wood fibre	Engineered wood fibre is processed new or virgin wood. It contains no twigs or leaves. The wood source should be checked prior to chipping for toxins and allergens. Installation over asphalt or concrete can result in reduced impact results. With a 300 mm (11.81 in) depth of material, a critical height of more than 3 m (118.11 in) can be obtained.	– Wheelchair accessible – Fairly durable – Easy to obtain – Less abrasive than sand – Retards insect infestation and fungal growth – Free of twigs and leaves – Free of contaminants – Stays in place better than other loosefill surface material (e.g., sand, pea gravel) – Can be installed over hard surfaces under certain conditions	– Initially more expensive than other loose-fill options – Can conceal insects, animal excrement, and sharp objects – Supports microbial growth when wet – Moisture, high humidity, and freezing temperatures can reduce its effectiveness – Decomposes and compacts over time	– Can have higher ongoing maintenance costs (due to kick-out, redistribution, topping-up, etc.) – Requires regular inspection, periodic raking, and removal of foreign matter – Requires periodic addition and replacement of engineered wood fibre, typically every 3 to 5 y – Adequate drainage is essential and will lower long-term maintenance costs – Engineered wood fibre should not be worked or loosened

(*continued*)

TABLE 7.4   Comparison of Protective Surfacing Materials *(continued)*

Material type	Characteristics	Advantages	Disadvantages	Maintenance
Loose fill materials				
Shredded tire crumb	Rubber crumb is created by the grinding up of tire material. For playground use, rubber crumb should be free of metal or wire from the reprocessing of tires. Suppliers should also be able to confirm that the rubber does not contain lead, other toxins, or allergens such as latex. Installation over asphalt or concrete can result in reduced impact results. With a 200 mm (7.87 in) depth of material, a critical height of more than 3 m (118.11 in) can be achieved.	– Durable – Easy to install – Non-abrasive – Does not support microbial growth – Less attractive to animals – Some types of rubber crumb are wheelchair accessible	– Can conceal insects, animal excrement, and sharp objects – Wide variation in quality – Can contain wire or metal, or other toxins (e. g., lead, latex) – Can be thrown or scattered – Can hide foreign matter – Can be lodged in ears or nose, or dust particles can enter and remain in lungs	– Can have higher ongoing maintenance costs (due to kick-out, redistribution, topping-up, etc.) – Requires regular inspection, periodic raking, and removal of foreign matter – Requires periodic addition and replacement of surface material typically every 2 to 5 y
Unitary synthetic materials				
Tiles	Synthetic tiles and mats are a combination of a chemical binder and a rubber filler. Tiles are available in various thicknesses, lengths, colours, and patterns. The tiles must be installed according to the manufacturer's instructions. Installation over asphalt or concrete can cause	– Wheelchair accessible – Stay in place – Easy to clean – Consistent impact-absorbing qualities – Lower maintenance costs over the long term – Decompose slowly – Tend to be more stable than poured-in-place rubber surfacing	– More expensive than other surfacing materials because tiles typically have a shorter lifespan than the equipment – Require professional installation – Wide variation in quality – Will lose impact-attenuating properties over time	– Regular inspection for damage and debris – General maintenance cost involves sweeping, blowing, or vacuuming debris from surface – Damaged or worn tiles can be replaced – Tiles will need to be replaced when they lose their impact-absorbing ability

TABLE 7.4   **Comparison of Protective Surfacing Materials (*continued*)**

Material type	Characteristics	Advantages	Disadvantages	Maintenance
Loose fill materials				
	poor impact results without adequate subgrade preparation. A critical height of up to 3 m (118.11 in) can typically be achieved; however, the attenuation results are highly variable depending upon the manufacturer, type of rubber, depth, pattern, etc.			– A blower or vacuum is sometimes required to remove debris from air pockets found in tile surfaces
Pour-in-place	Pour-in-place is a seamless synthetic surface that is formed with a chemical binder and a rubber filler. It can be installed on concrete or asphalt but must be used at suitable thickness and be well anchored. A critical height of up to 3 m (118.11 in) can typically be achieved; however, the attenuation results are highly variable depending upon the manufacturer, type of rubber, and depth.	– Wheelchair accessible – Stays in place – Easy to clean – Consistent impact-absorbing qualities – Lower maintenance costs over the long term – Decomposes slowly – Tends to have better impact attenuation properties than tile surfacing	– More expensive than other surfacing materials because pour-in-place typically has a shorter lifespan than the equipment – Requires professional installation – Wide variation in quality – Will lose impact-attenuating properties over time	– Regular inspection for damage and debris – General maintenance cost involves sweeping, blowing, or vacuuming debris from surface – Surface can be repaired – Rubber surface will need to be replaced when it loses its impact- absorbing ability – Must be swept free of dirt and other debris that can collect and decrease its shock absorption – A blower or vacuum is sometimes required to remove debris from air pockets found in tile surface

TABLE 7.5   Some Elements that May Appear in a Supervised Play Area

A.3.1 Shelter

Consideration should be given to providing some protection from sun and inclement weather. Creative play activities and fine-motor activities can also be provided in such shelters. The design should be such that children can be easily supervised.

A.3.2 Storage

Some storage space is required in most supervised playgrounds. This should be a secure space for maintenance, materials, and equipment storage. If the design of the storage area allows for play use by children, there should be no possibility of children being trapped inside. The supervisor should be able to lock the door in an open position as well as lock it shut.

A.3.3 Water play areas

When possible, play areas should provide access to water to promote creative, social, and intellectual (cognitive) development. Play facilities that encourage playing with water are recommended. These can take the form of play streams, water channels, faucets, or manual pumps.

A.3.4 Loose materials

Loose materials are an essential ingredient for creative play and should be provided wherever possible. They should be provided in a supervised area with defined limits, such as an enclosure. A flat area, separated and protected from physical play activities that can interfere, should be provided.

Recommended loose materials include the following:

(a) large unit blocks and boards [20 × 200 mm (0.79 × 7.87 in)] in various lengths and hollow wooden blocks with recommended dimensions of 200 × 200 × 200 mm (7.87 × 7.87 × 7.87 in) and 200 × 200 × 400 mm (7.87 × 7.87 × 15.75 in). These should be stable enough to allow children to build small-scale spaces. All edges should be rounded, and the blocks and/or boards should possess the characteristics of a safe toy for young children. They should be finished for outdoor use and suitable in size, weight, and bulk for handling by small children;

(b) containers of all kinds;

(c) blankets, rugs, pieces of cloth; old clothes for dress-up;

(d) wagons and other wheeled toys, including wheelbarrows;

(e) paper and craft materials;

(f) balls and other objects;

(g) bolsters, cushions, and other soft and foam objects; and

(h) play parachutes and other elements for co-operative games.

Handles and grips on items should enable young children to achieve secure gripping and manipulation.

Other loose materials to be used outside the specified creative play area may also be offered. These can include props to encourage role play and dramatic play by young children, and tools and hardware for the activities of older children.

(continued)

equipment and promptly report problems and concerns. The next time you walk by a school or public playground, stop and examine the condition of the protective surfacing under the climbing equipment. You may have legitimate cause for concern for children's safety!

Depending on the problems with equipment, educators decide whether children can use a particular piece of equipment. Ultimately, staff are responsible for the children's safety. Staff are accountable if they knowingly permit children to use defective equipment or if it is shown that an apparent defect was not identified. In addition, educators take children off-site to other playgrounds and need to be able to assess the safety of that environment. Placing children at risk in an inherently unsafe environment, regardless of the level of supervision, is not ethically acceptable and can affect liability.

CRITICAL THINKING

One winter day, eight-year-old Joanna is playing on the climber in the school playground. The protective surface under the climber is covered with ice. Her hands slip from the rungs, and she falls to the ground. She is admitted to the hospital's emergency department with a broken arm. Her friend, Michael, had to run to tell an educator that Joanna was lying on the ground. What risks should have been identified? How could Joanna's injury, and other injuries, have been prevented?

Conducting Safety Checks

Educators' observations obviously play a significant role in preventing injuries throughout the day. Children, activities, issues, concerns, and other distractions will prevent any educator from identifying every potential safety risk in the environment. For this reason, regular safety checks are an essential component of injury prevention. Each day, the first educator who arrives in the morning, preferably before the children arrive, will walk through the interior of the space and playground, looking for items that must be attended to immediately. This could include replacing a burned-out light bulb in the stairwell, putting the plastic outlet covers in unused electrical outlets, or removing cat feces from the outdoor sandbox. As well, cupboards may have been left unlocked or hazardous products left out on a counter or floor when the space was cleaned the night before.

Before children go out to the playground each morning, educators need to conduct a quick check, looking for garbage, sharp objects (e.g., broken glass, discarded needles), discarded condoms, animal feces, protruding nails, puddles of water, ice on the protective surfaces, or wood chips that have been scattered by the wind or through use. Many early childhood facilities, depending on municipal regulations, must complete written checklists daily, often in both the morning and the afternoon. Ask to see and perhaps assist one of the educators complete the checklist at your practicum placement. Like our homes, early childhood facilities experience considerable wear and tear. Ideally, directors design standard checklists that are relevant to their particular building and playground. Weekly, monthly, and yearly **safety checklists** can be used to identify hazardous items, faulty equipment, and general maintenance requirements. These are available from a variety of sources, including the Canadian Paediatric Society's *Well Beings* (2008) and your municipal and provincial or territorial licensing agencies.

Documenting these checks and subsequent actions is part of an overall risk management program that also reduces the risk of legal liability. There are three levels of potential hazards on the playground. Any hazard needs to be dealt with to promote a safe environment:

- A condition that could cause a major injury or fatality needs to be corrected immediately (e.g., an entanglement point on a slide).
- A condition likely to cause serious injury with temporary disability needs to be corrected as soon as possible, before the next scheduled inspection (e.g., sand needs topping up under a climber).
- A condition likely to cause minor injury or that doesn't meet CSA standards may require long-term planning or budgeting but must be attended to in a timely fashion.

Reference must be made to the CSA's publication whenever a playground evaluation, a new playground, or changes or additions (i.e., retrofitting) are under consideration to make the most informed decisions and reduce the risk of legal liability in the event of an injury.

Supervision of Children

Child care regulations have established minimum educator–child ratios and maximum group sizes for the different age groups. Do you know your province or territory standards? Refer to your early childhood regulations to complete the following information:

Educator–Child Ratio	Group Size
infants:	___ : ___
toddlers:	___ : ___
preschoolers:	___ : ___
school-agers:	___ : ___

Adequate staffing is essential in the supervision of children. Children are naturally curious and often do not understand the potential dangers or consequences of their actions. Combine this fact with the excitement felt by children who are having fun or trying something new, and the potential for children to forget safety rules or use equipment unconventionally is much higher. While supervising children, educators should always assume that children can do more today than they could do yesterday. The comment "I didn't think Tony could roll over yet, so I thought it was safe to leave him on the diaper change table for a few seconds!" indicates the educator's inability to apply developmental theory to early childhood practice. This comment points out that the educator did not follow a very basic safety practice with infants and toddlers. In some ECE training programs, this student's behaviour would be grounds for expulsion. Making assumptions about children's abilities can lead to injuries. Therefore, educators must actively supervise children.

Afternoon naps usually begin after lunch, when children are naturally tired and have full tummies. This is the time when educators take their own lunch breaks. With some staff off for lunch, fewer educators are working, unless additional adults come in to cover during these times. Here is the challenge: How do the remaining educators adequately supervise all the children? Both those children who are napping and those who are playing require supervision. For preschoolers, the nap and play areas are usually in the same room, which facilitates supervision. However, for infants and toddlers, the nap room is usually separate from the play area. As well, infants and toddlers typically sleep at different times during the day and for extended periods. Educators regularly go into the nap room to check on, resettle, or bring out the children who have awakened. Baby monitors are an inexpensive but valuable piece of equipment for educators to use in addition to regular supervision. What program could support having an educator in the nap room most of the day? (As an aside, position young infants on their backs or sides to sleep. Research has indicated a link between sleeping on the tummy and sudden infant death syndrome, or SIDS. Once children can reposition themselves while sleeping, this practice is not applicable.)

During Indoor Play

Equipment, toys, supplies, furniture, storage, and physical space should be developmentally appropriate for the children using them, so that much of the educators' supervision is focused on facilitating play and guiding children's social behaviour. From the standpoint of injury prevention, the level of supervision depends on the inherent risks of the activity, the ages of the children, and the applicable rules.

- Infants and toddlers must never be left alone during water play. Older preschool children do not necessarily need an educator to be directly at the water table at all times.
- Preschoolers and school-agers involved in woodworking must be supervised directly.
- A small group of school-agers are playing a board game in the hall. Although they are out of view, you know where they are; they are still within earshot.

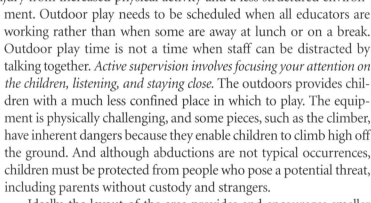

During Outdoor Play

Outdoor play presents educators with unique supervisory challenges because of the greater risk of injury from increased physical activity and a less structured environ-

ment. Outdoor play needs to be scheduled when all educators are working rather than when some are away at lunch or on a break. Outdoor play time is not a time when staff can be distracted by talking together. *Active supervision involves focusing your attention on the children, listening, and staying close.* The outdoors provides children with a much less confined place in which to play. The equipment is physically challenging, and some pieces, such as the climber, have inherent dangers because they enable children to climb high off the ground. And although abductions are not typical occurrences, children must be protected from people who pose a potential threat, including parents without custody and strangers.

Ideally, the layout of the area provides and encourages smaller groups of children to gather throughout the playground (e.g., sandbox, garden plot, water table, painting easels, places in the shade, swings, slides, climber) rather than congregate in one or two areas. Educators should spread out throughout the playground and move among the play spaces for which they are primarily responsible. Equipment, especially the climber, should have one educator who is directly responsible for supervision. Another person could supervise children on the swings and slide. Tubular slides present special safety concerns because the tube blocks educators' view of children sliding down. Furthermore, a child's clothing, hood, or scarf could become caught and cause strangulation. Although a national voluntary standard requests that Canadian manufacturers not make clothing with drawstrings, it is not always honoured, as these items remain available. This is why programs should have a policy that bans drawstrings on hoods and that requires scarves, if worn, to be tucked into the coat. A neck warmer provides a safe alternative to a scarf. As well, educators must be vigilant in ensuring that skipping ropes, cords, ropes, and so on have not been tied to play structures and, when found, are taken down immediately. A program policy should spell out that only ropes designed for climbing should be attached to such structures. In addition, if a child is wearing a helmet while riding a toy, ensure that it is removed before the child plays on the equipment. The helmet's straps pose a risk for strangulation.

Outdoor play is a time for preschool and school-age children to choose the activities they will take part in. Although these older children do not always need educators to take as active a role in their activities, educators should not be any less involved in supervising what the children are doing. Joining in children's activities on their level often means the adult is jumping in a leaf pile, playing tag, or being a partner in ball play. Following the child's lead doesn't mean that the adult cannot suggest new ideas to extend play, and then the children decide whether or not to accept your suggestion (Theemes, 1999, p. 70). Remember, being active outdoors is good role modelling as well as good for the educator's well-being!

For infants and toddlers, educators cannot let their guard down for a second. Infants who haven't yet learned to creep or crawl can sit on a blanket with toys and books. But once they can travel, there is no end to what they can do. Of course, it is wonderful that they have opportunities to explore their world physically and cognitively. However, this reality also means that educators must be vigilant in supervising their outdoor play. Take a close look at what young children can find in the grass and soil.

· ·

Although a stone could cause choking, the potential risks should not exclude these children from outdoor play. Even very young children can begin to learn what they can and cannot safely put in their mouth, with educators' guidance. Of course, the educators will be carefully checking the environment first to reduce the likelihood of hazards!

· ·

Beyond the regular level of supervision, more vigilant supervision is required at certain times, such as when a new piece of equipment is added to the playground. At first, this piece of equipment will be more popular, and children will need extra supervision until the novelty wears off. Children need time to become familiar with any necessary safety rules; children aged four and older can be involved in developing them. Field trips are also times when additional supervision is required. Directors generally arrange for volunteers, often parents, to provide extra adults to improve the adult–child ratio (see Walks and Field Trips, page 414).

CRITICAL THINKING

On a field trip to the zoo, a group of 24 preschoolers and 3 educators take time out to use the small playground. While there, two children crash into each other and another child is hit by someone on the swing. What can you learn from this scenario? What would you do differently next time to prevent injuries?

Prevention of Missing Children

Educators must know the whereabouts of all children at all times. Preventing children from wandering away from the group on a field trip or out of the playground is far easier than trying to locate a child after he or she has gone missing—and easier than suffering the emotional consequences experienced by the child, other children, educators, and, of course, the parents.

Implement the following measures to ensure children's personal safety:

- Maintain a daily attendance record that provides educators with a head count and tells them quickly who is absent or who has already gone home with his or her parent.

- Secure all exits from the building and ensure that young children cannot open them.

- Control entry into the building with a security system, which in some regions may involve simply locking the outside doors.

- Lock the playground gate when children are outside and have one educator responsible for conducting regular head counts.

- Establish the steps to follow if a child goes missing from the program, the playground, or a field trip. Design a search plan for the building, playground, and surrounding neighbourhood. Staff may find it useful to contact an agency that deals with missing children, or the local police department, to assist them in developing a plan that meets their needs (see Planning Successful Field Trips: Preschoolers and School-Agers, page 416).

Safety Rules: A Learning Process

Most of us don't consciously think about the fact that our daily lives are governed by rules. Yet we don't plug in the electric radio near the bathtub. We follow traffic laws while driving and understand the consequences if we are stopped by the police. And we read the instructions before connecting a propane tank to the barbecue—or at least we should!

Society must have rules so that people can coexist. We cannot get a driver's licence until we are 16 years old or older. Society has determined that by that age, we are physically and cognitively ready to operate a vehicle, understand and follow traffic laws, and accept the serious responsibility of driving.

Adults guide children with rules necessary for their own safety and the safety of others and for respecting shared property. The ultimate goal is to learn to behave responsibly and to develop self-control during childhood. To promote this development, we try to provide children with an early childhood environment that respects their need for autonomy and independence, their need to have some control over their world. The process of learning takes time. Children gradually gain more independence and responsibility based on their level of cognitive, physical, emotional, and social development. Children start to learn to follow rules with a simple rule for an activity, and, gradually, they work toward an understanding of rules that are more complex. This process enables older children to learn problem-solving and decision-making skills based on their own safety and their respect for others and property. At this point, they rely on the attitudes, knowledge, and skills that they have developed and less on adult guidance and supervision. Rules learned in childhood pave the way for lifelong patterns of behaviour.

An educator guides a toddler to pedal her riding toy along the path. As a preschooler, Allison learns not to ride double on tricycles, to slow down on the curves of the path, and to wear a bike helmet. As a school-age child, she attends a bicycle safety course and rides to and from school. By the time she is a teenager and young adult, Allison is capable of making her own decisions about riding bikes and can transfer this knowledge and these skills to driving a vehicle.

Whose Need for Control?

Most of us, children included, want to enjoy the feeling of independence and a sense of control over our lives. Consequently, young children often say, "You're not the boss of me!" in response to an adult's power over them. Children react this way for one of two reasons. They naturally want to be in complete control, so the rules imposed by adults are considered to be an infringement on their freedom and desire for independence. Nurturing educators recognize this, but also know that a secure environment for children includes consistent expectations. Second, the children may be legitimately reacting to adults who are inappropriately using their own need for power to control children. When educators are in a power struggle with children, they must always ask themselves whether a particular rule is really in the children's best interest or is simply a way to control them. Educators who have overwhelmed children with rules for absolutely everything have set themselves up for countless power struggles with children. In the long term, this practice increases the potential for making children feel incompetent and lacking in the confidence to make independent decisions.

There are always situations that require educators to act immediately, regardless of the child's response, because the child or others are in danger. Following the incident, the educator can then talk with the child about what has happened and help him or her understand the reasons behind the safety rule.

- A toddler stands up to run down the slide.
- Two children are fist-fighting.
- A school-age child jumps from the top landing of the stairwell.

Often educators observe a child breaking a safety rule but putting no one in danger. To prevent a power struggle with the child, the educator takes a moment to reflect on the intent of the rule rather than react immediately:

- Should the rule be adapted or eliminated because the child's skills and abilities have increased?
- Has the rule any foundation? If not, it should be eliminated.

Educators should meet regularly to evaluate the safety rules. This enables them to validate their assumptions about the rule by considering the children's changing skills and abilities, the activities and inherent risks, the condition and maintenance of equipment, and the children's responses to the rules. This can also be an opportunity to evaluate other rules and to revise or eliminate unnecessary ones. Whenever possible, children should be included in developing and evaluating rules for specific activities. These are opportunities for children to begin learning to look at the bigger picture of safety, developing observation skills, identifying risks and anticipating possible outcomes, understanding the rationale behind the rule, and so on. A potential danger to children can be our own attempt to protect them. If they can't understand the rationale for rules, or if the rules are unbending, we could be setting up children for injuries. They will be denied opportunities to build their decision-making skills, develop their confidence in their ability to think for themselves, and consider the reasons for their being asked or pressured to do something by others.

Guidelines for Safety Rules

Whenever you are in the process of developing safety rules, remind yourself that rules play a role in injury prevention, but they should not be the primary preventive. Rules alone cannot ensure children's safety. Educators will consider the following elements in developing rules:

- the age of the children
- whether the activity is developmentally appropriate
- the potential risks in the activity or play equipment and possible outcomes
- the design of the physical environment
- the level of supervision and modelling
- previous injuries related to this activity

Obviously, if an activity is not developmentally appropriate, it should either be adapted or cancelled. A long list of rules does not ensure injury prevention. In many instances, rules are unnecessary or can be reduced in number when the proper prevention strategies have been implemented.

- Before permitting children to use the climber in a neighbourhood playground for the first time, educators check that the climber is developmentally appropriate and well maintained. They will be sure that enough staff are available to supervise the climber and the remainder of the playground before developing rules for the preschool children.
- A three-year-old can say, "Stop, look, and listen before you cross the street." However, even though the child does that when you're there, you cannot assume that he or she is able to cross the street safely alone.

No one list of safety rules fits every early childhood program's requirements. Rules depend on the philosophy of the program and the age of the children, as well as the particular group of children, types of equipment, design of the physical indoor and outdoor space, and so on. Rules are ever-changing, requiring an ongoing awareness for appropriateness and utility. It is better not to have a rule than to have one that has lost its value. Similarly, it is better to have fewer rather than more rules.

You are invited to participate in an activity, but before you begin, you are presented with this list of rules:

- Don't run.
- Don't eat during the activity.
- Stay away from the red area.
- Keep your hands to yourself.
- Keep your voice down.
- Keep your shoes on.
- Don't climb on the furniture.
- Put everything away when you're done.

Now close your eyes and recite all the rules you have just read. Then repeat them tomorrow morning without reading the list. Unless you have a photographic memory, you probably will not remember more than one or two rules either now or tomorrow. Then how can we expect children to remember and follow a list of rules for each piece of play equipment and activity? How many of these rules are stated in positive terms?

It is often easy to come up with many rules for using equipment or other activities. When a piece of equipment or activity has more rules attached than are essential, they may reduce everyone's enjoyment, may cause children to become frustrated, and may, in fact, be either unsafe or developmentally inappropriate. Educators who continually restate the same rule many times a day probably should reevaluate either the rule or the activity. Limit the number of rules by prioritizing what is most important for the children's safety. To ensure that safety rules are appropriate and effective, think about the following criteria:

- Consider children's development. (A rule that expects toddlers to share is frustrating for everyone, yet older preschoolers can be expected to share. Instead, positively reinforcing toddlers when they do share helps promote sharing.)
- State rules in positive terms. They should focus on what children can do rather than what they can't do.
- State rules in clear and simple language, especially those for younger children.
- Make sure rules are realistic, with enough freedom to encourage creative play but enough restrictiveness to prevent unsafe behaviour.
- Enforce rules consistently using gentle reminders and positive acknowledgment when children follow them. Threats, yelling, sarcasm, or any other tactics that can scare, intimidate, or embarrass children should never be used—this

is emotional abuse. Children who have difficulty following important safety rules, even after being reminded, should be removed from that particular activity with an explanation of why removal is a logical consequence.

The educator says, "Sand can get in children's eyes when you throw it. You need to find something else to do right now." However, give the child the opportunity to return to the activity later, which demonstrates your confidence in the child's ability to follow the rule.

- Rules are modelled by educators. Modelling helps children understand the importance and necessity of rules.
- Rules are developed, whenever possible, with the involvement of preschoolers and school-agers. (When a new toy is available, you can ask children what could happen if…? and what would then be important guidelines or rules for using it.)
- Rules provide teachable moments to point out sensible safety guidelines.

When a child or adult trips over a toy, it is an ideal time to mention why the rule about putting toys away before moving to the next activity is important. Yet care must be taken not to lecture or nag children constantly, or else they are likely to tune us out!

- Rules are reviewed with children before they begin an activity that they haven't done for several months (e.g., woodworking, using the riding toys outside now that the snow has melted).

➤ I. RULES AND BALL PLAY

Let's use ball play to demonstrate some possible rules for children in different age groups and how the type and number of rules would evolve.

Infants and Toddlers

Ball play involves exploring, throwing, or rolling balls with little accuracy across a room, in a playground, or to an educator. Infants' and toddlers' eye–hand coordination is still developing, they are just becoming aware of cause and effect, and they are not yet ready to share. Therefore, a rule for ball play is usually unnecessary for this age group. Instead, educators should provide children with plenty of soft, light, midsize balls to prevent problems. Constant active supervision and guidance are required.

Preschoolers

Between the ages of two and five, children improve their accuracy in throwing balls. They may play simple games with peers, such as pitch and catch, hot potato, or soccer. It is a good idea to continue using softer rubber or inflated balls and light ones. Appropriate rules for this age group would be the following:

- Throw the ball to someone, not at someone.

- Put away the balls when you are finished so no one trips over them.
- Keep balls in the large area when playing inside.
- When outside, you can bounce the ball on this wall because it doesn't have windows and people won't be walking between you and the wall.
- When a ball goes over the fence, an adult will get it.

Obviously, only one or two of these rules would be needed at any one time!

School-Agers

These children develop more complex ball skills, play cooperative and competitive games and sports, and often break up into teams. They may be quite accurate and powerful in throwing balls and using bats. Except for the general guidelines about not harming self, others, or property, rules depend on the particular ball game. While they are learning a ball game such as soccer, dodge ball, street hockey, baseball, or volleyball, educators can help them develop and understand the safety rules of the game. In baseball, for example:

- Play in an area away from other children.
- Wear a helmet when at bat.
- Put the bat down after swinging. Don't throw it.

In dodge ball (if permitted in the program), for example:

- Use a light, soft rubber ball.
- Aim below the waist.

II. RULES AND SWINGS

We'll use swings to demonstrate some possible play equipment rules for children in different age groups and how the rules might evolve.

Infants and Toddlers

Educators usually have to lift children into a swing. Because an educator has to be right there with an infant, rules aren't needed. Older infants and toddlers may need rules such as these:

- Hold on with both hands.
- Stay sitting until the swing stops.

Preschoolers

These children are learning to use swings with less direct adult involvement. There is quite a difference between the ability of a two-year-old and that of a five-year-old on swings. The following examples are more appropriate for children who have become competent on swings and can use them independently:

- Stop the swing completely before getting on or off.

(continued)

- Look carefully when walking in front of or behind moving swings.
- Only one child may be on the swing at any time.

School-Agers

Most children who are still interested in swings are already competent to use them the regular way and find new and challenging ways to swing (e.g., shinnying up the swing poles, twisting the chains and letting them spin out, jumping off a moving swing, standing on the seat). Some rules for swings may be as follows:

- Only one child on the swing at any one time.
- Make sure that no one is near when you jump off.

School-age programs may permit more innovative uses of swings depending on a number of factors, such as the skill levels of the particular children, the condition of the protective surface, and whether younger children are using the playground at the same time. Think how you might handle a question from preschoolers about why older children are allowed to jump off swings, but they aren't. Remember, rules are not static: they can change with children's development or the situation.

Children are permitted to jump off moving swings. During a safety check of the playground, the educator sees that the sand underneath the swings is hard-packed. To prevent an injury, until the sand is worked up, this is shown to the children, who are asked to wait until the swings stop moving before getting off. Children will understand the reason why and that this rule is only temporary.

OBJECTIVES

To describe safety issues related to seasonal changes.

To discuss the principles and practices in planning and conducting field trips.

To list the reasons why children are more vulnerable to environmental contaminants than adults.

To identify environmental concerns known to affect children's health.

To be aware of situations in which child protection is a concern.

WHAT'S THE REST OF THE STORY?

The remainder of this unit is devoted to other safety-related issues that educators should consider. Some of these pertain to safety on a daily basis, such as protecting children from the seasonal elements and going for walks; others are of a more general nature, such as injury reports and responding to emergencies.

Being Outdoors Safely: Summer and Winter

Can you imagine living in a place where the weather is always the same? Maybe you can if you're reading this unit in the middle of winter with a wind chill of −34°C (−29°F)! Canada's changing seasons provide us with wonderful opportunities to participate in a variety of activities and sports, but the hot and cold weather pose certain safety considerations.

A written policy includes all routine practices regarding both summer and winter outdoor safety. The policy is communicated to families and staff at the beginning of spring and late fall, is posted in the centre, and is reinforced in newsletters or other communication vehicles to ensure that everyone is aware of the practices and their rationale. The policy includes practices around

- sun safety, smog alerts, mosquito and other insect control measures, summer excursions, and any other specific issues relevant to the specific program, and
- outdoor play, wind-chill reports, and appropriate winter clothing for the age groups in your care.

Summer

Sadly, the suntan remains popular—a symbol associated with health, active living, and attractiveness. Cases of melanoma, the deadliest form of skin cancer, are on the rise. Between 1980 and 2004, the annual incidence of melanoma among women between the ages of 15 and 39 increased by 50%. But rates among young men remained stable over the same time period (Ogilvie, 2008). In addition to inadequate sun safety practices, the popular use of tanning beds may be a factor.

After a long winter, the allure of the sun can be overwhelming, especially when one feels the warmth on the face and skin. In the past few years, however, there has been a concerted effort to educate the public about the dangers of sun exposure. Pamphlets, magazine articles, and television commercials outline the relationship between ultraviolet (UV) radiation and skin cancer (e.g., melanoma), eye damage, and premature aging of the skin.

➤ INTERESTING FACTS ABOUT THE SUN

Fiction: A tan is healthy.

Fact: A tan indicates that your skin has already been damaged.

Fiction: A tan will protect me from the sun.

Fact: A dark tan in a white person offers an **SPF** of about 4.

Fiction: Black skin will protect me from the sun.

Fact: People with black skin can get sunburns and skin cancer. Black skin gives an **SPF** protection of about 8.

Fiction: You can't get burned on a cloudy day.

Fact: Up to 80% of the sun's rays can penetrate light cloud, mist and fog.

Fiction: You can't get burned if you're in the water.

Fact: Water offers minimal protection. Water's reflection can intensify the sun's rays on you.

Fiction: Baby oil is a good sun lotion.

Fact: Baby oil intensifies the effects of the sun and causes skin to burn faster.

Source: *A Parents Guide to Sun Protection: Sun Fiction and Fact,* Health Canada, 2007. Reproduced with the permission of the Minister of Public Works and Government Services Canada, 2008.

Children are more sensitive to UV exposure than adults because they have thinner skin and, on average, spend more time outdoors than adults, especially in the summer. One in seven children will get skin cancer in his or her lifetime. The skin can suffer a lot of damage in childhood. In fact, one of the conditions that puts people most at risk for skin cancer is two or more blistering sunburns as a child or adolescent (Health Canada, 2007b, p. 2).

UV Index and the Humidex

While ozone can be found through the entire atmosphere, the greatest concentration occurs at an altitude of about 25 km. This band of ozone-rich air is known as the "ozone layer". . . . Ozone's unique physical properties allow the ozone layer to act as our planet's sunscreen, providing an invisible filter to help protect all life forms from the sun's damaging ultraviolet (UV) rays. (Environment Canada, 2002a, pp. 1, 2)

Basically, the more UV rays we are exposed to, the faster our skin is damaged. Cloudy days don't necessarily protect us from UV rays. The darker and thicker the clouds, the more UV rays that are blocked. Fluffy and thin clouds don't block UV rays, and UV rays that are reflected off bright surfaces (e.g., sand, concrete, water, snow) increase our exposure. In Canada, people living at higher elevations (e.g., in the mountains) get more UV rays because the air is cleaner and thinner. And UV exposure increases the closer you are to the equator, so there will be more UV exposure in southern Ontario than in the Arctic (Environment Canada, 2002a).

UV rays are strongest in the summer, but during other seasons, too, educators need to be aware of UV rays (e.g., a sunny winter day in the Rockies). In the summer, the weather reports usually provide the **UV index** for the day. UV is measured on a scale of 10, with 10 indicating the shortest sunburn time, typically on a sunny summer day. Tables 7.6 and 7.7 put the UV index into practical and relevant terms so that educators can prevent skin damage to children and themselves.

TABLE 7.6   What Does the UV Index Mean to Me?

UV INDEX	CATEGORY	SUNBURN TIME
over 9	extreme	less than 15 minutes
7–9	high	about 20 minutes
4–7	moderate	about 30 minutes
0–4	low	more than 1 hour

When the UV index is over 9, UVB is extremely strong, and you will burn in less than 15 minutes. (Sunburn times are for light, untanned skin; the times are somewhat longer for those with darker skin.) Even if you do not get a burn, you may still be damaging your skin.

Source: Adapted from *Living With Ultraviolet*. © Her Majesty The Queen in Right of Canada, Environment Canada, (2002). Reproduced with the permission of the Minister of Public Works and Government Services Canada.

TABLE 7.7	The UV Index: Typical Summer Midday Values	
CANADIAN COMMUNITIES COMPARED WITH THE TROPICS AND THE NORTH POLE		UV INDEX
Tropics		10.0 (extreme)
Toronto		8.0 (high)
Halifax		7.5 (high)
Edmonton		7.0 (high)
Yellowknife		6.0 (moderate)
Iqaluit		4.8 (moderate)
North Pole		2.3 (low)

Source: *Living With Ultraviolet.* © Her Majesty The Queen in Right of Canada, Environment Canada, (2002). Reproduced with the permission of the Minister of Public Works and Government Services Canada.

Depending on where you live, you may be used to hearing weather reports on the radio or television include not only the day's temperature but also the UV index and the humidex (e.g., "It's 32°C today, but the relative humidity makes it feel like 42°C"). The more moisture there is in the air, the less sweat evaporates off skin, which is why people feel hot and sticky when it's very humid outside. Basically, the humidex value is calculated using the temperature and the relative humidity. How does the humidex tell us what it's like outside?

- 20° to 29°C (68° to 84°F): It's comfortable for most.

- 30° to 39°C (86° to 102°F): Most will feel discomfort, some more than others.

- Over 40° (104°): Almost everyone will be uncomfortable. Most activities and work must be restricted.

Educators use their discretion when the humidex reading is high to ensure that children playing outside do not become dehydrated or sick. Perhaps outdoor activities could be limited in duration and restricted to quieter play in the shade, or perhaps water play could be made available.

What Is SPF?

SPF stands for the Sun Protection Factor provided by a sunscreen. It refers to a product's ability to stop your skin from burning. The higher the number of the SPF, the longer you can stay in the sun before burning. (Health Canada, 2007c, p. 1)

Source: *A Parents Guide to Sun Protection: Sun Fiction and Fact,* Health Canada, 2007. Reproduced with the permission of the Minister of Public Works and Government Services Canada, 2008.

It takes about 10 minutes for unprotected skin to burn in the summer sun. Therefore, a lotion with a **sun protection factor** (**SPF**) of 15 ideally provides children with 150 minutes of protection, although sweat and water reduce its protection time. An SPF of 15 blocks more than 92% of the UVB rays. Skin may still tan even if a sunscreen is used, since all chemical sunscreens allow some UVA rays to penetrate (Health Canada, 2007c, p. 1). Choose lotions that

- are broad spectrum, acting against UVA and UVB rays;

- have at least an SPF of 15;

- are creamy, as they don't usually contain alcohol (which may sting skin and eyes);

- are unscented (will not attract insects);

- don't contain para-aminobenzoic acid (PABA), although it is rarely used now because of its link to allergic sensitivity, and

- screen out most of the UVB and UVA rays as stated on the label.

Source: *A Parents Guide to Sun Protection: Sun Fiction and Fact,* Health Canada, 2007. Reproduced with the permission of the Minister of Public Works and Government Services Canada, 2008.

"REMEMBER: Sunscreens are not intended to increase sun exposure time but to increase protection during unavoidable exposure" (Health Canada, 2007c, p. 1).

Apply sunscreen 15 to 30 minutes before you go outside. Don't forget that sunscreen should be applied in the early spring and also late into the fall. Liberal application means at least 5 mL (1 tsp) on the face and on each arm, for example. Remember to apply lotion above where shorts and sleeves stop, since they ride up the legs and arms while the children are playing, and to the top of the children's feet when they are wearing sandals. When children are very active and sweating, lotion should be applied more often to give 100% UV protection. Children using wading pools or sprinklers either need to wear a waterproof sunscreen or have regular sunscreen reapplied when they get out of the water. As added sun protection, children can wear T-shirts over their bathing suits to protect their shoulders, back, and chest. Remember to have the children change into dry T-shirts once they are finished playing in the water, as the wetness reduces the fabric's sun protection. If parents do not wish their child to use sunscreen (perhaps due to allergies), alternative arrangements for sun protection must be made. *For example, the child will need to wear a wide-brim hat; a lightweight, loose-fitting, long-sleeved shirt; full-length pants; and socks whenever outdoors.*

Programs may prefer to use communal bottles of lotion, since it is much faster to do one child after another than to use 20 different bottles of lotions and try to keep them all straight. As well, all the bottles must be kept out of reach of children. In these programs, staff check with parents to ensure that they approve of the type that is used. Some children may have a skin reaction to a particular brand of sunscreen, most often ones that contain PABA. Educators do not have to wash their hands after each application. Not only is that time consuming, but also the risk of spreading infection through sunscreen is negligible even when someone has a cut or scrape because these should be covered with either clothing or a Band-Aid. The only time that hand washing may be warranted is when a child has an allergy to the sunscreen brand used by the program; then the educator needs to wash off the program's lotion before applying this child's own. Older preschoolers should be learning to apply their own lotion. These children need supervision to ensure that they don't get lotion in their mouth or eyes and that they adequately cover all exposed skin. By the time they are school age, most children should be responsible for this task.

Additional Sun Protection

How do educators protect themselves and children while outside during the summer? They can begin by limiting or avoiding outdoor play and walks between 11 a.m. and 3 p.m. (Peak hours may vary by an hour one way or the other.) However, if children are to get outside even twice a day, a compromise needs to be reached: shade must be available, fluids must be offered, and sunscreen, hats, sunglasses, and clothing must be used.

Everyone should wear hats, preferably with a wide (7.5 cm or 3 in.) brim that shades the face, ears, and neck. Some children don't like wearing hats but may be more likely to wear baseball caps, which are very popular. Don't forget to put sunscreen on their ears and the back of their neck. Child-sized shatterproof sunglasses with 100% UV protection are now available at low prices; parents should be encouraged to provide their child with a pair. Although many toddlers and young preschool children may not keep them on, this at least introduces them to the idea. Ideally, children wear long-sleeved shirts and long pants, although this seems impractical when it is very hot or humid. Whatever clothing is worn, it should be loose fitting and cool to help reduce sweating.

Ensure that shade provided by trees, table umbrellas, awnings, or other structures is accessible to children to play in. Children should be encouraged to come into shade every half-hour while outside. Wading pools should be placed in the shade. Sunscreen is not a replacement for shade.

Physical activity in hot weather puts children at risk of becoming dehydrated because the body loses water through sweating. Offer water to children before they go outside and encourage them to drink water several times while outside and again after they are back inside. Pay particular attention to children who are using the play equipment and running around, as they will be losing more water through sweat. Children can be dehydrated and not complain of thirst.

Remember how germs are spread and do not use a communal drink bottle or shared cups. If you don't have access to running water outside, bring out a jug and enough cups for everyone.

Keep in mind that infants

- should be shaded from the sun at all times. Their skin protection system is not fully developed, and for most of their first year, they cannot move out of the sun on their own. And they can't tell you when they are getting too hot or thirsty.

- should get plenty of fluids even if they are just lying on a blanket in the shade. Young children can become dehydrated very quickly because they have more surface area (skin) in relation to their body mass than adults do. Signs of dehydration and treatment are discussed in the section on diarrhea (see page 173).

- should wear T-shirts over their bathing suits when they are in the wading pool.

- should not, when under the age of six months, have sunscreen applied, because they may put lotion-covered hands or feet in their mouth. Also, the lotion may irritate their skin.

- should, whenever possible, be dressed in loose-fitting clothes that have long sleeves and pants (or long-sleeved cotton jumpers) and should wear hats.

Certain medications can cause skin reactions such as rashes, swelling, blisters, or redness that looks like an exaggerated sunburn. Photosensitivity reactions are relatively common. Symptoms can appear immediately once the skin is exposed to sun or several hours after exposure has ceased. Interestingly, symptoms may develop only on skin that wasn't covered by clothing or may appear anywhere on the body. Symptoms can last for several days, even after the prescription is completed. Some of the commonly prescribed medications that can cause photosensitivity are some antibiotics, antihistamine creams, oral contraceptives (the pill), and sunscreen containing PABA. Some of the medications prescribed for the management of diabetes, cystic fibrosis, and mental health disorders can cause photosensitivity reactions (see Administering Medication, page 180).

Do you ever hear adults say to children, "Just do what I say because I'm the parent" or "I don't have to do that because I'm the adult"? Take a moment to think about the behaviour that educators model if they sunbathe, compliment one another on their tans, or refuse to wear hats and sunglasses or to apply sunscreen at work. The adult who tells children that they must do things because he or she told them so is, in fact, controlling children and certainly not being a positive role model.

Insects and Repellent

To avoid attracting insects, wasps, and bees, avoid serving sweet food and beverages outside and keep garbage containers far from the play area. Exercise caution when a child has an allergy to bees or wasps and be sure that his or her adrenaline kit is outside with the educators and the child. Remember that if the insects are prevalent and are biting, the best option may be to keep the children inside or to arrange to use a community centre or school gym to get physical exercise, even if it's only for a few days.

Repellents are used to repel mosquitoes, ticks, fleas, and biting flies. Repellents are poisonous and must be kept out of reach of children. The West Nile virus is becoming more of a concern across Canada. But we also need to put this virus into perspective, as the risk of infection is low for most Canadians and the risk of serious health effects from the virus is even lower (Health Canada, 2005). Eliminating places for mosquitoes to breed is a first step. In early childhood programs, the staff are likely already doing that for the safety of children:

- Empty all water-holding containers (e.g., wading pools, pots, pails, birdbaths) at the end of each day.
- Ensure that all areas of standing water, such as puddles or under drainpipes, dry up at least every other day; if not, do so manually.
- Monitor the length of the grass (if applicable) in play areas and the buildup of debris and inform the director of the need for immediate action when a situation warrants.
- Encourage families to provide light-coloured, tightly woven clothing for their children and long pants, long-sleeved shirts, and socks for their children to use during early morning and late afternoon and for walks where there is a lot of foliage.
- Programs must ensure that the window screens fit properly.
- Mosquitoes are most active at dawn and dusk, which are times that are outside the hours of operation for most programs. Even so, at those times of day, it is very unlikely that staff and children would be outside.
- Pay attention to the provincial and regional reports during the summer.

Do not apply DEET on children under six months old. Use clothing or mosquito netting over strollers and carriages or avoid going outside if the insects are particularly bad. A drop of white vinegar or oil of citronella behind the ears, knees, and wrists may help keep insects away.

For children between six months and two years old, repellent with DEET should not be applied more than once a day and only at a concentration of 10% or less. For children between 2 and 12 years old, a product with 10% or less is recommended, and it shouldn't be applied more than 3 times in a day. For anyone older than 12, a concentration of no more than 30% DEET should be used (Pest Management Regulatory Agency, 2004).

Remember the following points if you use repellents:

- Choose lotions rather than sprays.
- Look for a product that is not combined with a sunscreen.
- Apply sparingly and only on exposed skin, not under clothes or diapers.
- To prevent children getting the repellent in their mouth, do not apply it on their face, hands, and fingers.

- Never permit young children to put repellent on themselves or others. Older preschoolers may apply it with supervision, and most school-agers should have learned how to apply it safely.
- Once children are back inside, wash off the repellent.
- Obtain the parents' written permission before using repellent.

Winter

Winter conjures up pictures of chattering teeth, knee-high snowdrifts, and icy roads. Yet winter also has beautiful blue skies, clean crisp air, and snow that sparkles like diamonds. Snow is a wonderful play medium for winter activities and sports. Children can have great fun in playgrounds, even though in most regions of Canada, it will be very cold. Getting outside in the winter provides all of us with much-needed physical activity, fresh air, and sunlight, which is the best source of vitamin D.

Dressing appropriately for the weather goes a long way toward making winter activities enjoyable and safe. Scarves and hoods can become caught on play equipment, resulting in strangulation. Families should be encouraged to provide neck warmers rather than scarves for children. If scarves are used, ensure that they are tied, with the ends tucked into the coat or parka, and that hoods are tied snugly around faces. Some clothing manufacturers are now making cordless hoods that fasten with Velcro rather than cords.

Most of our body's heat is lost through our head. Wearing appropriate winter hats, toques, hoods, and so on is equally important for adults and children in protecting us from chill and our ears from **frostbite**. Exposed skin freezes in just a few minutes when it is cold enough outside. Noses, cheeks, ears, fingers, and toes are most prone to frostbite. Watch the children to ensure that their hats, hoods, and scarves do not slide out of place and that someone hasn't got a boot full of snow.

Watch for children who take off their mitts when using play equipment. Toddler snowsuits often come with mitts (without thumbs) that snap onto the cuffs. Toddlers quickly become frustrated with mitts and pull them off because they can't do anything with their hands. Parents should be encouraged to provide toddlers with nonslippery mittens with thumbs. Unless the mitts or gloves are leather, they get wet quickly during play. Wet mitts not only chill children's hands but also increase the likelihood of frostbite. Programs may have mitt-drying racks, or parents can be asked to send two or three pairs of mitts each day so that children have a dry pair to wear during the afternoon.

As discussed in the section on summer safety, educators have a professional responsibility to dress appropriately for the weather conditions when supervising outdoor play. If it is cold enough for children to be wearing hats, mitts, winter boots, and zipped-up coats, educators should wear the same. This is not only to model the behaviour for the children but also to protect themselves from chill and frostbite.

Children may complain that they are cold or wet. Obviously, if they are wet, they must go indoors and change into something dry before going back outdoors. However, some children will tell you that they are cold from the moment they step out the door. Often they need to be encouraged to start moving around so that they warm up. Educators can help them by moving around themselves and inviting children to join them. Yet after being outside for some time, some children will be cold and should go inside to warm up. Keep in mind that children have less muscle mass than adults and therefore don't generate as much body heat, which is a natural response to being out in the cold.

We often begin our winter mornings by listening to the day's temperature and **wind-chill factor**. "Wind chill describes a sensation, the way we feel as a result of the combined cooling effect of temperature and wind" (Environment Canada, 2002b, p. 2). Canada's wind-chill index is reported using temperature-like units, but because it is not the actual air temperature, it is given without the degree sign. "The index likens the way your skin feels to the temperature on a calm day. *For example, if the outside temperature is −10°C and the wind chill is −20, it means that your face will feel as cold as it would on a calm day when the temperature is −20°C"* (Environment Canada, 2002b, p. 1).

The Canadian Paediatric Society (2008, p. 81) suggests that children remain indoors under the following conditions:

- when the temperature is below −25°C (−13°F), regardless of the wind-chill factor.
- when the wind-chill factor is reported as −28°C (−15°F) or below, regardless of the temperature.

Source: Canadian Paediatric Society, *Well Beings: A Guide to Health in Child Care.* (Ottawa: Canadian Paediatric Society, 2008), 81. Reprinted with permission.

Some early childhood regulations stipulate an outdoor temperature below which it is deemed too cold for children to play outdoors. Obviously, in some regions of Canada, people are accustomed to long, cold winters and have appropriate winter clothing to minimize the amount of exposed skin. In other regions, where cold weather occurs less frequently, children may have to remain indoors for several consecutive days. Table 7.8 identifies possible health hazards and what to do to prevent them for a range of wind-chill temperatures. Centre staff may want to explore options within the community that would provide space for children to be physically active every day.

TABLE 7.8   Wind-Chill Hazards and Risk of Frostbite

WIND CHILL	RISK OF FROSTBITE	HEALTH CONCERN	WHAT TO DO
0 to –9	Low	– Slight increase in discomfort	– Dress warmly, with the outside temperature in mind.
–10 to –27	Low	– Uncomfortable – Risk of hypothermia if outside for long periods without adequate protection	– Dress in layers of warm clothing, with an outer layer that is wind-resistant. – Wear a hat, mittens and scarf. – Keep active.
–28 to –39	Increasing risk: exposed skin can freeze in 10 to 30 minutes.	– Check face and extremities (fingers, toes, ears, and nose) for numbness or whiteness – Risk of hypothermia if outside for long periods without adequate protection	– Dress in layers of warm clothing, with an outer layer that is wind-resistant. – Cover exposed skin: wear a hat, mittens and a scarf, neck tube or face mask. – Keep active.
–40 to –47	High risk: exposed skin can freeze in 5 to 10 minutes*	– Check face and extremities (fingers, toes, ears, and nose) for numbness or whiteness (frostbite) – Risk of hypothermia if outside for long periods without adequate protection	– Dress in layers of warm clothing, with an outer layer that is wind-resistant. – Cover exposed skin: wear a hat, mittens and a scarf, neck tube or face mask. – Keep active.
WARNING LEVEL** –48 to –54	High risk: exposed skin can freeze in 2 to 5 minutes*	– Check face and extremities for numbness or white-ness (frostbite) – Serious risk of hypothermia if out-side for long periods	– Be careful. Dress very warmly in layers of clothing, with an outer layer that is wind-resistant. – Cover all exposed skin: wear a hat, mittens and a scarf, neck tube or face mask. – Be ready to cut short or cancel outdoor activities. – Keep active.

WIND CHILL	RISK OF FROSTBITE	HEALTH CONCERN	WHAT TO DO
–55 and colder	High risk: exposed skin can freeze in less than 2 minutes	DANGER! – Outdoor conditions are hazardous	– Stay indoors.

*In sustained winds over 50 km/h, frostbite can occur faster than indicated.

**In parts of the country with milder climate (such as Southern Ontario and the Atlantic provinces except Labrador), a wind chill warning is issued at about –35. Further north, people have grown more accustomed to the cold, and have adapted to the more severe conditions. Because of this, Environment Canada issues warnings at progressively colder wind chill values as you move north. Most of Canada hears a warning at about –45. Residents of the Arctic, northern Manitoba and northern Quebec are warned at about –50, and those high Arctic, at about –55.

Source: *Wind Chill Hazards.* © 2003 Her Majesty The Queen in Right of Canada, Environment Canada, 2003. Reproduced with the permission of the Minister of Public Works and Government Services Canada.

Catching falling snowflakes on our tongue is a lot of fun. Blankets of fresh white snow are inviting to eat. Yet children should be discouraged from eating fallen snow (on the ground, fences, benches, etc.) or licking icicles, which can be contaminated with dirt or pollution or animal or bird feces or urine. On mild days, it's hard for any of us to resist picking up snow and making snowballs. Children naturally want to throw balls, and snowballs are no exception. However, people can easily be injured by snowballs that are thrown too hard or that contain stones or ice. Perhaps you can reach a compromise on snowballs. Designate a wall (without windows) or a tree that snowballs can be thrown at, although you will still

have to supervise to ensure that children do not throw balls at one another. Children can also be encouraged to build walls, animals, people, and so on with snow.

It would be hard to find an adult who grew up in Canada who didn't try to stick his or her wet tongue on cold metal, contrary to parental warnings. So you won't be surprised if some children freeze their tongue to metal objects and perhaps suffer a painful injury. Frostbite occurs when the skin and underlying tissue get frozen. Frostbite may not always be painful, but the skin or patch of skin (e.g., nose, cheeks) looks white and in advanced cases may be blistered. Your first-aid course should cover how you will respond to children in either of these situations.

Activities in the Winter

Winter sports such as skating, tobogganing, and skiing all have the potential to cause injuries. To reduce the risk of injury, educators must ask themselves five safety questions when they are planning winter sports:

1. Is this activity developmentally appropriate for the children?

2. Is the location designed for children to use (e.g., the height of the tobogganing hill), and are there potential hazards—trees, walking paths, ditches, or a road—at the bottom of the hill?

3. What are the potential dangers? How can they be reduced or eliminated?

4. What safety equipment must children wear? Is there enough equipment for each child?

5. Can we recruit enough staff or volunteers for supervision?

Toboggans and sleds are dangerous if improperly used and can cause head, pelvic, and back injuries.

If planning such an activity, please keep the following safety considerations in mind:

- Avoid sliding near roads, driveways, trees, poles, rocks, and water.
- Make sure children wear protective helmets.
- Stay seated and don't overload toboggans or sleds.
- Remove all scarves and drawstrings.
- Climb the hill to the side, away from others sliding down.
- Be extra careful on icy hills, as children will go faster than they expect.

We can get sunburned in the winter, too, because snow and ice reflect the sun's rays. Sunscreen and lip balm with SPF should be used when children are outdoors for several hours. The lotion also helps protect the skin from windburn.

Walks and Field Trips

Children need to expand their world in many ways and directions, and walks and field trips provide opportunities for learning and enjoyment. Yet unfamiliar surroundings increase the opportunity for injuries, especially for children. Whether educators are taking a small group for a walk to the public park or a group of six- and seven-year-olds to the planetarium by public transit, advanced planning ensures that the outing is safe as well as developmentally and educationally relevant.

Programs have developed written policies and procedures regarding walks and field trips. Walks are often a regular part of an early childhood program, as when infants and toddlers go out in strollers or wagons every day. Educators at programs without a playground need to walk children to neighbourhood playgrounds daily. In both cases, staff obtain written parental permission for walks at the time of enrollment. Parents then know that their children are frequently being taken off the premises and can discuss any concerns that they may have with the staff.

Stroller Walks with Infants and Toddlers

Stroller walks and regular outside time are the best way to meet the needs of infants. Field trips at this age are not developmentally appropriate, as they take the children away from their comfort and routines for long periods of time. Daily walks in the community around the early childhood setting, where infants are talked to, responded to, and exposed to interesting sights, smells, and sounds, are developmentally appropriate and very exciting for them. There is no need for transportation in addition to "active transport" (i.e., walking) with young children in strollers or wagons. Getting to know shopkeepers and other people in their neighbourhood will help them build trust in significant adults and community (e.g., shopkeepers waving from the windows of their store). Take different routes for interest and variety; ensure that the director or other designate knows which route will be taken. Ensure that you have covered the safety considerations that are relevant to infants and toddlers (see Safety Considerations for Walks and Field Trips, page 419).

Although infants (or toddlers) may fall asleep during the walk, avoid that as a goal: view the walk as a wonderful opportunity for them to begin to enjoy the many wonders of the outdoors (see Environmental Contaminants, page 421). Take opportunities for children to be taken out of the stroller and explore when safely possible. Toddlers, who are developing autonomy and like to practise their new skills, may enjoy a trip involving a short walk or wagon ride. On these short walking trips, one adult to every two children is a safe ratio. Of course, toddlers need opportunities to be physically active without a lot of restriction. They need outdoor time in a fenced playground to fulfill that criterion. Toddlers who are approaching preschool age may be ready for a short field trip, again ensuring that it is planned and implemented with safety and age-appropriate considerations. They may enjoy a half-day trip where they will still be able to eat and sleep in familiar surroundings.

Before putting children in strollers, for each trip, ensure that the brakes, wheels, and handles are in good working order. Check very carefully that the five-point harness system and lap belt are solidly attached to the seat or frame and that the child is securely buckled to prevent falls out of the stroller, which can cause serious injuries, including head trauma.

"Active Transportation" with Preschoolers and School-Agers

When motorized transportation is unnecessary, short excursions and field trips are less complicated in planning and implementing, although safety precautions are always essential. On any walk with preschoolers and school-agers,

> ensure the supervisor or staff remaining at the centre are notified about the children participating in the outing. The destination, the route to and from the outing and the expected time of return to the centre should be documented in the daily log/communication book. A local map with the walk route marked is always helpful for parents arriving after the group has left. (Toronto Children's Services, 2004, p. 4)

Ensure that you have covered the safety considerations that are relevant to walks and field trips with preschoolers and school-agers (see Safety Considerations for Walks and Field Trips, page 419).

Planning Successful Field Trips: Preschoolers and School-Agers

The key to safe field trips is careful planning. All aspects of your field trip planning are clearly outlined in the program's field trip policy, including permission forms that families need to sign. It is important to reiterate the educators' responsibility for children's safety at all times. Remember that you need to consider all aspects of the field trip, including

- preparing the children and adults,
- transporting the group to and from the destination,
- assessing the actual activity and physical environment, and
- evaluating the trip on returning.

An itemized list is useful in planning, but educators also have to brainstorm to anticipate other issues that may come up and determine how they can prevent confusion or injuries. Organizing the routine walk to the local playground is quite different from bussing a group to a conservation area. Posting a checklist for walks saves time and ensures that educators take everything they need. But even a routine walk may present a surprise that requires educators to make a decision and ensure the group's safety. You have probably planned an event down to the last detail, and then something unexpected happens. That invariably happens on field trips, too. Educators need to think on their feet and apply their safety knowledge and skills to make responsible decisions.

- Finding that half a block of sidewalk has been ripped up, educators and toddlers have to walk along the road past the construction to get to the playground. This is not ideal, but the staff carry it out as safely as possible. Responsible educators will talk about what happened with the children on returning to the program and next time choose a new route, if possible, until the construction is completed.
- Two of the parents who had volunteered to accompany your group to the children's theatre presentation announce at the last minute that they are unable to attend. What do you do: cancel the trip, phone around for other volunteers, or…?

Educators have some basic but important questions to ask themselves when they plan field trips:

- Is the trip developmentally appropriate for the age group? Taking young preschoolers to a traditional museum where there are no interactive opportunities will not hold their interest, but a fire station where they experience a fire truck up close is likely more in tune with their interests.
- Is the trip educationally appropriate? Taking a preschool group to the mall because the adults want to shop is irresponsible. Trips that do not relate to the interests and learning needs of the children are also more likely to be unsafe, because bored children of any age tend to look for other stimulation, such as pushing one another or wandering away from the group.

- Do the educators believe that the children are able to understand and follow the trip's guidelines?

Taking a newly formed group of preschoolers on a field trip that requires several rules may be asking for problems. Instead, start with short walks and excursions, helping children develop an awareness of safety rules, and progress from there.

- With regard to pedestrian safety, it is important to remember that children are at higher risk than adults for several reasons. Their small size and more restricted peripheral vision mean that they may not notice approaching cars. Until older school age, they don't have the ability to determine a car's speed and distance, may be impulsive, and are curious (Canadian Paediatric Society, 2008, p. 125).

When you're out walking, remind children of these simple **road rules**, and model them yourself at all times:

- Look left-right-left for traffic at every intersection. Preschoolers can be taught to look ALL WAYS.
- Cross only when the street is clear of traffic and the signal says it's time to go.
- Keep looking for cars as you're crossing the street.
- Do not walk between parked cars.

Constant supervision in and around motor vehicles and roadways and meticulous use of appropriate child restraints are the best protections you can provide while transporting children in your care. Being a good model yourself and sharing information with parents will also help to instill a lifetime's worth of safe behaviours. (Canadian Paediatric Society, 2008, p. 125)

- Is there a consistent way to quickly identify the members of their group while out in a public place where there may be other groups of children (e.g., T-shirts, smocks, or ball caps all in the same colour, or a visible tag with the program logo and phone number). School-age children don't want to be embarrassed; involve them in the decision of identifiable clothing. Why is it important not to have the child's name on a tag on his or her clothing?

Ensure that one educator does regular head counts before leaving the program, several times during the trip, before leaving again, and on arrival back at the program. Educators are encouraged to have a recent colour photograph of each child as well as his or her age, height, weight, and eye colour. If a child is missing, a photo and description will be useful (see Prevention of Missing Children, page 396).

- Are there enough adults to ensure safety? Make sure to have more than the legislated minimum number of adults—that is, improve on the adult–child ratio, especially on trips with younger children or children with specific needs. Some programs find it difficult, if not impossible, to recruit volunteers or family members to join them on trips. Staff may take smaller groups of children at a time, over a few days (on visits to the fire station on Tuesday, Wednesday, and Thursday, for example). These programs may have included this model in their field trip policy.

- Is there quick access to a phone? Bringing a cell phone is the best solution; if this is not possible, ensure that a phone is nearby in case it is needed.

In addition to the safety considerations (page 419) for walks with preschoolers and school-agers, further considerations for field trips include the following (not an exhaustive list):

Preparation before the Field Trip

- Obtain reliable information about the destination, including washroom and drinking water availability, accessibility for all children and adults, including wheelchairs and strollers, and shade if outdoors. If possible, have a staff member visit the destination to ensure correct information. Find out about costs, hours of operation, etc.
- Inform staff at the destination of your estimated time of arrival and find out where and how they will greet your group upon arrival.
- Notify parents **at least** 24 hours in advance, with trip details including when you are leaving and returning to the early childhood setting.
- Although parents may have signed an all-inclusive permission form for walks and field trips at admission, many programs have an additional form signed for specific off-site field trips.
- Establish your route and leave a copy of directions with the director and parents.
- Prepare children for the trip, including what to expect and rules for safety and appropriate conduct (also review on day of trip). Remember the "rule about rules": if there are too many of them, you need to reevaluate whether this trip is appropriate.
- Ensure that at least one educator going on the trip has first-aid training. Know the location of the nearest hospital and how to get there.
- Prepare for food safety if applicable (e.g., ice packs for transporting).

Preparation for the Day of the Field Trip

- Follow the list of safety considerations (page 420) for taking preschool and school-age children for walks.
- Each adult is given a list of children for whom she or he is responsible during the trip and additional instructions as appropriate.
- Ensure that all necessary items are packed.
- When reviewing safety rules with children, include what to do if they get lost or separated from their group:
  - Choose a central, recognizable meeting spot, which is pointed out to the group upon your arrival at the destination.
  - Have a consistent message for the children about what to do if they get lost.

After the Trip

It is always important to evaluate a field trip, as soon as possible, upon your return. When possible, get children's feedback. Some questions for the evaluation include:

- Did any issues arise with reference to the transportation/route back and forth?
- Did any issues arise with staffing and volunteers with regard to supervision, group size, or best practices?
- Were there any health or safety issues with the location and facilities?
- Although you planned the trip with age-appropriateness in mind, was it suitable for the children's interests and developmental levels?
- Learning and enjoyment: how did the trip rate?
- Would you consider attending this site again? Why or why not?
- If you would go back, are there any suggestions for groups attending this site in the future?

A planned field trip that involves motorized transportation, such as cars, school buses, or public transportation (e.g., buses, subway), has additional risk and safety considerations with young children. The Canadian Paediatric Society's *Well Beings* (2008) has a complete chapter dedicated to transportation safety, providing very specific guidelines for transporting children in early childhood programs. The information is prefaced with this proviso:

> Every child care facility should have a transportation policy that specifies when child care practitioners may transport children, the rules to follow when transporting them, the responsibilities of staff members who are driving or accompanying children, and emergency procedures. Share this policy with parents at the time of enrolment and with all staff. (Canadian Paediatric Society, 2008, p. 111)

Source: Canadian Paediatric Society, *Well Beings: A Guide to Health in Child Care.* (Ottawa: Canadian Paediatric Society, 2008), 111. Reprinted with permission.

Toronto Children's Services (2004, pp. 1–2) notes that decision making about trips and outings will depend on many factors and that, by focusing on the children's interests, there may be valuable learning opportunities close to the centre without the expense and effort of elaborate field trips. The realities of safety and liability issues and stretched budgets may also mean that early childhood settings view program enhancement as an alternative to field trips. *For example, bringing in one or two visitors to the centre to provide a unique experience rather than the cost and transporting issues to take all children off-site may be the most effective way to achieve the goals and objectives for the group.* Field trips can offer wonderful opportunities for children's learning and enjoyment. Comparing the advantages and challenges of field trips and program enhancements may come down to a case-by-case basis.

Safety Considerations for Walks and Field Trips

Safety considerations for walks and field trips will depend on many factors, such as the location of the early childhood setting (urban, rural) and the age and needs of children. Specific details will be outlined in the program's policies. This list is not exhaustive and is based on infants and toddlers going for walks in strollers and the preschoolers and school-agers going for walks and on field trips.

SAFETY CONSIDERATIONS	AGE GROUPS
A first-aid kit and emergency information for all children and staff in the group is taken on each outing, including medication that may be needed for specific children with chronic conditions (e.g., EpiPen® (epinephrine) Auto-Injector or Twinject® auto-injector, asthma inhaler). A charged cell phone is taken by staff. Maintain child–staff ratios at all times. Do "head counts" regularly during the outing and match with names. This is applicable to toddlers if they get out of the strollers in a green space. Children are dressed appropriately for the weather (e.g., hats and sunscreen in summer). Obey traffic signs and signals at all times.	Infants Toddlers Preschoolers School-agers
Children wear identification (of the program, not the child's name) on all outings. Assign one adult to the front of the group and one to the back. Other adults should be close to children who require assistance. Use the buddy system for children four years old and up. Buddy checks should be done throughout the trip in addition to regular attendance checks. Consider packing a snack for longer walks. Accompany children to public washrooms when away from the early childhood setting. Take along a knapsack for additional items such as a snack or water for longer walks and a camera to take pictures on the trip.	Preschoolers School-agers

Walking While Holding on to a Rope?

Many programs use a walking rope for children to hold when walking as a group outside the program's property. Staff believe that by holding on to a knot or handle attached to a rope, the young children are safer. Educators assume that they are able to keep track of the children because they are in an orderly line and that children will not dash off. The use of ropes is a debatable issue among educators. We do not, however, support the use of ropes, for a number of reasons:

■ The use of ropes implies that the educators don't believe that the children are competent enough to follow the rules for walks. Toddlers who aren't ready to follow the rules should be in strollers or wagons that they can get out of to walk around in a park or playground.

- When one child trips, all the children holding on may also fall, which is potentially more hazardous than not having a rope.
- Educators who rely on the rope as a security measure may not notice when one child lets go.
- Holding on to a rope is not a natural way to walk and thus doesn't provide young children with a realistic experience. It also may encourage them to depend on educators rather than to develop a natural awareness of their surroundings and safety.
- Some people in the community already view early childhood as an institutional setting. Seeing children walking along the street holding on to a rope may reinforce that negative view of early childhood.

Environmental Contaminants

We have discussed concerns about UV rays, humidity, and wind chill, but there are many other environmental factors that environmentalists and researchers are bringing to our attention. Since the 1940s, hundreds of thousands of new chemicals have been introduced into our world in the name of progress and a better standard of living.

The impact of this chemical onslaught on the environment, wildlife, and humans is alarming and still unfolding. Many toxic substances are classified as neurotoxins, hormone disruptors, carcinogens, and respiratory irritants. Some chemicals fit into more than one of these categories. Cell and reproductive changes are becoming more evident as affected generations develop and reproduce. Largely unknown, however, is the impact of synergy: the effect of chemical combinations to which we are exposed. We all breathe the same air and drink the same water, so these chemicals know no boundaries, and that makes pinpointing their effects even more complex. The effects of climate change (global warming), much of which is the result of dependence on carbon fuels, are resulting in a scramble for solutions. In addition to broad social policy changes, which, of course, are essential, our favourite Canadian environmentalist, David Suzuki, is supporting Canadians in making small changes. Everyday changes found on the David Suzuki Foundation website make a difference and help us feel that we have some control over our future (see Resource Materials, page 439).

In addition to the toxic substances in the environment, our health is also affected by contaminants that aren't necessarily chemical additives. *For example, the tragedy in Walkerton, Ontario, was caused by* E. coli *bacteria in the cattle manure that had been spread onto the fields near the wells that supplied the town's drinking water. This contamination resulted in a number of people dying and many more becoming ill. The aftermath of this incident highlights the crucial role of accountability and strict government policies and procedures on a societal health promotion level.* Many Canadians assume that safe drinking water is available in all regions of Canada. Health Canada revealed in the summer of 2006 that 76 Aboriginal communities were under an advisory to boil drinking water, despite $2 billion being spent by the federal government over the last 5 years to upgrade their water treatment systems (First Nations Voices, 2006, p. 1).

Awareness and action by government, groups, and individuals are the keys to moving away from a destructive path. As environmental science continues to evolve, new information seems to surface daily, making it challenging but important for educators to keep updated on legislative and regulatory changes in environmental safety issues that affect children. We still know far less than we should about the impact of these environmental factors on children and youth, making biological indicators of environmental substances important to research (Leitch, 2007, p. 88). In *Reaching for the Top: A Report by the Advisor on Healthy Children and Youth*, Leitch (2007, p. 94) calls for a longitudinal cohort study in Canada to research the effects of chemicals, such as lead and mercury, on the well-being of children. "The need for this study is enormous. Over the last number of years there has been an explosion of allergies. Asthma rates have skyrocketed and chronic disease rates have increased. The environment is believed to be a substantive factor which, following further research, should lead to appropriate clinical and environmental changes that will positively impact the health of Canadian children and youth" (Leitch, 2007, p. 90).

The discussion here focuses on why children are more vulnerable to environmental contaminants, environmental concerns known to affect children's health, and possible actions using the

- health promotion action plan (see Revisiting the Health Promotion Action Plan, page 437) and
- Environmental Health Childproofing Checklist (see Resource Materials, page 439).

For further information and to stay current on the ever-changing information on environmental safety issues, consult the resources listed at the end of this unit. At the forefront, the Canadian Partnership for Children's Health and Environment (CPCHE) is an affiliation of groups with overlapping missions to improve children's environmental health in Canada. Working across traditional boundaries, their website includes downloadable resources with a comprehensive guide entitled *Playing It Safe* (see Resource Materials, page 439).

Children's Exposure and Vulnerability to Environmental Toxins

Although a wide range of opinion exists among professionals regarding the impact of environmental factors on health and safety, there is no doubt that fetuses and young children are more exposed and vulnerable than adults to environmental contaminants, both immediately (acute reactions) and in the long term (chronic effects). Children's environmental exposures and vulnerabilities are unique. Even before conception, parental exposure can affect a child's lifelong health. For example, sperm, which is produced continuously in adult males, may be damaged by occupational or environmental exposure.

A striking study in a First Nations community near Sarnia, Ontario (Mackenzie, Lockridge, & Keith, 2005), highlights how the proximity of this community to a group of large petrochemical, polymer, and chemical industrial plants has potentially changed the ratio of male-to-female births quite dramatically. The proportion of male live births of the Aamjiwnaang First Nation had been declining continuously from the early 1990s to 2003 (the research period), with the most pronounced decrease observed during the most recent 5 years studied. "A community health survey is under way to gather more information about the health of the Aamjiwnaang community and to provide additional information about the factors that could be contributing to the observed decrease in the proportion of male births in recent years" (Mackenzie et al., 2005, p. 1).

After conception, fetuses are vulnerable to chemical exposure.

A well-known example is the story of diethylstilbestrol (DES), a synthetic estrogen hormone prescribed to women between the 1940s and 1971 to prevent miscarriage, with the promise of healthy, full-term babies. The legacy of this exposure has been generational, with daughters and sons of the women who took DES exhibiting high rates of reproductive organ abnormalities, reduced fertility, and other outcomes, including a rare form of cancer. Possible effects to the third generation are as yet unknown.

The term "**windows of vulnerability**" refers to periods of fetal development or other sensitive stages of childhood when "safe" doses for adults are not necessarily safe for children. *For example, there may be lifelong effects on lung function from early exposures to air pollution, permanent brain damage to preschool children exposed to lead, or reproductive abnormalities of children in utero whose parents worked with organochlorine pesticides.*

Several reasons contribute to the increased exposure and vulnerability of children when it comes to environmental toxins (CPCHE, 2005, pp. 20–24):

■ Proportionality

The surface area in a child's lungs is larger in proportion to the rest of the child's body, and, proportionally, a child breathes in more air than an adult. In addition, a child's brain is proportionally larger and therefore receives more blood flow per unit weight compared with an adult. Children eat more food and drink more liquids in proportion to their body weight than do adults. Therefore, their potential exposure to toxins such as lead, pesticides, and nitrates is greater.

- Behaviour

Young children explore their environment by spending more time close to the ground (e.g., crawling) and often put their hands or toys in their mouth and swallow nonedible items. These actions expose them to toxins in dust, soil, and carpets, as well as to pesticide vapours floating close to the ground. This also can increase the different pathways or routes of exposure: inhaling, skin contact, and ingesting.

- Physiology

Physiology refers to how living organisms function. The physiological differences between children and adults place children at higher risk. Children's tissues and body systems (e.g., nervous, respiratory, reproductive, digestive, and immune) are not fully developed and are thus more susceptible to damage. Their growth is regulated by hormones, and many environmental toxins are possible "hormone disruptors." Young children's rate of breathing is normally faster, slowing down as they get older. Therefore, young children inhale toxins more quickly than older children and adults, and the rate of intake speeds up as they are more active, especially outdoors (South Riverdale Community Health Centre, 2003). Children absorb nutrients in the gastrointestinal tract more quickly than do adults, increasing their susceptibility. *For example, children have a greater need for calcium, they absorb more of this mineral when it is present in the gastrointestinal tract, but the body will absorb lead instead of calcium if it is present.* Another physiological difference is that the blood–brain barrier is more permeable in a child, resulting in easier access by toxic contaminants to the brain of a child than to an adult's. "In infancy, skin is more permeable than in later life, allowing the passage of substances through the skin into the bloodstream. Additionally, a child's airways and lungs develop from the early years through adolescence, during which time exposure to toxic substances can overburden the respiratory system. These exposures can cause temporary symptoms, or can actually affect the physical development of lung tissue, such that the lungs are more susceptible to pollutants later in life" (CPCHE, 2005, p. 24).

- Metabolism

"Metabolism is the combined package of all the life-sustaining chemical processes occurring in any living organism. Children tend to have a faster metabolism than do adults. They need to take in more oxygen per unit of body weight per minute to support their growth and activity needs, which are driven by their higher metabolic rates" (CPCHE, 2005, p. 24).

- Life expectancy or latency

Another aspect of risk for children is what is called a "latent effect." Being exposed at a younger age gives more time for health-related problems to develop. Substances that build up in the body, perhaps in fat cells or bones, may not result in health effects until the child has reached adulthood. This is particularly a concern with exposure to carcinogens, such as radiation.

There are additional risk factors for some children, particularly those living in poverty, with inadequate nutrition, or living in a home with smokers (CPCHE, 2005, pp. 28–29).

Children who live in poverty are disproportionately at risk of exposure to environmental toxins: they are more likely to live in industrial areas and closer to smokestacks, garbage dumps, and highways with exhaust fumes. Their home environments are more likely to be improperly designed and poorly maintained buildings, with poor indoor air quality, old paint (which may result in lead exposure), old plumbing, and parking lots backed onto apartment buildings (Chaudhuri, 1998, p. S26). Indoor dampness causing mould growth, dust mites, and cockroach and rodent problems can all be factors in respiratory difficulties.

Poor nutrition can be experienced by any children, but, again, children who live in poverty likely have less access to the range of foods needed to reduce intake of environmental contaminants. For example, a "poor diet can compromise a child's immune system and the ability to detoxify and excrete pesticides. Some pesticides may have larger effects on the immune systems of children who lack iron" (CPCHE, 2005, p. 28).

Environmental tobacco smoke (ETS), formerly referred to as secondhand smoke, is associated with respiratory system problems, especially the development and irritation of asthma. It is also common knowledge that ETS contains over 40 known carcinogens. When other risk factors are present, the risks of ETS are multiplied.

Environmental Concerns and Children's Well-Being

The following section covers four environmental issues of concern to children's health and safety: air pollution, lead, pesticides, and chemicals in plastics. These are certainly not the only contaminants of concern. Further information, and keeping current in the area of environmental safety, is an important responsibility of educators and parents.

Air Pollution

Climate changes are contributing to increased air pollution. How? Greenhouse gases in our atmosphere hold in the heat. These trapped gases are increasing with the use of fossil fuels (i.e., oil, coal, natural gas) to create power and heat. This blanket-type effect is gradually increasing the average temperatures in Canada, which can have serious consequences to our health. As billions of tons of greenhouse gases, including harmful pollutants such as ground-level ozone, sulphur dioxides, and nitrogen oxides, are added to the atmosphere every year, smog is produced. Health Canada estimates that air pollution is the cause of 5,000 premature deaths a year (Canadian Institute of Child Health, 2002). For reasons listed earlier, children are severely affected by air pollution. Air pollution, both indoors and out, can affect respiratory health and influence children's behaviour (e.g., irritability may result from mild reactions to air contaminants). Although there is controversy about the overdiagnosis and the causes of asthma, there is substantial evidence that asthmatic and nonasthmatic children have significant adverse health responses to many air contaminants (see Asthma, page 189). The leading concerns in outdoor air pollutants have been ozone, suspended particles, and sulphur compounds.

Indoor air pollutants include substances such as tobacco smoke, carbon monoxide, radon, formaldehyde, mercury, and asbestos. Ironically, use of these substances was intended to improve quality of life. The presence of some of these substances has resulted in better insulation, decreased ventilation (which has contributed to problems with airtight buildings), increased indoor humidity and higher temperatures, and more furniture and conveniences.

There are a number of ways to improve indoor air quality and reduce children's exposure to environmental contaminants. One obvious way, which has been successful in public places in Canada, is to ban smoking indoors. Parents and educators who have not yet been able to quit smoking need to recognize the importance of smoke-free environments for children. Some jurisdictions have taken the concern about the effects of ETS on children one step further by banning smoking in cars when children under 19 are present. Nova Scotia became the first province in Canada to do so in 2007, followed by British Columbia and Ontario, and likely others will follow.

Other suggestions for improving indoor air quality concern children's exposure to dust and other potentially harmful substances. Ensure that the facilities' surfaces, furniture, counters, and shelves are easy to clean and that they are cleaned on a regular basis. Use unscented cleaning and laundry products and encourage staff not to wear perfumes or colognes, which some people are allergic to. Limit the amount of carpet used within a program. Avoid its use in high-traffic areas where people are wearing shoes or boots and where food or play materials such as paint and play dough are used. Purchase carpeting that is hypoallergenic and cleans well. Ensure that it is vacuumed daily and steam-cleaned regularly. In programs without infants and toddlers, consider eliminating carpeting altogether. Even in those programs with infants and toddlers, other things could be used on the floor instead of carpets (e.g., mats). Window coverings, especially horizontal blinds, tend to trap dust. When selecting window coverings, consider roller blinds. Select fabrics and designs that can be removed and washed easily.

To help protect children outdoors, enforce a no-idling zone during pickup and drop-off times and prohibit smoking close to the building.

Lead

Lead exposure has been associated with serious illness and even death. Scientists now know that even low-level lead exposure can affect a child's brain development and nervous system, leading to possible behavioural and learning difficulties and reduced intelligence (Harvey, 2003, pp. 1–5). It is impossible to avoid lead exposure completely, but safety awareness and precautions limit exposure, which is important because no level of lead is considered safe. A great public health success in the 1970s was the elimination of lead from gasolines. Lead-based paint, found in and on the exterior of older buildings (lead was used as a pigment in paints until shortly after World War II), remains a hazard for many children. Information about how to determine if this is a problem and how to safely remove lead-based paint is readily available.

Exposure to lead in dust and soil is a main concern because preschoolers are likely to ingest dust and soil every day. Houses and apartments and early childhood settings situated near industries that have used lead, or are situated on busy streets, may contain high levels of lead because lead can remain in the soil for decades and contaminate vegetables grown in that soil. Another source of lead contamination is lead-soldered pipes. Municipally treated drinking water is almost lead-free when it leaves the water plant, but it may pick up lead from the plumbing systems of older houses or apartments or from a lead-containing solder common in newer copper systems. In some areas, plumbing codes now limit the content of lead in solder. Lead accumulates when water stands in the pipes, so the first water out of the tap generally contains the most lead and should be flushed for a minute every morning. Even if your facility is new and doesn't have lead pipes and solder, the water travelling through your community's water system will have passed through lead pipes.

Health Canada's *Children's Jewelry Regulations* came into effect in 2005 and make it illegal to import, advertise, or sell children's jewelry items that contain more than 600 mg/kg total lead and 90 mg/kg migratable lead (Health Canada, 2007d).

How can you tell if a toy contains lead?

- Dull, grey-looking metal.
- Pieces that seem heavy for their size.
- If you rub a piece of jewelry against a sheet of paper and it leaves a grey line, it's probably made of lead.
- Bright colours, especially orange and red.
- Soft plastics, as lead is used as a stabilizer to help keep the plastic soft.

> You can test for lead in toys and jewelry on your own. There are several lead testing kits available, mainly through paint stores, large hardware store chains and online. Health Canada no longer tests toys or jewelry suspected of lead contamination, but encourages consumers to contact the National Capital Region Consumer Product Safety Bureau if they have concerns. (CBC News, 2007, p. 2)

Source: *Lead in Toys: What to Look For,* Health Canada, 2007 and CBC. Reproduced with the permission of the Minister of Public Works and Government Services Canada, 2008 and Canadian Broadcasting Corporation.

If a family is concerned that their child may have been exposed to lead, suggest that they ask their physician for blood testing.

Pesticides

Pesticide products registered by the federal government to control pests such as insects, rodents, and weeds have been an ongoing concern because of their obvious toxicity. Recently, there have generally been more stringent standards and regulations to prevent acute (immediate) episodes of toxicity, although children may be more liable than adults to experience latent (delayed) effects over the course of their lifetime (CPCHE, 2005, p. 23). Using chemicals to treat our lawns and gardens and to deflea our pets exposes us to long-term hazards. Insect repellents are likely more hazardous than the bug bite itself (South Riverdale Community Health Centre, 2003, p. 32). A number of health concerns—allergies, hormone disruption, and developmental neurotoxicity, to name a few—have possible associations with pesticides.

In 2000, the Supreme Court of Canada upheld a bylaw passed by the town of Hudson, Quebec, that banned the cosmetic use of pesticides within the town's borders. This ban includes both public land, such as parks, and private property. This landmark decision has paved the way for a number of communities in Canada to pursue similar bylaws. Of course, the attempts are challenged by lawn chemical companies, but it seems that the movement to ban pesticide use is gaining momentum. The general public is becoming more aware of natural alternatives to pest control, as many municipalities have put bylaws in place banning cosmetic use of pesticides, with subsequent fines. Where does your community stand on this important issue?

Plastics

In our modern world, we have come to depend on plastics in much of our everyday life. Plastics can be in our clothing, toys, eyeglasses, computers, phones, dishes, utensils, and furniture—the list goes on. One look around (indoors and outdoors) any early childhood setting and it is obvious that we have come to depend on plastic toys, equipment, and utensils. Historically and currently, most plastics are made from petroleum, a nonrenewable resource, and petroleum-based chemicals. The manufacturing of plastics pollutes air, land, and water and exposes workers to toxic chemicals. In terms of health risks after manufacturing, there is growing evidence that hormone-disrupting chemicals used in manufacturing some plastics, such as BPA, leach into foods or beverages, especially when heated. This is why, for example, there has been alarm and Health Canada's response concerning the use of BPA in baby bottles and sippy cups. "Bisphenol A is found in hard, clear plastics, as well as the epoxy resins used in the lining of some food containers, dental fillings and a slew of other products. The chemical can cause damage to reproductive and developmental systems during vulnerable states of human development, such as early childhood and in the womb" (Environmental Defence, 2008, p. 1).

Leaching of chemicals used in making plastics increases when the plastic comes in contact with oily or fatty foods, during heating, and from old or scratched plastic. Types of plastics shown to leach toxic chemicals are polycarbonate, polyvinyl chlorides (PVCs), and styrene (Institute for Agriculture and Trade Policy, 2005, p. 2).

PVCs are used to produce plastics for cling wrap, some plastic squeeze bottles, cooking oil and peanut butter jars, and detergent and window cleaner bottles. These plastics last for many years and are difficult to destroy, adding to our overflowing landfills. When they are burned, the fumes are even more toxic, emitting dioxins and other known toxins, which then settle on land and are often ingested by grazing animals. Humans then ingest them in food.

PVCs and the phthalates that are added as a plastic softener captured a lot of national and international media attention in the late 1990s due to efforts to ban their use in mouthing and teething toys and rattles. The most immediate concern with phthalates in PVCs is that they leach out of the plastic fairly easily and are thought to be hormone disruptors (i.e., they interfere with the hormone systems) in children. In 1998, Canada's federal government followed the lead of the European Union and banned the use of phthalates in teething rings and other infant toys. Another concern with plastics is the use of lead, cadmium, and other heavy metals, along with various chemicals, in their manufacturing to make them stronger or more flexible. The consumer may incorrectly assume that any product intended for children would have undergone stringent testing before being put on the market. To ensure children's safety, the precautionary approach (see page 375) has been adopted by Health Canada in the banning of BPA use in the manufacturing of baby bottles. In April 2008, Canada became the first national jurisdiction to designate BPA as a toxin.

Some good news is that it is likely that hazardous substances can soon be replaced with safer alternatives in the production of biobased plastic products. "Given the environmental and cost advantages of starch-based biopolymers, it won't be long before we see a far greater acceptance of biobased plastics" (National Research Council Canada, 2007, p. 1).

We may also find that rethinking the use of some plastic products is worthwhile. Suggested ways to reduce children's exposure to hormone disruptors found in PVCs include the following:

- Never microwave food in plastic containers, as the chemicals leach out. Use glass, Pyrex, china, or ceramic dishes. Baby bottles should be warmed in hot water. Silicone nipples and pacifiers or soothers do not contain phthalates.
- Use fabric teethers when possible.
- PVC mini-blinds contain lead that breaks down and becomes a dust on the surface. Wash this away carefully and often.

The following are tips for safer, more sustainable food use of plastics (Institute for Agriculture and Trade Policy, 2005, pp. 2–3):

- Avoid using plastic containers in the microwave. Chemicals are released from plastics when heated (especially for fatty foods because of more leaching of chemicals into fatty foods).
- Beware of cling wraps, especially for microwave use. Use waxed paper or paper towel instead for covering foods.
- Use alternatives to plastic packaging whenever possible. *For example, bring reusable bags or cardboard boxes to the grocery store.*
- Avoid water in plastic bottles unless you're travelling to or live in an area where the quality of water is questionable. Bottled water is less regulated and has less certain purity and safety than tap water.
- If you do use plastic water bottles, take precautions. If you use a polycarbonate water bottle, to reduce leaching of BPA, do not use the bottle for warm or hot liquids and discard old or scratched bottles.
- Use alternatives to polycarbonate plastic baby bottles and sippy cups.

Source: *Smart Plastics Guide Healthier Food Uses of Plastics: For Parents and Children*, 2005. Reprinted with permission of Institute for Agriculture and Trade Policy.

Actions to Promote Environmental Health and Safety in Early Childhood Settings

When we consider the vast and still relatively unknown aspects of environmental contamination, we can become overwhelmed and feel powerless to make a difference. However, there are everyday strategies we can incorporate into early childhood programs that reduce exposure to known environmental contaminants. The *Environmental Health Childproofing Checklist* is a tool for students and educators to evaluate their facility from the perspective of environmental health (see Resource Materials, page 439).

Is there action we can take to address the concern about lead in our water source? Lead-soldered copper plumbing, although banned in the late 1980s, is still quite widely available in existing plumbing. When water sits overnight (or all weekend!) in contact with these joints, lead can go into the water. This is particularly true if the source water is "soft" or acidic, such as can occur on the Canadian Shield.

Since lead is probably harmful at any exposure level, the precautionary approach has meant that some jurisdictions, Ontario for one, legislate that all early childhood settings flush their water system for at least one minute every morning from a cold water tap on the branch of plumbing where water is used for drinking. The Ontario legislation requires that this process is documented in writing and the records are kept for at least five years.

Never use water from the hot water tank for cooking or drinking, as hot water picks up more lead than cold water.

The following are some of the recommendations related to children, youth, and the environment for the Government of Canada to undertake as set out in *Reaching for the Top: A Report by the Advisor on Healthy Children and Youth* (Leitch, 2007, p. 94):

- Conduct a 10-year longitudinal cohort study encompassing fetuses at pregnancy to children 8 years old that monitors their health status and outcomes.
- Ban toxic substances on children's toys, develop a proactive mechanism of evaluation, and implement real enforcement.
- Create and phase-in a "best practice" labelling program for children's products that identifies products that do not contain harmful chemicals (e.g., are lead-free).
- Ensure that imported toys are rigorously tested to ensure that they do not exceed minimum levels of lead.
- Strengthen the protection and monitoring of ground-water sources to reduce the potential exposure to chemical hazards such as mercury, lead, PCBs, dioxins, and polybromonated diphenyl ethers.
- Modernize both the *Hazardous Products Act* and the *Canadian Environmental Protection Act* to better protect children from health and safety hazards associated with consumer products.

Source: *Reaching For The Top: A Report By The Advisor on Healthy Children and Youth* by K. Leitch, Health Canada, 2007. Reproduced with the permission of the Minister of Public Works and Government Services Canada, 2008.

Being Prepared for Emergencies

Educators should have an up-to-date first-aid certificate that equips them with the knowledge and skills

- to help them remain calm,

- to administer basic first aid or at least to ensure that their actions do not make an injury worse while waiting for emergency medical services (make sure you know the number for dialing emergency medical services),
- to use the supplies in a first-aid kit, and
- to know when to call emergency medical services.

Throughout your ECE training, you will work in programs, and one of your first tasks when starting in a new program will be to familiarize yourself with its emergency policy and procedures and take part in fire and evacuation drills. In response to our changing society, programs are now required to be ready to respond to a wide range of situations beyond fires, such as

- possible violent situations,
- bomb threats,
- lock-down situations (e.g., a school-age program located in a school, a section of the neighbourhood that is locked down), and
- environmental situations such as chemical spills and weather emergencies (e.g., blizzards, tornados).

Be sure you know where the following are located in the building:

- emergency exits and posted evacuation routes (floor plan with exits indicated)
- first-aid kits
- fire extinguishers and fire alarms (read the operating instructions)
- smoke detectors and carbon monoxide detectors
- emergency phone numbers within the community, as well as the children's parents' numbers
- blankets and flashlights

Injury Reports

An injury report should be completed whenever a child or educator is injured— even when the injury appears to be minor. Minor cuts can become infected. A head injury may show no immediate observable symptoms, but changes in behaviour can develop hours later. When in doubt, always complete an injury report. Educators should also document the injury in the child's file and make reference to the completed injury report. The injury report provided at the end of this unit covers the pertinent information, including the time and date, educator's signature, and who was notified. A line drawing is provided so that educators can mark where the injury is on the body.

The primary purpose of the injury report is to serve as a legal document. Clear and succinct documentation is required to report the injury as objectively as possible. Depending on the child's injury and the outcome, these reports may be reviewed by the early childhood office, police, or lawyers if the question of professional liability or suspected child abuse is raised. A copy of the injury report is usually placed in the child's file.

The report also serves as a tool for staff in developing injury prevention strategies. Educators use the report to evaluate a specific injury or a series of similar injuries in their program. From this information, educators first consider the five W's of safety:

- who
- why, such as the level of supervision, what the child was doing at the time, and his or her developmental stage
- where, such as on a particular piece of play equipment, its general condition, the protective surface, or on a walk or field trip
- when, such as the time of day and weather conditions
- what happened in chronological order, the type and extent of the injury, and what the injury looks like (size, colour, location on the body)

Educators then consider everything they learned about this incident to determine and implement the necessary changes to prevent similar injuries in the future or at least to reduce the severity. More serious injuries will be reported as serious occurrences (see Serious Occurrences, page 376). The following are a few possible alterations either in practice or to equipment:

- Increase the level of supervision.
- Modify, repair, or remove a piece of play equipment.
- Review the safe use of play equipment with the children.
- Reorganize a particular planned curriculum with children (e.g., reduce the number of steps in a preschool cooking activity and the number of children to supervise them better with cutting and cooking).

- Eliminate a particular planned event with children (e.g., a field trip to horseback ride with preschoolers).

Children's Safety at Pickup Times

Educators are responsible for the safety of children until the children leave the premises with their parents or persons authorized by the parents. Program staff may be faced with a situation in which an unauthorized person arrives to pick up a child, conditions are deemed unsafe for releasing a child to the parent, or no one comes to pick up the child at the end of the day, or school-agers are permitted to leave unattended.

School-Age Children

School-agers range in age from 6 to 12, and their abilities, skills, and need for independence vary. Some parents feel that their children are competent and can handle the responsibility of being at home alone, and the children may want it that way. Other families feel they have no option but to leave their children at home on their own after school. In response, many communities have a phone number that children can call if they are lonely, need someone to talk to, or are worried about something. The community in which they live may also play a role in parents' sense of safety and their level of comfort in having children home alone. According to the Canadian Institute of Child Health, school-age children who are at home alone are clearly at increased risk for injury, missing meals, and other health and well-being problems (Canadian Institute of Child Health, 2000, p. 93).

The law requires that parents provide reasonable provision for the safety of children under age 16. However, this law is vague in terms of what is considered reasonable. School-age programs are then faced with the dilemma of creating a policy on the release of school-agers at the end of the day. Programs' policies depend on their philosophy, their setting (urban versus rural), their location within a city, and the parents using the program. Ultimately, educators and parents all want children to gain increasing levels of independence and responsibility. Most adults realize that developing autonomy through opportunities to manage some risk is beneficial for children.

The program can foster autonomy in school-age children by integrating the concept of "intermittent supervision" (Young, 1994, pp. 43–44). "While children benefit from a gradual expansion of boundaries, attention must be paid to the abilities of the child and the potential risks present in the environment" (Young, 1994, p. 43). When developing an intermittent supervision policy, the program considers issues such as program philosophy, physical layout, and length of time for transitions. In addition, depending on the perception of community safety, this policy may include the requirement of peer buddies (i.e., children are with a peer during these non–adult-supervised times).

- Children in pairs move independently of an adult from their classroom to the school-age program within the building or outside to a portable.
- Children go inside the school to use the washroom (e.g., in buddy pairs) and then return to the playground.

At the time of a child's enrollment, parents are made aware of this approach to supervision and are given an opportunity to discuss any concerns they may have. School-age programs may require that parents sign a permission form regarding intermittent supervision within the program. There are a number of reasons why children may leave the site without adult supervision: they may walk home from the school-age program, go to an off-site after-school activity, or walk to the corner store on an errand as a way to gain autonomy. But no educator would permit unsupervised activities such as these without prior consultation.

Programs work out the specific arrangements for each child with the parents. This agreement is put in writing in the child's file. Before parents permit their children to walk home alone, for instance, school-agers' educators and parents determine the child's readiness and safety factors. As stated above, a program policy or guideline may include a peer buddy system. The following questions should be asked:

- Has the child asked his or her parents to allow walking home alone, and does the child understand what it will be like to be home alone? If this request has not been made by the child, he or she is unlikely to be ready for this responsibility.

- Does the child's teacher feel that the child is developmentally ready? Teachers can provide parents and educators with valuable insights into children's behaviour (e.g., "Every time I step out of the classroom, Sandra is doing something that endangers her safety," or "Danny follows guidelines well and demonstrates initiative").

- What are the potential risks for the child on the way home from the early childhood facility?

- What kind of adult support is available to the child at home (e.g., neighbour, clerk in the corner store, children's telephone help line, telephone access to parents)?

Unauthorized Persons

Parents must feel confident that educators will not permit an **unauthorized person** to take their child from the program. To protect children from abduction, programs require an authorization policy and procedures that ensure that only authorized individuals pick up children. Parents and the program must have a written agreement that lists the people that parents authorize to take their children from the program. (Some parents will authorize one person only.)

If the list is part of a contract with the parent and an employee releases a child to a person not named in the list, the program will be in breach not only of contract but also of their provincial or territorial regulations. If the child is injured, a negligence action (lawsuit) may follow. Staff cannot release a child to anyone who has not been authorized in writing. A parent cannot add a name to the list over the phone. However, due to unexpected work responsibilities or travel problems, parents may find themselves in situations in which they can't get to the program in time to pick up the child. A parent might then call and tell the educator that a friend will come to the program even though this person isn't on the authorized list. These situations are grey areas. Educators have to be practical and exercise common sense. The parent has called the program first and authorized the person for this specific day, and the child knows that person. It would be unlikely that the staff would refuse to release the child to this individual. There may be times when someone arrives who is not on the list and the parent has not called the program. Even if the child is happy to see that person and would be comfortable leaving with him or her, educators are legally responsible not to release the child to this unauthorized person. In this situation, the educators must call the parents. The parent may simply have forgotten to tell the staff that morning. To avoid a similar situation in the future, the parents can add this person's name to the written agreement. The least likely occurrence, but the one of most concern, is that this person is, in fact, attempting to take the child without the parent's permission.

Noncustodial Parents

Many children live in families in which parents are either separated or divorced. Many of these families have workable agreements for child custody and visitation. In cases of joint custody, there usually aren't concerns for the child's safety. However, there are situations in which agreements are not straightforward. From educators' perspectives, parents must provide a copy of the custody order and a photograph of the noncustodial parent. If situations arise when the custodial parent releases the child to the other parent, the custodial parent must provide the staff with written permission. All educators must be apprised of these custody agreements to ensure that a child is not released to a noncustodial parent without authorization. Educators should be cautious if the noncustodial parent arrives on a day other than the one that had been agreed on. Staff can't assume that releasing the child is acceptable to the other parent simply because it's a different day. Parents, not strangers, are responsible for most child abductions.

What do staff do when an unauthorized noncustodial parent insists that the program release the child to him or her? Educators may face a verbal or physical confrontation with this parent. In this situation, staff need to

- calmly ask the parent to move to an area with more privacy (more than one educator should be with the parent) or at least have staff move all children away or outside.
- have someone call the custodial parent so he or she knows what is happening. Depending on their rapport, the custodial parent may be able to talk to the other parent or quickly come to the program.
- call the police if the parent loses control or tries to leave with the child.

Children in Need of Protection: Intoxicated Parents

It may be hard to imagine that parents could actually arrive to pick up their children while intoxicated with alcohol or drugs. Yet it does happen, and educators must know how to handle such situations for the safety of the child and the parent. Educators have a number of concerns:

- releasing the child to a parent whom they consider to be incompetent to care for the child
- the safety of parent and child on the way home
- the safety of others if the intoxicated parent is driving
- the child's safety and well-being once at home, especially if there is no second adult in the home
- the potential liability of the program if staff knowingly allow an intoxicated parent to drive and a motor vehicle mishap occurs

From both an ethical and a legal perspective, educators cannot release a child to someone who could cause the child harm. Each situation is different. Each depends on the age of the child, the staff's relationship with the parent, whether the problem is a recurring one, and so on, and, as such, releasing the child is a subjective decision on the part of staff. The situation could be difficult to handle. Educators should

- offer the parent coffee and calmly talk about safety concerns for the child and parent (the child should not be present);
- ask the parent whether someone could come and pick them up and ensure that the child is cared for when they arrive home, such as
  - the other parent, if he or she is active in the child's daily life, or
  - another authorized adult;
- in extreme cases, call the child protection agency and discuss the situation with them; and
- if the parent is belligerent or confrontational, or wants to or has already taken the child from the program and is driving away, call the police and tell them that a drunk driver is leaving the program with a child. If possible, provide the police with the make, model, and colour of the car, as well as the licence plate number.

When No One Arrives

What happens if half an hour after closing the program, the parents have not yet arrived and cannot be reached by phone? Staff should try contacting the following people:

- the alternative adults listed in the emergency information
- people on the authorized list
- as a last resort, the child protection agency, which will provide staff with guidance in handling the situation

REVISITING THE HEALTH PROMOTION ACTION PLAN

With reference to the health promotion action plan introduced in Unit 1, the following are examples of what we can do to reduce exposure to and production of environmental contaminants.

Individual Problem Solving and Self-Reliance

- Install and maintain carbon monoxide monitors as well as smoke detectors.
- Pay attention to air-quality advisories and the air-quality index.
- Limit activities that contribute to air pollution.
- Minimize contact between food and plastics (e.g., use glass containers in microwave ovens).
- Minimize the use of plastic mouthing toys.
- Run the water taps (or water fountain) for a few minutes each morning to reduce the contaminant load, including lead.
- Eat pesticide-free foods (e.g., organic fruits and vegetables) when possible.
- Use nontoxic repellents to control pests (e.g., dab white vinegar behind ears, knees, and wrists; spray a hot pepper and water mix on leaves to deter caterpillars).
- Minimize the ingestion of toxic chemicals through routine hand washing.
- See resources and stay current on environmental safety issues.

Collective Self-Help

- Insist on nonsmoking environments.
- With other educators in your early childhood program, follow the *Environmental Health Childproofing Checklist* (see Resource Materials, page 439).
- Test for lead in paint, soil, dust, solder, and drinking water (see Resource Materials, page 439). Share your findings with others in your neighbourhood.
- Demand full disclosure if pesticides are used in public places (school yards, parks, and roadsides).

Community Action

- Interested citizens can meet with the local supermarket manager to request organic produce or start a "fresh food box" program. A number of communities in Canada have started programs in which affordable locally grown produce (both organic and nonorganic) is made available on a weekly or monthly basis.
- Find out if your community is or is in the process of becoming a pesticide-free zone. If it is not, find out how to advocate for this.

- Join or start a group to learn about environmental contaminants and how to reduce them.

Societal Change
- Join a national organization that advocates for children's environmental health.
- Advocacy that results in legislated changes benefits everyone. Support the campaign for a cleaner environment and health protection laws in Canada, especially those that will protect children. Refer to Leitch's recommendations related to children, youth, and the environment (see page 430). The public is encouraged to send messages to key federal officials to continue reforming and updating the *Canadian Environmental Protection Act.*

CONCLUSION

Since 1980, the rate of hospitalization due to injury has been decreasing. We must remain vigilant and act on behalf of children to decrease the injury rate further in the coming decades. One senseless death of a child is too many. Air bags in cars, for example, are a preventive measure that can be detrimental to young children. The ongoing role of social public policy and legislation to continue Canada's trend to reducing children's injuries is paramount. On a daily basis, families and educators have an integral role in helping children learn lifelong safety behaviour. As children grow and develop, the educators' role moves from one of protecting children to one of enhancing their understanding of safety, identifying potential risks, and preventing injuries. Our communities and society have an important role in safety promotion through research, education, and legislation based on children's needs.

What's Your Opinion?

TO WEAR HELMETS OR NOT?

Safe Kids Canada (2007, p. 18) states that helmets have been proven effective in preventing head injury from all types of falls and crashes. With this information, what is your opinion on whether and how to translate that important safety information into early childhood programs? Are there particular activities that warrant helmet use? What are potential challenges, and how can they be solved to create safer programs and start young children on lifetime safety practices?

ASSESS YOUR LEARNING

Define terms or describe concepts used in this unit.

- Canadian Standards Association (CSA)
- considerations for walks and field trips
- encroachment area
- environmental contaminants
- four components of safety promotion

- frostbite
- injury prevention strategies
- precautionary approach
- protective surfaces
- safety checklists
- serious occurrences
- sun protection factor (SPF)
- UV index
- unauthorized person
- who, why, where, when, and what of safety
- wind-chill factor
- windows of vulnerability

Evaluate your options in each situation.

1. The daily routine usually ends with outdoor play, and parents pick up their children from the playground. Children need active supervision on equipment, but parents also need the opportunity to speak with an educator about their child's day.

2. School-agers on the playground are inundated with a long list of rules and often feel that they have no autonomy. Many children are trying to feel more powerful by deliberately breaking rules when educators' backs are turned.

3. The winter has been extremely cold and windy, yet a number of the school-agers are not wearing their boots and hats because "it's just not the thing to do." Before and after school, the children have a choice between staying in and going out to the playground. These same children choose to stay indoors. Some haven't played outside all month.

4. You are on a long summer walk with the preschoolers before lunch and suddenly you remember that none of you are wearing sunscreen.

5. The carpeting in the play area of the infant room needs a good cleaning, and your director wants to have it professionally cleaned. You and your room partner are aware of the environmental toxins, not only from the chemical cleaners but also from the carpet. The infants crawl around on it daily, with ongoing exposure.

RESOURCE MATERIALS

Organizations

Abotex Enterprises Ltd., 3031 Wildwood Drive, Windsor, ON N8R 1S7. Tel: 519-735-8645 or 1-800-268-5323 for nearest retail location; http://www.leadinspector.com (suppliers of lead test kits)

Canadian Institute of Child Health, 384 Bank Street, Suite 300, Ottawa, ON K2P 1Y4. Tel: 613-230-8838; fax: 613-230-6654; http://www.cich.ca

Canadian Standards Association (CSA), 5060 Spectrum Way, Mississauga, ON L4W 5N6. Tel: 416-747-4000 or national toll-free 1-800-463-6727; fax: 416-747-2473; http://www.csa.ca

Safe Kids Canada, 180 Dundas Street West, Toronto, ON M5G 1Z8. Tel: 416-813-6766 or national toll-free 1-888-723-3847; fax: 416-813-4986; http://www.safekidscanada.ca (Monitors children's injuries and develops prevention programs; Safe Kids coalitions are located across Canada.)

Other Websites of Interest

Best Start: Ontario's Maternal Newborn and Early Child Development Resource Centre: http://www.beststart.org/index_eng.html

Canada Safety Council: http://www.safety-council.org

Canadian Partnership for Children's Health and Environment (an affiliation of groups with overlapping missions to improve children's environmental health in Canada. Most comprehensive organization and website on children's environmental issues): http://www.healthyenvironmentforkids.ca

Canada Safety Council: http://www.safety-council.org

Canadian Toy Testing Council: http://www.toy-testing.org

David Suzuki Foundation: http://www.davidsuzuki.org

Environmental Defence:

- Protecting the Environment and Human Health: http://www.environmentaldefence.ca

- Toxic Nation: http://www.toxicnation.ca

Environmental Safety: http://www.healthyenvironmentforkids.ca

Environmental Health: http://www.hc-sc.gc.ca/english/protection/environment.html

Health Canada's Consumer Product Safety:

- General Consumer Information: http://www.hc-sc.gc.ca/index-eng.php

- Children's Products: http://www.hc-sc.gc.ca/cps-spc/child-enfant/index-eng.php

- Playground Equipment: http://www.hc-sc.gc.ca/cps-spc/sport/equip-play-jeu/index-eng.php

- Warnings and Advisories: http://www.hc-sc.gc.ca/cps-spc/advisories-avis/aw-am/index-eng.php

Pest Management Regulatory Agency, Health Canada: http://www.hc-sc.gc.ca/pmra-arla/english/index-e.html

Public Health Agency of Canada:

- For parents: http://www.phac-aspc.gc.ca/dca-dea/injury/en/parents.html

- For children: http://www.phac-aspc.gc.ca/dca-dea/injury/en/enfants.html

Stay Safe (Health Canada): http://www.healthcanada.gc.ca/staysafe

The Lung Association: http://www.lung.on.ca

The War Amps:

- PLAYSAFE: http://www.waramps.ca/playsafe/home.html

- Safety Walk Program: http://www.waramps.ca/playsafe/walk.html

Water Safety Services, Canadian Red Cross: http://www.redcross.ca/article.asp?id=000881&tid=001

Printed Matter

Children's Playspaces and Equipment (2007), by the Canadian Standards Association. To order a copy, call 1-800-463-6727 or visit http://www.csa.ca.

Environmental Health Childproofing Checklist (2006), by Best Start: Ontario's Maternal, Newborn and Early Childhood Development Resource Centre and the Canadian

Partnership for Children's Health and Environment. To download a copy, visit http://www.beststart.org/resources/env_action/pdf/envirostrategies.pdf

Field Trips and Program Enhancement (March 2004), by Toronto Children's Services. To download a copy, visit http://www.toronto.ca/children/pdf/fieldtrip.pdf

Guide to Less Toxic Products, by Environmental Health Association of Nova Scotia: To download a wide variety of information, visit http://www.lesstoxicguide.ca/index.asp?

Is Your Child Safe (2006), by Health Canada. To download a copy, visit http://www.hc-sc.gc.ca/cps-spc/alt_formats/hecs-sesc/pdf/pubs/cons/child-enfant/child-enfant-eng.pdf

Let's Go Outside! Designing the Early Childhood Playground (1999), by Tracey Theemes (High Scope Educational Research Foundation).

Playing It Safe: Service Provider Strategies to Reduce Environmental Risks to Preconception, Prenatal and Child Health (2006), by Best Start: Ontario's Maternal, Newborn and Early Childhood Development Resource Centre and the Canadian Partnership for Children's Health and Environment. To download a copy, visit http://www.beststart.org/resources/env_action/pdf/envirostrategies.pdf

The Toy Report (annual). To download reports, visit http://www.toy-testing.org/CTTCmm.htm

Videos/DVDs

Cutting the Risk, Keeping the Magic (1997), by Metro Toronto Community Services.

Toxic Trespass: Taking Action on Children's Health and the Environment (2007), by the National Film Board of Canada. To order a copy, contact the Women's Healthy Environments Network at 416-928-0880 or visit http://www.whenvironments.ca

BIBLIOGRAPHY

Canadian Cancer Society. (2008, May 13). *What you can do to avoid pressure-treated lumber.* Retrieved July 2008 from http://www.cancer.ca/ccs/internet/standard/0,2939,3172_372059_372110_langId-en,00.html

Canadian Institute of Child Health. (2000). *The health of Canada's children: A CICH profile* (3rd ed.). Ottawa: Author.

Canadian Institute of Child Health. (2002). *Fact sheet: Air pollution.* Retrieved July 2008 from http://www.cich.ca/PDFFiles/ClimateChangeFactSheets/English/AirPollution.pdf

Canadian Paediatric Society. (2008). *Well beings: A guide to health in child care* (3rd ed.). Ottawa: Author. The material on p. 417 is reprinted with permission.

Canadian Partnership for Children's Health and Environment. (2005). *Child health and the environment – a primer.* Retrieved July 2008 from http://www.healthyenvironmentforkids.ca/img_upload/13297cd6a147585a24c1c6233d8d96d8/Primer.pdf. The material on p. 423–425 is reprinted with permission.

Canadian Standards Association. (2007). *Children's playspaces and equipment.* Mississauga, ON: Author.

CBC News. (2007, August 14). *Lead in toys: What to look for.* Retrieved July 2008 from http://www.cbc.ca/news/background/consumertips/lead.html

Chaudhuri, N. (1998). The case for child development as a determinant of health. *Canadian Journal of Public Health, 89*(Suppl. 1), S26–S30.

Cooper, K., et al. (2000). *Environmental standard setting and children's health. Report by the Children's Health Project.* Toronto: Canadian Environmental Law Association and Ontario College of Family Physicians.

Environment Canada. (2001, September). *A Canadian perspective on the precautionary approach/ principle*. Retrieved July 2008 from http://www.ec.gc.ca/econom/pp_e.htm

Environment Canada. (2002a, September 20). *Stratospheric ozone: Frequently asked questions*. Retrieved June 2008 from http://www.ec.gc.ca/ozone/docs/UO/faq/en/faq.cfm#1

Environment Canada. (2002b, December 12). *Wind chill fact sheet*. Retrieved July 2008 from http://www.msc-smc.ec.gc.ca/education/windchill/windchill_fact_sheet_aug_10_e.cfm

Environment Canada. (n.d.). *Wind chill hazard*s. Retrieved July 2008 from http://www.msc-smc. ec.gc.ca/education/windchill/windchill_threshold_chart_e.cfm

Environmental Defence. (2008, February). *Toxic baby bottles in Canada*. Retrieved July 2008 from http://www.toxicnation.ca/files/toxicnation/report/ToxicBabyBottleReport.pdf

First Nation Voices. (2006, Summer). *First Nations, the environment and health*. Retrieved July 2008 from http://www.firstperspective.ca/voices_template.php?path=2006voices_ summer_first

Harvey, R. (2003, April 13). A silent danger still unheeded. *The Toronto Star*.

Health Canada. (2005, August). *It's your health: West Nile virus* (Catalogue No. H50-3/148-2005E-PDF). Retrieved July 2008 from http://www.hc-sc.gc.ca/hl-vs/iyh-vsv/ diseases-maladies/wnv-vno-eng.php#is

Health Canada. (2007a, November 16). *A parent's guide to sun protection: Sun fiction and fact*. Retrieved July 2008 from http://www.hc-sc.gc.ca/hl-vs/securit/sports/sun-sol/facts-realites- eng.php

Health Canada. (2007b, November 16). *A parent's guide to sun protection: Why be careful?* Retrieved July 2008 from http://www.hc-sc.gc.ca/hl-vs/securit/sports/sun-sol/careful-soi- gneux-eng.php#child

Health Canada. (2007c, November 16). *A parent's guide to sun protection: What is SPF?* Retrieved July 2008 from http://www.hc-sc.gc.ca/hl-vs/securit/sports/sun-sol/what_spf- que_fps-eng.php

Health Canada. (2007d, September 6). *Health Canada advises Canadians about children's poten- tial exposure to lead* (Advisory 2007-114). Retrieved July 2008 from http://www.hc-sc.gc.ca/ ahc-asc/media/advisories-avis/_2007/2007_114-eng.php

Health Canada. (2008, May 29). *Health Canada responds to concerns raised about bisphenol A in canned food: Information update*. Retrieved July 2008 from http://www.hc-sc.gc.ca/ahc-asc/ media/nr-cp/_2008/2008_84-eng.php

Institute for Agriculture and Trade Policy. (2005). *Smart Plastics Guide healthier food uses of plastics: For parents and children*. Retrieved July 2008 from http://www.healthyenvironment- forkids.ca/img_upload/13297cd6a147585a24c1c6233d8d96d8/Smart_Plastic_Guide_IATP. pdf

Leitch, K. (2007). *Reaching for the top: A report by the advisor on healthy children and youth* (Catalogue No. H21-296/2007E). Ottawa: Health Canada.

Mackenzie, C. A., Lockridge, A., & Keith, M. (2005). Declining sex ratio in a First Nation com- munity. *Environmental Health Perspectives, 113*(10). Retrieved July 2008 from http://www. ehponline.org/members/2005/8479/8479.html

National Research Council Canada. (2007, September 1). *Ingredients for greener plastics: NRC overcomes major hurdles in producing plastic from vegetable sources*. Retrieved July 2008 from http://www.nrc-cnrc.gc.ca/highlights/2007/0709bio_e.html

Ogilvie, M. (2008, July 10). More young women getting skin cancer. *The Toronto Star*. Retrieved July 2008 from http://www.thestar.com/article/457852

Pest Management Regulatory Agency. (2004). *Safety tips on using personal insect repellents* (Catalogue No. H113-1/33-2003E-IN). Retrieved July 2008 from http://www.hc-sc.gc.ca/ pmra-arla/english/pdf/pnotes/deet-e.pdf

Safe Kids Canada. (2007). *Child and youth unintentional injury: 10 years in review 1994-2003*. Retrieved July 2008 from http://www.sickkids.ca/SKCForPartners/custom/ SKW06NationalReportENG.pdf. The material on pages 359, 361, 362, 363, 369, 371, 372, 374, 379 and 438 is reprinted with permission.

South Riverdale Community Health Centre. (2003). *Hidden exposures: A practical guide for creating a healthier environment for you and your children.* Toronto: Author.

Theemes, T. (1999). *Let's go outside! Designing the early childhood playground.* Ypsilanti, MI: High Scope Educational Research Foundation.

Toronto Children's Services. (2004, March). *Field trips and program enhancements.* Retrieved July 2008 from http://www.toronto.ca/children/pdf/fieldtrip.pdf

Toronto Public Health. (2003, July). *Chromated copper arsenate-treated wood (pressure treated wood).* Fact sheet. Retrieved July 2008 from http://www.toronto.ca/health/factsheet_ptw.htm#06

Young, N. (1994). *Caring for play: The school and child care connection.* Toronto: Direction 2000.

Preventing Child Maltreatment

CONTENTS

The United Nations (UN) Convention on the Rights of the Child, proclaimed in 1989, is the first legally binding international instrument to incorporate the full range of human rights for all children. The Convention spells out the basic human rights that children everywhere are entitled to:

- survival
- optimal development
- protection from harmful influences, abuse, and exploitation
- full participation in family, cultural, and social life

(See Appendix 8.1, page 501.)

Although most children in Canada do develop in safe, predictable environments in which their rights are met, this is not the reality for many others. Trained and experienced educators often identify child maltreatment as an area in which they need further education. Although it is impossible to know the true extent of child maltreatment, because much goes unreported, even conservative estimates of the number of reported cases make it likely that educators will come in contact with children who are victims of maltreatment. Participating in continuing education opportunities, combined with work experience and collaboration with professionals and agencies, enhances your understanding and skills in the area of child maltreatment: abuse and neglect. Since educators are frontline professionals and work closely with children and families, they are in a position to identify children whom they suspect are being maltreated and are able to activate primary, secondary, and, in some situations, tertiary prevention. In other words, early childhood programs can contribute to the prevention of child maltreatment in several ways:

- by ensuring that the environment in the program is rich with responsive, respectful role modelling in relating to both children and adults (primary prevention)
- by early identification of suspected child maltreatment and by reporting suspected maltreatment to a child protection agency (secondary prevention)
- by supporting both children and their families when child maltreatment has been confirmed (secondary or sometimes tertiary prevention if educators are asked to be involved in the treatment process)

As professionals, educators are required by law to report their suspicions of child maltreatment. Suspected child maltreatment reporting requirements are under provincial/territorial jurisdiction; educators must know these requirements. Their relationship with children and their families also creates an ethical responsibility to report. These reports make it possible for child protection agencies to provide protection for children who are at either immediate or future risk and to assist the children and their families in recovery.

Failure to recognize and to help stop child maltreatment can result in serious consequences for children, including long-term emotional and physical problems and, in extreme cases, death. Another devastating consequence is that adults who were maltreated as children may themselves become abusive or be further victimized (e.g., spousal abuse), so the cycle of abuse continues.

EXPLORING YOUR FEELINGS

As individuals, we need to understand our own feelings about this sensitive and emotional subject. Working with families involves a wide range of philosophies, parenting practices, and lifestyles. Educators' openness to diversity in values and customs contributes to their sensitivity and effectiveness on a personal as well as a professional level.

About Child Maltreatment

Each of us brings different life experiences and spiritual and cultural beliefs to the program. Some people find it incomprehensible that someone could inflict emotional and physical pain on a child, or they may feel anger and hatred for those who maltreat or neglect children. Others are themselves survivors of child maltreatment. Even if you were not maltreated as a child, you probably know someone who was. For survivors, the realm of emotional and physical reactions to child maltreatment may be overwhelming. Attempting to understand child maltreatment from a professional rather than personal perspective is challenging. Even if we have only read or heard about child maltreatment, we may still have strong feelings.

What do we do with all these emotions and responses? You may feel the need to acknowledge and work through your feelings to respond effectively to this complex issue in your work.

- You are so angry at the thought of a parent hurting a child that you question your ability to provide further support to the child and family.
- As an adult survivor of child maltreatment, you feel that this is the time for you to seek professional help.

Child maltreatment of any kind can generate a range of intense emotional reactions. We all experience some reaction when faced with disturbing behaviour. *For example, when you read a newspaper article or hear a story on the television or radio about sexual abuse, such as sexual exploitation of children by a doctor or religious leader, how do you feel? Perhaps you feel disbelief that anyone could do such a thing to a child. Perhaps you feel anger at the child for not telling someone when it started.* It is important for anyone caring for children to explore her or his feelings about sexual abuse. Our reactions can affect our understanding of sexual abuse and the way we respond to children who have been sexually abused.

Those who have concerns about their confused feelings or about approaching issues that may not have been resolved since childhood may find it necessary to talk with a trusted friend or a counsellor. Your college's counsellors and instructors can provide students with names of referrals (e.g., social workers, counsellors, or psychologists) and community services.

About Family Diversity

The region of Canada we live in and, more specifically, the location of the program we work in, may determine the diversity of families' structures, living styles, social and economic situations, ethnocultural backgrounds, religions, and so on. It is important to realize that you don't have to adopt someone else's values and beliefs, but you do need to develop a level of understanding and respect for others' values and beliefs. Many practices are obviously not harmful to children, even if they are different from your experience. Many foods, rituals, and family practices are an important part of cultural or religious heritage and socialization. However, when it is possible that a practice may be harmful, the child protection agency must be consulted.

While helping preschoolers with their bathing suits for the wading pool, you notice that Khoa has small circular bruises over his chest and back. When you ask, "I see you have marks on your back. What happened?" the four-year-old replies, "Mommy used a spoon to make me better." The child is not upset and is generally a content child who is always happy to see his mother at the end of the day.

A manifestation of bad wind (a notion derived from Chinese medicine) such as a cough can be released by creating small bruises on the body, commonly effected by rubbing the body with a coin or a spoon or by cupping—that is, by placing a hot cup on the body and letting it cool until the air contracts and draws the skin upward. When bruise lines appear, the bad wind has come to the surface and left the body (Dinh et al., 1990, p. 194).

In this example, the educator needs to contact the child protection agency because using an object and leaving marks are indicators that need to be followed up. The worker will direct the educator whether to talk to the parent. Every situation is different, but in many jurisdictions, child protection agencies ensure that families connect with personnel who help them learn about alternatives to traditional health practices that conflict with child protection standards in Canada.

Learning to work effectively with diverse families requires an open attitude and skills. These skills can be developed from

- the family, in a respectful manner,
- coworkers,
- postdiploma courses and antibias workshops,
- relevant agencies in the community, and
- literature and audiovisual training materials.

To summarize, you must ask yourself two important questions before you can manage suspicions of child maltreatment in a practical way in early childhood programs:

1. What are some of the feelings I have about child maltreatment—such as fear, anger, frustration, sadness—and how can I deal with these in a way that enables me to work effectively with families?

2. How open am I to living styles, values, and parenting practices that are different from my own?

OBJECTIVES

To define and describe each category of child maltreatment: physical abuse, emotional abuse, sexual abuse, neglect, and exposing children to family violence.

CHILD MALTREATMENT

The definition of **child maltreatment** has evolved over time and will continue to do so. Thirty-five years ago, child maltreatment was thought to concern mainly children who were severely physically abused. Since then, we have become aware of the high incidence of child sexual abuse, especially when considering the far-reaching consequences of child pornography on the Internet. We are more aware of the consequences for children who have been abused emotionally, including issues such as children witnessing the abuse of their mother or other family member. The various ways that children are neglected has also become much more evident, making neglect the most prevalent type of child maltreatment reported to child protection agencies in Canada (see Appendix 8.2, page 502). Child maltreatment is always a misuse of power—a person with greater physical, intellectual, or emotional power and authority controls a child in a way that does not contribute to the child's health, growth, and development. Although we use the term "parent" in this unit, it is important to note that the offender could be another family member, such as an aunt or grandfather, or another caregiver in the child's life, such as a babysitter, educator, or coach. In all four categories of substantiated abuse, in the first nationwide study to examine the incidence in Canada, the majority of alleged perpetrators (93%) were family members or other persons related to the child (Trocmé, Fallon, MacLaurin, & Copp, 2001).

Child maltreatment means that the child's rights are not being met, as outlined in the UN Convention on the Rights of the Child. Child maltreatment can occur within the home, in institutions, and even at the community or societal level:

- Parents or other individuals may abuse children.
- Institutional practices may be abusive to children, such as the inappropriate use of physical restraints.
- The physical, emotional, and social consequences can be devastating for the more than one million children in Canada who live in poverty.

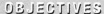
OBJECTIVES

To develop a heightened awareness of the complex consequences of maltreatment on children.

Types of Maltreatment

Generally, child maltreatment is categorized into four types: physical abuse, emotional abuse, sexual abuse, and neglect. Although this categorization can be useful, it implies distinctions that don't always exist. In reality, the four types of maltreatment do not operate exclusively of one another. In fact, it is common to find that categories of child maltreatment coexist.

Gemma is being physically abused and is also abused emotionally or at least suffers emotionally as a result of pain inflicted on her. A child is being emotionally abused when she or he witnesses violence against a parent. This child may also be the victim of physical abuse through injury intended for that parent, such as being cut by shards of glass from a bottle thrown across the room or suffering a blow while trying to "protect" the nonoffending adult. An educator who belittles a child's attempts at mastery of a skill and who ignores the child's needs for comfort when needed is being both emotionally abusive and neglectful.

Neglect

Neglect occurs when parents and caregivers fail to meet the child's physical, emotional, and social needs, through inattention or omission.

The Canadian Incidence Study of Reported Child Abuse and Neglect (Trocmé et al., 2005) identified neglect as the highest substantiated form of child maltreatment (30%) (see Appendix 8.2, page 502). The consequences of neglect can be extreme, especially for infants and young children. Inadequate emotional and physical stimulation and malnutrition cause a condition known as "failure to thrive." Infants who suffer from this condition gain little weight, with no medical explanation, and experience delays in development, particularly in language, during the second year of life.

The Canadian Incidence Study of Reported Child Abuse and Neglect (Trocmé et al., 2001, pp. 35–37) outlines eight forms of neglect, with failure to supervise being the most prevalent form reported:

■ Failure to supervise or protect leading to physical harm

The child is left alone on a balcony and falls over.

■ Failure to supervise or protect a child from possible sexual abuse

The parents leaves a child with a babysitter even though they suspect the babysitter may be sexually fondling her.

■ Physical neglect

The caregiver failed to care for the child adequately: inadequate nutrition or clothing and unhygienic or dangerous living conditions.

■ Medical neglect

The caregiver refused to allow medical treatment or to alleviate physical harm or suffering

■ Failure to provide treatment for mental, emotional, or developmental problems

The caregiver did not provide treatment for a child suffering from severe anxiety, depression, withdrawal, self-destructive or aggressive behaviour, or a condition that could seriously impair his or her development.

■ Permits maladaptive or criminal behaviour

A child has committed a criminal offence with the caregiver's encouragement or because of the caregiver's failure to supervise the child adequately.

■ Abandonment or refusal of custody

> The caregiver has died, without making adequate provisions for care and custody, or the caregiver refused to take custody of a child.

■ Educational neglect

> A caregiver knowingly allowed a child to miss school regularly or repeatedly kept the child at home (at least five days a month) or failed to enroll the child in school.

Source: *Canadian Incidence Study of Reported Child Abuse and Neglect* by N.B. Trocmé, B. Fallon, B. MacLaurin, and B. Copp. Public Health Agency of Canada, 2001. Reproduced with the permission of the Minister of Public Works and Government Services, Canada, 2008.

Physical Abuse

Children who have suffered injuries that were inflicted by parents, older siblings, extended family members, or others have been **physically abused**. In some cases, abuse occurs only once, but in most situations, the child is abused over a period of time. The physical abuse usually becomes more severe over time; the abuser often justifies his or her actions in terms of discipline and may not have initially intended to hurt the child. There are as many types of injuries as there are ways and objects with which someone can physically abuse. Physical injuries that result from physical abuse can be grouped into four categories (Ayoub et al., 1990, pp. 239–242):

1. Injuries to the skin and soft tissue underneath include bruises, abrasions (e.g., cuts, scrapes), hematomas (swellings containing blood), bites, and burns. Bruises or abrasions can be caused by being hit by hands or blunt instruments (e.g., belts, hairbrushes, or rope) or by being kicked. Severe bruising, especially on the buttocks or legs, often results from excessive discipline involving objects such as fly swatters or wooden spoons. Bruises often take on the shape of the object used. Tying children's arms or legs together or to a chair or bed can cause burn marks or cuts to wrists or ankles. Dunking children in hot water can cause burns. "Isolated burns on the buttocks, palms of the hands, or soles of the feet are particularly suspicious. Another kind of contact burn is from cigarettes" (Ayoub et al., 1990, p. 241) (see Figure 8.1)

2. Injuries to the head and central nervous system include bleeding inside the eyes or brain tissue (often from being violently shaken), spinal injuries, and asphyxia (from choking or suffocating). Shaking a young child, especially an infant, is a common cause of serious injury or death. Adults may not realize that the use of force in a moment of anger can lead to a lifetime of ill effects.

3. Internal (abdominal) injuries are serious and can lead to death. Internal organs such as the spleen and pancreas can be crushed or ruptured. A punch or kick to the abdomen can rupture the child's stomach. If a child is thrown, the impact could tear the liver or spleen.

4. Injuries to the skeletal system can result from shaking, squeezing, or a direct blow. Actions such as pushing the child down the stairs can result in fractures of the arms, legs, or skull. An infant's skull is thin and pliable, so a blow to the head by a hand or foot can easily cause a fracture.

FIGURE 8.1	Children's Bruises

Areas of Bruising

Common (over bony prominences)

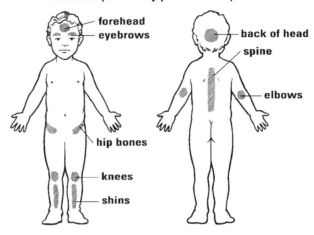

Questionable (over soft, fleshy areas)

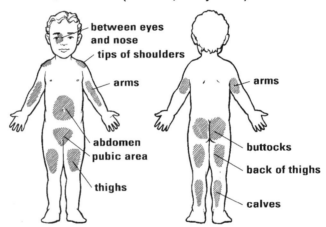

Shaken Baby Syndrome

Shaken baby syndrome, a form of nonaccidental head injury with or without impact, occurs when an infant or young child is shaken violently, usually by a parent or caregiver. It is believed that the demands of caring for an infant, especially a baby's crying, may trigger a frustrated parent or caregiver to shake the infant (Canadian Paediatric Society, 2001, p. 664). Although it can happen with small children, shaken baby syndrome is so named because infants under the age of one are the most common victims. They are particularly susceptible to injury because of their large head, heavy brain, and weak neck muscles, coupled with the fact that the offender is much larger and stronger than the infant.

It is never acceptable to shake a child. There are usually no outward signs of trauma even if the shaking occurred against something (it is often something soft, such as a mattress), but the damage to the brain can be very serious (Canadian Paediatric Society, 2001). The rotational force cuts off blood vessels around the brain and leads to internal bleeding, sometimes resulting in swelling of the brain, which causes further damage. Depending on the severity of the symptoms, a physician may not diagnose a head injury. *For example, a physician may observe a baby who is mildly shaking or trembling and experiencing some vomiting.* This could be explained by the flu. On the other hand, the baby's symptoms could include seizures or loss of consciousness, or the baby could die. Approximately 25% of children who were clinically diagnosed die, and about 80% of those who survive have lifelong neurological damage, such as blindness, cerebral palsy, learning disabilities, and behavioural problems (Barr, 2006).

Experts suspect that the incidence of shaken baby syndrome is substantially underestimated due to missed diagnoses. The Canadian Paediatric Society (2001), together with other organizations, endorsed the "Joint Statement on Shaken Baby Syndrome" to contribute to public awareness and endorse the development of prevention resources available from agencies at the community and federal levels. Shaken baby syndrome may be reduced through universal educational programs delivered early to new parents. Programs and resources help parents understand that crying is normal, recognize its ability to frustrate caregivers, and learn positive ways to cope with it. The National Center on Shaken Baby Syndrome is the only worldwide organization that is dedicated solely to the prevention of this form of child abuse and encourages the widest distribution possible to health care facilities and the general public (see Resource Materials, page 496).

Female Genital Mutilation

Female genital mutilation (FGM), also known as female genital cutting, is an extreme form of physical abuse that has come to the attention of the general public in Canada since the early 1990s. The severity of the mutilation is classified into the four types described below (World Health Organization, 2008, p. 24):

1. partial or total removal of the clitoris and/or prepuce (clitoridectomy)

2. partial or total removal of the clitoris and the labia minora, with or without excision of the labia majora (excision)

3. narrowing of the vaginal orifice with creation of a covering seal by cutting and appositioning the labia minora and/or the labia majora, with or without excision of the clitoris (infibulation)

4. all other harmful procedures to the female genitalia for nonmedical purposes, for example, pricking, piercing, incising, scraping, and cauterization (unclassified)

Source: *Eliminating Female Genital Mutilation: An Interagency* Statement, 2008. Reprinted with permission of World Health Organization.

The short- and long-term health effects of this practice can be physically, emotionally, and socially devastating to the girls and women who are subjected to it, causing excruciating pain and sometimes death. According to the World Health Organization (2008), approximately 100 to 140 million girls and women worldwide have been subjected to this violence. Each year, approximately three million girls are at risk of undergoing FGM. Most live in 28 African countries, although some live in Asia or the Middle East and increasingly are immigrants to the West, including Canada. Growing migration has increased the number of girls and women living outside their country of origin who have undergone FGM or who may be at risk of being subjected to the practice (Yoder, Abderrahim, & Zhuzhuni, 2004). It is usually done when girls are between the ages of 4 and 10 years, without anesthetic and under unsterile conditions. Culture, tradition, and religion are used as justification for this violent abuse, but in reality, no religion dictates this practice. Therefore, using religion as a rationale for violence is insupportable. The World Health Organization (2008, p. 8) holds the following position regarding female genital mutilation:

> Seen from a human rights perspective, the practice reflects deep-rooted inequality between the sexes, and constitutes an extreme form of discrimination against women. Female genital mutilation is nearly always carried out on minors and is therefore a violation of the rights of the child. The practice also violates the rights to health, security and physical integrity of the person, the right to be free from torture and cruel, inhuman or degrading treatment, and the right to life when the procedure results in death.

The UN Convention on the Rights of the Child (see Appendix 8.1, page 501) refers to the evolving capacity of children to make decisions, but due to cultural or religious expectations, a girl's decision to undergo FGM is not free of coercion. A common, coordinated approach promoting positive social change at community, national, and international levels could lead to FGM being abandoned within a generation, with some of the main achievements obtained by 2015 (World Health Organization, 2008).

Many girls and women who come to Canada are victims of FGM. A range of issues may emerge for these girls and women, and they must be treated with sensitivity. If you have had this procedure, seek out caring and enlightened physicians and other professionals who will be supportive to your physical, emotional, and social well-being. Child protection agencies, particularly those in large Canadian cities, have developed a policy to respond to victims of FGM. These policies acknowledge that girls who have already undergone the practice need compassion and support—particularly culturally relevant support. Child protection agencies also aim to protect young girls where there is the risk of this physical abuse. Canada's *Criminal Code* prohibits citizens and landed immigrants from being removed from the country and subjected to FGM. Parents who insist on continuing this practice do so illegally, using untrained persons in unhygienic conditions and putting their daughter at substantial risk.

Discipline versus Punishment

The practice of corporal punishment, often a hotly debated issue in parenting, illustrates how difficult it is to define physical abuse. Violence in our society is not only accepted but is often also revered. Some of the most popular movies of our time depict extreme violence. At the same time, the media bombard us with images of war and political unrest, institutional and family child abuse, date rape, murders of young women, spousal abuse, and elder abuse. "Our society is so used to seeing and accepting violence that it is not uncommon to excuse the violence or blame the victim. We say, 'It was the alcohol,' or 'He had a bad day.' We may even ask, 'What did she do to provoke the violence?'" (Caring Communities Project, 1994, p. 12).

Federal and provincial/territorial governments have acknowledged the prevalence of child and intimate-partner abuse and have begun to take a stronger stand against violence in the home. Children are not their parents' property, nor is a wife owned by her husband. It may be hard to believe that only in the last 25 years was the *Criminal Code* amended to state that husbands have no legal right to force their wives to have sex.

Corporal punishment is the use of physical force to discipline children. It is not against the law in Canada, but it is illegal in over 20 countries, most of which are in Europe. The *Criminal Code of Canada* defines assault as the use of physical force on an individual without consent. Assault charges can be laid any time an adult strikes, shakes, or kicks another adult. However, Section 43 of the *Code* gives adults permission to use physical force on children. Children are the only people in Canada who can be legally "assaulted." Their assailants need not fear legal reprisal unless the force is deemed to be unreasonable. This difference between the way the *Criminal Code* deals with hitting children and hitting adults reflects a lack of societal respect for the child. The *Criminal Code of Canada* defines the degree to which corporal punishment is legal, beyond which it is excessive and is considered child abuse. "Excessive" is sometimes difficult to distinguish from "not excessive," and the difficulty can lead to a vast range of interpretations. Some examples of when punishment crosses the line include leaving marks, shapes, bruises, cuts, or scrapes; when the skin is burned; when bones are broken; and when hair is pulled out in clumps.

Many parents who adhere more closely to authoritarian discipline believe that corporal punishment in the form of slapping, spanking, or even beating is an appropriate form of punishment. These parents may use the familiar refrain "spare the rod and spoil the child" or insist that their own parents spanked them as children and they've turned out fine. Much of raising children has been subtly or overtly concerned with being master over them—controlling children or breaking their spirit. Even when parents or educators have some understanding of child development, they may feel an overriding need to exert authoritarian control over children. In some early childhood programs, we hear phrases such as "Can the teacher control the children?" or "Does she have control over the group?" This is not surprising because many adults have been raised with these principles. No one is implying that children shouldn't learn respect for others, but we must be aware of methods and motivations in guiding children if our goals are to promote self-esteem and model self-control. Children benefit when parents learn to guide their children with positive discipline, instead of viewing corporal punishment as an option.

Corporal punishment often results from an adult's failure at self-control—as a means to relieve their anger, stress, and frustration. Who benefits? What are children learning from being slapped, spanked, shaken, beaten, constantly yelled at, or told hurtful things? Antispanking advocates believe that children learn that

- it's permissible to hurt and humiliate someone, especially someone smaller than you ("My parents do it to me, so it's acceptable"),
- the reason they need to obey rules is to avoid being hit,

- when they get bigger, they will have power over others, and
- violence is an acceptable way of expressing anger and solving problems.

Parents who believe that spanking is acceptable and appropriate may justify their actions in the following ways:

- "We are teaching them right from wrong." In reality, spanking teaches children only what is not acceptable. They will not learn right from wrong without being taught what they should be doing. Spanking may also communicate to children that they are "bad" persons.
- "It is an act of love." This is a confusing message for children, who learn that people who love them also hurt them. It's not surprising, then, that so many women choose husbands and boyfriends who abuse them, since traditional gender socialization teaches girls to be submissive and boys to dominate.
- "It's a cultural practice." Hitting children is a widespread practice throughout Canada. Many adults today, regardless of culture or race, were hit as children and believe that it is an acceptable parenting practice.
- "They need to respect adults." Rather than respecting the adults who spank them, they fear them. Eventually, when they are beyond fear, they often lose respect for those adults.
- "I don't want them to become spoiled." Children who are "spoiled" learn disrespectful behaviour from inconsistent parenting, insufficient provision of necessary structure, and neglect of children's needs, not from a lack of spanking.

In 1999, a large population survey study linked slapping and spanking in childhood with psychiatric disorders in adulthood (MacMillan et al., 1999). It found that although being spanked as a child didn't necessarily result in having later psychiatric disorders, compared with the general adult population, children who were spanked were twice as likely to develop drug and alcohol problems in adulthood. They also had increased rates of anxiety disorders, antisocial behaviour, and depression. According to the study, "spanking remains one of the most hotly debated issues among professionals working with children and families and among the general public" (p. 806).

The debate over spanking becomes relevant when we discuss child abuse. Corporal punishment by parents is not, in itself, against the law, but child advocates agree that it is not a positive way to discipline children. Many cases (69%) of physical abuse in Canada have involved the child protection agency's difficulty in distinguishing between corporal punishment and physical abuse (i.e., punishment that went too far) (Trocmé, 2002, pp. 4–5). Built into the use of corporal punishment is a lack of societal respect for the child. This is evident in the legal ambiguity. Assault charges can be laid whenever an adult strikes, shakes, or kicks another adult. There is no ambiguity here. It is important to realize that children benefit when parents, rather than viewing corporal punishment as an option, learn to guide their children with positive discipline, not punishment.

The many good reasons not to use corporal punishment for the long-term well-being of Canada's children should motivate policymakers, educators, and parents to put much effort into alternatives. In 2004, the Supreme Court of Canada decided to uphold several national and regional groups concerned with children's rights who advocated for a number of years for the repeal of Section 43. These groups continue to advocate for the criminalization of any kind of corporal punishment, including spanking. To date, Section 43 has been successfully used by some parents as a defence for injuring their children. Repealing this law would send a strong message to the community that this method of "child rearing" is no longer condoned. In handing down the 2004 decision, the Supreme Court offered certain parameters for assisting a court in deciding whether the physical force was "reasonable," such as forbidding use of an object and slaps across the face or blows to the head.

CRITICAL THINKING

As you know, Canada has not yet joined the countries that have abolished corporal punishment, including spanking. Identify how the parameters discussed above (a) support or (b) do not support a child's rights according to the UN Convention on the Rights of the Child (see Appendix 8.1, page 501).

Two essential components of effective parenting skills are responsiveness and discipline. Appropriate discipline is firm but not excessively restrictive and does not involve humiliating or shaming. There are clear limits to and expectations regarding children's actions; children are encouraged to take responsibility for their actions and learn from the consequences of their behaviour. When confrontation becomes necessary, parents should encourage children to find acceptable alternatives to actions that are not acceptable. The parenting style that combines a high level of caring and involvement with high but reasonable expectations is most likely to help children develop the confidence and coping skills needed to maintain competence and the sense of perspective that shapes how they react to stress. The interaction of these factors also contributes to the development of resiliency.

Emotional Abuse

Emotional abuse is likely the most widespread type of abuse, yet it is also the most difficult to prove. Children are unlikely to escape emotional harm when they are physically or sexually abused or neglected. Although the physical injuries may heal, the scars of emotional abuse may be long lasting. Although no parent or caregiver is immune from getting angry or frustrated at times, emotional abuse is characterized by the following pattern of behaviour (Boost – Child Abuse Prevention & Intervention, 2008a):

- rejecting (e.g., saying "I wish you were never born")
- criticizing (e.g., saying "Why can't you do anything right?")
- insulting (e.g., saying "I can't believe you would be so stupid")
- humiliating (e.g., embarrassing a child in front of other people)
- isolating (e.g., not allowing a child to play with friends)
- terrorizing (e.g., scaring a child by saying "The police will come and take you away")

- corrupting (e.g., always swearing in front of the child or getting the child to participate in things against the law)
- not responding emotionally
- punishing a child for exploring the environment

Source: Boost Child Abuse Prevention & Intevention. Adapted with permission from Rimer, P. and Prager, B. (1998), *Reaching Out: Working Together to Identify and Respond to Child Victims of Abuse.* (Toronto: Nelson Education Limited).

Emotional abuse can occur without children being abused in any other way. Parents who never use physical discipline may not realize that they are being abusive when they ridicule children, frequently use sarcasm or harsh criticism, or make inappropriate demands. This ongoing rejection is harmful to children's feelings of self-worth. "Emotional abuse derails the child's sense of mastery and competence. The push to conquer the environment is fueled by curiosity, autonomy, and a positive sense of self, all of which are often damaged in these children" (Ayoub et al., 1990, p. 235). For some parents, particular times create situations that trigger feelings of anger, disapproval, frustration, etc. Perhaps it is at the time of a developmental milestone (e.g., learning to use the toilet) or a time of the day (e.g., bedtime). In some family situations, one child is singled out as the scapegoat—the target at which the parent's anger is inappropriately directed.

Family Violence

Both women and men are victims of intimate-partner violence, although women make up the majority of cases. We refer to women as the victims in these discussions; however, this in no way should be interpreted as negating the abuse of men in interpersonal relationships. Also, family violence occurs across all ethnic, cultural, racial, and class backgrounds (Menjivar & Salcido, 2002).

Exposing children to family violence is now recognized in a number of provinces as a form of emotional abuse and in other provinces/territories as a separate category of abuse. The majority are cases in which the child's mother is being abused by her partner (e.g., the child's father or stepfather, the mother's boyfriend or same-sex partner). However, the child may be witnessing abuse of another or additional family members, such as grandparents. Statistics Canada reports that 7% of women who were living in a common-law or marital relationship reported to the 2004 General Social Survey that they had been physically or sexually assaulted by a spousal partner at least once during the previous five years. This is a small but statistically significant drop from 8% in 1999. These figures represent approximately 653,000 women in 2004 and 690,000 in 1999. In 1993, 12% of women had been assaulted by a spousal partner in the preceding 5 years. The figures for men were 7% in 1999 and 6% in 2004 (Statistics Canada, 2006).

Children exposed to family violence often experience a variety of problems similar to those caused by other forms of abuse (Baker, Jaffe, & Moore, 2001b, p. 15). They live in an atmosphere of threat and fear, even though they themselves may not be assaulted, and are in physical and psychological danger. They are caught up in a complex dynamic of physical or verbal violence in which they feel powerless. In addition, if they escape violence in the home by leaving with their abused parent, children often live in poverty. Children under age five make up the largest proportion of children living in women's shelters in Canada (Baker, Jaffe, & Moore, 2001a, p. 10). Approximately 106,000 women and children were admitted to shelters between April 1, 2005, and March 31, 2006, most often to escape abuse (Vaillancourt & Taylor-Butts, 2007). Violence often escalates after leaving home, so the fear continues. Because so many incidents of family violence are unreported, the estimate that 1 in 10 women are abused is conservative, and the number of children who witness violence in their home is substantial.

Sexual Abuse

Child **sexual abuse** is generally defined as the involvement of children in sexual activity in which the offender uses power over the child. The offender seeks sexual gratification from the child, who may or may not be of the same gender. Sexual abuse includes oral, anal, genital, buttock, and breast contact or the use of the penis, fingers, or objects for vaginal or anal penetration, fondling, and sexual stimulation.

Exploitation of the child for pornographic purposes and making a child available to others as a child prostitute are also forms of sexual abuse. Inappropriate solicitation, exhibitionism, and exposure to erotic material for the purpose of sexually arousing a child, or for adults to use to stimulate themselves, are also forms of sexual abuse. Over the past decade or so, the emergence and proliferation of Internet sexual exploitation have added a terrifying level of sexual abuse. J. Rimer's (2007) comprehensive literature review highlights the magnitude of this issue. Rimer states that the accessibility, production, and trade of child pornography through the various popular forms of Internet-related technology have provided a means by which child pornography can flourish as an industry. This industry is worldwide through cyberspace, and its perceived anonymity, instant and adaptable capabilities (such as webcam, digital photography, and pseudomorphing images, to name a few), and ease of electronic transmittal have created a "monster" industry for child sexual abuse. Even old images and films of child abuse from the 1960s and 1970s are scanned or uploaded and digitized, adding to the estimated many thousands of child pornography images being sent weekly.

> Sexual exploitation of children on the Internet encompasses three major forms of maltreatment against children:
>
> - child pornography (more appropriately termed "child sexual abuse images");
> - child luring/unwanted sexual solicitation; and
> - child prostitution/child sex tourism.
>
> Canadian police estimate that there are more than 100,000 websites that each contain thousands of child abuse images (Alcoba, 2008)....Internet use knows no borders, and identifying children is very difficult and time consuming. Although there are over one million child sexual abuse images in circulation over the Internet, with approximately 100,000 different child victims, only about 800 children worldwide have been identified (Chapman & McGarry,

2007). There are more than five million children worldwide drawn into child prostitution and child sex tourism, including over 200,000 in Canada (Flowers, 2001, p. 149–150).

Source: Used with permission from Rishchynski, G., P. Rimer, and J. Rimer. (2008) *Looking for Angelina: A Learning Guide on Family Violence.* Toronto: Second Story Press.

In recent years, the *Criminal Code of Canada* has been amended to create new criminal offences relating to child sexual assault and amending the provisions on child sex tourism. Currently, Bill C-15 proposes legislation to protect children from sexual exploitation by criminalizing a number of specific actions, including luring children on the Internet; transmitting, making available, or exporting child pornography on the Internet; and intentionally accessing child pornography on the Internet (Department of Justice Canada, 2008).

Abuse is never the child's fault. Some offenders use the excuse that the child or adolescent initiated the contact ("She came onto me") or was a willing participant. This assumes incorrectly that the child had the choice to refuse. The offender is in a position of power and must exercise self-control. Children are vulnerable not only because of their physical size but also because they depend emotionally and economically on adults and are easily manipulated due to their limited understanding of adult sexuality (Caring Communities Project, 1994, p. 12).

It is more common to observe emotional indicators of sexual abuse than physical indicators, although it is possible that the genitals have been injured, irritated, traumatized, or infected, including genital discomfort, pain on passing urine, and blood in the diaper or underwear. The more common indicators are unexplained changes in personality, nightmares and sleep disturbances, clinging or extreme seeking of affection or attention, and age-inappropriate sexual behaviour or knowledge (Rimer, P., 2007, p. 28). Children may also complain about headaches and stomachaches, which are related to the stress of sexual abuse.

The National Clearinghouse on Family Violence (2006) reports that the vast majority of sexual abuse offenders are men. Yet women, too, can be offenders. A small unknown percentage of offenders are pedophiles who are sexually excited only by children. Pedophiles are more likely to abuse a large number of children, and in these cases, the victims are more likely to be boys than girls. However, most sexual offenders are heterosexual males who have sexual relationships with adult women as well as the children they sexually abuse.

In most cases of all types of maltreatment, including sexual abuse, the offenders are well known to their victims. Approximately 25% of the offenders are adolescent, but offenders can be found among all ages, ethnocultural communities, and social classes. Most sexual abuse takes place in the context of an ongoing relationship between the abuser and the child. This longer term relationship provides the offender with the opportunity to manipulate the child's desires and fears to exploit the relationship.

Due to the nature of these relationships, the abuse can go on for years. Even in cases in which sexual abuse happened only once, children may experience an enormous degree of emotional turmoil. The sooner children are able to seek professional help, the better.

Children often feel confused, especially because, in many cases, the sexual abuse is not painful and may even feel somewhat pleasurable. For some children, this contact may be the only physical affection they receive. When children realize that a trusted adult has betrayed them, children may feel guilt about "causing" the abuse or shame that it felt good sometimes. Children with a strong sense of self-worth and communication skills may be less likely to be sexually abused, but it is clear that the abuse is never the child's fault. It is almost impossible for the child to resist the abuse; offenders put a great deal of thought into how they will manipulate children.

Behavioural and Emotional Indicators of Maltreatment

This section examines some of the **behavioural and emotional indicators** that educators may observe in children who suffer from any type of maltreatment. What are behavioural and emotional indicators? They are signs, symptoms, or clues seen in a child, or in the adult in the child's life, that lead educators to suspect that the child is being maltreated. Unless we actually witness abuse, or a physician diagnoses physical injuries or symptoms consistent with abuse, we must remember that no single behaviour confirms child maltreatment.

Lars, usually a cheerful, sociable seven-year-old, now acts withdrawn. To suspect abuse immediately in his case is making a big leap. We must know more about what is happening in Lars's life and family. Perhaps his whole family is anxious about his mother's loss of her job. Maybe Lars is afraid of being bullied on the school playground.

Maltreatment can lead to serious emotional distress in children and a diminished sense of self-worth. Behavioural indicators differ depending on the child's personality and temperament.

The following short list focuses only on general behavioural indicators that may be exhibited in children who are being maltreated in any way. The child may

- either be overly compliant or overly aggressive;
- either resist physical contact or not hesitate to go to unfamiliar persons for affection;
- either be overanxious to please or resist all limits and react with temper tantrums or rage;
- be afraid to go home or fearful when a parent or a particular adult arrives at pickup;
- experience delays in development, particularly in language and motor development, or in the development of age-appropriate social relationships with peers;
- be overwhelmed with sadness, anger, or apathy;
- lack confidence in his or her abilities;
- not be emotionally attached to anyone;

- demonstrate regressive behaviour, for example, a five-year-old who wets his or her pants or reverts to constant crying, rather than using words;
- lack curiosity and interest in the surroundings (e.g., not interested in play); or
- disclose to educators that someone, for example, has caused an injury (physical abuse), constantly puts down the child (emotional abuse), has had sexual activity with the child (sexual abuse), or has left the young child without supervision or other basic needs for periods of time (neglect).

These behavioural indicators can apply to any of the four types of maltreatment. However, because of the individual nature of the different types of abuse, some indicators tend to be more relevant to one type of abuse than another.

- In physical abuse, the child often demonstrates aggressive, acting-out behaviour.
- In emotional abuse, the child sets unreasonably high expectations for self and refuses to try again if he or she doesn't succeed the first time.
- In sexual abuse, the child has an unusual level of sexual knowledge, sexual play, or excessive self-stimulation (masturbation) for his or her age and developmental level.
- In neglect, the child hoards food or continues to ask for helpings at lunch beyond what seems a reasonable amount of food for a child.

Possible Consequences of Maltreatment

> Child abuse can have devastating consequences for victims. Depending on its form(s), duration and severity, abuse may affect every aspect of a child's life; it may have consequences that are psychological, physical, behavioural, academic, sexual, interpersonal, self-perceptual or spiritual. (Department of Justice Canada, 2008)

Each child is unique in terms of development, personality, and temperament. It is impossible to make generalizations about all children or about children who are survivors of maltreatment. The effects may appear at the time of the abuse or neglect or surface only in adolescence or adulthood. No one can predict the outcomes that children will experience as a result of maltreatment. We don't understand why one child who experienced one incident of abuse may suffer far more than another who had been abused for a number of years. Resilience is the individual's ability to bounce back from stress and adversity and take on new challenges (Hall & Pearson, 2004, p. 1).

Stress and adversity create feelings of helplessness and wanting to give up in some people. However, in others, difficult experiences trigger problem solving, learning, and growth (Werner & Smith, 2001). One study of 6- to 11-year-olds found that the maltreated children who were resilient exhibited self-reliance and self-confidence, along with positive future expectations (Cicchetti & Rogosch, 1997). Resilient children usually have the capacity to find allies outside their family and to identify that things should be different than they are in their family. However, the concept of resiliency can also minimize the impact of children's suffering because it's impossible to know the full potential that has been lost to abuse even though the child appears to be resilient and develops coping strategies (Sundelin, 1994, p. 715). It is also essential to recognize that resilience is culturally embedded, affecting children's choice of what they think will best help them survive (Unger, 2007).

Many studies continue to refer to the consequences of child abuse, which can be numerous and wide ranging. Table 8.1 provides some of the possible short- and long-term consequences often experienced by children and adults who have experienced maltreatment.

TABLE 8.1   **Some Consequences of Maltreatment**

Note: The following are overall conclusions drawn by various researchers. Don't assume that 100% of children who are abused behave in any one certain way, but be aware that a statistically significant number of children display similar characteristics.

Psychological Consequences

- extreme and repetitive nightmares
- anxiety or depressive symptoms, long bouts of sadness, social withdrawal
- sudden phobias, such as a fear of darkness or water
- psychosomatic complaints, including stomachaches, headaches, hypochondria, excessive blinking

Physical Consequences

(in addition to the obvious physical injuries related to the abuse)

- small body size and low weight
- permanent neurological damage (e.g., as a result of shaken baby syndrome, head trauma abuse)
- stress-related symptoms (e.g., gastrointestinal problems, migraine headaches, difficulty breathing, aches, pains, rashes that are not easily diagnosed or treated)

Interpersonal Consequences

- insecure attachments to parents and caregivers
- difficulty in trusting others
- relationship problems, such as overly sexualized or overly conflicted relationships

Self-Perceptual Consequences

- extremely low levels of self-esteem
- inaccurate body images, which often lead to eating disorders
- overwhelming sense of guilt or self-blame for the abuse

(continued)

TABLE 8.1   Some Consequences of Maltreatment *(continued)*

Behavioural Consequences

- developmental delays, including language delay

- clinging behaviour, extreme shyness, and fear of strangers

- troubled socialization with peers (constant fighting, bullying, teasing)

- poor school adjustment and disruptive classroom behaviour

- self-destructive behaviours, such as self-mutilation or burning

- early use of drugs or alcohol and substance abuse or dependence

- suicide and suicide attempts

Academic Consequences

- low overall school performance test scores and low language, reading, and math scores

- weak orientation to future vocational and educational goals compared with nonmaltreated children

Sexual Consequences

- engaging in open or excessive masturbation, excessive sexual curiosity, and frequent exposure of genitals

- premature sexual knowledge, sexualized kissing in friendships and with parents

Spiritual Consequences

- loss of a sense of faith, in a divine being as well as in themselves, other people, or the world around them, sometimes referred to as a "shattered soul"

Source: Adapted from *The Consequences of Child Maltreatment: A Reference Guide for Health Practitioners* by Jeff Latimer, National Clearinghouse on Family Violence, Public Health Agency of Canada, 1998. Reproduced with the permission of the Minister of Public Works and Government Services Canada, 2008.

P. Rimer (2007, pp. 81–82) lists a range of feelings that may impact a child who has been maltreated: self-blame, fear, powerlessness and vulnerability, betrayal, loss, destructiveness to self or others, and hopelessness. Any or all of these feelings can obviously influence the child's emotional and social well-being.

Emotional and social difficulties affect children in the areas of attachment, security, trust, confidence, motivation, social sensitivity, and play behaviour. Frustrated by their limited social skills, their lack of achievement, and difficulties in their home environments, children who have experienced maltreatment are frequently aggressive or withdrawn. During the first few years of a child's brain development, we know that a young child's genetic potential is optimized when her or his world is rich in nurturing relationships and learning opportunities. These are the conditions that strengthen higher level complex functions, such as self-regulation and problem solving, in the neocortex. However, the child who is exposed to threat and chaos strengthens the lower level limbic functions, activating the stress hormone cortisol and adaptive responses to help him or her survive. "A hyperarousal response is more common in older children, males, and in circumstances where trauma involves witnessing or playing an active role in the event.... Dissociation is more common in young children, females, and

TABLE 8.2	Six Core Strengths for Children: A Vaccine against Violence
Attachment:	being able to form and maintain healthy emotional bonds and relationships
Self-regulation:	containing impulses, the ability to notice and control primary urges as well as feelings such as frustration
Affiliation:	being able to join and contribute to a group
Attunement:	being aware of others, recognizing the needs, interests, strengths and values of others
Tolerance:	understanding and accepting differences in others
Respect:	finding value in differences, appreciating worth in yourself and others

For more information on the Six Core Strengths, visit the *"Meet Dr. Bruce Perry"* page at http://teacher.scholastic.com/professional/bruceperry.

Source: *Maltreatment and the Developing Child: How Early Childhood Experience Shapes Child and Culture* by Bruce D. Perry (2004). <http://www.lfcc.on.ca/mccain/perry.pdf> (April 2008).

during traumatic events characterized by pain or inability to escape" (Perry, 2004, p. 2). Boys, then, are more likely to externalize their response through aggression, delinquency, and later spousal abuse. Girls are more likely to internalize their response to abuse, resulting in psychological disorders, including eating disorders, low self-esteem, and thoughts of suicide (Alliance of Five Research Centres on Violence, 1999, pp. 5–7).

Research supports focusing treatment on socioemotional problems because an increased belief in oneself, trust in others, and positive social skills are springboards to developing other competencies. Perry (2004, p. 4) identifies what he calls "Six Core Strengths for Children," which are strengths that trained educators promote daily in a program of best practices (see Table 8.2).

Causes of Child Maltreatment

Child maltreatment is a complex issue that cannot be explained by any one theory. Many factors are involved in causing and perpetuating child abuse and neglect. Society consists of a number of interacting components, including economic, social, educational, cultural, individual, familial, and religious ones. The Department of Justice (2008, p. 4) acknowledges the connection between child abuse and marginalization:

> There is increasing understanding that a child's vulnerability to abuse may be increased by factors such as dislocation, colonization, racism, sexism, homophobia, poverty and social isolation. For example, in the past, many children sent to institutions experienced abuse. Most of these children were from marginalized groups in our society including, among others, children with disabilities, children from racial and ethnic minorities, Aboriginal children and children living in poverty.

It is well known that over several generations, many Aboriginal children and families in Canada have been plagued by numerous affronts, including institutional child maltreatment. Native residential schools across Canada in the mid- to late 1900s resulted in the maltreatment of and a cultural void for many Aboriginal children, often without recovery for individuals or Native communities.

Even today, Aboriginal children who experience maltreatment at home are placed in foster care at a rate twice that of non-Aboriginal children.

This highlights the added vulnerability that Aboriginal children and families face. Many foster homes may be positive environments for children, especially if culturally similar, but the opportunity to build families and communities "from the inside" is more complex when children are removed. On a positive note, child welfare consortia have begun to emerge across Canada (e.g., Prairie CW Consortium, Atlantic CW Consortium) to work together with representation from Aboriginal service delivery, government, and education to make changes based on the potential for community-based Native child welfare (McKay, 2007).

Although there are many stress factors that can affect parents' lives, not all parents under stress abuse or neglect their children. Just because parents are separating, for example, doesn't mean that you should look for signs of maltreatment. If you have developed a relationship with the family, you probably know how they have coped with stress in the past. If a family is experiencing several life events at the same time, the increased stress may be more than they are able to cope with, which can contribute to child maltreatment. Some families are under ongoing stress, such as those living in poverty or those in which one or more members have a chronic debilitating illness. Again, these families do not necessarily abuse their children. Similarly, a family's financial stability does not necessarily mean that a child cannot possibly be suffering maltreatment within the family.

We live in a mobile society, and one consequence of this is that many adults live far from their parents, siblings, or extended family. Having access to social support networks is one of the determinants of health. "Far too many children grow up without the number and quality of relational opportunities needed to organize fully the neural networks to mediate important socio-emotional characteristics such as

empathy" (Perry, 2004, p. 4). As a society, as a community, and as individuals, we can help parents raise children in more positive environments by reducing stressors and helping them cope. Some parents are fortunate enough to have a network of friends or extended family members who provide emotional support or help (sometimes in the form of respite) when they need it. Those families who are isolated, with no one to turn to in times of extreme stress, can be at higher risk for abuse or neglect. When the early childhood program is a support system for families, it reduces the sense of isolation. Families are then more likely to seek help when needed.

PREVENTING CHILD MALTREATMENT

Everyone in the community has a role to play in preventing child maltreatment. Educators are professional advocates for children, and they can make a significant contribution to prevention. Educators' roles can be divided into three levels of prevention: primary, secondary, and tertiary. We begin this section with a brief introduction to child protection agencies that are involved in prevention.

Child Protection Agencies

Child protection legislation and services are under provincial or territorial jurisdiction, as are health, education, and early childhood education. Although the laws themselves are quite similar in all provinces and territories, the application of the laws varies across the country. As a result, the delivery system varies not only across Canada but between regions within a province or territory. Due to differences, and for the sake of clarity, we use the term "child protection agency" throughout this unit. The primary goal in all jurisdictions remains the same: prevention and community support services. Child protection agencies are required by law to assess all reports of suspected child maltreatment and to take steps to protect children from further abuse or neglect. This discussion touches on the broad responsibilities of the agencies.

The job titles of the personnel working in an agency's office vary. We use "child protection workers" to describe the people who take the calls from directors or educators, teachers, and other members of the public and who are assigned to the child's case. They are usually social workers trained to assess situations in which children are "in need of protection." As it relates to early childhood programs, the child protection worker talks with the staff, family member, or other adult who is reporting and advises how to proceed. The staff may be asked to continue to observe the child and document observations in the child's file or to make a formal report to the agency. Based on this report, a child protection worker is assigned to the child's case, and an investigation begins. In the section Secondary Prevention, you will read more about this process. There will occasionally be situations in which the worker believes that the child is at immediate risk and the worker, perhaps with the police, may apprehend the child.

The agency's priority is to maintain the family unit while preventing further maltreatment to the child. There is recognition that in Canada today, significant changes to child welfare legislation are required to ensure that children's health and safety are the first priority. With that in mind, the agency's investigation determines what they believe is in the best interests of the child. Criminal charges are laid when the offender is found guilty of abuse according to the *Criminal Code of Canada*, which happens in only a small number of cases.

To describe the function of child protection agencies with regard to child maltreatment.

To define primary prevention and outline the educators' role in the early childhood environment and beyond.

To define secondary prevention and discuss the educators' role in identifying suspected child maltreatment and in documenting and reporting it to a child protection agency.

To define tertiary prevention and discuss the educators' role in working with children, families, and agencies.

Primary Prevention

Primary prevention refers to early childhood programs' policies and practices that support relationships with children and families so that child maltreatment doesn't happen. Educators are not immune to maltreating children. For this reason, programs' policies address child maltreatment, child guidance, child-centred programming, nutrition, and health and establish procedures that are consistently implemented by staff. These policies and practices, combined with training, enhance educators' ability to provide and model quality care.

The Educator's Role in Primary Prevention

Educators have a unique opportunity to demonstrate that maltreatment can be prevented. Prevention begins within early childhood programs by

- supporting children in developing their core developmental strengths (see Table 8.2, page 465),
- providing a positive role model for parents, and
- supporting parents in their parenting rights and responsibilities.

Creating a Positive Early Childhood Environment

High-quality early childhood education environments are caring and nurturing and respect children and their families. Parents see how educators interact with their child and other children and how they guide behaviour and provide a safe, suitable physical environment for children. Knowing that their child is well cared for in their absence alleviates stress for parents.

In terms of the children, a high-quality early childhood education program promotes children's health—and helps prevent child maltreatment. The most obvious example is promoting children's developmental strengths as an essential

FIGURE 8.2 **The Brain's Capacity to Change**

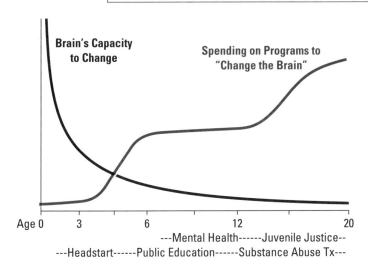

Source: *Maltreatment and the Developing Child: How Early Childhood Experience Shapes Child and Culture* by Bruce D. Perry (2004). <http://www.lfcc.on.ca/mccain/perry.pdf> (April 2008).

part of all practices and curricula. Children who are building their skills and confidence may be better protected from maltreatment than those who are not. They may be more aware of their rights and those of others. A high-quality program also helps prevent sexual abuse by integrating children's awareness of their bodies, healthy sexuality, and personal safety (see Sexuality, page 518). Recognizing the strength of the brain's capacity for growth in the early years through positive relationships and environments, the focus needs to be placed on resources to prevent the incidence of child maltreatment, resulting in fewer children and adults who need costly treatment with uncertain outcomes as a result of maltreatment (see Figure 8.2).

Enrollment interviews are ideal opportunities for directors (or educators) and parents to begin getting to know one another. Over time, educators develop meaningful partnerships with families. Often these result in parents sharing more personal information, such as their views on discipline, their support systems, or their relationship with a spouse or partner. Educators combine this information with observations of parents and children interacting to help them understand the parent–child relationship. Some parents do not feel comfortable sharing personal details about their family. This is perfectly acceptable, and they deserve the same respect as other parents. Educators need to be careful not to pry or make judgments based on the family's wish for privacy. They shouldn't assume that parents are trying to hide something. Providing parents with nonjudgmental support is a positive primary strategy.

A parent rushes into the program at the end of each day. She seems to be in a never-ending battle with her three-year-old. He doesn't want to go home and often has a tantrum. This is an upsetting way to begin the evening. As the educator, you have two options. You can either do nothing, which in some ways contributes to the tension—the tired, frustrated, rushed mother may yell at or slap her child—or you can recognize the stress she is under as she tries to leave work on time and travel across town to pick up her son. By acknowledging how difficult this is for her, by talking about how the two of you can work together, you can make the stress more manageable. Perhaps the mother could call the program when she is leaving work or try to arrive at the same time each day so that you can have her son prepared for the transition. As well, spending 10 minutes together in the play area before getting ready to leave, or sitting down and relaxing together over a snack before the commute home, may be options that the parent and child like.

Educators can contribute to promoting positive discipline strategies for families by

- role modelling positive guidance with children;
- being open to discussion with individual parents about discipline issues and avoiding being judgmental or prescriptive, which undermines a parent's authority; and
- providing access to resources on discipline and parenting such as articles, books, audiovisual materials, support groups or courses for parents;
- providing opportunities for group discussions such as parent meetings or workshops (e.g., see *Nobody's Perfect* and the organization The Incredible Years in the Resource Materials, page 496) and ensuring that culturally relevant facilitators are flexible, able to suspend judgment, and trained to recognize suspected child abuse;
- keeping abreast of community resources that may be of assistance to parents, including ethnoculturally relevant resources, if available; and
- becoming involved in organizations that are committed to reducing violence in society and, in particular, advocating for positive environments for children.

Child Maltreatment Prevention Programs for Children

Caring adults want children to be safe. Prevention programs seem, on the surface, an obvious way to help protect children from harm. Ultimately, it is essential for adults to be clear that it is their responsibility to protect children and that children should never be given the message that they are responsible for protecting themselves. Also, any prevention programs for children must take developmental and cultural appropriateness into consideration to meet the needs of children of different ages and populations. Before deciding to evaluate a specific prevention program for children, consider the following potentially misleading assumptions about such programs:

- The main challenge of primary prevention is that it is a socialization process as well as an educative one—child maltreatment, and particularly sexual abuse, occurs in a society that fosters the sexualization of children and the absolute power of adults. We want children to have tools that can help them in a potentially abusive situation, but we don't want them to feel responsible for protecting themselves or to believe that they failed in any way if they were unable to protect themselves from victimization. *For example, children may not believe they can say "no" to a powerful adult, or they may not be able to evaluate a situation for potential danger, including an adult's motives.*

- Prevention programs may be presenting concepts that make sense to adults but are beyond the young child's cognitive capacities. All children relate to prevention strategies on different emotional and cognitive levels and respond in accordance with their developmental stage (see Table 9.1, page 511).

- Young children can acquire skills and concepts, but the issue is whether they can retain the information over time. Interactive and comprehensive programs in which children can role-play and practise skills are likely helpful, although children won't necessarily be able to apply the skills in real-life situations. Programs that include relevant information and resource materials for parents and educators likely reinforce the learning and involve the adults in a meaningful way. This potentially reduces the burden of responsibility that children may feel.

- The inclusion of self-defence strategies is controversial. They may help the child develop self-confidence and skills to escape, but their use could potentially place the child in greater danger. The program must stress that the goal of using self-defence is flight, not fight.

- A child's disclosure of abuse already suffered is the most tangible result of these programs, which performs a secondary prevention function (Finkelhor & Strapko, 1992). It is important for educators to be both aware of and prepared for this possibility. However, there is also the possibility that a child may not understand the difference between "tattling" and "telling" (to get help).

- Educators must be committed to critically examining the assumptions behind a particular prevention program, as well as the specific content.

P. Rimer (2007) provides a helpful list of questions to ask when examining a prevention program for appropriateness:

1. Are the materials comprehensive, including information for staff, parents, and children?

2. Is the information in the program accurate?

3. Is the language clear, and appropriate to the ages and developmental levels of the children?

4. Does it empower the children, supporting development of problem-solving skills in a variety of situations (e.g., negotiating, expressing feelings)?

5. Does the program recognize the value of healthy relationships and include strategies for building them (e.g., activities that promote pro-social behaviour such as cooperation and helping)?

6. Does it reduce the child's sense of isolation, giving children the message that there are people who will help?

7. Is there a clear message that the child is not responsible for his/her own protection?

Source: Reprinted with permission from Rimer, P. (2007), *Making a Difference: The Community Responds to Child Abuse*, 5th ed. (Toronto: Boost – Child Abuse Prevention & Intervention), 114.

Networking with Community Resources

Every program has access to professionals and printed resources on child abuse. Access to parenting consultants and parenting courses may be limited to larger urban communities. Programs must have the name and phone number of the child protection agency and a clear understanding of the program's role in reporting and documenting suspected child maltreatment. In-service training for staff on child maltreatment is always beneficial. Educators are also in a position to respond to parents' requests for information or consultation with a specific agency related to parenting, health, housing, or finances. Programs should make it a priority to ensure that their staff are aware of ethnoculturally and language-sensitive resources.

Preventing Child Maltreatment by Educators

The primary focus of this unit is the prevention of child maltreatment within families. However, any person of authority, including educators, can violate their power over children. Factors that contribute to maltreatment in families are not unlike those that may lead to abuse within programs. Feelings of frustration or being trapped lead to short tempers and striking out physically or emotionally as a way of regaining a sense of control and power. Although it is unlikely that educators would hit or spank a child, they might be at risk of shaking or restraining, threatening, using sarcasm, or yelling at a child. Work environments that contribute to educators' physical, emotional, and social health are vital in providing educators with a true sense of autonomy, job satisfaction, and improved overall well-being. When graduates seek employment, it is important to ensure that prospective employers provide clear job descriptions, personnel policies, a process of staff orientation and performance review, and other ways in which educators'

rights and responsibilities are considered. Opportunities for professional development to address areas that require further educator knowledge and skill also reduce frustration and stress, while increasing competence and best practices with children and families.

CRITICAL THINKING

After half an hour, Shelly is still unable to comfort a toddler. She is becoming increasingly frustrated and has said, "I just want to leave him in the crib until he stops crying." You can see that she is handling the child less and less gently. How could you manage this situation to reduce Shelly's stress, and the stress experienced by the child, and reduce the risk of physical abuse? What may be steps to prevent these types of situations in the future?

To prevent the possibility of maltreatment in an early childhood program, try to pair new adults in the room, such as supply staff or students, with familiar staff. Listen to parents about any concerns they have and try to understand them from their perspective. This helps educators know best how to address the issue. Remember that if a parent believes her or his suspicion is warranted, it is also the right and responsibility of the parent to report the suspicion to the child protection agency.

One of the most important areas of professional development for early childhood educators is the working knowledge and problem-solving skills based on the Canadian Child Care Federation's Code of Ethics. The Code, which was adopted by the Canadian Child Care Federation and its affiliate organizations Canada-wide, consists of eight principles originally developed by the Early Childhood Educators of BC. The code guides practitioners in protecting the children and families with whom they work by working through ethical dilemmas using the principles put forward. Recognizing that ethical issues arise often, and the value of developing an ethical problem-solving approach to make the best decisions, the Manitoba Child Care Association (2007) offers a four-part ethics workshop series for educators: *The Ethical Journey*.

Sexual abuse in programs is rare, yet it is understandably alarming for parents to realize that this, and other forms of maltreatment, can happen when they entrust their child's care to others. This realization has had both positive and negative effects on early childhood programs. On the positive side, parents demand that programs have an open-door policy for parents. Parents may want to be more closely involved in the program to understand what the children are doing all day and to ensure that all policies and procedures are respectful of children.

Educators may be overly cautious about the physical affection they give to children. They may feel inhibited because of the possibility that parents will misconstrue appropriate behaviour as inappropriate. This is particularly the case for male educators, who may feel that they are suspect because of their gender (see Men Working in Early Childhood Settings, page 90). Although it is not common practice, there are programs in which staff are, unfortunately, discouraged from reciprocating children's hugs or having children sit on educators' laps. Policies and practices must provide checks and balances, combining warm, sensitive caregiving with ways to ensure that educators' behaviour is verifiable. The Canadian Paediatric Society (2008, p. 361) offers some commonsense practices to avoid misunderstandings that could lead to false accusations of abuse:

■ Exercise good judgment about the kind of language used with children (e.g., never use any words that could have a sexual connotation).

■ Avoid play or care in secluded areas and keep coworkers and parents informed of activities when you are alone with a child.

■ Be sensitive to how a child feels about being touched and ask permission if you're not sure.

■ Confine touching to a child's head, back, and shoulders when offering comfort, affection, or reassurance.

■ Learn to intervene and redirect children appropriately when they are engaged in self-stimulation or sexual play.

■ Use correct terminology for all body parts and encourage children in your care to do the same.

Source: Canadian Paediatric Society, *Well Beings: A Guide to Health in Child Care.* (Ottawa: Canadian Paediatric Society, 2008), 361.

Training in early childhood education is extremely important in all aspects of working with groups of children. Working with children is hard work, both physically and emotionally, and the difficulty can be compounded by educators' low status and wages. Trained staff should have the knowledge and confidence to create programs that are caring, interesting, varied, stimulating, and rewarding for both children and themselves. Those with little or no formal early childhood training often lack the knowledge and skills necessary to manage the everyday stresses of the work. Teamwork is a crucial component of working effectively in early childhood. Of course, new graduates want to focus their efforts on a high-quality team approach to their work and learn from their more experienced educators. This is ideal when educators are positive role models but not if a coworker uses harsh disciplinary strategies. In worst-case scenarios, a new graduate or any other educator takes on some of the negative behaviour, such as belittling children, using sarcasm, or grabbing, shaking, or restraining children. As trained educators, they should recognize that this behaviour is unacceptable and, indeed, reportable to the child protection agency. The director must take action with staff who begin to demonstrate inappropriate behaviour before it leads to child maltreatment, or the educator should ask the director for assistance.

Secondary Prevention

Secondary prevention encompasses

- identifying children who may be victims of maltreatment,
- documenting observations and possible indicators, and
- reporting to a child protection agency.

This is a balancing act for educators, whose role in secondary prevention is complex. First, educators are not "child abuse police." Although they must address the situation when a child comes into the program with a bruise or in dirty clothes or yells at a doll in dramatic play, educators don't leap to a conclusion of child maltreatment at first glance. Second, educators make numerous observations about dramatic changes in a child's behaviour, emotional state, or physical appearance. Using these indicators, the educator attempts to find out why the child's behaviour has changed. Third, educators must understand that it is a child protection agency's responsibility to respond to suspicions, decide whether to investigate, and identify the offender. It is not your job to prove that maltreatment has occurred and, if so, who the offender is. However, it is the educator's responsibility to document and phone a child protection agency whenever she or he has questions or suspicions.

Identifying Suspected Child Maltreatment

The identification of suspected child abuse or neglect and the subsequent intervention with children and families are complex and difficult issues. Since educators spend so much time with children, and because of their observation skills, they are often the first people in children's lives to suspect the possibility of maltreatment. They are also in a position to provide support to the family. This can often create a conflict for the educator. Stopping maltreatment now can have long-term positive effects for children and often for their entire family.

Educators who suspect a child in their care is being maltreated may have the following reactions:

- They may refuse to believe that this parent would do this to the child. This may be especially difficult if they've known the parent for a while and have established a relationship.

- They may be afraid
  - of the parent's anger and, as a result, fear for the child's safety or their own safety,
  - of having falsely suspected the parent, or
  - that the child will be removed from the home or withdrawn from the program.

Ultimately, the child's welfare is your overriding concern. Most families love their children and don't want to continue to hurt them once they understand the negative effects on children. Educators need to ensure that families always feel welcome in the program, regardless of the process or outcome with the child protection agency—otherwise, staff are not fulfilling their role as child advocates. It's important for educators to support positive change within the family and not to expect miracles to happen overnight. Educators are a part of the child's life for only a few years, whereas the family is involved for a lifetime.

Educators know each child's temperament, personality, and family. They observe children achieving developmental milestones and the normal range of behaviour. Educators draw on this experience in making judgments about children's behaviour and observing physical injuries. By asking themselves questions, educators rule out other possible explanations, such as illness, usual locations of bruises, vision or hearing problems, anxiety about specific stressors (e.g., a grandmother's recent death), developmentally appropriate fears, or developmental delays unrelated to abuse. In a scenario in which a child has signs of an injury, it is routine practice for an educator to ask the parent or other family member who accompanies the child to the program questions such as "Sam has a bruise on his knee. Do you know what happened?" The educator uses an interested but nonthreatening tone, asking what happened and how, not why it happened. However, if the cause of the child's injuries, account by the child, or behaviour of the child or adult is unclear, the educator should call a child protection agency to discuss concerns and seek direction. The child protection worker will guide the educator regarding whether or not to approach the parent or other adult and further direction about possible formal reporting. Such consultation may lead to a resolution that works in the child's best interests (e.g., feedback to the family, referral for counselling, a change in your program that may help the child during a crisis period).

Identifying Suspected Family Violence

Provinces and territories have mandated reporting to the child protection agency when there is knowledge that a child is witnessing (a better term may be "exposed to") family violence. Those that do not have mandated reporting nonetheless expect that reporting would ensue if there was concern that the child is in danger or that circumstances have changed that justify the involvement of the child protection agency (and possibly the police). Find out what the legal requirements are in your province or territory. When in doubt, call the child protection agency for direction.

Mandated reporting acknowledges the position that being exposed to family violence is a form of child maltreatment, whether the child actually sees or hears the violence, witnesses the aftermath of the violence (e.g., nonoffending parent's injuries or emotional upset, police intervention), or is an unintentional victim of the violence (e.g., the child is hurt while in the mother's arms). Also, due to the power and control tactics that are used by the offender, the child may be used as a pawn in the violence. For example, the offender may claim that the child's "bad behaviour" is the reason for the assaults against the nonoffending parent, may engage the child in the abuse of the other parent, or may hold the child hostage or abduct him or her to punish the victim or to gain compliance (Baker et al., 2001a, p. 4).

When faced with the knowledge or suspicion of any of the following indicators of family violence, a call to a child protection agency is required. The following are some examples of indicators that would require a call to a child protection agency when family violence is known or suspected:

- a child who has been physically harmed or almost injured by either partner, deliberately or "accidentally," during or after a violent episode
- a child who has "accidentally" been hurt when caught in the crossfire of objects thrown during a violent episode or injured in any way because of the situation (e.g., the child has cut his or her foot stepping on broken glass)
- a child who has been physically harmed while trying to protect a sibling or other family members
- a child who believes that she or he is responsible for precipitating or stopping the abuse
- a child who has been threatened with physical harm or death, or an abusive partner who says that she or he will harm the children
- the abusive partner has assaulted or thrown objects at someone holding a child
- a child is exhibiting serious symptoms of emotional distress because of exposure to family violence or is likely to suffer emotional harm (e.g., by being forced to observe or listen to the assault, expresses fear for his or her own safety or the safety of other family members
- the family returns to an abusive partner who is believed to pose a threat to the children
- conditions of release, probation or parole, or a restraining order with respect to the abusive partner not having access to the children have been violated, and no one has reported this to authorities (i.e., a child protection agency or police)
- the primary caregiver requires hospitalization, and there is no suitable alternate arrangement for the safe care and supervision of the children
- there is an awareness or suspicion that the alleged abuser is in a situation with access to other children

It is very important to support the nonoffending parent when she takes steps to disclose family violence. Although you may not feel ready or equipped to handle this type of disclosure, your level of acceptance and support for the victim are most important. Early childhood programs can display information that acknowledges family violence and a willingness to help (e.g., a poster from the local or regional women's shelter that includes a phone number).

The parent may decide to call the help line or may decide to talk to an educator or the director, believing that this must be a safe environment in which to talk about it. Remember that her safety and that of her children are paramount, so you must be very sensitive. Although you may believe that she should leave the abusive situation immediately, remember that the woman knows her reality and you don't. Violence often escalates when women leave, or try to, and afterward—sometimes resulting in murder.

Tables 8.3 lists suggestions to consider if a nonoffending parent approaches you about her situation.

Family violence is a very complex issue, with many other considerations in addition to those highlighted here. Graduates of an early childhood education program require further knowledge and understanding of their role in supporting families in these situations—particularly in supporting children exposed to family violence.

CRITICAL THINKING

The next-door neighbour notices that the children are playing outdoors without coats on in cold weather *and* does not realize that the mother has sent them outside to prevent them from witnessing her impending assault. This example is not meant to underplay the children's needs for proper clothing but to highlight the mother's assessment of risk and her strategy to protect her children from the greater risk. Consider all players in this scenario: children, the nonoffending mother, the offending partner. Identify each player's issue and decide what the neighbour's next step should be.

Suspecting Child Maltreatment

Educators' suspicions of physical abuse are based on

- the severity of the marks or injuries that can't be explained by a mishap during play and
- the type, number, size, and shape of the trauma to the skin.

Whenever a child is hurt, you must ask yourself, "How did this happen?" and "Did adults fail to protect the child?" Just as in programs, injuries that occur at home are understandable: bumps and bruises are a normal part of every child's life. Figure 8.1 (see page 452) illustrates the parts of the body on which educators are most likely to see bruises due to everyday activities, as well as the locations where bruises may be a cause for concern. Even though it is not your role to determine which bruises are suspicious or to interpret their origins, some markings do have identifiable shapes. Use nonleading questions such as "What happened to your arm?" followed by "What happened next?" Leading questions such as "Who did this to you?" or "Why did your mother hurt you like that?" not only put ideas or answers into the child's mouth but may also contaminate an investigation.

TABLE 8.3 Do's and Don'ts of Disclosures of Family Violence

If a woman divulges family violence, her concerns, fears, worries and situation must never be minimized or discounted. Her decision to talk to someone usually indicates her desire to consider options to change her situation. The response of the person to whom she discloses has a significant impact on her ability to take positive steps toward ending the abuse, or to reinforcing her guilt, isolation, feelings of powerlessness and loss of hope. Recognize that emotional abuse has as much of an impact on someone's overall well-being as physical violence.

If family violence is divulged, keep the following in mind when responding to the disclosure.

Control Your Emotions

- If she is calling you on the phone, determine how safe it is for her to talk.

- Try and stay calm and relaxed, no matter what she tells you—she needs to sense that you are able to help.

- Validate her feelings and experiences—never minimize how she has been treated. Give her the message that you think the abuse is a concern.

- Do not say negative things about her partner—although he/she has mistreated her, they may still care about one another. Do <u>not</u> confront the abuser.

- If your tone is judgmental and she chooses to stay with her partner, she may feel she cannot call back for additional help and support. Do not judge her inability to take action today.

Provide a Respectful Perspective

- Reinforce that domestic/family violence is a crime.

- Emphasize that she is not responsible for her partner's behaviour—she did not cause the abuse, no matter what he says she has said or done.

- Acknowledge any steps she has taken toward safety and change, no matter how small, including her disclosure to you.

- Always recognize the impact of cultural values and beliefs on someone's perception of choices.

Present Options

- Strongly encourage her to get medical treatment if she (or the children) has sustained any injuries.

- Brainstorm with her about her options and any formal or informal avenues where she might get help, but remember only she can decide what is right for her, taking into consideration what feels safe.

- Express your concern for her safety and the safety of her children. Help her to develop a safety plan for both staying and leaving (ensure she understands and knows how to dial emergency services [911 or the seven-digit number in rural areas]).

- Inform her that there are services available (including legal options) to protect and help families—abuse does not stop without outside intervention. Ask her if she wants to involve police. (Be sensitive to the fact that immigrant or refugee women who have been abused may have experienced police who are cruel and oppressive, and are therefore fearful of them.)

- Do not give advice or try to make decisions for her, even if you feel your advice is sound (e.g., "I think you should…" or "If it were me, I would…").

- Ask her what she wants to see happen, what are her main concerns now, and how you can help.

- Do not overwhelm her with too much information—she may have to begin with small steps on her way to taking control of the situation (e.g., making a list of who she can call for help).

Source: Reprinted with permission from Rimer, P. (2007), *Making a Difference: The Community Responds to Child Abuse*, 5th ed. (Toronto: Boost – Child Abuse Prevention & Intervention), 74-5.

It is important to stay within your role boundaries and to remember that you could potentially jeopardize the investigation if you seem to ask leading questions. Confirmation of trauma is made by child protection workers, often in consultation with physicians. One of the strongest indicators of suspected physical abuse is a delay in seeking medical treatment for extensive and serious injuries. Although some children are more injury prone, children who repeatedly injure themselves raise serious concerns about the possibility of physical abuse or the level of supervision and guidance at home.

Disclosures of Maltreatment

Educators often establish closer, more personal relationships with some children than with others. These relationships are essential for children if they are going to trust an educator enough to disclose maltreatment. There may be times when you have concerns about a child, although he or she hasn't said anything to you or any other educator. In this situation, the educator with the closest relationship with the child is probably best positioned to talk with the child. Discuss your observations of the child's behaviour. You might say, "I have noticed lately that you are getting angry with your friends and storming off a lot. Is something bothering you?" The child may actually have something to talk about that has nothing to do with abuse or neglect. Opening the door in this way may help the child to feel comfortable enough to talk. Children may not want to talk at first, but may approach you at another time when they know that an educator will listen and is concerned about them. However, if a child doesn't disclose abuse to you, but your observations lead you to suspect abuse, you must follow the steps in your program's child maltreatment protocol. For a number of reasons, a child may not disclose maltreatment or may recant, saying that it didn't really happen after an earlier disclosure.

When children decide to disclose, it is a call for help. When they approach educators, educators must listen to their account and support them. It is difficult for children to disclose abuse for a host of reasons. Here are a few:

- The child has only started to realize that something "not right" is happening to him or her.
- The child has been threatened with physical or emotional consequences if she or he tells.
- The child feels it is his or her fault and will be blamed.
- The child feels vulnerable or powerless and does not think she or he will be believed.

Responding Effectively to Disclosures

If you have seen or heard something that leads you to suspect child abuse, remember to:

1. Control your emotions.

   Try to be relaxed and casual.

   Do not look shocked, disgusted, or say nasty things about who you think may have abused the child.

- Do not assume that the abuse was a terrible experience (e.g., a child who has been sexually abused by an attentive and gentle person may perceive the abuse as pleasurable). Assuming the abuse was awful only adds to the child's guilt.
- Be aware and accepting of your own feelings.

  If you feel that you cannot control your emotional responses, talk to your immediate supervisor.

2. Offer reassurance.

Reassure children by letting them know that

- they were very brave to tell,
- you are glad they are telling you about this,
- it is not their fault,
- you are sorry that this has happened to them,
- they are not alone—this happens to other children too, and
- you will do everything you can to help.

Do <u>not</u> say things like:

- "How can you say those things about…?"
- "Liar."
- "How could you let him do those things to you?"
- "Why didn't you tell me this before?"

Children are further reassured when

- the child is given your undivided attention.
- the child's feelings are acknowledged and validated. If the child asks, tell the child you believe him/her. If a child discloses in a group setting say, "That sounds important. We can talk about that later," and try to find an unobtrusive way to speak with the child privately, as soon as possible.
- a trusted adult stays with the child, unobtrusively if necessary, until a child protection worker arrives.
- continued unconditional love and support are given to a child who has recanted.

3. Be aware of the child's developmental level and use of language.

Accept a child's terminology or slang words to describe an event, particularly as children often do not know the correct terminology for body parts or sexual behaviour. This is not the time to correct the words the child uses or his/her definition or description of what happened—it is critical for the investigation that the child use his/her language in giving the account of the abuse. Do not interrupt or fill in any silences with your own words, even if the account is incomplete or unclear.

- Answer the child's questions as simply and honestly as possible.

  Refrain from using trigger words or adult terminology such as rape, incest, abuse, wife assault, or jail since they may alarm the child or hamper the investigation.

4. Ask questions that are open-ended, that are not leading or suggestive of a specific answer.

   – "Can you tell me what happened?"

   – "What happened next?"

   – "How did you get that bruise?"

   Ask questions in a manner that does not suggest to the child/adult what happened or who did it—for example, "Did you get that bruise because mommy hit you with a brush?"

   Refrain from questioning the child/adult's account (e.g., "Are you sure it was Uncle Ted?").

   ■ Refrain from asking "Why?" Many children do not understand the motivation and may understand a why question to imply blame.

   Resist trying to change the mind of a child who has recanted, since coaching a child or suggesting that something did or did not really happen will hamper the progress of the case.

   Refrain from asking questions because you want to prove maltreatment.

5. Respect the person who discloses.

   ■ If a child/adult is telling, listen. Be patient—this may be difficult for the person to share with you.

   ■ If a child/adult is quiet, do not interrogate him/her.

   ■ Do not forcibly undress a child or forcibly remove clothing to view injuries.

   ■ Do not display a child's injuries to others indiscriminately.

6. Tell the child what will happen next.

   ■ Do not make promises you cannot keep. For example, do not agree to keep the disclosure a "secret." It is important to explain to the child that some secrets must be shared in order to get help, or to keep people from being hurt. Tell the child the information will be shared only with people whose job it is to help kids.

   ■ Do not answer questions for which you do not have the answers. For example, if a child asks, "Will Daddy have to go to jail now?" you can only say "I don't know. Other people decide that."

   ■ Do not agree if a child/adult asks that you not tell anyone else. You may be tempted to remain silent out of respect for his/her wishes, the confidentiality of the relationship, or out of loyalty. Silence places you in collusion with the abuser. The family and all those involved should know:

     – without outside intervention, the abuse will probably continue;

     – other children may be at risk of abuse; and

     – if any attempted intervention fails, and calling a child protection agency is used as a threat, then the child protection agency is seen as punitive and not a resource to families in need, as it should be seen.

7. Follow through on legal and ethical responsibilities.

- Know your agency's policies and reporting procedures.
- Record what the child said using the child's own words, as soon as possible.
- Document objectively any observations of the child's behaviour, or the behaviour of any others relevant to the situation.
- Write down the name of anyone the child has indicated as the possible abuser and any description that the child provides.
- Document any conversation between yourself and the child.
- Consult with a child protection authority before contacting the child's family.
- Do not tell the child to keep any of your discussions with him/her secret.
- Report your suspicions to the designated authorities.

Source: Adapted with permission from Rimer, P. (2007), *Making a Difference: The Community Responds to Child Abuse* 5th ed. (Toronto: Boost – Child Abuse Prevention & Intervention), 45–7.

Clarifying with Parents

Even when there are concerns about suspected child maltreatment, ongoing communication with families is of the utmost importance in promoting children's well-being. When approaching parents or other family members, your goal is to clarify a situation, not to suggest that they are the offenders.

Start with your observation and follow with a question:
- "Jacob has a black eye. Do you know how it happened?"
- "Josie has seemed very sad for the past week and hasn't been interested in playing. Have you found that she is behaving this way at home too?"

Additional observations or questions depend on the parents' responses to your initial observation and question.

- You may ask Jacob's mother, "Did he see the doctor? Were there any special instructions to care for him or concerns about his eyesight?"
- Josie's dad has noticed her lack of interest too. You respond by saying, "Do you have any idea why Josie seems so sad?"

Take the parents' lead while being careful not to put them on the defensive. Questions starting with "Why did you…?" or "Why weren't you…?" are inappropriate, and most parents, whether or not abuse is an issue, will feel they are being judged. In most instances, the parents' explanation is sufficient, and your questions and concerns are resolved. The parents usually appreciate your concern, and your positive relationship with them is maintained. Even in cases in which you are no longer concerned, it is important to document your initial concerns and the conversation in the child's file. Jacob may have recurring black eyes or other injuries that may begin to form a pattern that is of concern later on.

There are times when the parents' response reinforces your suspicion of child abuse. If the explanation for the black eye seems unusual, the parent seems nervous in her or his response, and perhaps the child looks fearful, you will likely question the validity of the explanation and call a child protection agency for guidance.

Educators are strongly discouraged from approaching parents for clarification in the following situations:

- Whenever sexual abuse is suspected. There are a number of reasons for this. If the offender is the mother's husband or boyfriend and he talks with the child's mother before the child protection worker or police do, he may convince her that he could never have done such a thing. After all, who would want to believe that her partner is capable of sexually abusing her own child? It is even more devastating for children if their mother does not believe them.

- When you are concerned that the child may be abused again as a result of your conversation with the parents.

- When you fear the family would disappear, making follow-up impossible. You may base this decision on the family's history of moving frequently.

In fact, child protection agencies prefer that any action beyond clarifying a situation be checked with them first. In other words, contact the child protection agency for direction. The child protection worker may indicate that they or the police will contact the parents. Or the child protection agency may advise the director to call the parents and ask them to come in for a meeting. It is important to follow the direction of the child protection agency.

No list of possible indicators for a suspected offending parent is given here, to avoid stereotyping. *An educator's role is to objectively and carefully document his or her observations (which aid the child protection agency in their investigation). It is not the educator's role to identify the abuser. Remember that as a professional you are legally and ethically obliged to report your suspicions of child maltreatment. If you are unsure of whether your observations are reportable, consult with your local child protection agency.*

Documenting Indicators

Educators may hesitate to document their suspicions in children's files for the following reasons:

- They don't fully understand the importance of documentation in proving a case of child maltreatment.
- They believe that they don't have time to document suspicions.
- They are concerned that their report may be made public.

Documentation is an important part of the administrative responsibilities of educators for a range of health care concerns. Every program's work schedule needs to provide staff with the time to write relevant notations in children's files concerning illness, observations on their development, or suspected child abuse. Due to the serious legal implications of child maltreatment, documenting your observations, concerns, and questions is critical in that it provides a reliable account for the child protection agency. Although the child's file and the educators involved may be called to testify in court, this is the exception rather than the rule.

The more complete and comprehensive the information is, the more able the agency is to fulfill its important role in protecting children. Verbal accounts based on your memory are not as reliable as careful documentation written at the time. Child protection agency staff view educators who document well as conducting themselves professionally, which builds credibility in the role of educators as child advocates.

Documentation: What Is Involved?

What makes a document objective, clear, concise, and complete? Every time you document, observe the following guidelines:

- Complete the correct form identified in the child abuse policy of your agency. Note that other incidents not related to suspected child maltreatment are completed on a different form (e.g., *Serious Occurrence Form* or *Injury Report*).

- Include the full name of the child, the date and time of recording, and the date and time of your observations.

- Describe clearly whatever you observed—the child's physical injury or behaviour—that is of concern. Note the type of injury (i.e., burn, bruise, cut, fracture), shape, size, colour, and number. A form that has a line diagram of a child's body makes it easier for educators to indicate where the mark(s) appeared on the body than to write, "It was 3 inches (6 cm) to the left of the belly button and maybe 2 inches (4 cm) above." In terms of behaviour, document any patterns that contribute to your suspicions (e.g., aggressive behaviour toward others, unexplainable fears) and direct quotations (if possible) of comments the child made during play (e.g., dramatic play).

- In chronological order and using direct quotations, write down anything that was said by the child, the parents, and you. This should make it evident that you did not ask the child leading questions, such as "When did your dad hit you so hard?"

- Document objectively what was actually seen or heard. Do not include how you feel about the incident or ideas about what you think might have happened.

- Include anything that someone else has said; it might be important.

- Documentation should be completed as soon as possible after you become aware of the physical or behavioural indicators or after a child's disclosure.

- Sign and date your form in ink.

- Record everything in your own handwriting.

- Use a new form if you have concerns on another day.

Unless otherwise instructed by the child protection agency, the educator will follow the child abuse policy and practices outlined by the early childhood program. Your municipal early childhood office may require notification whenever child maltreatment is suspected. This and other requirements should be outlined in the policy.

Reporting to a Child Protection Agency

Program staff are typically included in provincial/territorial child protection legislation's list of professionals working with children who are legally obliged to report to the local child protection agency when they have reasonable grounds to suspect child abuse. You are expected to become familiar with the child welfare legislation in your province or territory, read the section that covers children in need of protection, and understand your legal and moral responsibilities. In addition, you must know the child abuse policies and procedures of your agency.

The staff member, student, or volunteer who initially suspects abuse is required by law to call the child protection agency. Ways in which the person reporting can assist in a child abuse investigation are outlined below:

1. Be attentive to indirect disclosures and physical and behavioural indicators of maltreatment.

2. Document in detail the information that forms the suspicion of maltreatment or family violence.

3. Consult with a child protection agency worker before speaking with anyone else about the details of your suspicion.

4. Continue to monitor the child and be attentive to further indicators and/or potential risks to the child; complete new documentation each time. Report this to the child protection agency.

5. Be aware of emotional responses to the situation and deal with them to be as effective as possible

6. Do not inform a parent or caregiver that a suspicion of child maltreatment or family violence has been reported unless a child protection worker guides you to do so.

7. In consultation with the investigators, determine if it would be helpful to the child for the staff (student or volunteer) to be present in any investigative interviews. If present in the interview, follow the direction of the investigators regarding the level of participation.

8. Respect the confidentiality of the child, the family, and any proceedings in which staff (student or volunteer) may be involved. Child protection workers are also bound by policies of confidentiality regarding details of the case.

Source: Adapted with permission from Rimer, P. (2007), *Making a Difference: The Community Responds to Child Abuse*, 5th ed. (Toronto: Boost – Child Abuse Prevention & Intervention), 61.

As you are probably aware, reports can be made anonymously by educators or by anyone else. Educators are professionals, have specialized skills and knowledge, and have a relationship with the child and likely the family. They are able to work effectively with other groups of professionals. If an anonymous report is made, there is loss of the centre as a safe, familiar place that may be the best environment for the investigators to interview the child, if deemed a necessary part of the investigation. The child protection agency staff may incorporate educators into the child's treatment plan, but if they don't know who is calling, this obviously can't be done. For these and other reasons, it is in the best interests of the child to identify names and contact information when reporting.

A common fear of educators is that there is a chance that maltreatment has not occurred or cannot be proved. It is important to keep in mind that it is your legal duty to report suspicion and not your role to investigate or prove maltreatment. You are fulfilling your responsibilities under the law and are not making any accusations. The child protection agency investigates allegations and decides on action to be taken on behalf of the child. Even if maltreatment cannot be proved, someone who reports is not vulnerable to any consequences unless the report was made maliciously or without reasonable grounds. Educators have opportunities to get to know children, to understand what is "normal" for individuals, and to have a positive impact on the child's life when maltreatment is stopped early on. It is rare for educators' reports to be considered malicious. Malicious reporting comes into question at times during a custody battle, when one parent has wrongly accused the other of child maltreatment to prevent him or her from having access to the children.

What Happens during Investigations

The child protection worker decides if the reported concerns require an investigative response based on the conditions set out in the provincial or territorial child protection legislation. If the case doesn't meet at least one of the conditions, the agency does not have legal grounds to intervene. The worker will interview the person reporting her or his suspicions. If a decision is made by the child protection agency not to intervene, your report and the information obtained in the investigation are retained. The agency may not always inform the individual who reported of this decision. Every situation is unique, so the response depends on the circumstances.

Child protection workers may not conduct the investigation on their own, but may include others on the team. Many communities have put protocols in place that determine how investigations are responded to and conducted and by whom. *For example, a police officer may be involved, as defined by the community protocol or to decide if there are reasonable grounds for a criminal investigation.* Reports of suspected sexual abuse and family violence are usually investigated jointly with the police. For other types of maltreatment, police may be consulted. If there is concern for the child protection worker's safety, a police officer may accompany her or him when going to the child's or alleged offender's home. The agency staff often consult with other social service and health professionals during the investigation, calling on them to assess the child and the alleged offender. Investigative interviews are analyzed according to specific criteria, findings of medical exams are gathered, and a thorough assessment of the circumstances surrounding the allegations is conducted. Family dynamics and the presence or absence of indicators of abuse are taken into account.

Generally speaking, the two findings of a child protection investigation are

verified or not verified. If the investigators determine based on all the facts that maltreatment was likely, they then decide on next steps. If not verified, meaning the allegations were not confirmed or there may be another probable explanation, the report is filed and is available if there is future reporting. If further information comes to light, it is possible that a new finding of verified will result. Remember your legal and ethical responsibilities to contact a child protection agency whenever you have suspicions of child maltreatment. It may be your report that brings to light further evidence that makes the difference to the child and the family. (Rimer, 2007)

When we report suspected child maltreatment, children in difficult situations learn that someone significant in their life is telling them that this should not be happening to them. This information can be instrumental for children in the long term. We send important messages to children that they are not to blame for the maltreatment, that it should stop, and that someone cares enough to try to stop it.

Coping with Your Emotions

It is a very emotional experience to respond to a situation of suspected child maltreatment. Most educators experience a range of conflicting emotions, including anger, anxiety, empathy, frustration, concern, sadness, denial, and disbelief. There are often several multifaceted reasons for these emotions. Anxiety, for example, may be based on worry about the child's well-being, about the possibility of the alleged offender's reaction, about not having enough "proof," and about inadequacy in handling the situation. These feelings are normal. It is important, for your own well-being, to acknowledge your feelings and find ways to cope constructively with them. If you are fortunate, you will be working in a supportive environment where you can speak with your coworkers or the director about your feelings after reporting. Perhaps a counsellor would be helpful. You may find that your usual ways to relieve stress (e.g., physical activity, deep breathing, tai chi) are good coping mechanisms, too. In any case, you need to find ways to care for yourself and your own health and to ensure that you are in control of your emotions. This is important so that you have an effective response to the entire situation (e.g., the anger must not come through to the child or the frustration to the parent).

Suspected Child Maltreatment by Educators

The line between child maltreatment and excessive discipline may be blurred at times—when observing both parents' and educators' behaviour. Remember that corporal punishment and emotional putdowns are never to be tolerated in early childhood programs. Suspicions that a coworker is maltreating children physically, emotionally, or sexually or is neglecting their needs are stressful, to say the least.

Any allegation must be responded to immediately. Not responding quickly creates the feeling that the program is not prepared to deal with the situation and that there must be something to hide. When clear policies and procedures are in place, the agency can respond effectively.

Document any concerns, questions, or suspicions about educators maltreating children. If you witness physical or sexual abuse, your actions are much more clear-cut. Because emotional abuse can be more subjective than other types of abuse, you must carefully document what was said and by whom, what was going on at the time (e.g., the activity), and the child's behaviour in response to the educator. Commonly, an educator is emotionally abusive to certain children, perhaps only one or two from the group. Often, when talking with this educator about the group, you will find that she or he shows hostility toward those children. Comments such as the child "never listens" or "does things just to annoy me" and "is basically a bad kid" are objective clues that may support your suspicion.

An educator who has suspicions about another educator's behaviour with children should talk with the immediate supervisor about the observations and her or his intention to call a child protection agency. The individual who suspects maltreatment, whether an educator, a parent, or someone else, must call the child protection agency for advice and be assured that the matter will be kept confidential until the initial investigation is complete. The children's parents or other people involved will be notified according to the child protection agency's recommendations. It must be clear to the individual reporting that there are no sanctions or reprimands for phoning the child protection agency and no pressure from anyone not to do so. As a relatively inexperienced professional, it can feel somewhat overwhelming to have the legal and ethical responsibility to report suspected child maltreatment if this relatively infrequent scenario arises. However, it is likely that your director, another colleague, or the child protection agency staff will support you as you go through the process.

CRITICAL THINKING

Maltreatment by educators may be identified through the child's disclosure or by parents who approach the director with their concerns and perhaps their suspicion of a particular educator. How does the director proceed?

Another difficult situation arises when staff suspect the director of child maltreatment. The educator documents the concerns and follows the protocol set out by the program's policy. It is likely that the reporter will be expected to contact the president or chairperson of the board of directors (or owner, if applicable). The staff member who suspects maltreatment must also call the child protection agency to report. As with any suspicions of maltreatment, remember that you are legally bound to report, even if another party (e.g., board member or owner) tries to dissuade you from calling against your better judgment. The board member or owner must call the municipal early childhood office and speak with the consultant responsible for the program to inform that person of the situation. This consultant advises the board member regarding required steps. In most jurisdictions, an allegation of child maltreatment against any staff member, student, or volunteer is considered a serious occurrence.

Tertiary Prevention

Investigations into child maltreatment may confirm that a child has suffered maltreatment. The offender may be identified and criminal charges may be laid, although this is not a routine outcome. In **tertiary prevention**, there are a number of objectives. For the child, it means preventing further maltreatment and developing a care plan for the individual child's recovery. For the family, the objective is to work toward short- and long-term change. Beyond any criminal charges for the offenders, treatment must be explored to prevent maltreatment from recurring.

Educator's Role in Tertiary Prevention

The role of educators in tertiary prevention is threefold:

- They provide a secure and developmentally stimulating environment for the child.
- They support change in parents by providing good role modelling and resources.
- They may maintain ongoing communication with the child protection and other agencies' staff involved with the child and family and be part of a plan for the family. *For example, the child protection agency may request that a parent spend a couple of mornings a week in the program to role model positive discipline strategies.*

Communicating with Child Protection Agencies

High-quality early childhood programs recognize that staff can't be all things to all people. This is why directors establish connections with relevant professionals in their community and collect materials for the program's resource library and for distribution among parents. Depending on the issue, educators are called on to work collaboratively with other professionals—for example, the public health nurse during an outbreak of diarrhea. In the case of child maltreatment, educators may be team members with a child protection worker and possibly other specialists assigned to an individual child.

The director and educator are requested to participate in the child's recovery process along with the child's play therapist and behavioural therapist. The therapy is conducted and supervised by the trained therapists, but they may have particular recommendations for the educators to incorporate into the child's everyday program. Whether these are specific guidelines for play or for all the educators to manage a child's inappropriate behaviour consistently (i.e., the six-year-old's temper tantrums), the recommendations are an important aspect of the child's ongoing care.

Because children's situations and types of maltreatment vary so greatly, it is impossible to discuss fully the range of professionals and therapies that may be part of an individual child's recovery.

As part of the child's care plan, educators may be asked to observe, document, or complete developmental checklists to aid these professionals in assessing the child's progress. Educators are encouraged to call on the child protection worker when they are uncertain about a particular behaviour (e.g., self-mutilation) or other community agencies for guidance in supporting children and families who are going through the court process.

There are times when a child who has been maltreated is enrolled in a program for the first time by the child protection agency or another agency as part of the care strategy. Social workers recognize that trained professionals in high-quality early childhood programs enhance the child's well-being. Usually, the goals for enrolling a child who has been maltreated into a program include building positive relationships, overcoming developmental delays, and increasing feelings of self-worth, as well as providing modelling and support for parents. The decision to accept this added responsibility should not be taken lightly. It will not be in anyone's best interest, including the child's, if the educators can't cope with the complexities of the situation. Educators will not yet have an ongoing relationship with the new child and may therefore need increased support.

The *Helping the Child Who Has Been Abused Fact Sheet* (Boost – Child Abuse Prevention & Intervention, 2008b) lists the following strategies in working with children identified as victims of maltreatment. Professionals, which includes educators, help the child to

- develop positive self-esteem,
- trust,
- identify and express emotions,
- learn to communicate,
- identify and solve problem situations,
- catch up developmentally, and
- develop a safety plan (visit http://www.boostforkids.org for some specific strategies).

Source: *Boost Child Abuse Prevention & Intevention.* Adapted with permission from Rimer, P. and Prager, B. (1998), Reaching Out: Working Together to Identify and Respond to Child Victims of Abuse. (Toronto: Nelson Education Limited).

High-quality early childhood programs strive to provide most of these things for all children in their program. You are already participating in the child's recovery regardless of the specific therapies carried out by other professionals. If you refer back to the discussion on the consequences of being maltreated, you will see just how they interconnect with these strategies.

Providing a Secure Environment

Beyond the essentials included in the preceding list, certain aspects of your everyday work come into play when caring for children who have been maltreated:

- Provide predictability and security in the day's routine (e.g., bringing a transition object such as a toy back and forth between home and the program). Routines and rituals are important coping mechanisms for children, especially if their lives have been stressful or disorganized.

- Help children learn appropriate ways to have their needs met, even when that means learning to delay gratification (e.g., an educator explains to the preschooler that he will be able to ride on a tricycle as soon as the next tricycle is free).

- Build a spirit of community in the classroom, with children and adults helping each other, talking through issues, and solving problems together.

- Provide clear and firm, but kind and reasonable, limits as an important part of the early childhood environment. Since they suffer from injuries and pain or fear that someone will hurt them again, children who have been maltreated often feel unsafe. As a result, they may take risks even though they may know, or have been told, that an action can result in an injury. Or they may intentionally hurt others since they have learned that others have hurt them.

- Guide children to help them learn age-appropriate behaviour. Maltreatment may result in children having developmentally inappropriate behaviour.

- Be an active listener. Children can sense when they can trust an educator and express worries, fears, and concerns related to their family. This is not a counselling relationship, but one in which an educator can help the child cope with stress.

- A family's situation rarely changes from inadequate to wonderful overnight. The child probably feels frustrated and worried about the family or has fears and concerns about social services or a legal proceeding in which he or she is involved.

- Recognize that children's behaviour can have many different meanings. Consider a child with a short attention span. Although it may be a developmental stage, perhaps it is a learned behaviour that is used as a survival tool (e.g., he or she expects that any activity will be interrupted with yelling or a smack and so is overly attuned to every movement or conversation in the room, always ready to move quickly).

Supporting Change in Parents

Communicate respect for the parent and the parent's own ways of coping and adapting to his or her unique realities. When supported and respected as a person, a parent is more likely to use the early childhood program as a resource to develop the confidence and skills needed to interact successfully with other persons and institutions in his or her life. As was the case for children who are maltreated, educators' communication with the child protection worker is important in providing consistency and support to parents who have been abusive.

All parents bring strengths and weaknesses, past experiences, and expectations to parenting. Most parents who maltreat their children love them and want to stop. Parents and other family members can feel distressed and overwhelmed by the child's maltreatment, whether they were the offenders or believe they failed to protect the child from others. They may experience reactions similar to those of the child: they are preoccupied with the details of what happened, have feelings of helplessness and guilt, and are fearful that it could happen again (P. Rimer, 2007, p. 84).

The program may play a role in providing respite for parents. Parents may need to work on managing or eliminating stress factors or problems that directly or indirectly relate to their parenting (e.g., counselling or treatment sessions, resolution of marital, housing, education, or employment issues). Programs can provide high-quality care for the child during this time. The child protection worker may request that these parents enroll their children in a program for the first time. This may not only benefit the parents but also encourage the development and recovery of the children. As stated earlier, providing modelling of positive ways to interact with children (e.g., talking, playing) and positively guiding their behaviour may provide parents with ideas and strategies.

Ultimately, the child's rights must be at the forefront of our concerns. In recent years, tragic stories of children who have suffered further or who have been killed while in the care of known offenders have been terrible reminders that not all parents have the support or possibly the will to change their abusive behaviour. Educators who continue to have concerns about the well-being of a child whose report has already been filed must report any new information. In the big picture, re-evaluating existing child protection legislation, policies, and protocols is part of the solution to this important social problem.

REVISITING THE HEALTH PROMOTION ACTION PLAN

Child maltreatment is a major social problem that requires a multidimensional approach by all members and levels of society. With reference to the Health Promotion Action Plan introduced in Unit 1, the following examples demonstrate how the plan incorporates child maltreatment prevention.

Individual Problem Solving and Self-Reliance
As individuals, it is important that we reflect on our personal and professional values to determine whether we practise respect for children in our everyday lives, built on the UN Convention on the Rights of the Child. Continuing to build our knowledge and skills in child development, working with families, and policy and legislation contributes to best practices as professionals. Organize staff training on child maltreatment and invite a child protection worker to speak at a parent night. Follow your legal and ethical responsibilities if you suspect child maltreatment.

Collective Self-Help
After talking with single parents from the program, one educator who is also a single parent organized a support group. The group set up a baby-sitting exchange that allows a parent to go to the laundromat without the children. Besides making these errands less stressful, this arrangement provides the parent with respite time. They also exchange clothing and toys. This group provides valuable and enjoyable opportunities for the parents to establish friendships and reduce feelings of isolation.

Interested parents are offered a recognized parenting program with a trained facilitator on a weekly basis at the end of the day, while their children have dinner and are being cared for. Internal policies and procedures are regularly evaluated to maintain the focus on supporting children and families and on prevention of child maltreatment and family violence. Educators share the information they learn from professional development activities with their colleagues.

Community Action

From the grassroots, community action can include the establishment of parent resource centres; book, toy, and clothing exchanges; and telephone help lines (e.g., Kids Help Phone). Within some communities, professionals who work in the area or have an interest in child maltreatment form a child protection team (e.g., professionals working in the fields of education, medicine, public health, mental health, social work, law enforcement, law). These teams improve communication among professionals and coordinate more effective prevention programs, training, and child maltreatment response in the community. Educators and parents should be encouraged to become involved as participants. Another possible way to contribute is to serve on the board at a women's shelter (or family shelter), often affiliated with a range of services. Educators contribute valuable knowledge and skills. Early childhood systems are developing initiatives that focus on collaborative community-based approaches to create neighborhoods for learning, by enhancing and promoting the developmental assets of all children and families.

Societal Change

As child advocates, educators can be involved in organizations that work to reduce the acceptance of violence in our society, which is a root cause of maltreatment. Child advocacy associations, for example, are working toward laws against any type of corporal punishment of children.

An important focus is to help support parents in raising their children. Social policy that reduces poverty would lower stress for families. To address the many other stressors for families, governments should have adequate child welfare budgets for prevention and quality services. In addition, the 2007 *Reaching for the Top: A Report by the Advisor on Healthy Children and Youth* (Leitch, 2007) calls for a national office of child and youth health, with one of its three priorities being mental health. This suggested office would have the mandate to raise awareness, develop policy, collaborate and coordinate, and undertake and champion research and surveillance. The ultimate goal is to take Canada closer to its potential to be the most healthy place in the world for children to grow up. At the time of this report, Canada ranks 13 out of the 21 richest countries in the world, as identified by the Organisation for Economic Co-operation and Development. This poor ranking is shameful. Immediate action is needed for Canada's children and youth to reach the potential that is possible with Canada's immense resources and capabilities. Understanding why individuals maltreat children is only part of prevention. As a society, we must move from focusing on individuals to addressing the root causes of maltreatment, which will take a multifaceted approach. Recognizing the work that needs to be done by all levels of government in addressing the social determinants of health, such as income inequality, housing and food security, and social exclusion (see Social Determinants of Health, page 4), would also have a major impact on preventing child maltreatment in Canada.

CONCLUSION

Whether we are referring to primary, secondary, or tertiary prevention, the prevention of child maltreatment has a lot to do with working collaboratively. This issue, more than any other in the early childhood program, acknowledges that promoting children's health is not done in isolation.

The safety and well-being of every child in Canada should be a priority for each adult and each level of government. Regrettably, this is not the case. As part of a process of public education, we need to persuade the community to begin to look at children as a shared natural resource that represents society's future—rather than as solely the responsibility of their parents (Steinhauer, 1998, p. 91).

What's Your Opinion?

WHAT'S IN A WORD?

The term "child rearing" is commonly used to mean bringing up children. Some child advocates would argue that this term perpetuates the use of corporal punishment, whereas a term such as "child raising" would be better suited to positive parenting and the respect to which all children are entitled. Do you think that language is powerful in this regard? Back up your opinion.

ASSESS YOUR LEARNING

Define terms or describe concepts used in this unit.

- behavioural and emotional indicators
- child maltreatment
- family violence
- neglect
- primary prevention
- sexual abuse
- tertiary prevention
- emotional abuse
- female genital mutilation
- physical abuse
- secondary prevention
- shaken baby syndrome

Evaluate your options in each situation.

1. A coworker remarks that there are probably a lot of children in your program who are maltreated because most are part of single-parent families.

2. A month after you reported a case of suspected maltreatment to the child protection agency, there has been no news. The child continues to come to the program each day and is demonstrating the same behaviour that led you to make the report in the first place. You are angry and confused by the lack of response from the agency.

3. A coworker who spanks her children starts a conversation at lunch time about repealing Section 43 of the *Criminal Code*. She suggests that doing so would mean parents would be charged for "a little slap."

4. Lily, one of the five-year-old children who attends the program in the mornings and school kindergarten in the afternoon, is quiet and listless this morning. When you sit with her for a while, she tells you that she's scared to go home tonight. Lily says that last night her dad was really mad and hit her mom. She comments that she is going to be a good girl tonight so it won't happen again.

5. The director meets with the educators to inform everyone that the child protection agency has requested that a child who has been maltreated be enrolled in your program as part of his treatment. He requires a caring, consistent environment to help reduce developmental delays and build self-confidence. Although you are flattered, and the director obviously wants to say yes, you are concerned because you and the other educators are already feeling stretched meeting the needs of the present children.

RESOURCE MATERIALS

Organizations

Boost – Child Abuse Prevention and Intervention, 890 Yonge Street, 11th Floor, Toronto, ON M4W 3P4. Tel: 416-515-1100; fax: 416-515-1227; http://www.boostforkids.org

Canadian Council on Social Development (CCSD), 190 O'Conner Street, Suite 100, Ottawa, ON K2P 2R3. Tel: 613-236-8977; fax: 613-236-2750; http://www.ccsd.ca

Canadian Institute of Child Health, 384 Bank Street, Suite 300, Ottawa, ON K2P 1Y4. Tel: 613-230-8838; fax: 613-230-6654; http://www.cich.ca

Canadian Society for the Prevention of Cruelty to Children, 362 Midland Avenue, Box 700, Midland, ON L4R 4P4. Tel: 705-526-0214; fax: 705-526-5647; http://www.empathicparenting.org

Child Welfare League of Canada (CWLC), 226 Argyle, Ottawa, ON K1P 5E7. Tel: 613-235-4412; fax: 613-235-7616; http://www.cwlc.ca

Family Violence Initiative, Department of Justice Canada, 284 Wellington Street, Ottawa, ON K1A 0H8. Tel: 613-957-4222 or national toll-free 1-888-373-2222; fax: 613-954-0811; http://www.canada.justice.gc.ca/eng/pi/fv-vf/index.html

Kids Help Phone, National Office, 439 University Avenue, Suite 300, Toronto ON M5G 1Y8. Tel: 416-586-5437 or national toll-free for children 1-800-668-6868; fax: 416-586-0651 (or contact regional office). Corporate site: http://org.kidshelpphone.ca/en; kids site: http://www.kidshelp.sympatico.ca

National Clearinghouse on Family Violence, Family Violence Prevention Unit, Public Health Agency of Canada, 200 Eglantine Driveway, Address Locator: 1909D1, 9th Floor, Jeanne Mance Building, Tunney's Pasture, Ottawa, ON K1A 1B4. Tel: 613-957-2938 or national toll-free 1-800-267-1291; fax: 613-941-8930; http://www.hc-sc.gc.ca/hppb/familyviolence/index.html (excellent website for resources)

Vanier Institute of the Family, 94 Centrepointe Drive, Ottawa, ON K2G 6B1. Tel: 613-228-8500; fax: 613-228-8007; http://www.vifamily.ca

Other Websites of Interest

Canadian Society for the Investigation of Child Abuse (CSICA): http://www.csicainfo.com/

Centre for Children and Families in the Justice System (excellent site to download resources): http://www.lfcc.on.ca

Department of Justice Canada (excellent site for resources): http://www.canada.justice.gc.ca

National Center on Shaken Baby Syndrome (excellent site for resources): http://www.dontshake.com

Springtide Resources (formerly known as Education Wife Assault) (excellent site for resources): http://www.springtideresources.org

Suspected Child Abuse and Neglect Program (SCAN) (The Hospital for Sick Children): http://www.sickkids.on.ca/scan/default.asp

The Incredible Years: http://www.incredibleyears.com

Printed Matter

Bi-Monthy E-Bulletin, by the National Clearinghouse on Family Violence. To subscribe, visit http://www.phac-aspc.gc.ca/ncfv-cnivf/familyviolence/e-bulletin/suscri_e.html

Canadian Incidence Study of Reported Child Abuse and Neglect – Selected Results, by Nico Trocmé and David Wolfe (Minister of Public Works and Government Services). To download a copy, visit http://www.phac-aspc.gc.ca/publicat/cissr-ecirc/pdf/cmic_e.pdf

Child Abuse: A Fact Sheet from the Department of Justice Canada, by Department of Justice Canada. To download a copy, visit http://www.justice.gc.ca/eng/pi/fv-vf/child-enf.pdf

Discipline Without Hurting, by Child Welfare League of Canada. To download a copy, visit http://www.cwlc.ca/files/file/pubs/DisciplineWithoutHurting.pdf

Family Violence in Canada: A Statistical Profile 2007, by Canadian Centre for Justice Statistics (Statistics Canada), Catalogue No. 85-224-XIE. To download a copy, visit http://www.phac-aspc.gc.ca/ncfv-cnivf/familyviolence/pdfs/fv-85-224-XIE2007001.pdf

Little Eyes, Little Ears: How Violence Against a Mother Shapes Children as They Grow (2007), by Alison Cunningham and Linda Baker. To download a copy, visit http://www.lfcc.on.ca/little_eyes_little_ears.html

Making a Difference: The Community Responds to Child Abuse, 5th ed. Toronto: Pearl Rimer, Boost – Child Abuse Prevention & Intervention. To purchase a copy, visit http://www.boostforkids.org

Maltreatment and the Developing Child: How Early Childhood Experience Shapes Child and Culture (2004), by Bruce D. Perry. To download a copy, visit http://www.lfcc.on.ca/mccain/perry.pdf

Nobody's Perfect, by the Public Health Agency of Canada, Division of Childhood and Adolescence (Health Canada). For more information, visit http://www.phac-aspc.gc.ca/dca-dea/family_famille/nobody_e.html

Reaching Out: Working Together to Identify and Respond to Child Victims of Abuse (1998), by P. Rimer and B. Prager (ITP Nelson).

Spanking and Disciplining Children: What You Should Know About Section 43 of the Criminal Code (2007), by Public Legal Education and Information Service of New Brunswick. To download a copy, visit http://www.legal-info-legale.nb.ca/assets/pdf/SPANKINGBrochure-E.pdf

Sexual Abuse and Exploitation of Children and Youth: A Fact Sheet from the Department of Justice Canada (2008), by Department of Justice Canada. To download a copy, visit http://canada.justice.gc.ca/eng/pi/fv-vf/sex_abu.pdf

Understanding the Effects of Domestic Violence: A Handbook for Early Childhood Educators (2005), by Linda Baker, Peter Jaffe, and Kathy Moore. Ontario Women's Directorate. To download a copy, visit http://www.lfcc.on.ca/ecehandbk.PDF

What's Wrong with Spanking? (2004), by Department of Justice Canada and Health Canada. To download a copy, visit http://www.phac-aspc.gc.ca/ncfv-cnivf/familyviolence/pdfs/nfnts-spanking_e.pdf

BIBLIOGRAPHY

Alcoba, N. (2008, March 21). Child-porn fighter to head cybercrime research centre. *National Post.*

Alliance of Five Research Centres on Violence. (1999). *Violence prevention and the girl child: Final report.* Ottawa: Status of Women Canada.

Ayoub, C., et al. (1990). Working with maltreated children and families in day care settings. In S. S. Chehrazi (Ed.), *Psychosocial issues in day care.* Washington, DC: American Psychiatric Press.

Baker, L., Jaffe, P., & Moore, K. (2001a). *Understanding the effects of domestic violence: A handbook for early childhood educators.* London, ON: Centre for Children and Families in the Justice System.

Baker, L., Jaffe, P., & Moore, K. (2001b). *Understanding the effects of domestic violence: A training manual for early childhood educators.* London, ON: Centre for Children and Families in the Justice System.

Barr, R. G. (2006). Crying behaviour and its importance for psychosocial development in children. In: R. E. Tremblay, R. G. Barr, R. DeV. Peters (Eds.), *Encyclopedia on early childhood development* (pp. 1–10). Montreal: Centre of Excellence for Early Childhood Development. Retrieved April 28, 2008, from http://www.child-encyclopedia.com/documents/BarrANGxp.pdf

Boost – Child Abuse Prevention and Intervention (2008a). *Child abuse facts.* Retrieved April 2008 from http://www.boostforkids.org/whatChildAbuseFacts.asp

Boost – Child Abuse Prevention and Intervention (2008b). *Helping the child who has been abused fact sheet.* Retrieved April 2008 from http://www.boostforkids.org/whatCAFHelpingTheAbused.asp

Canadian Paediatric Society. (2001). Joint statement on shaken baby syndrome. *Paediatrics & Child Health, 6,* 663–667.

Canadian Paediatric Society. (2008). *Well beings: A guide to health in child care.* (3rd ed.). Ottawa: Author.

Caring Communities Project. (1994). *Child sexual abuse prevention: A resource kit.* Book 1. Ottawa: Canadian Institution of Child Health.

Chapman, R., & McGarry, B. (2007, March 7). *Victim identification/background analysis.* Paper presented at the Provincial Strategy to Protect Children from Sexual Abuse and Exploitation on the Internet, Multi Disciplinary Training Conference, Gravenhurst, Ontario.

Cicchetti, D., & Rogosch, F. A. (1997). The role of self-organization in the promotion of resilience in maltreated children. *Development and Psychopathology, 9,* 797–816.

Department of Justice Canada. (2008, April 23). *Child abuse: A fact sheet from the Department of Justice Canada.* Ottawa: Author. Retrieved April 2008 from http://www.justice.gc.ca/eng/pi/fv-vf/child-enf.pdf

Dinh, D. K., et al. (1990). The Vietnamese. In N. Waxler-Morrison et al. (Eds.), *Cross-cultural caring: A handbook for health professionals in Western Canada.* Vancouver: University of British Columbia Press.

Finkelhor, D., & Strapko, N. (1992). Sexual abuse prevention education: A review of evaluation studies. In D. J. Willis, E. W. Holden, & M. Rosenberg (Eds.), *Prevention of child maltreatment: Developmental ecological perspectives.* New York: John Wiley.

Flowers, R. B. (2001). The sex trade industry's worldwide exploitation of children [Electronic version]. *Annals of the American Academy of Political and Social Science, 575,* 147–157.

Hall, D. K., & Pearson, J. (2004). *Reaching in … Reaching out. Resilience training: Introducing thinking skills that help children bounce back.* Toronto: The Child Development Institute.

Latimer, J. (1998). *The consequences of child maltreatment: A reference guide for health practitioners.* Ottawa: Family Violence Prevention Unit.

Leitch, K. (2007). *Reaching for the top: A report by the Advisor on Healthy Children and Youth* (Catalogue No. H21-296/2007E). Ottawa: Health Canada.

MacMillan, H., et al. (1999). Slapping and spanking in childhood and its association with lifetime prevalence of psychiatric disorders in a general population sample. *Canadian Medical Association Journal, 161,* 805–817.

Manitoba Child Care Association. (2007). *Human resource management guide for early childhood programs.* Winnipeg: Author.

McKay, S. (2007). Introduction: Development of the Prairie Child Welfare Consortium. In F. Brown, et al. (Eds.), *Putting a human face on child welfare: Voices from the Prairies.* Regina, SK: Prairie Child Welfare Consortium.

Menjivar, C., & Salcido, O. (2002). Immigrant women and domestic violence: Common experiences in different countries. *Gender & Society, 16,* 898–920.

National Clearinghouse on Family Violence. (2006). *Child sexual abuse.* Ottawa: Health Canada. Retrieved April 2008 from http://www.phac-aspc.gc.ca/ncfv-cnivf/familyviolence/pdfs/nfntsx-2006-csa_e.pdf

Perry, B. D. (2004). *Maltreatment and the developing child: How early childhood experience shapes child and culture.* Inaugural lecture. London, ON: The Margaret McCain Lecture Series, Centre for Children and Families in the Justice System. Retrieved April 2008 from http://www.lfcc.on.ca/mccain/perry.pdf

Public Health Agency of Canada. (2005). *Canadian Incidence Study of Reported Child Abuse and Neglect.* Retrieved April 2008 from http://www.phac-aspc.gc.ca/media/nr-rp/2005/pdf/cis100405_e.pdf

Rimer, J. (2007). *Literature review: Responding to child & youth victims of sexual exploitation on the Internet.* Toronto: Boost – Child Abuse Prevention & Intervention.

Rimer, P. (2007). *Making a difference: The community responds to child abuse* (5th ed.). Toronto: Boost – Child Abuse Prevention & Intervention.

Rishchynski, G., Rimer, P., & Rimer, J. (2008). *Looking for Angelina: A learning guide on family violence.* Toronto: Second Story Press.

Statistics Canada. (2006). *Measuring violence against women: Statistical trends 2006.* Ottawa: Minister of Industry. Retrieved April 2008 from http://www.statcan.gc.ca/english/research/85-570-XIE/85-570-XIE2006001.pdf

Statistics Canada. (2008). Prevalence and severity of violence against women. In *Measuring violence against women: Statistical trends 2006.* Retrieved April 2008 from http://www.statcan.gc.ca/english/research/85-570-XIE/2006001/findings/prevalence.htm

Steinhauer, P. (1998). *Developing resiliency in children from disadvantaged populations: Canada's health action, building on the legacy: (Vol. 1. Children and youth.* Ottawa: Health Canada.

Sundelin, W. (1994). Developmental and survival: A study of children at risk living in adverse psychological milieu. *Child Abuse and Neglect, 18,* 715–723.

Trocmé, N. (2002). *Responding to changes in reported child maltreatment: Federal program and policy implications* (OIS 1993/1998). Ottawa: Health Canada Policy Forum on the Canadian Incidence Study of Reported Child Abuse and Neglect.

Trocmé, N., et al. (2005). *Canadian Incidence Study of Reported Child Abuse and Neglect – 2003: Major findings.* Ottawa: Minister of Public Works and Government Services Canada.

Trocmé, N. B., Fallon, B., MacLaurin, B., & Copp, B. (2001). *Canadian Incidence Study of Reported Child Abuse and Neglect.* Ottawa: Health Canada.

Unger, M. (2007). Contextual and cultural aspects of resilience in child welfare settings. In I. Brown, et al. (Eds.), *Putting a human face on child welfare: Voices from the Prairies* (pp. 1–23). Regina, SK: Prairie Child Welfare Consortium.

Vaillancourt, R., & Taylor-Butts, A. (2007). *Transition homes in Canada: National, provincial and territorial fact sheets 2005/2006* (Catalogue No. 85-404-XWE). Statistics Canada, Canadian Centre for Justice Statistics. Ottawa: Minister of Industry. Retrieved May 2008 from http://dsp-psd.pwgsc.gc.ca/collection_2007/statcan/85-404-X/85-404-XIE2007000.pdf

Werner, E., & Smith, R. (2001). *Journeys from childhood to midlife: Risk, resilience, and recovery.* Ithaca, NY: Cornell University Press. World Health Organization. (2008). *Eliminating female genital mutilation: An interagency statement.* Geneva: Author. Retrieved April 2008 from http://www.who.int/reproductivehealth/publications/fgm/fgm_statement_2008.pdf

Yoder, P. S., Abderrahim, N., & Zhuzhuni, A. (2004). *Female genital cutting in the demographic and health surveys: A critical and comparative analysis.* Calverton, England: Macro International Inc.

UN Convention
on the Rights of the Child

In Child Friendly Language

"Rights" are things every child should have or be able to do. All children have the same rights. These rights are listed in the UN Convention on the Rights of the Child. Almost every country has agreed to these rights. All the rights are connected to each other, and all are equally important. Sometimes, we have to think about rights in terms of what is the best for children in a situation, and what is critical to life and protection from harm. As you grow, you have more responsibility to make choices and exercise your rights.

Article 1
Everyone under 18 has these rights.

Article 2
All children have these rights, no matter who they are, where they live, what their parents do, what language they speak, what their religion is, whether they are a boy or girl, what their culture is, whether they have a disability, whether they are rich or poor. No child should be treated unfairly on any basis.

Article 3
All adults should do what is best for you. When adults make decisions, they should think about how their decisions will affect children.

Article 4
The government has a responsibility to make sure your rights are protected. They must help your family protect your rights and create an environment where you can grow and reach your potential.

Article 5
Your family has the responsibility to help you learn to exercise your rights, and to ensure that your rights are protected.

Article 6
You have the right to be alive.

Article 7
You have the right to a name, and this should be officially recognized by the government. You have the right to a nationality (to belong to a country).

Article 8
You have the right to an identity – an official record of who you are. No one should take this away from you.

Article 9
You have the right to live with your parent(s), unless it is bad for you. You have the right to live with a family who cares for you.

Article 10
If you live in a different country than your parents do, you have the right to be together in the same place.

Article 11
You have the right to be protected from kidnapping.

Article 12
You have the right to give your opinion, and for adults to listen and take it seriously.

Article 13
You have the right to find out things and share what you think with others, by talking, drawing, writing or in any other way unless it harms or offends other people.

Article 14
You have the right to choose your own religion and beliefs. Your parents should help you decide what is right and wrong, and what is best for you.

Article 15
You have the right to choose your own friends and join or set up groups, as long as it isn't harmful to others.

Article 16
You have the right to privacy.

Article 17
You have the right to get information that is important to your well-being, from radio, newspaper, books, computers and other sources. Adults should make sure that the information you are getting is not harmful, and help you find and understand the information you need.

Article 18
You have the right to be raised by your parent(s) if possible.

Article 19
You have the right to be protected from being hurt and mistreated, in body or mind.

Article 20
You have the right to special care and help if you cannot live with your parents.

Article 21
You have the right to care and protection if you are adopted or in foster care.

Article 22
You have the right to special protection and help if you are a refugee (if you have been forced to leave your home and live in another country), as well as all the rights in this Convention.

Article 23
You have the right to special education and care if you have a disability, as well as all the rights in this Convention, so that you can live a full life.

Article 24
You have the right to the best health care possible, safe water to drink, nutritious food, a clean and safe environment, and information to help you stay well.

Article 25
If you live in care or in other situations away from home, you have the right to have these living arrangements looked at regularly to see if they are the most appropriate.

Article 26
You have the right to help from the government if you are poor or in need.

Article 27
You have the right to food, clothing, a safe place to live and to have your basic needs met. You should not be disadvantaged so that you can't do many of the things other kids can do.

Article 28
You have the right to a good quality education. You should be encouraged to go to school to the highest level you can.

Article 29
Your education should help you use and develop your talents and abilities. It should also help you learn to live peacefully, protect the environment and respect other people.

Article 30
You have the right to practice your own culture, language and religion - or any you choose. Minority and indigenous groups need special protection of this right.

Article 31
You have the right to play and rest.

Article 32
You have the right to protection from work that harms you, and is bad for your health and education. If you work, you have the right to be safe and paid fairly.

Article 33
You have the right to protection from harmful drugs and from the drug trade.

Article 34
You have the right to be free from sexual abuse.

Article 35
No one is allowed to kidnap or sell you.

Article 36
You have the right to protection from any kind of exploitation (being taken advantage of).

Article 37
No one is allowed to punish you in a cruel or harmful way.

Article 38
You have the right to protection and freedom from war. Children under 15 cannot be forced to go into the army or take part in war.

Article 39
You have the right to help if you've been hurt, neglected or badly treated.

Article 40
You have the right to legal help and fair treatment in a justice system that respects your rights.

Article 41
If the laws of your country provide better protection of your rights than the articles in this Convention, those laws should apply.

Article 42
You have the right to know your rights! Adults should know about these rights and help you learn about them, too.

Articles 43 to 54
These articles explain how governments and international organizations like UNICEF will work to ensure children are protected with their rights.

This text is not an official version of the UN Convention on the Rights of the Child. Access the official text of the Convention at www.unicef.org/crc/crc.htm. Art courtesy Doubleday Canada. Illustrations Copyright © 1997 Darcia Labrosse

Source: Adapted from the poster entitled *UN Convention on the Rights of the Child In Child Friendly Language.* To view the poster in its entirety visit www.ece.nelson.com. Reprinted with permission of UNICEF Canada.

Canadian Incidence Study of Reported Child Abuse and Neglect

8.2

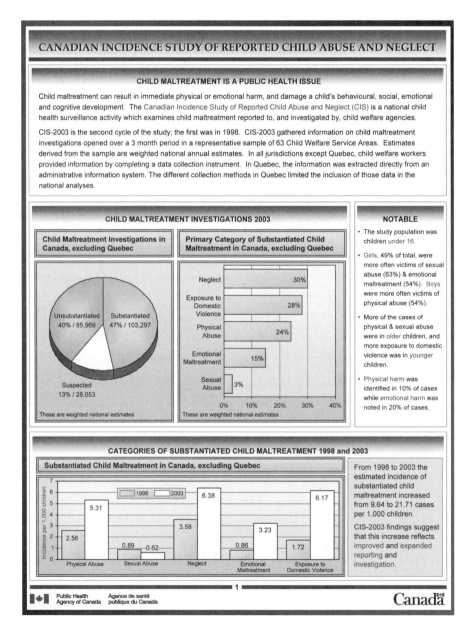

CANADIAN INCIDENCE STUDY OF REPORTED CHILD ABUSE AND NEGLECT

CHILD MALTREATMENT IS A PUBLIC HEALTH ISSUE

Child maltreatment can result in immediate physical or emotional harm, and damage a child's behavioural, social, emotional and cognitive development. The Canadian Incidence Study of Reported Child Abuse and Neglect (CIS) is a national child health surveillance activity which examines child maltreatment reported to, and investigated by, child welfare agencies.

CIS-2003 is the second cycle of the study; the first was in 1998. CIS-2003 gathered information on child maltreatment investigations opened over a 3 month period in a representative sample of 63 Child Welfare Service Areas. Estimates derived from the sample are weighted national annual estimates. In all jurisdictions except Quebec, child welfare workers provided information by completing a data collection instrument. In Quebec, the information was extracted directly from an administrative information system. The different collection methods in Quebec limited the inclusion of those data in the national analyses.

CHILD MALTREATMENT INVESTIGATIONS 2003

Child Maltreatment Investigations in Canada, excluding Quebec

Unsubstantiated 40% / 85,969
Substantiated 47% / 103,297
Suspected 13% / 28,053

These are weighted national estimates

Primary Category of Substantiated Child Maltreatment in Canada, excluding Quebec

Neglect — 30%
Exposure to Domestic Violence — 28%
Physical Abuse — 24%
Emotional Maltreatment — 15%
Sexual Abuse — 3%

These are weighted national estimates

NOTABLE

- The study population was children under 16.
- Girls, 49% of total, were more often victims of sexual abuse (63%) & emotional maltreatment (54%). Boys were more often victims of physical abuse (54%).
- More of the cases of physical & sexual abuse were in older children, and more exposure to domestic violence was in younger children.
- Physical harm was identified in 10% of cases while emotional harm was noted in 20% of cases.

CATEGORIES OF SUBSTANTIATED CHILD MALTREATMENT 1998 and 2003

Substantiated Child Maltreatment in Canada, excluding Quebec

Incidence per 1,000 children

1998 / 2003
Physical Abuse: 2.56 / 5.31
Sexual Abuse: 0.89 / 0.62
Neglect: 3.58 / 6.38
Emotional Maltreatment: 0.86 / 3.23
Exposure to Domestic Violence: 1.72 / 6.17

From 1998 to 2003 the estimated incidence of substantiated child maltreatment increased from 9.64 to 21.71 cases per 1,000 children.

CIS-2003 findings suggest that this increase reflects improved and expanded reporting and investigation.

Public Health Agency of Canada   Agence de santé publique du Canada

Canada

1

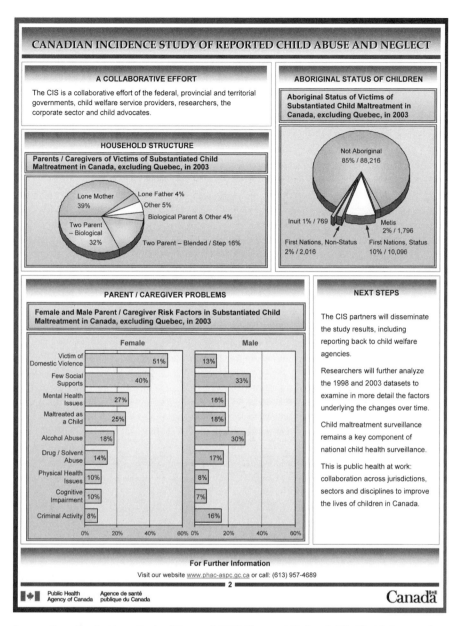

CANADIAN INCIDENCE STUDY OF REPORTED CHILD ABUSE AND NEGLECT

A COLLABORATIVE EFFORT

The CIS is a collaborative effort of the federal, provincial and territorial governments, child welfare service providers, researchers, the corporate sector and child advocates.

HOUSEHOLD STRUCTURE

Parents / Caregivers of Victims of Substantiated Child Maltreatment in Canada, excluding Quebec, in 2003

Lone Mother 39%
Lone Father 4%
Other 5%
Biological Parent & Other 4%
Two Parent – Biological 32%
Two Parent – Blended / Step 16%

ABORIGINAL STATUS OF CHILDREN

Aboriginal Status of Victims of Substantiated Child Maltreatment in Canada, excluding Quebec, in 2003

Not Aboriginal 85% / 88,216
Inuit 1% / 769
Metis 2% / 1,796
First Nations, Non-Status 2% / 2,016
First Nations, Status 10% / 10,096

PARENT / CAREGIVER PROBLEMS

Female and Male Parent / Caregiver Risk Factors in Substantiated Child Maltreatment in Canada, excluding Quebec, in 2003

Risk Factor	Female	Male
Victim of Domestic Violence	51%	13%
Few Social Supports	40%	33%
Mental Health Issues	27%	18%
Maltreated as a Child	25%	18%
Alcohol Abuse	18%	30%
Drug / Solvent Abuse	14%	17%
Physical Health Issues	10%	8%
Cognitive Impairment	10%	7%
Criminal Activity	8%	16%

NEXT STEPS

The CIS partners will disseminate the study results, including reporting back to child welfare agencies.

Researchers will further analyze the 1998 and 2003 datasets to examine in more detail the factors underlying the changes over time.

Child maltreatment surveillance remains a key component of national child health surveillance.

This is public health at work: collaboration across jurisdictions, sectors and disciplines to improve the lives of children in Canada.

For Further Information

Visit our website www.phac-aspc.gc.ca or call: (613) 957-4689

2

Public Health Agency of Canada
Agence de santé publique du Canada

Canada

Source: *Canadian Incidence Study of Reported Child Abuse and Neglect*, Public Health Agency of Canada, 2003. Reproduced with the permission of the Minister of Public Works and Government Services, Canada, 2008.

UNIT

9

Supporting Children's Development

504

High-quality early childhood programs strive to support children's growth and development in all areas. Educators think about each child holistically to achieve a balance in his or her physical, emotional, and social health. This is particularly important as our further understanding of health and illness makes the interconnections between the mind and body obvious, such as the physical wear and tear of stress.

Students and, ultimately, graduates integrate their knowledge of health, illness, safety, and nutrition with what they learn about child development, curriculum, families, diversity, and inclusion to create early childhood programs that meet the needs of both the group and each child. Recent research confirms that the brain is the key to our overall health and well-being, including our abilities and coping skills. Prolonged exposure to stress will have a negative effect on a child's brain development. Children enrolled in high-quality early childhood programs have been found to have lower stress hormone levels than those children enrolled in poor-quality programs (Canadian Child Care Federation, 2001, p. 1). Although many elements influence development, there is general agreement that human development follows predictable sequences in all areas—cognitive, emotional, social, and physical—but that individuals have unique "timing" and a sociocultural context. Children learn through interacting with people, objects, and the environment.

Children's growth and development are an early childhood education (ECE) course in themselves, and you will have taken it before you graduate. This textbook examines certain issues relating to children's well-being that readers can integrate with their knowledge of child development, developmental psychology, and sociology. The topics covered here will add to your understanding and ability to support children's well-being. Educators are in an ideal position to support children in their learning of lifelong healthy habits and positive attitudes. The latter portion of this unit is devoted to the health curriculum for children in early childhood programs.

HEALTHY BRAIN DEVELOPMENT

OBJECTIVE

To outline educators' roles in supporting each child's emotional well-being in terms of the child's self-regulation and relationship development, stress levels, and sexuality.

Brain research is continuing to help inform parents and educators about the types of relationships, environments, and experiences that support optimal brain development. The brain, as master control of our health and well-being, is paramount in all aspects of cognition and emotion (Bertrand, 2001, p. 8).

The importance of our emotional and social well-being and how these relate to physical well-being cannot be overstated. How you feel about yourself and the effectiveness of your relationships with others profoundly affect your health. For example, several longitudinal studies have documented that between half and two-thirds of children who have undergone adversity have overcome the odds and manifest resilience, the term often used to describe a set of qualities that include successful adaptation in the face of risk (Benard, 1995, p. 1). "We are all born with an innate capacity for resilience, by which we are able to develop social competence, problem-solving skills, a critical consciousness, autonomy, and a sense of purpose" (Benard, 1995, p. 1). Two aspects of long-term emotional–social health, self-regulation and relating to others, are discussed below.

Self-Regulation

Self-regulation and our ability to relate to others are two complex and recurring emotional and social tasks that are themes in our lives from birth. Self-regulation refers to the ability to focus attention, control emotional energy, and initiate and recover from anger, disappointment, joy, or other emotions, as well as manage facial and body movement. How well a child (or adult) can self-regulate has a dramatic effect on that individual's quality of daily life. To adapt, the child must be capable of flexible regulation, because life requires action and reflection, intensity and calm, and concentration and split attention.

Responsive relationships are the cornerstone of emotional development and self-regulation. A newborn needs the educator to regulate his or her state. As the child grows, regulation becomes dyadic—child and educator work together. During the preschool years, the child begins to self-regulate. The child learns to tolerate strong emotions and recover from arousal in secure, responsive relationships that support regulation. Self-regulation develops when children are exposed to manageable levels of stimulation and are protected from overarousal. Differences exist among children in their ability to regulate emotions and behaviour and to tolerate stress. Children use a variety of sensory and motor skills to regulate. **Temperament** also accounts for individual differences in a child's emotional arousal and reactivity. But it is through the relationship that the child learns to recover from arousal and stress. When educators remain emotionally available and are sensitive and responsive to individual differences, children learn to regulate. When children anticipate the empathy and understanding of their educator, they are more likely to cope with distress.

Children need to experience a full range of emotions and feel that it is safe to express them. When they do, they learn to regulate emotions and practise the culturally determined display rules for expressing emotions. For example, they learn when to make eye contact and how to show gratitude. They must know how to regulate emotions and behaviour to choose actions that will achieve their goals when exploring and relating to others. A child who wants to play with peers needs to regulate the impulse to take all the toys. Self-regulation is therefore central to the child's social, cognitive, and emotional development. Focusing on self-regulation means understanding individual capacities for stimulation and patterns of recovery from arousal. Educators need to use this information to create a safe environment and relationship for exploration and the development of self-regulation. As the child develops new language and cognitive and social skills, they are used for regulation. These new skills are practised and sorted out in the context of secure educator–child relationships.

Relating to Others

Relating to others refers to children's ability to build relationships, which begins at birth with their parents and develops with other significant people. In addition to relationships with adults, peer relationships are very important. The three major tasks of early childhood relationships are peer group entry, conflict resolution, and maintaining play (Guralnick & Littmann, 1992). Children need to regulate their emotional energy to accomplish all three tasks. Individual differences exist in the speed, intensity, and duration of emotional responses. Educators must know each child's emotional reactions to promote regulation and recovery before the child can make progress.

Educators support self-regulation when they

- initiate and maintain communication with parents and staff that increases sensitivity to the individual child's security and exploration;
- create an environment that is safe for exploration and the expression of impulses;
- observe and record individual sensory and motor skills that are used to regulate;
- are responsive to the child's signals and intentions;
- remain emotionally available;
- pair novel stimulation with familiar experience;
- remain sensitive to individual differences in coping and relating;
- expose the child to stimulation that matches the individual's ability to cope and, when the child is overstimulated, support recovery within the relationship;
- avoid the following measures that violate the relationship: emotional withdrawal, punishment, imposition of educator control, and intense expression of the educator's negative emotion;

- create optimal individual stimulation, taking into consideration the type of stimulation, its form, its intensity, and variations in presentation;
- increase stimulation over time in small increments that are responsive to the individual's ability to cope;
- respond to the child's signals and intentions (signals can be bids for regulation or requests for assistance to deal with feelings; signals are not only an expression of an internal state but also an outward show of feelings);
- ensure that the child's voice is heard and that the child is able to participate meaningfully in matters that directly affect him or her (as per the UN Convention on the Rights of the Child, see Appendix 8.1, page 501);
- observe the child's behaviour and figure out the meaning that his or her experience has for that individual;
- create spaces in the playroom with reduced stimulation;
- create stimulus shelters and comfort zones in the playroom; and
- create spaces for one-to-one interaction in the playroom.

Source: Adapted with permission from M. Goulet and R. Schroeder, *How Caring Relationships Support Self-Regulation: Video Guide* (Toronto: National Association for the Education of Young Children, 1998), 37–45.

Educators must observe the children to determine how each individual regulates emotional energy, preferences for other children, the familiar play situations chosen, the types of toys, and the pretend themes in which the child engages. When these things are known, educators can design environments that maximize the child's interactions with other children.

Making friends during the early years forms the basis for children's future relationships (Guralnick & Littmann, 1992). *Early Learning for Every Child Today* (Best Start Panel on Early Learning, 2006, p. 38) identifies making friends as the dominant skill in the social developmental domain for preschoolers (2½ to 6 years). Indicators of the child's developing skill are

- seeking out others to play with
- offering play materials and roles to others
- playing with others co-operatively
- inviting others to play
- exchanging ideas, materials, points of view with others
- sustaining play with others

Educators can enhance children's opportunities to make friends through social play by

- providing equipment and activities that help children learn social rules and roles and practise taking turns and ownership as they are developmentally ready;
- observing children's individual strengths and interests and using these to involve the child with others;
- engaging in play with children, taking turns, exchanging ideas, and modelling how to make friends and sustain play (Best Start Panel on Early Learning, 2006);

- actively guiding children to initiate play with one another when an educator observes an opportunity to foster a friendship. Insisting, however, that children play together, or that "we are all friends," is artificial and does not help children make friends. The reality is that although we all need to show respect for one another, children choose friends;

- choosing and arranging furniture to promote social interaction;
- providing equipment that provides the child with the opportunity to release emotional energy; and
- recognizing those school-agers who are having difficulty making friends and using observation to determine how educators can foster these skills. This may also mean making changes in the program (Musson, 1999).

Helping Children Cope with Stress

We have heard many times that stress is one of life's realities and that a certain degree of stress is important and positive; it challenges the individual to learn and grow. We also know that the causes of stress are varied. Some stressors are situational and **short-lived**, such as an upcoming birthday party, breaking an arm, or planning a wedding, and some are chronic and **long term**, such as living in an abusive home environment, the death of a loved one, or working at a high-pressure job. In addition, stress factors are unique to individuals: adults should be sensitive to each child's stress factors, realizing that they have meaning for the child. Urging a child to stop worrying, or suggesting that he or she shouldn't be upset, trivializes a child's concerns, causing more stress. Almost anything can cause stress. Regardless of the cause, however, stress management is crucial for a child. In some ways, children can be very resilient, but emotional vulnerability that begins in childhood can affect someone for a lifetime. How?

As complex and dynamic research on brain development is, one piece of evidence stands out clearly: "The neural pathways involved with how we respond to stressors and new information seem to be particularly powerful in shaping brain development and learning, behaviour and health" (Bertrand, 2001, p. 11). Stressors arouse pathways in the brain, and very early in life, individuals establish physiological stress responses that either contribute to life-long health or detract from it. You are encouraged to look at other references for descriptions of what is known about these physiological stress responses (Bertrand, 2001). A dramatic example involves cortisol, a chemical produced to respond to the stress. Higher cortisol levels are produced in response to stress, and repeated or prolonged elevated cortisol levels can damage organs, including the brain, or body systems. In other words, lifelong health can be affected by the patterns of stress response established early, and this response is highly influenced by early experiences interacting with the brain. The most critical early experiences involve the quality of interactions with primary caregivers.

Although infants, toddlers, and younger preschoolers have personality strengths, they don't yet have the cognitive skills to develop optimal coping on their own. They need adults to create environments that are low in stress and to help them find ways to cope with stress. Young children hear about things that relate to the outside of their bodies (e.g., changing a diaper, putting a coat on because it's cold outside, tying shoes), but beginning in the preschool years, their awareness of how they are affected by stress involves the inside as much as the outside of their body (e.g., their heart beats faster, their mouth becomes dry, and butterflies in their tummy). When children become aware of their internal body cues, they can recognize when they are experiencing stress. This leads to adults helping children to learn to regulate their internal responses and acquire coping strategies, such as relaxation techniques (e.g., taking slow, deep breaths) or moving away from the situation that is causing the stress. Coping skills are usually more developed in older children, because they have developed the sequential and logical thinking skills to be able to think about their problems and anticipate consequences.

Most children can cope with the usual stress factors arising from growth and development and everyday living, especially with the support of adults. Separation protest is a healthy and normal reaction in young children because of the lack of control young children have to effect their environment; in other words, despite the child's protest, the parent can leave anyway. However, as the adults (parents and other significant caregivers) in the child's life show consistent and caring responses, the young child begins to integrate feelings of trust and self-control. "Confidence in the caregiver becomes confidence in the self with the caregiver and, ultimately, confidence in the self" (Sroufe, 1995, p. 186). Early childhood program policies and practices on entry into the program should identify ways to reduce stress on infants and young children. An individual's control or perceived control reduces elevations in cortisol. Children who are more certain about their ability to control their distress, and who develop strategies to do so, exhibit less stress and have lower levels of cortisol. Educators must support the development of children's personal control over the environment and over their own internal body state to reduce stress and regulate the production of cortisol.

Children's Stress Factors

It can be difficult to categorize stress factors into those that are less serious and usually of short duration and those that are not because a stressor is defined by how the individual perceives it. Generally, the following stress factors are often less serious or short term:

- those related to developmental milestones with no other mediating forces (e.g., toilet learning, separation anxiety, new baby in the house, making friends, learning to read, most fears)
- those related to everyday frustrations, such as too many choices, no choices, or no or little control over decisions that affect their life
- common but often anxiety-inducing experiences, such as visits to the doctor (e.g., for immunization shots or blood tests), the dentist, or a hospital emergency room; short stays in the hospital for minor ailments; short separations from family; moving; transition to an early childhood program; leaving that program to attend school; transitions within a program or school (e.g., from infant to toddler room); rejection from a peer

Table 9.1 lists some of the common fears of children at different ages.

TABLE 9.1	Common Childhood Fears
Under 2 Years Old	■ loud noises or the dark. If unable to eliminate the noise or the lighting, adults need to be present and reassuring to reduce stress. ■ separation anxiety Dealing with it sensitively and consistently will help the child learn to trust that the parent will return. *For example: Ensuring that parents have a ritual of goodbye when dropping off the child, and not supporting a practice of 'disappearing' without the child's awareness.*

(continued)

TABLE 9.1　　**Common Childhood Fears** *(continued)*

2 to 4 Years Old	■ At this age, children have vivid imaginations, and have difficulty distinguishing reality from fantasy.
	■ They may also have scary nightmares that wake them up, and need reassurance that the things they saw in the dream are not real. 　When that happens, they may need a trusted adult with them until they fall asleep.
	■ The fears may seem rational (e.g., a fear of dogs), or irrational to adults (e.g., being afraid of what's under the bed). 　Either way, we must remember that they are real fears to the child.
	■ By age three, most children can separate from their parents with little or no crying.
5 Years Old and Older	■ Exposure to visual media from any of the many possible media formats may create fears in young children including news reports of war on television (some children arriving in Canada have firsthand experience), or terrorist attacks. 　This is also true for younger children if their exposure is not carefully monitored.
	■ Younger school-agers might be afraid of ghosts and other supernatural beings. As they get older, they may have more concrete fears, such as being lost or kidnapped, being disliked, or real-life catastrophes (e.g., floods, fires, armed conflicts).
	■ Their concrete fears, however, are usually out of proportion to their likelihood in the child's life. As they develop cognitive understanding of this fact, these fears generally lessen or cease.
	■ Fear of being humiliated, or looking or acting "strange" in front of their peers.
	■ Older children often worry about their parents' relationship or health, and may exaggerate mild arguments or complaints that they hear and being a victim of physical violence.
	■ Night terrors, not uncommon in 5 to 9 year olds, are characterized by not fully arousing from sleep, but seeming to wake up, and they are screaming and thrashing. Although they seem awake, they will not respond, and will have no recollection of the event.

Source: Canadian Paediatric Society, *Behaviour and Parenting,* http://www.caringforkids.cps.ca/behaviour&parenting/Fears.htm, Ottawa: Canadian Paediatric Society, 2004. Reprinted with permission.

CRITICAL THINKING

Last week, two-year-old Priya, who had just started using the toilet, slipped while seated and almost fell in "bottom first." She now refuses to use the toilet again and cries and points at it whenever she needs to go, but insists on wearing diapers. Priya's mom has requested to bring in a potty as Priya feels safe with it and uses one at home. However, the public health department has a policy against potties for hygiene reasons. How can you support Priya in coping with her fear?

The following stress factors are often more traumatic or long term:

- parents' separation or divorce; death of a family member
- everyday life in poverty; homelessness
- living with violence in the family
- bias (e.g., racism or a home culture perceived as very different from and not accepted by that of the early childhood program or school)
- extreme fears or phobias
- bullying (generally in school-age children)
- repeated hospitalizations or a long stay in a hospital, particularly between the ages of six months and four years, especially when separated from parents
- refugee experiences (e.g., war, the witnessing of torture or death, the separation or loss of family members, different climate or weather, different language)
- witnessing a catastrophe or disaster (e.g., hurricane, tornado, fire, kidnapping, terrorist attack)

Although these lists are incomplete, they convey the idea that children can have a range of stress factors, some of which they resolve or cope with over time or with experience. Others are overwhelming or begin as something relatively minor and then escalate, resulting in a major negative effect on how the child functions every day.

Identifying Children Who Are Experiencing Stress

Many people assume that signs of stress are easy to pinpoint in children. However, with the exception of some very obvious signs, identification relies on educators' observation skills and sensitivity to individual children. Each child's temperament and personality traits have an effect on how they perceive stress and on their response. Identifying that the child is experiencing stress is only the beginning. Effective communication with parents is critical in determining the stress factors and deciding how you can work together to support the child. Possible signs are endless, but these are some common ones:

- The child seems sad, has a vacant expression, whines a lot, or has frequent temper tantrums.
- The child clings to educators, although he or she has been in the program for an extended period, or hasn't connected with at least one educator.
- The child is constantly worried.
- The child complains about physical symptoms (e.g., headaches or tummy aches, especially for school-agers). Some school-agers do not complain about aches but indicate stress through behaviour such as nail biting, nervous twitches, or sucking their thumb.
- The child seems to be tired and rundown and gets sick a lot (e.g., has frequent colds).
- The child has nightmares or night terrors.

- Bodily functions are not working properly—the child may have trouble with feeding, be constipated, have diarrhea, be unable to sleep or relax, or want to sleep all the time.
- The child self-stimulates constantly (e.g., rocking back and forth, thumb sucking, **self-pleasuring**).
- The child's overall behaviour suddenly changes drastically (e.g., becomes very aggressive or withdrawn).
- The child's development regresses.
- The child is hypervigilant and lives in a state of anxious readiness.

Suggestions for Reducing Children's Stress

Supporting children in their coping with their stress—helping them develop healthy ways to cope with what is usually normal stress—is one of the educators' roles in promoting the child's emotional well-being. Developing coping skills contributes to children's self-control and feelings of self-worth. Although we tend to think of stress as primarily affecting emotional health, educators should help children become aware of the mind–body–emotion interconnection whenever possible, as there are many physiological connections as well.

Help children develop coping skills by responding to needs and cues (e.g., comfort a distressed infant as promptly as possible, respect a toddler's need to try a task independently, offer a preschooler a choice whenever possible, provide a school-ager with opportunities for decision making without adult interference).

Asking a school-ager who has started biting his or her nails lately what the child is thinking and feeling at that moment can help make this connection.

To reduce overall stress for the children in their program, educators can implement a number of strategies to create a **"stress-aware" environment**. Here are some of those strategies:

- Provide a secure, calm environment in which schedules, routines, and transitions contribute to stability, not to heightened stress. Do what you can behind the scenes to reduce stress.
- Maintain an emotional climate of trust. Children will feel that they can express a range of emotions and be supported.
- Be calm and provide security for children.
- Recognize and respond to children's feelings, taking your cues from the child.
- Create a curriculum that supports the development of children's learning about self—feelings, rights, and responsibilities.
- Honour children's right to participate. Ensure that each child's voice is being heard so that children can express their views according to their developing capacities. This supports the UN Convention on the Rights of the Child.

Equally important, it helps reduce stress for the child because it contributes to a sense of control.

- Create developmentally appropriate stimulus shelters where a child can choose to be away from the group (e.g., pillows in a cozy corner for infants and toddlers, lofts or tents for preschoolers and school-agers).

- Evaluate the level of stimulation. Remember that some children are very much affected by sensory stimulation. For example:
  - Is the environment too busy and disordered, which can contribute to unfocused play, or uncluttered and organized, to help children feel in control?
  - Is the noise level conducive to focused play? Are there quiet times during the day to encourage calmness?
  - Is music playing, and, when it's playing, does the music fit the mood of the room?
  - Is the lighting natural and adequate or artificial and inadequate?

Helping infants and toddlers start to learn they can reduce their own stress levels usually means comforting them, but it also means helping them find ways to comfort themselves, identifying for them what they are experiencing, and guiding them to activities that help them work out some of their anger or frustration (e.g., large motor activities, water and sand play). With preschool and school-age children, educators can help them identify the "inside and outside" body cues for their stressful feelings and suggest ways in which they can alleviate those feelings now and in the future. As children learn about what makes them feel stressed and how they react, they learn a lot about themselves that will be beneficial in the long term.

Some older children may express their fears about terrorist attacks or armed conflicts (i.e., war). The following list of suggestions may help children process these fears. These strategies are similar to those used by parents and educators when helping children deal with other types of fears:

- Reassure children that they are safe, that you will protect them from danger, and that you will continue to help them when they feel afraid, sad, etc. If what is happening is in a far-off location, identify where we are on the globe or map compared with the geographic location of the conflict they fear.

- Know that reactions are usually short term.

- Take the time to listen actively.

- Answer questions as well as you can, but don't make promises you can't keep.

- Take their fears seriously; never ridicule or belittle children's fears.

- Be a role model. Share feelings and appropriate ways in which you cope with feelings.

Here are some examples of coping strategies that educators can help children develop:

- deep, slow breathing to help slow down the body

- stretching exercises (e.g., tensing and relaxing muscles), which can be incorporated into a creative movement activity for preschoolers (e.g., jungle animals), or relaxation exercises, which use imagery (e.g., the children lie down with eyes closed and an educator takes them on an imaginary journey)

- discussions in small groups, in which the children are asked what they would do if a big dog came up to them, if they got lost, or if they smelled smoke in their bedroom. Helping children think of options encourages them to participate in overcoming or managing fears. Note that such discussions would be inappropriate if any child in the group had an intense fear of dogs or fire; in that case, a one-to-one conversation with that child would help gauge her or his reactions.

- helping individual children identify what is a stress release for them. Some need vigorous physical activity, others prefer time alone looking at books or listening to music, and others may need to pound clay.

- asking children to identify what causes their stress and what they can do to prevent a reaction (e.g., remove themselves from a stressful situation if possible, think about something else)

- resolving conflict—much of school-agers' stress, in particular, is related to interaction with peers. Supporting children in learning to negotiate and ensuring that there are consistent expectations for managing conflict in the program help children build conflict resolution skills.

Terry Orlick's *Feeling Great: Teaching Children to Excel at Living* has more than 100 activities designed to help children cope effectively with stress (see Resource Materials, page 562).

Helping Specific Children

Educators create a stress-aware environment for all the children, but there are times when an individual child needs extra support because stress is affecting her or him significantly. Educators use their observation skills to identify signs and possible stress factors. The director may also be involved, and certainly parents are fully involved, unless there is a strong suspicion of child abuse.

The example below highlights the benefits of program involvement with parents in managing children's stress factors that may be developmentally based and, it is hoped, short term.

When children's stress is due to a very serious or long-term factor such as child abuse, the death of a parent, or an experience as a refugee, educators will likely need to collaborate with others in ensuring that the child receives consistent support. Other agencies may be involved, and educators may be given recommendations from play therapists or other developmental specialists and counselling services.

Some stressors may need additional help for some children and not for others, depending on aspects such as the complexity of the issue and, of course, how it is affecting the child. *For example, divorce may result in minimal or drastic changes to the child's everyday life situation.* Bullying, now recognized as a critical public health issue in many countries, including Canada, can lead to serious and lasting harm. Children

When children's stress reactions are developmentally based, educators and parents are often able to support children through this process in a positive way. Here is an example of a preschooler who expresses his fear of doctors and hospitals and how educators offer support along with his family:

- Desmond is four years old. He has always been afraid of the doctor's office, mainly because of the immunization shots that he hates so much. Next month, he is to be hospitalized to have minor surgery. His mother, Lorna, tells you that he is terrified. His stress is evident in the program as well as at home. He is not sleeping well and is having recurring nightmares. At the program, he can't lie still to rest, although he is obviously tired and irritable. Desmond is usually quite involved in play—able to concentrate for periods of time at the blocks and in dramatic play. Lately he flits around aimlessly, unless an educator spends one-to-one time with him.

Lorna and Desmond's educators have decided to try to help Desmond in the weeks leading up to the surgery in a number of ways:

- Desmond and Lorna are scheduled to take the guided tour of the hospital, which is designed for children about to have surgery. The goal of these tours is to decrease children's anxiety about the unknown, including the operating room, the playroom, and their own room.

- Educators will be particularly sensitive to providing Desmond with one-to-one time whenever possible, reading books and encouraging him to discuss his feelings when he is comfortable.

- Because Desmond enjoys dramatic play, the educators have set up this area as a hospital. The setting encourages him to act out his feelings and experiences. Since children tend to play about what they already know, the educators realize that his most meaningful play will be after the surgery. However, it is helpful for Desmond to handle the medical instruments and for educators to listen to his fears. He hasn't been able to articulate those fears when asked, but he does in the context of play with dolls.

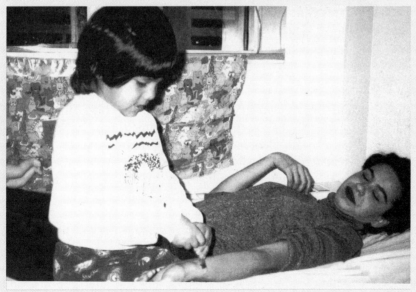

(continued)

Desmond is worried that when he is in the hospital the doctor will remove a leg or an arm rather than just perform the minor surgery. He's afraid that the doctor is mad at him because he always cries when he gets his shots. He's afraid he is going to be punished. This is helpful information to share with Lorna, because until now she thought his only fear was that she was going to leave him in the hospital. During the hospital tour, Lorna focuses her questions on issues that help reduce Desmond's fears.

- She finds out that she can stay in the hospital room with him.
- In the children's playroom, Desmond talks with two children who had minor surgeries and sees that they have both arms and legs.

After the visit, Desmond is more focused at the program. Although he is still stressed, he's playing with other children again and isn't as hesitant to voice his fears. He isn't crying as much or talking about cutting off arms during play in the hospital play area. Lorna says that Desmond is sleeping better and has had only two nightmares.

The day of surgery arrives. When the doctor comes in to see Desmond, she assures him that she will only fix what she said she would and that he has done nothing wrong. When Clarissa, an educator, comes to visit with two of Desmond's friends from the early childhood program the day after surgery, he is happy to see them and shows them his room and the playroom before checking out of the hospital. Within a week of his return to the program, Desmond seems to be back to his old self, proudly showing the pictures that his mother took at the hospital. Lorna isn't anticipating that he will love the doctor from now on, but she believes that the preparation and positive hospital experience alleviated Desmond's stress and fear. Educators observe a change in his dramatic play, which reflects Desmond's positive experience and ability to cope with this fear.

as young as early school age can be the victims and/or perpetrators, especially when we consider that bullying has now been defined as encompassing four categories: physical, verbal, relational, and cyberbullying (Canadian Council on Learning, 2008). As with all concerns, educators need to remember the scope and limits of their responsibility in supporting children's development, identifying when children need further help, and working with parents and other professionals in seeking that help.

Sexuality

"Canada is a pluralistic society in which different people have different values and perspectives towards human sexuality. At the same time, Canadians are united by their respect for basic democratic values" (Sex Information and Education Council of Canada 2004, 2). The interplay of these two realities requires that democratic values are upheld in policies and practices, while recognizing the rights of individuals in upholding their cultural values as long as these respect human rights and freedoms.

Sexuality is part of all of us, regardless of our age. Yet this topic often makes adults feel uncomfortable because they may be hesitant to acknowledge young children's sexuality. Young children's sexual feelings provide sensory pleasure, but without the erotic overtones that develop during and after puberty. Children's sexuality is an integral part of growth and development.

When children touch or stimulate their genitals in some way, it is often termed self-pleasuring or self-stimulation. Masturbation is an act of stimulating oneself to reach orgasm. Touching oneself for pleasure is a normal and natural behaviour, and in keeping with this positive view, we use the term "self-pleasuring" in this textbook. In fact, self-pleasuring more closely describes the child's intent. The word "masturbation" may evoke negative feelings for some adults due to taboos or messages learned as they were growing up. Self-pleasuring is a healthy behaviour for children unless it becomes the focus and interferes with the child's involvement in activities. When you observe children self-pleasuring, your reaction should be to help children learn social parameters, as with all behaviour. Acknowledge the child's pleasure and help him or her regard it as private, to be performed when alone. If children feel shame or embarrassment for normal, curious, or stimulating behaviour, this negativity about sexual matters may stay with them.

Developing Human Sexuality

With knowledge of child development, educators are able to predict the normal patterns of sexual behaviour and are prepared for and respond calmly to them.

Infants:

- Early experiences with sucking and being held, rocked, and cradled provide a foundation that fosters positive feelings toward self and relationships.
- Touching or fondling the genitals when the diaper is off is normal as infants explore all parts of their body.
- Activities such as bouncing, swinging, and jumping may produce sexual pleasure; boys may have an erection, and girls may have vaginal secretions, although they are less noticeable.

Toddlers:

In addition to the experiences and activities listed above for infants,

- they learn words for private body parts and toileting, and
- they have increased interest in others' genitals, an interest heightened by learning to use the toilet.

Preschoolers:

- They have concerns about their genitals. Boys might worry about their penis falling off, or girls might wonder why they don't have a penis. If they tell an educator of their concern, children must be reassured and not teased. Boys need to know that their penis won't fall off, and girls need to know that they have all their sexual parts, some of which are inside their body and not as obvious as boys' genitals. The following are typical preschooler behaviour:
- They self-pleasure or explore their genitals.
- They observe each other during washroom routines.
- They may sex-play, including "You Show Me and I'll Show You" and "Doctor" and so on.

- They question educators about how their body works, where babies come from, why those two dogs in the park are stuck together (i.e., mating), why girls and boys are different, and so on.

School-Agers:

- They may sex-play.
- They possibly self-pleasure in public, although most school-agers understand privacy rules.
- They use slang or swearwords for private parts, sexual acts, or sexual orientation.
- They ask educators questions similar to those that preschoolers ask but are somewhat more sophisticated (e.g., "How do babies get into a uterus?" or "What are those animals doing?"). Questions such as "What does homosexual mean?" and "How do people get AIDS?" or those related to puberty (e.g., "When will I get hair down there?") are common. ECE students and educators should also be prepared for personal questions from school-age children, such as "Do you have sex with your boyfriend?" These questions are personal. You should feel confident in responding respectfully by saying that this is a personal question and that you will not answer a question that is private. By asking questions, children learn which questions are private and which we will answer. Here again, educators help children learn social skills. A positive tone is important to ensure that children know they haven't done anything "wrong" by simply asking a question.

Knowledge Promotes Healthy Attitudes

Knowing about sex does not encourage children to become sexually active too early. Of course, this doesn't mean that four- or five-year-olds are interested in sexual intercourse or should be taught about it. A five-year-old may have an idea that a man and a woman rub bodies (and may even play this out with a partner in dramatic play with clothes on). However, the child probably does not understand the specifics of intercourse, and if he or she does, the educators should explore the possibility of sexual abuse. Educators should be prepared to discuss anatomical facts related to gender identity and sexual differences. Adults' comfort level concerning sexuality may reduce children's anxiety about this topic. However, developing a common approach to this topic is difficult because of differences in opinion.

Educators should not offer their opinion on sexual intercourse outside of marriage. It is the family's right to convey their moral beliefs. Educators must try not to be judgmental about family beliefs and teachings. However, if there is concern that the child is being physically, emotionally, or sexually abused as a result of the family's sexual mores, educators cannot ignore this possibility and must explore it further.

Around two years of age, children begin to be interested in parts of the body—both theirs and those of the opposite sex. Giving nicknames to genitals rather than the anatomically correct term, or discouraging children from mentioning these body parts, leads to confusion later. When children hear another child or adult call a penis a "wee-wee," they begin to assume that there is something wrong with using the word "penis," although it's acceptable to use the correct names for other body parts. The same confusing message is learned by infants. Adults smile at them when they play with their toes but slap them or say no when they touch their genitals. If these messages are reinforced as children grow, they will view self-pleasuring and their genitals as bad or dirty.

Preschoolers and young school-agers between the ages of three and eight may be eager to explore similarities and differences in their bodies with peers. Sexual games such as "Doctor" or "You Show Me and I'll Show You," often while playing "House," are motivated by natural curiosity, not by erotic drive. Although these games are predictable and part of development, adults often overreact to them.

For preschoolers, one of the important aspects of their emerging sense of self is awareness of their gender. Around age four or five, many focus on gender stereotypes, much to the chagrin of parents and educators who foster less rigid roles for males and females. When children reach the school-age years, many are naturally drawn to stereotypes in clothing, hairstyles, toys, and play behaviour. They also observe and experience gender stereotypes around them. Without devaluing individual children's interests and inclinations, educators must give the same kind of care and attention to girls as to boys and continue to offer them the same range of choices. Ongoing commitment to a nonsexist approach in the program helps counteract the gender stereotypes that children face in society. Adapting to a stereotype is harmful because it replaces behaving in accordance with your own personal identity with behaving in accordance with expectations of how you should behave.

A relatively common stereotype is that boys should not cry. This may result in a boy's reluctance to talk to anyone about what is worrying him for fear that he will cry. This can negatively affect his long-term emotional health.

Parents' Perspectives on Children's Sexuality

We have made some strong comments in this textbook on the advantages of direct communication about children's sexuality. Just as it is important to acknowledge parents' views on issues such as guidance, illness, and safety, the same principle applies to sexuality. Some parents may not agree with this open approach, and educators must respect their position, as parents and guardians are the primary and important source of sexual health education. So how do educators handle situations in which a child's sexual question or behaviour is one that you know the parent discourages or forbids?

First, educators need to come to an agreement among themselves on how they approach sexual questions and behaviour. This type of discussion provides opportunities for staff to talk about differences of opinion. Staff may benefit from additional postdiploma training (in-service) or consultation with a sexual health educator, often affiliated with the local public health agency. Libraries, too, provide educational materials. Some adults grew up with negative feelings or attitudes about bodies and sexuality. Some have values based on religious or ethnocultural beliefs about sexuality or sex roles. Although you must respect these views, it is inappropriate for a professional working with children to impart them to children.

- John believes that children should not touch or stimulate their genitals under any circumstances. He recognizes that he needs to explore why he feels this way. Meanwhile, he knows that he must avoid reacting negatively to children's self-pleasuring.

- A child asks how babies are born. Madeline is tempted to answer, "A stork drops them from the sky." Madeline must recognize that giving children false information is not helpful. The child will eventually find out that she wasn't telling the truth. Older children already have some idea and may be testing their educator's honesty.

Second, programs' policies on child guidance and curriculum should clarify staffs' commitment to answering children's questions, including ones of a sexual nature. Written information that educators develop for parents should mention that children's awareness of self, others, and the world is part of the ongoing curriculum. To avoid misunderstanding, include examples such as "We use anatomically correct names for all parts of the body" and "A preschooler who is exploring his or her genitals is redirected if this occurs in a social situation. The child is reminded that this is a private activity, which is acceptable at nap time."

Third, meeting with the parents at the time of enrollment allows the director to raise this issue and discuss the parents' views and how they wish to handle their child's questions. Differences of opinion may arise, and in those cases, a workable and practical compromise can be reached. In the future, if a sexuality issue arises that is relevant to all parents, it would be beneficial to have a parent meeting facilitated by a sexual health educator (or other expert).

Some children have shown a keen interest in playing "Doctor," and parents have concerns that individual children may be hurt either physically or emotionally. At a parent meeting, a staff person outlines how educators manage these situations in the program:

- The children are clearly told that their individual rights are to be respected and that no one has a right to touch them in a way that makes them feel uncomfortable. They are also not permitted to touch another person against that person's wishes. This rule applies at all times, whether it concerns aggressive behaviour (e.g., hitting, pushing) or sexual behaviour (e.g., kissing, touching private body parts).

- No child is permitted under any circumstances to insert parts of the body (e.g., fingers) or other objects into any part of another child's body.

- If one child is being forced to play "Doctor" against her or his wishes, the children are reminded of individual rights and the importance of respecting those rights. If children are discovered playing "Doctor" (e.g., with clothes off), the educator responds by calmly instructing children to put their clothes on and redirecting their play to another area (i.e., the rule is that children keep their clothes on at the program).

The sexual health educator facilitates a discussion to identify concerns and issues that need to be addressed. Changes in a program's policy or practices may be required.

Role of Educators as Sex Educators

Parents are the primary sexual health educators in children's lives. But educators too have a significant role to play as sex educators, whether they are aware of it or not. How? Children are constantly learning about their sexuality by

- listening to adults and other children,
- observing the way adults interact with each other and react to events and comments,
- absorbing attitudes that are communicated in adult conversation and action, and
- interacting with adults and other children.

In other words, educators are teaching about sexuality simply by the way they act, their body language, what they say, and what they don't say.

A school-age girl is looking at a magazine that has a picture of a girl about the same age posing in a way that looks seductive. The educator who remarks, "Isn't she gorgeous?" is teaching something different from the educator who asks, "What do you think of this advertisement?" The question may initiate a conversation between the girl and the educator about how advertisers use children in inappropriate ways and how they affect the way that girls and boys view females.

Educators contribute to children's sexual learning in a number of ways:

- They contribute to children's positive body image and self-worth by helping them feel proud and in control of their body.
- They help children value themselves as female or male by using implicit and explicit messages about real similarities and differences and celebrating these similarities and differences.
- They encourage knowledgeable and responsible behaviour by being informed about sexuality, answering questions simply and honestly, and responding gently to normal, curious sexual behaviour—while at the same time setting clear limits that help children learn about boundaries.
- They serve as role models by helping children understand acceptable and unacceptable private and public behaviour.

- They help protect children from exploitation or sexual abuse by teaching pre-school and school-age children about the idea of privacy and about private body parts and by teaching that sexual touching between children and adults is inappropriate (Brick et al., 2008, p. 2).

Body Image

Body image is defined as the "mental picture" someone has of her or his body and one's thoughts and feelings about that picture (Peel Public Health, 2007). Over the past couple of generations in North America, body image and self-esteem have seemed to be entangled in a "tug-of-war." One of the roles of parents and educators as sex educators is to support children's positive body image, which, it is hoped, will influence their development into later childhood and beyond.

Think about your body image as defined above. Is it positive? If not, reflect on your own attitudes about weight and shape and how these can shift to promote your own body image. Granted, many of the obstacles to positive body image are the messages we are inundated with in a society obsessed with a narrow definition of beauty, as well as excessive value placed on attractiveness in this narrow view. In the real world, people come in many shapes, sizes, colours, and abilities. Images in the media are altered in many ways to make the models "appear" perfect. Educators can do their best to counteract this focus on looks by commenting on children's strengths and attempts, not their looks. *For example, "Ali, you run so fast" instead of "Ali, you look so pretty in that outfit" or "Ramon, your drawing includes such an interesting variety of colours" instead of "Ramon, your hair looks perfect today."* Ensure that children are valued for qualities (having a great imagination, being a good listener to friends, problem-solving abilities, etc.) rather than body size and appearance.

Children's Questions about Sexuality

Questions about sexuality emerge from children as they become interested. Sexuality, like any other aspect of what is going on inside and around children, is something they naturally want to know about—their body, how it works, and sex. Be sensitive and follow the child's lead. Remember, the story unfolds for children over many years, along with their cognitive development. It is inappropriate to provide a long, detailed explanation that holds more information than the child wants or needs. Even for many older school-agers, the whole idea of sex can sound disgusting (Greenspan, 1993, p. 240). Many children ask questions when you least expect them. Don't be surprised when at times you feel uncomfortable with a question or panicky at the prospect of answering it. Many educators feel this way. Part of this reaction stems from the fact that you aren't the child's parent and want to avoid saying anything that contradicts what the parents have told, or will tell, their child.

Often a simple answer is all the younger child wants or needs. If he asks, "What are those two dogs doing?" you could answer, "The dogs are making puppies." Remember three key points when answering children's questions at any age:

1. Be sure you understand what it is the child wants to know. For example, when Chantal asks, "Where did I come from?" she might not be interested in the sexual act but rather what city or country she originated from or that she came from her mother's uterus.

2. Find out what the child already knows. For example, ask Chantal, "Where do you think you came from?" This will help you clarify what she is actually asking and what she already knows.

3. If you can't answer immediately, be sure to get back to the child soon.

CRITICAL THINKING

An ECE student who is pregnant is approached by an eight-year-old boy who asks, "How did you get pregnant? Were you raped?" The student responds angrily, "That's not a very nice question. Do you know you could hurt someone's feelings by asking that?" How would you respond?

Sexual orientation, like race, gender, class, and religion, is part of an individual's identity and must be respected as such. When children ask what the words "gay," "homosexual," or "lesbian" mean, or when they use derogatory names for sexual orientation to name-call, this is a very important learning moment. Some children may be part of a family with gay parents or be friends with someone who has gay parents. However, even these children may use negative remarks or stereotypes based on a lack of knowledge or misconceptions due to overwhelming stereotypes.

The scenario below occurred between a four-year-old and a five-year-old on a walk in the early childhood program's neighbourhood:

Child 1: "Why are those two men holding hands?"

Child 2: "They're probably gay."

Child 1: "What does gay mean?"

Child 2: "I don't know how to explain it. Let's ask the teacher."

Our classroom's book shelf, for instance, was well-stocked with stories about diverse family forms or tales whose primary characters were gay or lesbian themselves. Of these titles, I used a classroom favourite ("Daddy's Roommate") to offer an age-appropriate definition of 'gay.' According to one of the story's main characters, "Gay is another kind of love. And love is the best kind of happiness." To elaborate further on this definition, it was explained to the children that gay is when a man loves a man or a woman loves a woman. Opportunities for further questions were offered but this experience ulti-mately seemed to resolve the initial curiosity expressed on the neighbourhood walk. (Campbell cited in Janmohamed, 2006, pp. 20–21)

Source: *Building bridges: Lesbian, Bay, Bisexual, Transgender, Transsexual and Queer Families in Early Childhood Education* by Zeenat Janmohamed. Toronto Coalition For Better Child Care, 2006, 20. Reprinted with permission.

For most children, it is not the homosexual or heterosexual sex act that they generally want to know about but the importance of different kinds of families and relationships. What is important for adults to focus on is the caring part of the relationship in all family structures. *For example, other children may ask a child whose parents are lesbian, "Who is your real mom?" If the child being asked is upset with the question or unsure how to answer, the educator can say that both his moms are real and that both of them are there to love and care for him as he grows up. Similarly, for a child who is adopted, regardless of parents' sexual orientation, we would respond that the "real mom" is the mom who is there for the child growing up, and the "birth mom" is the woman who carried the baby in her uterus and birthed the baby.*

Gay families are much the same as any other family! The legalization of same-sex marriages in Canada (July 2005) supports this fact. In many centres, there are parents or coworkers who are lesbian, gay, bisexual, or transgendered. They may have "come out" or possibly have not. There will also be children whom we are caring for now in programs who will become aware of their lesbian or gay sexual orientation as they get older. Most individuals who are homosexual were raised by heterosexual parents, and the children of most lesbian and gay parents grow up to have heterosexual orientation. "The psychosocial research into lesbian and gay parenting indicates that there are essentially no differences in the psychosocial development, gender identity or sexual orientation between the children of gay or lesbian parents and the children of heterosexual parents" (Canadian Psychological Association, 2003, p. 1). Perhaps this reality helps highlight the importance of educators' attitudes in acknowledging families with same-sex parents as we do single parents, stepparents, blended families, grandparents bringing up their grandchildren, and so on. This is as integral a part of a child's identity as his or her race, religion, and socioeconomic level.

Older children are bombarded by stereotypes from the media and possibly from adults in their lives. They may repeat some of what they've heard. They may ask more direct questions such as "How do you get to be gay?" To respond appropriately to children's questions, comments, and behaviour, educators need to explore their attitudes and knowledge about homosexuality. People who hold negative attitudes about a sexual orientation that is different from their own must recognize that this bias is discriminatory. Discrimination perpetuates unjust treatment of individuals based on their identity. Although educators may not agree with someone's sexual practice (just as they may disagree with some religious beliefs), they must tolerate diversity. Children and parents need to be accepted and supported as families, and if educators are either subtly or overtly disapproving, they are not contributing to emotional health. Educators can seek out community resources to help them understand more about homosexuality and gay families.

RHYTHM OF THE PROGRAM

The rhythm of a program refers to the pace of daily routines and activities. Establishing a rhythm that respects and responds to the children is an educator's daily role, beginning with greeting and talking with parents and children at drop-off. The rhythm is influenced by the ages of the children and other factors, such as group size, ratios, interests of the children, time of day, weather, space available, mood of the group, and individual children. Adequate opportunities for physical activity, cognitive stimulation, and nutrition must be balanced with opportunities for rest and relaxation. Children of all ages need opportunities to reduce stimulation and stress. Respect for individual children is paramount in planning and carrying out the day's activities, as some children need more opportunity for downtime. This unit includes a discussion of the need for rest and relaxation. The need for physical activity is discussed in Unit 6, and nutritional needs are discussed in Unit 5.

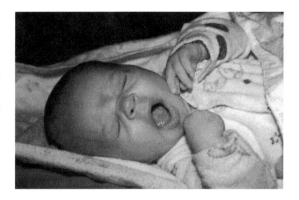

The Need for Rest and Relaxation

Napping or resting is an issue that arises in every program and with every age group. Educators balance the needs of the group with those of the individual. This requires acknowledging the limitations of group care while recognizing and carrying through with practices and routines that endorse the child's uniqueness. When this is not done, children may be negatively affected. For example,

- they may not get the rest they need;
- they may be forced to comply with rigid rules, such as lying on a cot for over an hour even if they don't need to nap; and
- they may be involved in a lose–lose situation, with the child and the educator developing unhappy relationships around routines such as napping or resting.

It is evident, then, that even with a physical need such as rest, emotional and social needs are interrelated.

Opportunities for rest and relaxation take into account the developmental and individual needs of children in the group:

- Infants follow their own individual nap schedules, which should be somewhat consistent with nap times at home.
- Some toddlers may need only one nap, whereas others need two. While the latter group naps, the other will need physical areas and opportunities to do quiet, relaxing, less stimulating things (e.g., being read to, working at puzzles).
- Preschoolers, especially older ones, don't require a nap any longer but still need to slow down and rest. They are only expected to lie on cots for a half-hour, and then they can get up and do quiet activities. However, even some older preschoolers need nap time, and provisions should be made for this.
- School-agers are provided with comfortable furniture or spaces where they can wind down or do quiet activities, if they would like to, after school.

Massage has gained recognition as an effective relaxation technique. But there are differing opinions on the appropriateness of infant massage in programs. Some people believe that massage can be soothing or stimulating for infants and involves caring touch. Others believe that infant massage is an intimate practice that should be done only by parents (if they choose). Some infants enjoy being massaged. Others are not comfortable with a tactile approach and show signs of distress. When an infant is obviously not relaxing or enjoying it, the educator must stop the massage. Not stopping indicates a lack of respect for the infant's physical and emotional needs. Educators who practise infant massage recognize the importance of following infants' cues and should seek training from appropriate resources in the community and obtain the parents' permission.

The need for rest and relaxation must be balanced with the need for physical activity. *Canada's Physical Activity Guide for Children* calls parents, educators, physicians, and community leaders to action to support children's daily active time (see Appendix 6.1, page 352). You know the reasons behind this call to action, which are outlined in detail in Unit 6. As a reminder, educators who model a physically active lifestyle contribute to the children's interest in activity. When educators participate with children and observe them in active play, they use their observations to design the environment and to facilitate so that children can challenge themselves and enjoy all the benefits of daily physically active play.

OBJECTIVES

To identify and describe four factors that influence children's understanding of health.

To discuss the guidelines in developing an appropriate health curriculum and identifying inappropriate practices.

HEALTH CURRICULUM

As with all aspects of the curriculum, the **health curriculum** should be designed using this principle: curriculum design requires that teachers identify the play and learning priorities for the young children in the program. In this step, teachers rely on information about individual children based on their observation and assessment of children's developmental levels and needs (Shipley, 2008) and cultural context. In other words, children's health education should be integrated into the program in ways that relate to these needs and interests.

Children's Understanding of Health

Children's understanding of health is influenced by the interaction of a number of factors:

- stage of cognitive development and temperament
- family and cultural context (i.e., cultural identity, socioeconomic circumstances, parenting styles)
- peers, their community, and the media

Cognitive Development

Young children's growing cognitive abilities affect what and how they think about health, prevention, and health promotion. Combining Piaget's theory of cognitive development and Natapoff's research on children's understanding of health, Table 9.2 provides examples of how children perceive concepts of health and prevention at each level. The term "prevention," for example, assumes an understanding of future and causality—actions that you take today can affect your health in 20 years. Does a three-, five-, or seven-year-old understand this concept? No. To fully understand and talk about these and other concepts, we have to reach Piaget's formal operational level in our cognitive development (at about age 12). Does that mean that teaching young children about health is pointless? No. It means that the health curriculum, to be relevant, should be based on children's cognitive abilities. Content that fits children's ability to process information is more likely to have a positive effect on long-term health behaviour (Natapoff, 1982).

Appropriate health education focuses on what children want and need now, not on what they'll need in future. In a study in which four- and five-year-olds were interviewed in a preschool setting, the results revealed that young children's understanding of health was largely related to their ability to perform activities and participate in a supportive, everyday context (Almqvist, Stefansson, & Granlund, 2006).

Explaining to Jamie, a preschooler, that if he brushes his teeth every day they will be healthy in 20 years is too abstract.

Memorizing rules is fairly easy for children. Yet we can't assume that when Jamie repeats "Brushing my teeth every day will keep them healthy in 20 years," he fully understands what he has said. For him, 20 years from now holds no meaning. It makes more sense to Jamie if we relate health education to his everyday life.

Brushing your teeth takes all the sticky food off your teeth so you won't get cavities (or a hole in the tooth). Brushing cleans your mouth and makes it smell good, too.

Cognitive development is a natural process. We can no more speed up its progress than we can speed up physical development and get a two-month-old to sit up independently. A comparison of five studies that set out to determine whether

OBJECTIVES

To identify developmental health needs and interests for each age group.

To offer suggestions for integrating the health curriculum in each age group on topics such as environmental education, dental health education, and hand washing and germs.

To identify the who, what, when, where, and why of cooking with children.

To discuss how educators promote dental health with each age group.

TABLE 9.2 Cognitive Understanding of Health

CONCEPT	SENSORIMOTOR: BIRTH TO 2 YEARS	PREOPERATIONAL: 2 TO 7 YEARS	CONCRETE OPERATIONAL: 7 TO 11 YEARS
Health	■ Concept too abstract for a pre-symbolic child. Groundwork is laid for later cognitive stages through child's experiences of healthy environments.	■ Only the physical dimension of health ■ Egocentric (e.g., if candy makes me feel good, it must be good for me) ■ Can't focus on the whole and the part at the same time; e.g., child believes that someone with a Band-Aid on the knee is not healthy (the physical signs of injury or illness are less of an abstract concept)	■ Beginning awareness of health as more than a physical dimension (e.g., understanding that emotional stress can cause physical symptoms) ■ Has conservation—believes it's possible to be partly healthy and partly not healthy (e.g., realizes that the child is still healthy even with a sprained ankle)
Causality	■ Too abstract—repeated experiences with cause and effect will contribute to development in this realm	■ Has "magical thinking" and is intuitive rather than logical—sometimes unrelated practices are thought to affect health or illness (e.g., child believes that getting sick must have been a result of misbehaviour—"Why did Rena give me chickenpox? I wasn't mean to her.")	■ Has cause-and-effect reasoning—understands that certain actions or inactions can affect health (e.g., eating breakfast helps you concentrate at school)
Time	■ Too abstract—consistent daily routines provide some predictability in their day (e.g., toddlers know that after lunch they will have a nap; they understand sequence)	■ Present oriented—here-and-now orientation; does not have an understanding of the future	■ Still present oriented ■ Has reversibility, enabling child to think through a chain of events and back—important in beginning to see more long-term orientation to health
Body	■ Beginning awareness of body parts will contribute to later stages	■ Has some body awareness but not a holistic view of how systems interrelate ■ Perceptually bound ■ Developing an awareness of body cues	■ More aware of the body and mind and how they work together ■ Beginning awareness of body cues (e.g., child with asthma recognizes early symptoms of an episode and by acting on these cues takes medication)

preschoolers understand a biological germ theory of illness concluded that they do not. Most children in the studies did not link the origin of a symptom (the germ) to transmission. A few children reasoned that certain kinds of symptoms are contagious (e.g., all tummyaches are contagious). These answers followed the adults reading storybooks about children getting sick (Solomon & Cassimatis, 1999).

Learning is an interactive process, and children's exploration and interaction enhance their development. Using the concept of the body as an example, educators can provide experiences, materials, and questions that promote children's learning. Children build on their experiences. During diaper changes, educators can talk to infants about their tummy, knees, and toes and ask them to help lift their bottom to take off the diaper. Toddlers are learning the names and locations of body parts and beginning to identify feelings. Educators help preschoolers progress in their understanding of the body by asking them questions such as "How do you know when you are tired (or hungry, afraid, sick, happy)?" Educators can thus encourage children to become more aware of concrete body cues. School-agers begin to understand how the internal circulatory, digestive, and other systems work.

Temperament

The sequence of development is similar for children, although temperaments are unique. Temperament is generally considered to refer to characteristic patterns of emotional reactions and emotional self-regulation. Biological characteristics influence behaviour very early in life. Renowned psychologist Jerome Kagan studied shyness in children for many years. He believes that approximately 20% of infants are born with an inhibited temperament. By two months old, these infants show sensitivity to unfamiliar stimuli, such as strangers and loud noises. Their anxiety is apparent in louder crying and a faster heart rate (Kagan, 2001, p. 25). Often such behaviour begins to be labelled as shyness as the child grows older. Shyness doesn't always mean that the child is more anxious than a more outgoing child. However, anxiety in a child is an important consideration because temperament has an effect on the child's understanding and view of health.

Irena's parents let her walk to the corner store by herself. She feels proud, excited, and independent. On the other hand, her older sister Thea is relieved now that Irena can go to the store when the family needs milk or bread. She has always felt anxious about going because she worries about all the things that could go wrong (e.g., she could trip and fall, not have enough money, be hit by a car, be approached by a stranger).

Thea has an inhibited temperament compared with her sister. She views many of life's challenges as risky and threatening, whereas Irena sees challenges as positive and exciting. People's temperaments are on a continuum, with those more fearful on one end and those who believe they are invincible on the other. Of course, feeling invincible can also be influenced by development. As we noted in Unit 7, young children may not as yet understand the risks involved in their activity. A preschool child cannot estimate how long it will take a moving vehicle to reach the child's location and therefore may take undue risks, such as running across a street to retrieve a ball. When developing and implementing a health curriculum, educators need to consider the range of temperaments in their group. Remember that increasing children's anxiety or feelings of vulnerability to encourage them to take positive health action has serious ethical questions. We must be careful not to raise anxiety levels in children, because increased stress for children does not mean increased health, as discussed earlier.

Educators are planning to teach children to be cautious about crossing streets, ingesting poisons, or approaching animals by focusing on all the dangers. Educators are concerned about some of the children who feel invincible. Although their approach may have a positive effect on the safety behaviour of some children, it may have a negative effect on those who worry. Their fears about crossing streets, exploring new things, or approaching animals are intensified. This negates children's confidence in striving toward self-care.

The Family and Cultural Context

Family is an essential connection to children's identity. The connection between children and their families is a powerful one that has a significant effect on their understanding of health. Members of various ethnocultural groups connect the cause of disease, to varying degrees, to certain theories, such as the imbalance of hot and cold in the body, spiritual or supernatural powers, or magic (e.g., the evil eye causing fever, vomiting, or diarrhea). Illness may be viewed as an invasion of body, mind, soul, and spirit (Waxler-Morrison, Anderson, & Richardson, 1990). A family's health beliefs and practices may be effective in maintaining the health of an individual and his or her family, even if these practices are not based on contemporary medical theories. In fact, traditional remedies may at times help someone feel better when conventional medicine has failed or has no recommendation.

It is critical that the early childhood program respect the significance and dignity of each family's cultural beliefs and practices. Of course, this must be qualified with regard to concerns that children are being mistreated, malnourished, or neglected in any way by a particular family practice. Remember that culture is a broad term and can be defined by both **"inherited" culture** (i.e., race, ethnicity, language, religion) and **"personal" culture** (i.e., acquired, often reflecting values, attitudes, and ideologies).

Influences that may stem from culture are beliefs about health care professionals (e.g., conventional versus complementary practitioners) and types of treatment (e.g., prescription medicine versus herbs). Clearly, a practice that is unfamiliar to an educator is just that—unfamiliar. In their work with families, educators learn about health beliefs and practices other than those learned in their own families or at school and use this knowledge and experience in health curriculum development. The differences in inherited cultural practices can be overshadowed by socioeconomic factors.

There may be more similarities between the health beliefs or practices of different ethno-cultural groups at the same socio-economic level than there are among the people within the same ethno-cultural groups who are from different socio-economic levels. (Masi, Mensah, & McLeod, 1993, p. 8)

In other words, if you are wealthy, you probably have more in common with others who are wealthy than you do with people who are poor and from your ethnocultural background. The reverse is true also.

Socioeconomic Factors Affecting Well-Being

The socioeconomic gradient in health status has been a pattern for over a century in all industrialized, wealthy societies. This pattern can be stated simply: "From birth to death, higher socio-economic status is related to better academic achievement, lower rates of illness and even lower rates of accidents and suicides" (Bertrand, 2001, p. 4). Children who are poor are likely to be living in unhealthy environments that are beyond their ability to change. Poverty usually means food insecurity, substandard housing (e.g., cold, damp, drafty, crowded) in unsafe areas, inadequate clothing, and no access to safe play and recreation opportunities. These living conditions result in a higher incidence of disease, hospitalization, and deaths due to injuries. Families in poverty rarely see a reason to hope for improvement in their situation.

It is difficult for children to develop a future-oriented attitude toward health (e.g., health prevention) when the world they live in is filled with daily crises (e.g., uncertainty over when they will have food). Children who live in families who are comfortable financially have more reason to believe that they have control over and can affect their health.

Peers, Community, and the Media

As children grow older, the influence of their peers, community, and the media can have either a positive or a negative effect on their health. Sam was eating a variety of nutritious foods until he was six years old; then he told his mom that he could bring in only those foods that his friends approved. Similarly, Olivia stopped washing her hands because it wasn't "cool" with her friends. On the other hand, if peers are excited about healthy habits or have positive views of health, they tend to influence one another positively. Children's willingness to try new foods that peers, possibly from different ethnocultural backgrounds, bring in fosters an openness that promotes health. Friends who are willing to wait while their peers wash their hands are making a statement about health.

The community—neighbourhood, early childhood program, school, recreation centre, place of worship—in which children live also affects their overall well-being and influences their view of health.

Every morning the program's playground is strewn with broken glass and discarded needles, syringes, and condoms from the night before. To date, nothing proactive has been done to change this, and the children are getting the impression that we have to accept the situation.

Children, educators, parents, and the police work together to develop a plan of action that results in changing the situation. Children see firsthand that it is possible to have an impact on our health.

The media influence children's understanding of health and perceptions of what is healthy. This varies with the age of the children and how much television they watch. Children who watch a lot of television and use the Internet regularly are inundated with themes and messages, some of which have negative influences on their understanding of physical, emotional, and social well-being. Parents must take an active role in selecting the types of TV programs, videos, and computer games to which their children are exposed. Whenever possible, parents should interact with them to answer questions, clarify, and ensure that they are getting positive, health-promoting messages.

Developing and Implementing a Health Curriculum

Many of the programs' healthy practices are important for all of us in our everyday lives—hand washing, dental care, healthy eating, physical activity, stress management. The hygiene practices described in Unit 3 are not of particular educational interest to children, even though they have a direct impact on their health (e.g., food storage, sanitation of mouthing toys). Providing a health curriculum in a program is more than occasionally reading a children's book about a health-related issue. Table 9.3 consists of guidelines for appropriate and inappropriate health curricula for children that educators can refer to in evaluating their ongoing curriculum.

CRITICAL THINKING

Your partner in the preschool room uses her Internet search engine on a regular basis for finding curriculum ideas. She has found a theme-based set of activities on learning about germs, all of it focusing on children learning that germs are not visible to the naked eye, they are everywhere, and we must kill them all. What feedback will you offer, and what would you suggest as an alternative?

Health Needs and Interests of Children

Certain health education topics or behaviour are more appropriate to introduce at particular ages and developmental stages. Beginning to learn about germs, for example, makes much more sense to preschoolers than it does to infants. The following discussion is by no means exhaustive, but it indicates typical health areas of need or interest for each age group. Of course, each group of young children in early childhood programs is unique, and these general ideas must be responsive to the group's needs and interests.

Infants and Toddlers
The focus in a health curriculum for infants and toddlers is on adults caring for children's health needs and modelling healthy attitudes and behaviour. Environments that support infants' and toddlers' emotional health and development are ones in

TABLE 9.3   **Developing a Health Curriculum: Guidelines**

APPROPRIATE HEALTH CURRICULUM	
GUIDELINES	**EXAMPLES**
focuses on the children's developmental needs, interests, and level of under-standing	Preschoolers' interest and readiness to learn simple safety rules that can be practised, such as "stay away from matches" or "stop, drop, and roll" if clothes catch fire.
is interactive—children learn best when they interact with people and materials in their environment (play based or fit into their daily lives)	Toddlers are encouraged, but not forced, to try new foods (e.g., pineapple). They can see peers and educators eating the food, hear its name, observe it with their other senses, and have opportunities in the home-living centre to play with lifelike fruit and vegetables. They are learning about the food and are therefore more likely to try it.
acknowledges children's rights through participation	The educator supports the children's ideas for incorporating a safety rule for a new activity according to their developing capaci-ties.
has clear and reasonable objectives for children's learning based on develop-mental areas (cognitive, physical, emo-tional, social)	The primary objective for the preschool cooking experience is to encourage the child to follow a sequence. Secondary objectives include sensory exploration, cause and effect, promoting turn taking, and small-motor skills.
is organized so that much of the health curriculum happens as part of the pro-gram's routines—hand washing, rest and relaxation, physical activity, healthy eating, and so on	Infants' hands are washed by the educator after diapering and before eating; school-agers are encouraged to respond to their body cues, such as needing to rest or drink water after vigorous physical activity.
includes practices modelled by educators	Children see educators washing their hands after helping a child in the washroom and before eating with the children.
fits into the natural daily, weekly, monthly, and seasonal rhythm of the program	From the spring to the fall harvest is an ideal time to learn about growing vegetables and flowers from seeds.
is integrated into all curriculum areas—music, movement, science, literature, and so on	Preschooler body awareness: ■ art—body tracing on paper; children paint in body parts ■ music—songs about bodies ■ creative movement—body games, challenging children to explore their bodies with questions such as "How tall/small can you be?" "How high can you jump?" "How angry/happy can you look?" ■ science—use a magnifying glass to look at skin ■ literature—many children's books (e.g., *The Bare Naked Book*) ■ numeracy—graph particular body characteristics (e.g., skin, hair and eye colour, "inny" or "outy" bellybuttons) by printing names or placing photos of children on paper ■ dramatic play—a full-length mirror

(continued)

TABLE 9.3   Developing a Health Curriculum: Guidelines (*continued*)

APPROPRIATE HEALTH CURRICULUM	
GUIDELINES	**EXAMPLES**
is flexible so that educators can take advantage of teachable moments or one-to-one interactions	Answer a preschooler's question during a food experience (e.g., "Why are vegetables good for me?"); show a toddler how to sneeze into the sleeve after the child has sneezed without covering his or her mouth.
builds self-esteem and competence, moving from simple to complex	Use simple three-step recipe cards for "ants on a log" (celery, cream cheese, raisins), allowing children to feel accomplishment in completing a task independently.
is respectful and inclusive of family beliefs, practices, and situations	A parent regularly comes in and teaches tai chi to the school-age children and educators and discusses its advantages to reduce stress in mind and body.
focuses on the concrete rather than the abstract and on present rather than future health	Say "Physical activity helps your body work better" rather than "Physical activity now lowers your risk of heart disease when you are an adult."
emphasizes all aspects of health so that children begin to develop an awareness of holistic health involving physical, emotional, and social well-being	Healthy eating is viewed not only in terms of its effect on growth and physical well-being but also on mental alertness: if you eat well, you learn better and you have opportunities to spend enjoyable, relaxed social time with your friends while eating.
moves toward increased understanding and responsibility for their own health with knowledge about what aspects of their health are in their control	Emphasize to preschoolers that making hand washing a habit before eating and after toileting is something they can take responsibility for, something that helps them take control over how often they get sick; let preschoolers know that they have no control over how safely an adult drives a car, but they do have control over putting on their seat belts to protect themselves.

INAPPROPRIATE HEALTH CURRICULUM	
PRACTICES	**EXAMPLES**
a series of lessons are formally taught to children	Talking (or lecturing) to children about the do's and don'ts of hygiene without hands-on practice does not allow interaction with children; reading a book about sexuality in group time is inappropriate.
is based on themes, so a health area is highlighted for a week but is not a priority for the rest of the year	Peacemaking is introduced as a week's theme in the school-agers' room when a conflict is in the news. For the remainder of the year, the principles of peacemaking are ignored by educators, and children are not developing the skills to put peacemaking into practice.
is based on the adults' health interests rather than the children's interests	An educator who does aerobics every day conducts daily instructional exercises and loses patience with the toddlers when they don't seem interested in the activity.
is designed or implemented in a way that instills fear, an inappropriate sense of responsibility, or groundless vulnerability in the child	An educator pressures preschoolers to eat everything on their plate because children elsewhere are starving; an educator cautions children to never talk to strangers because they may hurt them.

which children feel safe and secure and trust that adults will meet their physical, emotional, and social needs and respond to their cues. To achieve such environments, early childhood programs need to

- establish effective ongoing communication with parents (e.g., practices around separation for child and parent that promote trust)
- implement good hygiene practice, ensure safety, and actively involve children in routines. This would include as many one-to-one or small group experiences as possible. The very young child learns about health by experiencing healthy environments and by educators' actions. For example:
  - responding to infants' and toddlers' verbalization and talking about the activity's process, including naming parts of the body while diapering, while toileting, and during other routines
  - encouraging the child's involvement in undressing (e.g., diapering, getting into a sleeper for a nap after outdoor play) and older toddlers' involvement with dressing
  - hand washing with children, who become increasingly involved as time goes on
- provide opportunities for children's bodies moving in space, minimizing restriction except for safety reasons
- relate physical activities to growth and development, such as short flexible tunnels for budding crawlers and large foam blocks for climbers
- ensure that infants are given a spoon and are encouraged to be as involved as they would like to be in self-feeding. Be patient with toddlers' learning table behaviour and respectful of cultural practices in eating that differ from yours (e.g., using hands to eat or an adult feeding a child). Establish basic limits: Food is not to be thrown, for example.
- offer opportunities for various sensory experiences, including foods with interesting natural colours and textures, as appropriate
- serve nutritious food, encouraging preference for whole foods without a lot of processing and added sugar, salt, and additives
- monitor and control sudden loud noises in the program because of young children's fears. When adults who are unfamiliar to the children visit the program, or when the children are outside, be sensitive to the children's responses. Support children in daily separation from parents.

Toilet learning often begins somewhere between 18 and 36 months. The term "learning" highlights children's active role in this process. As with most aspects of working with children, educators should follow the child's lead. Readiness for using the toilet is demonstrated when all three of the following are observed in a child:

- physical maturity—stays dry for several hours, can get to the toilet, pulls down loose-fitting pants
- awareness—of a full bladder or bowel; the child understands that she or he has wet or soiled diapers
- desire—to use the toilet (or potty) and to have a dry diaper

When all three aspects of readiness are in place, toilet learning is usually a positive process. Educators in toddler (or preschool) rooms often find that children's desire is high when peers are using the toilet. Children's feelings of self-esteem are paramount in the approach to toilet learning. In the best interests of the child, together parents and educators work to provide support through this period. When there is a difference of opinion on the timing or approach to toilet learning, educators and parents work together to reach a compromise.

Preschoolers

This group of children is particularly interested in learning about

- cleanliness, toilet learning and toileting, good grooming, dressing themselves;
- germs and sickness;
- health and safety rules (e.g., cover your mouth when you cough and sneeze, look both ways before crossing the street);
- safety and injury prevention, at least on an early-awareness level, and especially using simple rules;
- personal safety, again on an early-awareness level, and following child-centred guidelines (see Child Maltreatment Prevention Programs for Children, page 471);
- community helpers (e.g., role of firefighters, police officers, doctors, nurses, dentists) and especially what happens in a hospital if the child or a friend has been a patient;
- some common fears: fear of the dark, monsters, loud noises (e.g., thunder, truck backfiring), abandonment (especially if divorce, death, hospitalization, or other trauma has occurred);
- food and good nutrition, how and where foods are grown or are eaten, different foods eaten by people and animals;
- the role of sleep and relaxation; and
- the role of physical activity and movement.

The following are usually of more interest and more appropriate developmentally for older preschoolers:

- body awareness, interest in more complex body parts and systems (e.g., internal organs, respiratory system)
- regular brushing, primary teeth coming out, new teeth coming in
- emotions, own feelings, awareness of similarities and differences (e.g., gender, race), manners, own family and others' families, having babies
- beginning awareness of conflict resolution and peacemaking
- basic understanding of importance of caring for the environment

School-Agers

School-agers are interested in more complex issues and want more details, but they still haven't developed abstract reasoning. The following are some examples that particularly interest them:

- illnesses
- loss of primary teeth, emergence of permanent teeth
- body awareness that is more complex than when younger (e.g., interest in body secretions and body noises, changes with puberty)
- consumer health, especially as reflected in advertisements in television commercials, magazines, product labels, prices
- environmental health issues, particularly issues around landfill sites, overpackaging, air quality, depletion of the ozone layer, animal extinction, and actions we take, such as observing the three R's (reduce, reuse, recycle), composting, returning bottles and cans, and renewing and refinishing
- personal feelings, making friends, family dynamics, getting along with others (e.g., bullies, peacemaking)
- human rights: racism, sexism, classism, homophobia, and concern for those whose rights have not been respected
- safety and injury prevention (e.g., bicycle, pedestrian, playground, home safety, first-aid treatments)
- awareness of own stressors and positive ways to deal with stress
- how the body works (e.g., how nutrition, rest, and physical activity interrelate)
- physical fitness
- foods friends eat that may be different from theirs and nutrients in foods
- self-care, as in learning to make snacks and meals independently, knowing what to do in an emergency, finding out about personal safety and street proofing
- community awareness and with support from adults work with others to affect health in the community (e.g., neighbourhood, school, early childhood program)

Getting Down to the Health Curriculum

When health is viewed holistically, countless topics and issues can be included in a program's health curriculum. Although this section does not include a multitude of ready-to-use activities for different age groups, it does offer suggestions for implementing health curricula in a selected number of health-related topics (see Resource Materials, page 562). From here, students will be able to take what they learn from the entire discussion on health curricula and develop a curriculum on topics of their choice. Of course, any specific curriculum must always be based on the needs and interests of the particular group of children as they emerge. The following topics are discussed in more detail in connection with the guidelines for the various age groups:

- environmental health
- nutrition education
- dental health
- hand washing and germs

Environmental Health Education

Over the past two decades, concern about the health of our planet, which ultimately affects all life, has been a major educational focus for everyone. A lot of resources are available that encourage public involvement in environmental health and safety. Of course, increased knowledge about climate change, energy use, land and water use, waste, and other environmental issues is essential for changes in public and personal attitudes and behaviour that will positively affect the earth. Canadians are becoming environmentally literate and are engaging in environmental stewardship to contribute to a healthy future.

Children can learn good helping habits and may even be involved in community action to improve the environment. However, we must never imply or state that children are solely responsible for the future of the planet. Because children have reached only the early stages of cognitive and moral development, they are liable to take this message seriously. Feelings of guilt (e.g., whenever a child uses a paper product), fear or hopelessness for the future, and other feelings will contribute to children's stress levels. They may begin to view the onerous task of saving the planet as theirs alone and become consumed by it.

Environmental health education can be a part of everyday life at home and in programs. Adults who "live gently" or are aware of their "carbon footprint"—

both of these terms are used to refer to a way of living that respects life, uses resources without wasting, and causes minimal harm to the planet—are helping children to learn about environmental health. Programs model these practices by

- participating in recycling programs, where available. The most common recycling programs are community-wide and accept glass, plastics, cardboard, and newspapers. Recycling can also include clothing, winter boots and coats, skates, and toy swaps in early childhood programs and between early childhood programs.

- composting. Some local waste management programs also accept food waste for composting.

- choosing products that are safer for the environment (e.g., cloth diapers or use of a recycling system for disposable diapers, biodegradable products) (see *Child Health and the Environment—A Primer* in Resource Materials, page 563).

- using energy efficiently

- repairing, remodelling, and reusing, when possible

- respecting ecosystems

Refer to Healthy Spaces, the interactive website hosted by the Canadian Institute for Child Health and the Canadian Child Care Federation that provides information on healthy indoor and outdoor child care and home environments (see Resource Materials, page 562).

Within programs, educators need to be aware of the messages they are sending to children about their role in saving the earth. Our goal is for children to develop a positive attitude and belief that they can make change happen and be

TABLE 9.4   Hands-On Contact with Nature and Children's Mental Health and Well-Being

BENEFIT	EFFECT
Benefits associated with seeing growth and change, the cycles of life	Builds resilience
Contact with nature is calming	Reduces disruptive behaviour
Gives children a sense of freedom to innovate, be creative, to discover	Enhances self-esteem
Engages the senses	Creates feelings of wellness
Provides enjoyment	Children enjoy being outside in nature
Gives a sense of achievement, empowerment	Increases self-esteem

Source: Hands-on Contact With Nature in Primary Schools as a Catalyst for Developing a Sense of Community and Cultivating Mental Health & Wellbeing by D. Maller, 2005. *EINGANA: Journal of the Victorian Association of Environmental Education,* 28(3), 17–22. Retrieved from http://www.vaee.vic.edu.au/resources/eingana/einganadec05.pdf#page=18. Reprinted with permission.

part of a community of change by incorporating actions that contribute to that change, but not to be overwhelmed with a sense of personal responsibility. When environmental education is integrated through contact with nature, there is the potential for various benefits for children, as listed in Table 9.4.

Infants and Toddlers

Environmental education for infants and toddlers should focus on role modelling. Children observing educators who respect plants, trees, animals, and insects on walks and children guided by gentle reminders when handling nature inappropriately (e.g., plucking flower petals, stomping on earthworms) are on their way to becoming environmental advocates. Opportunities for walks in the park or other natural environments provide awareness of nature; music recordings of nature sounds such as rain falling, birds singing, insects chirping, or waves lapping may also provide comfort and familiarity when children experience the "real" sounds. It is important to remember that, developmentally, these very young children are egocentric and that going beyond this level of environmental education would not be good practice.

Preschoolers

As with all learning, preschoolers build on what they have already experienced with the environment. For preschoolers to develop respect for the natural environment, they first need to be part of it and learn about it. However, environmental concepts and issues are complex. Since children learn from the simple to the complex, educators begin with simpler versions of relevant concepts for preschoolers. They learn best when they interact with people and objects.

    The environmental concept of life cycles can be introduced at the preschool level in a number of ways. Planting and harvesting, composting, and observing trees change with the seasons are ways that help preschool children begin to understand nature. Ideally, a respect for nature is a part of everyone's value system. Individuals don't necessarily have to love earthworms or spiders to respect the role they play in the environment. Vermicomposting (or red worm composting), for example, is a convenient way for organic waste to decompose. It is a practical, indoor option to help preschoolers see the process of composting "in action." Educators can easily find information on the health and safety considerations for this process.

Educators need to provide experiences through the seasons that serve as springboards for observing, investigating, discovering, and learning about the environment through nature. Adults, including ECE students and educators, sometimes feel that they do not know enough about nature, but they can learn along with children. Adults who demonstrate a quest for learning, rather than pretend to know everything, actually provide very good role modelling.

Children can express their interest in the environment in all areas of the program's curriculum:

- *Art.* Use easels outdoors to inspire children to paint their representation of trees or their feelings about trees; make leaf rubbings; create from recycled materials (e.g., sound-makers, collages).
- *Music.* Sing songs about nature or create chants; identify sounds of nature.
- *Creative movement.* Express the rhythms of the earth or move like wind, water, and so on.
- *Science.* Care for a living thing through planting and gardening; adopt a tree in the park and see how it changes with the seasons.
- *Literature.* Read and discuss books about nature or about legends that involve nature, possibly stories from the children's backgrounds (e.g., Aboriginal Canadian legends embody nature).
- *Numeracy.* Compare sizes and shapes of plants or pebbles to seriate, classify.
- *Dramatic play.* Add a small recycling box in the home-living centre; play jungle animals; transform the play area into a forest with trees and animals.
- *Field trips.* Walk in your neighbourhood in the different seasons; visit a botanical garden, recycling plant, community playground, garden centre, farm, orchard, bird sanctuary, pond.

Although they are still young, preschoolers could become involved at a simple level with community action, along with their parents or educators.

City developers were planning to cut down trees in the program's neighbourhood to build a parking lot. Educators and concerned parents involved the children in a walk of support for the park, the trees, and the play area. The event got media attention. As well, pictures the children drew of the park and trees were enclosed in a letter to the mayor.

Educators must be careful to ensure that participation of this kind does not instill fear, that children understand the purpose of what they are doing, and that they are not being exploited to gain public support for adults' issues. Many complex environmental issues are beyond a preschooler's cognitive level of understanding (e.g., animal extinction).

Today's preschoolers will become the adults who make major environmental decisions in the future. The interest in, knowledge of, and concern for the environment that begin in their preschool years will eventually benefit everyone.

School-Agers

This age group is already targeted more than any other with regard to environmental education resources. School-agers, especially those who have reached a concrete operational level of thinking, can have a fuller understanding of environmental issues, particularly if they have had environmental experiences earlier in life. Children are becoming interested in the democratic process. Those who have been developing decision-making and coping skills may have been involved in some social action. Any number of approaches and activities can be part of school-age early childhood programs. Through a discovery approach supported by educators who believe in the importance of living gently, school-agers can get involved in meaningful and practical experiences. For example, two books by Larraine Roulston, *Pee Wee and the Magical Compost Heap* and *Pee Wee's Great Adventure: A Guide to Vermicomposting,* were designed to teach 5- to 10-year-olds the facts and process of composting (see Resource Materials, page 562). They can also organize and lead regular school yard and neighbourhood litter cleanup campaigns. Through their experiences, school-agers acquire the knowledge and life skills to develop their confidence as change agents. They may also be interested in becoming involved in community action with such activities as writing letters to policymakers about environmental issues that affect them, such as residential pesticide use.

When children put their energy into contributing to change, a health promotion philosophy is put into practice.

By planning and networking with teachers in the children's school, ideally, the educators and teachers can coordinate their environmental health policies and practices. As well, they can find out how much time is spent on the environment in the classroom. Your efforts will be in vain if children become turned off when inundated with environmental education rather than motivated and excited by it.

Adults have a major role in protecting children from environmental hazards, as there are a number of factors about children that contribute to their greater exposure to substances in the environment (see Environmental Concerns and Children's Well Being, page 425). Protection must always be a priority, but there are many ways that educators and parents can "gently" integrate environmental health education into children's lives, recognizing their rights to participation in their own health promotion.

Nutrition Education

Nutrition is the easiest health area to integrate throughout the curriculum and from infancy to school age. The possibilities for learning are endless but usually centre on some general concepts. The following nutrition concepts can be appropriately incorporated into children's nutrition experiences:

- Everyone needs food to grow, feel good, and have energy to do things.
- A wide variety of foods are available, and it is best for our body if we have variety every day.
- Foods have unique colours, flavours, textures, smells, sizes, shapes, and sounds.
- Foods that are unfamiliar to you are enjoyed by other people. Trying new foods helps you learn about yourself and the world and gain respect for and insight into other ethnocultural backgrounds.
- Everyone has individual food likes and dislikes.
- Food should be respected for its role in fulfilling needs—and should not be used for art activities.
- Foods have different sources (e.g., some grow on trees or in the ground, some come from animals).
- Foods are made up of nutrients, and the foods that have more nutrients are better for our body.
- The way that food is handled and cooked affects the amount of nutrients in it, its safety, and its taste.
- Food provides the opportunity for social time, and the rights of self and others are considered through the sharing of food.

Nutrition experiences help children develop cognitively, physically, emotionally, and socially. Here are some examples of how food can be incorporated into all areas of the program's curriculum:

- *Art.* Use magazines and grocery store fliers to create collages of various foods; food cartons to be recycled after use can be painted or used in box sculpture; draw pictures of how you feel eating different foods (e.g., puckered face after eating a lemon). Using food that will not be eaten in art and craft activities is unacceptable and disrespectful of food and of those who do not have enough to eat.

- *Music.* Sing songs about foods; the words to familiar children's songs can be modified to include nutrition messages.

- *Creative movement.* Pretend to be fruit or vegetables planted, picked, harvested, falling to the ground.

- *Science.* Design activities using one or more senses (e.g., discovery box with foods inside to touch and describe before eating). Grow foods (e.g., gardening in plots or boxes). Compare fruit and vegetables (e.g., fresh, frozen, canned, dried).

- *Literature.* Read books about food, cooking, gardening (e.g., *The Sandwich* to support issues of diversity).

- *Numeracy.* Use scales and measures to compare weights of foods.

- *Social studies.* Share foods and eating customs with others—activities particularly relevant for older preschool and school-age children. Examples are foods eaten for Dwali, harvest foods, haggis, foods for Kwanza celebrations, the origin or invention of certain foods and eating implements, cooking equipment, utensils).

- *Dramatic play.* Set up a grocery store (e.g., empty cracker and cereal boxes), restaurant, or pizzeria and provide lifelike food. Use cooking and eating utensils that reflect ethnocultural diversity.

- *Field trips.* Visit a grocery store, market, bakery, farm, local garden, or health food store or invite a child's family member to come and cook a traditional dish.

Cooking with Children

Cooking with children is an ideal way to begin their nutrition education. Snacks provide an opportunity each day for children to have food experiences. Food preparation calls on children to use their five senses; to learn about colours, shapes, and textures; and to use simple kitchen utensils. Children can begin to learn the basic principles of hygiene and food safety and, of course, take pride in their accomplishments and eat the "fruit" of their labour. Even older infants love to squeeze bananas or help mash potatoes. When children enjoy cooking and eating nutritious foods and develop food preparation skills, they may be inclined to have a more balanced lifestyle as they get older. Current public health concerns about the mass consumption of unhealthy food, particularly convenience foods with high contents of trans fats, salt, and sugar, require changes in eating habits. Table 9.5 offers suggestions for snacks that children can make.

TABLE 9.5	Some Snacks or Lunches Children Can Make
AGE GROUP	**SNACK OR LUNCH IDEA**
Infants	simple fruit salad, mashed banana, applesauce, blended mango pudding, cottage cheese with a face made with Cheerios, frozen fruit juice on sticks, finger gelatin made with fruit juice and plain gelatin, well-cooked carrot sticks with yogurt dip,* smoothed avocado on crackers, fruit and yogurt blender drinks
Toddlers	devilled eggs using yogurt instead of mayonnaise, cottage cheese salad with crushed pineapple, porridge for a teddy bear picnic, ants on a log (e.g., bread sticks with apple butter and Rice Crispies), fruit or vegetable and cheese kabobs using Popsicle sticks, frozen bananas on sticks served with yogurt or applesauce dips, banana coins in orange juice, nutritious milk shakes
Preschoolers	English muffin pizzas, dippidy-doo and vegetables too,* guacamole and corn tortilla chips, pita sandwiches, unidentified frying objects (i.e., cut a circle out of a slice of bread and fry it with an egg in the hole), homemade butter (shake cream) for sandwiches or crackers, vegetable ("stone") soup, yogurt and fruit sundaes, "people" sandwiches (e.g., hummus on circles of bread with grated carrots, apple smiles, sunflower seeds, banana coins, etc., to make faces), scrambled eggs in an "ice cream" cone
School-Agers	tacos, three-bean salad, muffins, baked apples, rice pudding, Waldorf salad, banana-egg pancakes, chop suey, stir-fried vegetables, pretzels, fondue, stuffed pita, hummus with crackers, sticky rice, vegetable sushi, beans and rice, lentil soup

* Provide children with individual dishes of dip. Double dipping in a communal dish spreads germs.

The Five W's of Cooking with Children

Who?

The ideal educator–child ratios:

- infants 1:1
- toddlers 1:2
- preschoolers 1:3
- school-agers 1:4 maximum

The worst situation:
A large group of children with one educator

These ratios promote safe cooking practices and allow for individual participation.

What?

Two ways of cooking with children:

- small group with an educator, usually using a recipe that makes enough food for a number of children (e.g., baking)
- individual children following the recipe, often called "production-line cooking," usually using a recipe that makes individual portions

Select nutritious foods that are developmentally appropriate and do not pose a risk for choking. Ensure that allergies and food restrictions (religious, ethnocultural) are considered in planning any food experience.

Children learn from following recipes

1. the names of food and food mixtures

2. sequential learning: recipes that are based on developmental appropriateness, for example

- two steps for infants
- three to four steps for toddlers
- four to six steps for preschoolers
- eight steps maximum for school-agers

3. how to measure ingredients

Pictorial and written recipe cards are particularly useful for preschoolers and school-agers. They incorporate sequencing and prereading skills (or reading, for older children) into the experience, and children learn that a lot of food preparation involves recipes. For prereaders, there should be many illustrations with just a few words. It is possible to use one recipe card listing all the steps (e.g., on a piece of construction paper). For individual portion cooking, a set of recipe cards (one card for each step) makes it easier for children to do one step and then move to the next station.

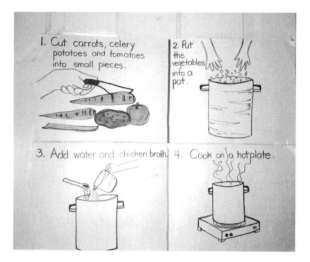

The following are tips for making recipe cards:

- Cut out pictures or drawings of food, cooking equipment, and utensils used in each step.
- Use a dot system rather than numbers to indicate each step, particularly for preschoolers (e.g., one dot on the first card, two dots on the second).
- Laminate the cards for durability with repeated use.

As children become more familiar with the printed word, you may want to create recipe cards that combine pictures and words (e.g., have a picture of the apple and print the word "apple" or use the dots and symbol for the number two). For readers, the recipe's steps can be presented in a chart format.

When?

The ideal time is during play time, as one choice among several activities. This way, you may be able to work with smaller groups at a time and repeat the recipe until all children who want to can do it. With the ideal number of children (or close to it), you are able to focus on each child's questions, reactions, and so on, and each child is truly involved in the process. Your role as facilitator is very important. If children are independently doing a production-line recipe, ensure that other children are not waiting in line. This creates an antisocial climate. Instead, children can sign up and come at their turn.

The worst time is during a circle time or other large group times. It is not realistic to expect a large number of children to work together at something that needs only a few. Passing a bowl around while each child has one stir is not learning—it creates frustration, and your role is focused on crowd control rather than on facilitating.

Where?

The ideal place:
In a low-traffic area located close to running water and an electrical outlet, if needed

The worst place:
In a noisy, busy area

Why?

Food experiences (or cooking) with children can be positive in many ways:

- Everyone needs to eat!
- When children are involved in food preparation, they are more likely to try the food.
- Cooking is usually an enjoyable experience for children. They are proud of their accomplishments, which builds self-esteem.

Any well-planned food experience has many advantages for children:

1. Cognitive opportunities are made available and facilitated through foods.
   - Children can see similarities and differences (classification).
   - They can experience temporal relations (sense of time and sequence).
   - They can develop a sense of quantity and measurement.
   - They can problem-solve (e.g., What will happen if . . . ?).
   - They can take part in matching (one-to-one correspondence).
   - They can learn about growing plants.
   - They can learn about the origins of foods, such as eggs from chickens, milk from cows and goats.
   - They can see the effect of temperature on substances (e.g., freezing fruit juice, frying potato pancakes, baking muffins).

2. Educators use opportunities to build language skills through food routines and nutritional learning experiences (e.g., by using the correct terms for foods, equipment, cooking processes, and discussions about foods and by following recipe cards).

3. Children regularly have the opportunity to participate in food preparation. This can be integrated into the everyday curriculum. In addition to viewing meal and snack preparation as important aspects of everyday life, children build their cooking skills and have opportunities for cooperation and for appreciating a wider repertoire of foods, enhancing their ethnocultural learning. Most ethnocultural groups have particular breads that are either staples or are familiar to them.

4. Food experiences involve both girls and boys, promoting an atmosphere of equity in both food preparation and cleanup.

To enhance the cooking experience, educators should follow these recommendations:

1. Prepare for the activity:
   - Try out the recipe before using it with the children.
   - Ensure that all ingredients and equipment are available and in working order.
   - Check carefully for any food allergies or restrictions.

2. Promote safety:
   - Have all necessary equipment and ingredients set out in a safe location before beginning the activity (involve school-agers in this aspect).
   - Explain and demonstrate all safety aspects to the children before starting (e.g., using knives) and practise these precautions during the activity.
   - Follow food safety tips:

- The table is cleaned and sanitized before you begin.
- Everyone, including you, washes their hands before setting up the ingredients, utensils, and equipment.
- Consider using an apron or some type of cover-up.
- If the snack is not to be eaten immediately, it is stored safely (e.g., blender drinks in the fridge).
- The utensils, equipment, and table are cleaned and sanitized when finished.

3. Facilitate the activity:
   - Encourage every child to participate.
   - Be receptive to the questions and feelings of each child.
   - Show interest and enjoyment in the activity through facial expression, tone of voice, body language, flexibility, and positive interactions with children.
   - Let the children's comments and questions guide you about what they want to learn.
   - Ask questions that encourage problem solving if children are not initiating questions.
   - Use positive guidance throughout the activity.

4. Evaluate the activity after it is over:
   - Were the expectations appropriate for children's learning?
   - Did each child have opportunities to actively participate?
   - Was the time frame appropriate?
   - What follow-up experiences would be meaningful?

It is important to involve families in your nutritional education curriculum. Some family members may be available to come in and make a favourite recipe with the children; others may send in a recipe or a food that has special meaning in ethnocultural or religious events. Programs may also find ways to share families' favourite recipes through newsletters, bulletin boards, cookbook projects (possible fundraiser), and potluck events throughout the year.

Dental Health Education

"Poor oral health can affect a person's quality of life. Oral pain, missing teeth or oral infections can influence the way a person speaks, eats and socializes. These oral health problems can reduce a person's quality of life by affecting their physical, mental and social well-being" (Canadian Dental Association, 2008, p. 1).

Dental health education is a good example of children learning through a daily routine. Dental care is a lifelong health habit. Educators are in an ideal position to take an active role in ensuring that children's teeth are protected while they are in the program and to help children learn good **dental health** practices. Taking good care of teeth and gums is essential, both for maintaining dental health and overall health.

For families who are financially comfortable or who have jobs that include dental benefits, professional dental care is usually not a problem. Families with a low income but not on social assistance are often in a position in which they do not have dental benefits, and the family budget may not be able to include the costs of dental care. However, some communities provide access to free or affordable dental care if they qualify, and it can be very helpful to make that information available to families in the program.

By around age two, children have 20 primary (or baby) teeth. Between ages 6 and 12, primary teeth start to loosen and fall out as the permanent teeth underneath begin pushing through the gums (see Figure 9.1). Most children start by losing the lower two front teeth and then the top two, creating the classic gap-toothed smile.

FIGURE 9.1	The Development of the Primary Teeth

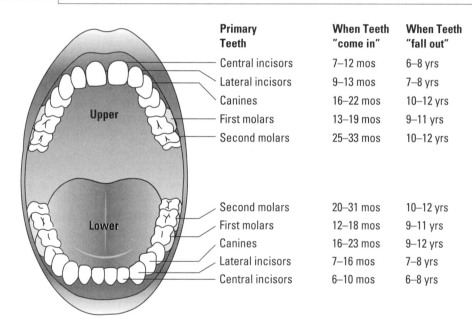

Primary Teeth	When Teeth "come in"	When Teeth "fall out"
Upper		
Central incisors	7–12 mos	6–8 yrs
Lateral incisors	9–13 mos	7–8 yrs
Canines	16–22 mos	10–12 yrs
First molars	13–19 mos	9–11 yrs
Second molars	25–33 mos	10–12 yrs
Lower		
Second molars	20–31 mos	10–12 yrs
First molars	12–18 mos	9–11 yrs
Canines	16–23 mos	9–12 yrs
Lateral incisors	7–16 mos	7–8 yrs
Central incisors	6–10 mos	6–8 yrs

Everyone gets plaque. This thick, sticky layer, mostly made of bacteria that live in our mouth and "feed" on the sugars and starches we eat, is constantly on our teeth. The bacteria in the plaque mix with food in our mouth in an "acid attack" that lasts up to 20 minutes after we eat. This attack begins eroding the enamel layer of our teeth. Some of us incorrectly assume that the natural sugar in raisins or other dried fruit, or the starch in snacks such as pretzels or crackers, is better for your teeth than less nutritive snacks such as candy or potato chips. Although saliva helps neutralize the acid and rinse food out of our mouth, especially at mealtime, when more saliva is produced, it can't do it all. Brushing and flossing are needed to remove food and plaque; if the plaque stays there, it hardens and causes tartar, which leads to tooth decay. When young children have the opportunity to learn effective toothbrushing, flossing will be a natural addition to their routine as they reach school age. Brushing our teeth before going to sleep is a good practice. When we are asleep we don't produce as much saliva, so the bacteria and food left in our mouth produce acid that eats at enamel.

How Do We Promote Dental Health?

Fluoride Fluoride is a mineral that strengthens tooth enamel, which helps prevent cavities. People who live in communities in which the drinking water is supplied through a water treatment plant probably haven't given much thought to fluoride. In many places, fluoride is added to the drinking water before it reaches our homes, which is a decision made by each community's public health agency. Other sources of fluoride are toothpaste, fluoride drops prescribed by physicians, and fluoride treatments by dental professionals.

The controversy, sometimes voiced, about fluoride is usually concerned that tap water may contain a higher level than it should. Fluorosis, causing chalky-white or brown blotches on teeth that are forming from birth to three years old, can result from overfluoridation. If educators or parents are concerned about fluoride levels, contact your regional public health agency.

Healthy Eating and Drinking Limit the amounts of high-sugar foods offered, particularly sticky ones (e.g., raisins, granola bars, pop, hard candies) or foods with cooked starch (e.g., potato chips, bread, potatoes, pretzels). Serve dentally friendly foods often, especially fresh fruit and vegetables, plain yogurts, cheese, and milk. Frequent snacking (or grazing) is discouraged because food is in our mouth so often that acid production is frequent. Encourage children to drink water between meals and snacks, ensuring that tap water is readily available and easy for preschoolers and school-agers to access independently. Limit fruit juice to no more than 120 mL (4 oz.) of fruit juice daily for preschoolers; it should only be drunk from a cup and served at meal- or snack times (Canadian Paediatric Society, 2008, p. 40).

Do not prop baby bottles or put children to sleep with a bottle. This is not advisable for the following reasons:

- These practices allow formula or milk (which contains natural sugars) to pool in the mouth for a long period of time. Babies' teeth are soft and very susceptible to acid and decay. Juice and non-nutritive high-sugar drinks are even more damaging. **Early childhood tooth decay (ECTD)** (formerly called nursing bottle syndrome) can happen very quickly, leading to the painful decay of primary teeth. Dull white spots or lines can appear on newly erupted teeth seemingly overnight. Parents are encouraged to see a dentist as soon as possible if this happens.

  ECTD has a negative impact on children's overall health and can cause pain, making it difficult to sleep, eat or speak. Pain can also affect a child's ability to concentrate and learn. Children who develop dental decay at an early age are more likely to suffer decay throughout childhood. By making appropriate cleaning practices part of the daily routine and helping families learn about nutrition and dental hygiene, you can play an important role in preventing ECTD. (Canadian Paediatric Society, 2008, p. 55)

- Children should not be put to bed even with a bottle of water. This practice increases the child's risk of choking. However, sucking is a natural and normal developmental need in young children. Many children derive comfort from sucking a thumb or soother (never dipped in sugary substances). Generally, dentists are not concerned about the child's teeth unless use continues as permanent teeth are beginning to emerge. In these situations, educators can suggest that the family seek the advice of their health care provider or dentist (Canadian Paediatric Society, 2008, p. 55)
- Children's eustachian tubes are shorter and straighter than adults'. When children lie on their back with a bottle in their mouth, the liquid and saliva may run back into the middle ear and cause an ear infection.

It is advisable to switch to a sippy cup for all drinks as soon as possible, preferably by one year of age.

Routine Toothbrushing By the time children are of preschool age, they can learn about "2 for 2": twice daily for two minutes each time. Although this really refers to once in the morning and once before bed, *if* the early childhood program can support a toothbrushing routine in the day, it reinforces the concept and gives children more practice.

Many centres choose not to brush the children's teeth during the day. There are several reasons for this decision, including

- the public health issue surrounding the logistics of storing the brushes in a manner that keeps them from touching, being able to air-dry, but not open to the air, and the labelling of both the brushes and each child's storage area. Due to the various styles of brushes, finding a hook system that accommodates the brushes is challenging. This being said, some programs have been successful in meeting these issues.
- children dropping the brush into the sink and onto the floor, resulting in the brush needing to be replaced.
- the time that it takes staff to supervise all the children during this routine.

For many programs, this routine follows lunch time as children begin the transition to a nap or quiet activity. On field trips, children can rinse their mouth with water. Flossing is difficult in programs because of the extra time and demands involved. Parents should floss their child's teeth once a day until the child has the skill to floss his or her own teeth, as flossing can reduce overall plaque significantly.

Tips for brushing:
- Use a soft toothbrush.
- Add toothpaste. Use a small dab for infants and toddlers; preschoolers need an amount only about the size of a pea. Be careful that the tip of the tube doesn't touch the brush. An educator will need to help younger children put on the paste.
- Follow the three-step method (see Figure 9.2) and brush or supervise the child's brushing. Start at the far lower back teeth, using a "wiggling," not a scrubbing, motion. Move around the mouth, wiggling the brush on all the surfaces. Don't forget to brush the tongue to fight bacteria and freshen the breath.

- Teach children not to swallow the toothpaste but to rinse with water and spit.
- Rinse the brushes well.

FIGURE 9.2   **Toothbrushing Pattern**

 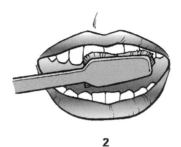 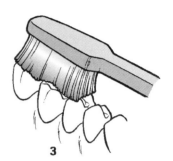

1   2   3

Tips for toothbrushes:

- Use a baby toothbrush for infants and toddlers and a child-size one for children up to 12 years old.
- Each child must have his or her own brush and must never share it.
- Label each child's toothbrush and store it to dry where air will circulate around it and where it doesn't touch other toothbrushes. Educators often have to be very creative in designing a convenient, hygienic storage method.
- Keep out of reach of children to ensure that brushes are not used by different children and as a safety precaution. Children must learn not to run or walk with a toothbrush in their mouth.
- Ideally, each child should have his or her own travel-size tube to reduce the likelihood of cross-contamination and promote independence. The tubes must be labelled with the children's names.

To prevent infections (Canadian Paediatric Society, 2008, p. 56):

- Ensure that toothbrushes are replaced every three months and always after a child has been ill with a cold or other respiratory infection.
- Ensure that each child's toothbrush is labelled to prevent cross-contamination.
- Store toothbrushes away from the toilet area, and out of reach of young children, until children are toothbrushing independently; rinse or ensure that the child rinses the toothbrush carefully after each use and that each toothbrush can dry without touching others.

Infants and toddlers:
Educators communicate with parents about wishes for their infant's daily dental care. If the parent agrees, the educator can wipe a young infant's gums with a soft,

clean, damp cloth daily. When first teeth appear, the Canadian Paediatric Society (2008) recommends cleaning them with a soft bristle toothbrush designed for babies while laying the infant on a flat surface or cradling the infant's head in your lap.

Families should take their 12-month-old infant for a first dental visit and monitor routinely for signs of decay on teeth or on the gum line.

When toddlers are able to stand at the sink, they are able to participate more in brushing. Standing behind the toddler and facing the mirror tends to be a convenient position. Educators may either do the brushing for the child or hold the brush with the toddler.

Preschoolers and school-agers:
With experience, older preschoolers become more skilled at brushing, and the educator eventually needs only to supervise and possibly offer a little help rather than be actively involved. Being able to print her or his name is usually an indicator that a child has the dexterity to toothbrush. Most school-agers have the dexterity to brush their teeth without supervision and have gained more responsibility and independence in self-care. Although some children simply don't like brushing their teeth or don't like one more routine, most children appreciate the immediate results: brighter teeth and a clean-tasting mouth. Involve children in planning and preparing dentally healthy snacks. Educators can also encourage children to be aware of healthy food choices and explain how some foods promote dental health.

The muffins offered at lunch time have raisins in them. The educator mentions to the children at her table that having something with dried fruit is best at lunch time because at a meal they have more saliva, which helps take the sticky raisins out of their teeth. Also, their routine is to brush their teeth after lunch.

Learning about dental health can be incorporated into all areas of the program's curriculum:

- *Art.* Paint and draw pictures of food that promote dental health.
- *Creative movement.* Children can wiggle their bodies like they wiggle the toothbrush, an activity more appropriate for younger preschoolers.
- *Music.* Sing songs (e.g., about smiles: Raffi's *You Brush Your Teeth*).
- *Science.* Place a hard-boiled egg in vinegar, which helps show how enamel dissolves with a lot of acid.
- *Literature.* Read books about keeping teeth, losing teeth (e.g., tooth fairy stories such as *Where Do the Fairies Keep All the Teeth?*), and dental health.
- *Numeracy.* Count teeth (e.g., how many molars); classify pictures of foods that are more and less healthy for your teeth.
- *Lunch time/snacks.* Discuss the importance of our strong teeth in crunching carrots and biting into apples.

- *Dramatic play*. Set up a dental office and provide a variety of real props, including a flashlight, a mirror, and a lab coat; avoid needles for safety as well as not to instill fear! If you are involved in the play, offer positive comments about going to the dentist and avoid using negative words such as "drill" or "hurt."
- *Field trips*. Tour a dentist's office; invite a dental hygienist to talk about dental health with children and/or for a parent meeting. Dental professionals often have positive and child-appropriate explanations for their questions.

Source: Canadian Paediatric Society, *Well Beings: A Guide to Health in Child Care.* (Ottawa: Canadian Paediatric Society, 2008), 56. Reprinted with permission.

Contact local resources such as the public health agency or a local college that teaches dental hygiene to inquire about possible (free) resources, such as "big teeth" and toothbrushes, models that children can practise with or observe and talk about.

Hand Washing and Germs

As we discussed in Unit 3, hand washing is the most important routine that we do every day to prevent the spread of infection. It is a health practice that children need to learn for it to become a lifelong health habit. Like dental health, education about hand washing is based on an ongoing routine in the program, and there are many opportunities to reinforce it.

Infants and Toddlers

The hand-washing routine begins in infancy as part of diapering and feeding routines. Educators talk with infants about what they are doing as they are doing it, making comments such as "The water is warm" or "The cloth feels soft and wet." Infants are aware of their hands being washed and feel that it is part of caring.

Once toddlers are physically able to stand at the sink, educators can help them learn to wash their own hands. It is easier for children to learn the proper way and to make it a habit with practice than it is to change poor habits once they are formed. Educators may make the routine enjoyable for children by singing action songs such as *This Is The Way We Wash Our Hands*.

Preschoolers

Preschool children are ready for basic information about germs and what hand washing does to germs. During the preschool years, children become skilled at hand washing when adults provide consistent support built on earlier experience. By the time they are independently washing their hands, with educators now only supervising, they can learn some basic information about germs (e.g., germs are on our hands even when they look clean and they hide between fingers and under nails).

How can preschoolers learn about germs when germs can't be seen on hands? As with all aspects of the curriculum, it is essential to encourage active involvement and introduce concepts in a concrete way. Educators reinforce the fact that we are trying to prevent as many germs as we can from entering our bodies. Because our hands touch many things, there are a lot of germs on them. Most children don't walk around with facial tissue in a pocket; rather than not covering their mouth when they sneeze, and rather than sneezing into their hands, they can put their arm in front of their mouth. This prevents germs from getting on their hands.

Since we can't see germs, educators can show preschoolers something to compare to germs. Use a spray bottle to spray water into the air; the water droplets seem to disappear in the air and fall onto objects. Germs in the water now float in the air and can land anywhere—including on someone else. When we cough and sneeze, droplets of saliva that carry germs spray out. This helps children understand why covering their mouth before sneezing is a good way to cut down on germs going from one person to another.

Learning about hand washing can be incorporated into different curriculum areas:

- *Art.* Draw what they think germs would look like if they could see them.
- *Music.* Sing songs (e.g., to the tune of *Row, Row, Row Your Boat*, sing "Scrub, scrub, scrub your hands, put the soap between, wash the germs right down the drain, make them nice and clean").
- *Science.* Put a piece of bread in a jar and over the next several days invite the children to watch mould grow. To compare, handle a second piece of bread with dirty hands and put it into the jar. Ask children to predict which piece of bread will grow mould (germs) more quickly and record their predictions and observations over the next week. Educators can explain that for us to actually see germs (like mould), there have to be many, many of them. Do not let the children touch the bread with mould.
- *Literature.* Read books.
- *Dramatic play.* Use the water table to wash dolls, including the hands.
- *Nutrition.* Show how food can be shared without spreading germs (e.g., serving spoons, cutting a sandwich in half rather than taking turns having a bite).

School-Agers

School-age children will be hand washing without supervision, although many need to be reminded. Developmentally, these children are at an age when discussions about germs and the role of hand washing can be more complex.

Germs are everywhere, and some of them help keep us healthy (e.g., penicillin, yogurt). Skin and nose hairs stop some germs from getting into our bodies. Our body has other ways to defend us: tears, saliva, and stomach juices kill some germs when they get into our body.

Discussion of products such as hand sanitizers and antibacterial soaps can encourage children to think about the pros and cons of killing all germs (see Receiving Mixed Messages, page 146). Are there benefits to killing even the "friendly germs" we have on and in our bodies? How do we find a balance?

Activities such as growing moulds on foods (e.g., apple core in a jar) or growing germs from fingers on agar in petri dishes are appropriate (contact your local hospital or make an agar mixture with the children). Children in the concrete operational stage of development can understand that the mouldy apple is the same apple a week later, and the same with the petri dish.

REVISITING THE HEALTH PROMOTION ACTION PLAN

Children need to be consulted and participate meaningfully in the decisions and activities that affect them. The skills that children develop in this process include expressing views, decision making, coping, and public participation. These skills don't happen overnight. It takes practice and confidence to develop them. As children get older, they need experiences that encourage them to see themselves as participants, helpers, or agents of change in their communities. Educators and parents assist children in finding a balance between having confidence in their own skills and abilities and knowing when to depend on adults, the community, and society.

Health promotion is based on the philosophy that individuals can have both personal and public control over their lives and can improve their own health. Through our awareness, we can make change happen from the individual level to the societal level. Using the four components of the Health Promotion Action Plan presented in Unit 1, the following example highlights this philosophy:

The *UN Convention on the Rights of the Child in Child Friendly Language* poster has a prominent place in each playroom at the centre for everyone to see. Parents and ECE students often read it over, and several of the four- and five-year-olds and the school-agers have asked a family member or one of the educators to read it to them. Due to the lengthy list of articles in the convention, however, the children lose interest quickly and run off to play.

Recognizing the importance of ensuring that the UN-legislated rights of all children are upheld in our early childhood program and that children become aware of their rights at an age-appropriate level, the director and educators decided to find ways to bring this document to life as their ethical and professional responsibility.

Individual Problem Solving and Self-Reliance

One of the educators designed an arrow with Velcro that points to the current article of interest on the poster. The arrow location is chosen by a child or children who show interest in the poster, and ways to enable discussion of this particular article are explored, ensuring children's input. Children express their views according to their developing capacities, supporting their sense of control and thereby reducing stress and building resilience. It is also evident from the UN Convention that guiding children in understanding their rights also means building relationships and maintaining respect for their families.

The room partners reviewed and identified those articles of most relevance to the early childhood program and are evaluating how well they believe the program is responding to those rights, as well as opportunities to strengthen this. They find ways to obtain children's input as their rights include participating meaningfully in matters that directly affect them. Those articles that seem of particular relevance to the program are as follows:

- Article 12
- Article 13
- Article 15
- Article 16
- Article 24
- Article 29
- Article 30
- Article 31

For the text of these articles, refer to Appendix 8.1: UN Convention on the Rights of the Child, page 501.

Collective Self-Help

At a monthly full program staff meeting, one of the ongoing discussion items is sharing ideas that are emerging from children, families, and educators on the UN Convention as they build it into the curriculum. There is also a discussion of possible policy and practice amendments for the centre that reflect a fuller vision of the UN Convention.

To address Article 30, amendments to the child's intake form were made. Now, parents or guardians, in the initial meeting with the director and educator, are asked if they have specific recommendations to ensure that their culture (however they define it) is reflected in the program. A new family has identified that they would appreciate if the educators would find natural, unobtrusive ways to intermittently ask their preschool son how to say what they are doing (such as eating fruit) in his first language. The family is concerned that using English all day without acknowledging his first language may contribute to negative feelings about the language. When educators and children reinforce their interest, it may help their child feel proud of speaking both languages. Although the educators may have followed through with this strategy without the family's request, this opportunity resulted in a connection from the beginning, hopefully opening the door for ongoing communication to support the child and family culture in the program.

With reference to Article 29, the educators, director, and, ultimately, the board of directors decided to initiate a policy around environmental protection. This policy includes several practices to reduce waste, eliminate toxins (e.g., audit of cleaning products, running water for a few minutes every morning to flush possible lead in the water pipes), and incorporate ways to build child respect for the environment in age-appropriate ways.

Community Action

The UNICEF website reminds us that "educators can engage parents, children and community members to promote children's rights by encouraging advocacy with local and national governments, initiating dialogue on children's issues and creating a forum for children to express their opinions and views" (UNICEF, n.d.a, p. 1). This fact spurred on the educators to get involved in their community concerning poverty and homelessness, both issues that are interconnected and dramatically affect the rights of children. The educators also noted the United Nations' vision for the five outcomes for every child if the Convention on the Rights of the Child are made a reality: being healthy, staying safe, enjoying and achieving, making a positive contribution, and economic well-being (UNICEF, n.d.b, p. 1). It is evident that the school-age children in the program can make a positive contribution, one of the five outcomes, while contributing to the health, safety, and economic well-being outcomes for other children.

Some of the school-age children are involved in volunteering at a food bank one day after school, and others are involved in helping in the community kitchen at a homeless shelter. A number of the parents and relatives of the children and educators are also becoming involved, and this community action is contributing to a cohesive vision for change.

Societal Change

Due to their further knowledge of the UN Convention on the Rights of the Child, and their involvement at the community level, educators and children have the impetus to become engaged in advocacy for broader societal change. Canada has some dynamic role models who became advocates as children and are making remarkable headway with regard to human rights. Two renowned examples are

- Hannah Taylor, who started *The Ladybug Foundation*, which addresses the homelessness issue in Canada, when she was five years old. Hannah is the youngest member of the jury panel of children from around the world that selects the annual recipient of the World's Children's Prize for the Rights of the Child in Stockholm and is the recipient of The 2007 Future Leader Award (Canada's Most Powerful Women: Top 100).

- Craig Kielburger, who founded *Free the Children* at 12 years old. It is the world's largest network of children helping children through education, with more than one million youth involved in their innovative education and development programs in 45 countries. The organization has received the World's Children's Prize for the Rights of the Child (also known as the Children's Nobel Prize).

Refer to the Resource Materials at the end of this unit for these foundations' websites (page 562).

With such inspiring young advocates, the school-agers have started on their long-term commitment to societal change that will one day benefit all children. Early childhood educators also recognize the importance of advocating for well-funded, integrated early childhood programs in Canada as one of the essential ways to address the desired outcomes of the UN Convention on the Rights of the Child. The educators are child advocates who are members of a professional organization with this goal.

CONCLUSION

A holistic view of children's health is based on the premise that the whole child must always be considered. This view is particularly important when discussing issues that at first glance seem to relate to only one dimension of well-being, such as stress (emotional) or rest (physical). We quickly realize that there are physical, emotional, and social considerations for all health issues. Health policies and procedures based on the program's philosophy are written and reviewed regularly to ensure that this holistic view of health is put into practice on an ongoing basis.

A health curriculum is determined by the developmental needs and interests of the children and their sociocultural context. It is integrated into the everyday life at the program. The relevance of the health curriculum to the children's lives and viewing children as partners are paramount in planning, implementing, and evaluating a health curriculum.

What's Your Opinion?

TO BRUSH OR NOT TO BRUSH?

You and the other preschool educators at your program are pleased that your brushing routine after lunch seems to be working well for the children. Most of the preschoolers independently follow the routine with some support from the educators and sometimes make comments such as "My mouth feels clean" or "Brushing takes the food out of my teeth."

It is quite challenging to ensure that each child's toothbrush does not touch the next one stored in the container, and a few times the container has toppled to the floor, requiring disinfecting all around. During the annual visit, the public health inspector was concerned about the risk of contamination, particularly because the name labels were coming off the wet brushes.

You and your colleagues now need to decide: can you arrive at a more stringent procedure and storage arrangement, or should you discontinue the routine at the program while encouraging the children to brush at home twice a day?

ASSESS YOUR LEARNING

Define terms or describe concepts used in this unit.

- body image
- children's understanding of health
- dental health
- early childhood tooth decay (ECTD)
- five W's of cooking with children
- health curriculum
- inherited culture
- personal culture

- rhythm of the program
- self-pleasuring
- self-regulation
- sexuality
- stress-aware environment
- stressors, long-term
- stressors, short-lived
- temperament

Evaluate your options in each situation.

1. You overhear an ECE student say to a three-year-old, "You have to play with Daniel. We are all friends at day care."

2. While you are on a field trip, a four-year-old boy points to a pregnant woman and asks, "Why is that woman's tummy so big?"

3. An eight-year-old in your program is being teased by her peers for being so tall. Katie has been growing quickly lately and is much taller than the rest of the children. She storms off crying, and when you go to comfort her, she asks you, "Will I always be different from everyone else? I hate being tall."

4. You and a classmate have been asked to plan a curriculum to help preschoolers learn about poison prevention. You agree that it would be a good idea to bring in real objects. Next day, your colleague arrives with a bag of potentially hazardous products, including oven, window, and toilet cleaners used at home.

5. The program where you are doing a placement does not promote good nutrition. You are responsible for the weekly after-school cooking club and have submitted your plan to the educator. You would like to begin with simple recipes such as "dippidy-doo and vegetables too" and move to more complex recipes, such as soups and breads. The educator discourages you with the comment, "This will never work. The children only want to make cookies and cakes."

RESOURCE MATERIALS

Other Websites of Interest

Dental Care for Children (Canadian Dental Association): http://www.cda-adc.ca/en/oral_health/cfyt/dental_care_children/index.asp

EcoKids: http://www.ecokids.ca/pub/index.cfm

Evergreen: http://www.evergreen.ca/en

Free the Children: http://www.freethechildren.com/index.php

Green Street: http://www.green-street.ca/home/index_e.html

Healthy Environments for Kids: http://www.healthyenvironmentforkids.ca/english/

Healthy Spaces, Canadian Institute of Child Health and Canadian Child Care Federation: http://www.cfc-efc.ca/healthy-spaces

Invest in Kids: http://www.investinkids.ca/ContentPage.aspx?name=home

Kids Have Stress Too!®: http://www.psychologyfoundation.org/kidshavestresstoo.php

Nature Canada: http://www.naturecanada.ca

Nature Challenge for Kids: http://www.davidsuzuki.org/kids

Pollution Probe: http://www.pollutionprobe.org

Reaching IN . . . Reaching OUT: Promoting Resilience in Young Children: http://www.reachinginreachingout.ca

Sierra Club of Canada: http://www.sierraclub.ca

The Ladybug Foundation: http://www.ladybugfoundation.ca/

Zero to Three: http://www.zerotothree.org/site/PageServer?pagename=homepage

Printed Matter

Around The World Cookbook: More Than 50 International Recipes for Children (2008), by A. Johnson Dodge (Dorling Kindersley Publishers).

Bread, Bread, Bread (1989), by A. Morris and K. Heyman (Lothrop, Lee and Shepard). *Child Health and the Environment—A Primer* (2005), by the Canadian Partnership for Children's Health and Environment. To download a copy, visit http://www.healthyenvironmentforkids.ca/Primer.pdf

Feeling Great: Teaching Children to Excel at Living (1998), by Terry Orlick (Creative Bound Publishers).

Chirp (for 3- to 6-year-olds), *Chickadee* (for 6- to 9-year-olds), and *Owl* (for 9- to 13-year-olds), Canadian magazines on nature and environmental topics. To subscribe, visit http://owlkids.com

The Optimistic Child: A Proven Program to Safeguard Children Against Depression and Build Lifelong Resilience (1996), by M. Seligman (Houghton Mifflin Publishers).

Pee Wee and the Magical Compost Heap and *Pee Wee's Great Adventure: A Guide to Vermicomposting*, by L. Roulston. To order a copy, contact roulstonlp @sympatico.ca.

Salad People and More Real Recipes: A New Cookbook for Preschoolers and Up (2005), by M. Katzen (also the author of *Pretend Soup*) (First Tricycle Press).

The Sandwich (1975), by I. Wallace and A. Wood (Kids Can Press).

BIBLIOGRAPHY

Almqvist, L., Stefansson, P., & Granlund, M. (2006). I can play—young childrens´ perceptions of health. *Pediatric Rehabilitation, 9,* 275–284.

Benard, B. (1995). *Fostering resilience in children.* Urbana-Champaign, IL: University of Illinois. (ERIC Clearinghouse on Elementary and Early Childhood Education No. ED386327). Retrieved July 2008 from http://resilnet.uiuc.edu/library/benard95.html

Bertrand, J. (2001). *Summary of research findings on children's developmental health.* Ottawa: Canadian Child Care Federation/Canadian Institute of Child Health.

Best Start Panel on Early Learning. (2006). *Early learning for every child today: A framework for Ontario early childhood settings.* Toronto: Ontario Ministry of Children and Youth Services.

Brick, P., et al. (2008). *Bodies, birth and babies: Sexuality education in early childhood programs.* Hackensack, NJ: Center for Family Life Education, Planned Parenthood of Greater Northern New Jersey.

Canadian Child Care Federation. (2001). *Child care and children's health: Quality is vital.* Ottawa: Canadian Health Network.

Canadian Council on Learning. (2008, March 20). *Lessons in learning: Bullying in Canada—how intimidation affects learning.* Retrieved June 2008 from http://www.ccl-cca.ca/CCL/Reports/ LessonsInLearning/LinL20080320BullyingConcernCanadians.htm

Canadian Dental Association. (2008). *Oral health: Good for life.* Ottawa: Author. Retrieved June 2008 from http://www.cda-adc.ca/en/oral_health/oral_health_life.asp

Canadian Paediatric Society. (2004). *Behaviour & parenting: Taming the monsters: Helping children deal with their fears.* Ottawa: Author. Retrieved June 2008 from http://www.cps.ca/caringforkids/ behaviour&parenting/Fears.htm

Canadian Paediatric Society. (2008). *Well beings: A guide to health in child care* (3rd ed.). Ottawa: Author. The material on pages 550 and 551 is used with permission.

Canadian Psychological Association. (2003, August 6). *Gays and lesbians make bad parents: There is no basis in the scientific literature for this perception.* Retrieved June 2008 from http://www.cpa.ca/ cpasite/userfiles/documents/old%20press%20releases/gayparenting-cpa.pdf

Cech, M. (1990). *Globalchild: Multicultural resources for young children.* Ottawa: Health and Welfare Canada.

Goulet, M., & Schroeder, R. (1998). *How caring relationships support self-regulation: Video guide.* Toronto: National Association for the Education of Young Children.

Greenspan, S. I. (1993). *Playground politics: Understanding the emotional life of your school-age child.* Don Mills, ON: Addison-Wesley Publishing.

Guralnick, K. M., & Littmann, E. (1992). *Making friends: A guide to using the assessment of peer relations and planning interventions* [Video and guide]. Ottawa: Department of National Health and Welfare.

Janmohamed, Z. (2006). *Building bridges: Lesbian, gay, bisexual, transgender, transsexual and queer families in early childhood education.* Toronto: Ontario Coalition for Better Child Care.

Kagan, J. (2001). Born to be shy? In R. Conlon (Ed.), *States of mind: New discoveries about how our brains make us who we are.* Toronto: John Wiley & Sons.

Maller, D. (2005). Hands-on contact with nature in primary schools as a catalyst for developing a sense of community and cultivating mental health & wellbeing. *EINGANA: Journal of the Victorian Association of Environmental Education, 28,* 17–22. Retrieved July 2008 from http:// www.vaee.vic.edu.au/resources/eingana/einganadec05.pdf#page=18

Masi, R., Mensah, L. L., & McLeod, K. A. (Eds.). (1993). *Health and cultures: Exploring the relationships—policies, professional practice and education* (Vol. 1). Oakville, ON: Mosaic Press.

Musson, S. (1999). *School-age care: Theory and practice* (2nd ed.). Don Mills, ON: Addison-Wesley Publishers.

Natapoff, J. N. (1982). A developmental analysis of children's ideas of health. *Health Education Quarterly, 9,* 130–141.

Peel Public Health. (2007, August 20). *Healthy body image: What is body image?* Retrieved June 2008 from http://www.region.peel.on.ca/health/commhlth/bodyimg/bintro.htm

Sex Information and Education Council of Canada. (2004). Sexual health education in the schools: Questions & answers. *The Canadian Journal of Human Sexuality, 13*(3&4), 67–81.

Shipley, C. D. (2008). *Empowering children: Play-based curriculum for lifelong learning* (4th ed.). Scarborough, ON: Nelson Canada.

Solomon, G. E. A., & Cassimatis, N. L. (1999). On facts and conceptual systems: Young children's integration of their understandings of germs and contagion. *Developmental Psychology, 35,* 113–126.

Sroufe, L. A. (1995). *Emotional development: The organization of emotional life in the early years.* Cambridge, UK: Cambridge University Press.

UNICEF. (n.d.a). *Convention on the Rights of the Child: What educators can do.* Retrieved June 2008 from http://www.unicef.org/crc/index_30221.html

UNICEF. (n.d.b). *Every child matters: The five outcomes and the UN Convention on the Rights of the Child (UNCRC).* Retrieved June 2008 from http://www.everychildmatters.gov.uk/_files/ F1B3FBF728B196018E9616C71D0BF592.pdf

Waxler-Morrison, N., Anderson, J., & Richardson, G. (Eds.). (1990). *Cross-cultural caring: A handbook for health professionals in Western Canada.* Vancouver: University of British Columbia Press.

INDEX

Note: Page numbers followed by an F refer to figures and page numbers followed by a T refer to tables.

E. coli bacteria, 422
Ear infections, 173
Early childhood education
    placements, 98–99
    positive and negatives of working in, 89T
    professional behaviours, 97–98
    quality, 35T
    worksite analysis, 79T
Early childhood program(s)
    high-quality, 32–34, 38–39
    licensed, regulations for, 33–34
    policies, 34–38
Early childhood tooth decay (ECTD), 552
Eating disorders, 220–21
Eating habits. *See also* Nutrition
    body image and, 220–24
    division of responsibility, 245
    economics and, 221–23
    effect of sensory experiences, 217
    emotional habits, 217
    factors affecting, 216–24
    food costs and, 222–23
    food insecurity, 222–23
    physical activity and, 216–17
    restaurant food, 222
    safe, 367
    social and cultural factors, 217–20
Eating habits, healthy, 245–63. *See also* Nutrition
    child nutrition programs, 268
    creating a positive eating environment, 248–50
    developmental characteristics, 246T–248T
    fats in foods, 227–28
    fibre, increasing, 227
    good food choices, 227
    infant nutrition, 251–58
    menu planning, 269–72
    nutrition issues, 325–32
    preschool nutrition, 262
    providing food, 263–68
    school-age nutrition, 262–63
    supporting, 323–36
    toddler nutrition, 258–61
    trust *vs.* control, 245
Eating Well with Canada's Food Guide. See Canada's
    Food Guide
Education
    social determinant of health, 5T, 6T, 22–24
    literacy and, 6T

Educator-child ratio, 392
Educator-child relationship, 85
Emergencies, 430–42
    first aid certificate, 430–31
    injury reports, 431–33
Emotional abuse, 457–58
    indicators of, 462
Employee health policies, 86–87
Employment and working conditions, 6T
Encroachment area, 381
Enrollment
    interviews, 469
    medical examination, 159
Entrapment, 370
Environment, outdoor. *See* Outdoor play;
    Playgrounds
Environment, physical, 377–91
    furniture, 378–79
    indoor play equipment, 379–81
    indoor space, organizing, 378
Environmental contaminants, 421–30
Environmental issues, 425–29
    air pollution, 425–26
    lead exposure, 426–27
    pesticides, 427–28
    plastics, 428–29
Environmental issues in the workplace, 83–84
Environmental toxins. *See also* Hazardous substances
    behaviour, and, 424
    children's exposure to, 423–25
    fetal vulnerability to, 423
    life expectancy/latency, 424
    metabolism, 424
    physiology, 424
    proportionality, 423–24
    windows of vulnerability, 423
Ergonomics, 74
Ethnocultural food habits
    development in children, 217
    ethnicity and, 219
Exclusion policy
    from early childhood programs, 168–69
    infectious diseases, 72

Falls, 361
    accident-prevention strategies, 364T, 366T
    head injuries, 385
    injuries, 371